A BOOK OF READINGS

Management of the Family of the Mentally Retarded

Edited by WOLF WOLFENSBERGER and RICHARD A. KURTZ

Parkinson Division
FOLLETT EDUCATIONAL CORPORATION

 Manufactured in the United States of America.

Designers: Russ Coombs and Rick Springer
Editorial Preparation: Dorothy M. Reynolds and Elizabeth H. Abele

Library of Congress Catalog Card Number: 68-30810

1234567872717069

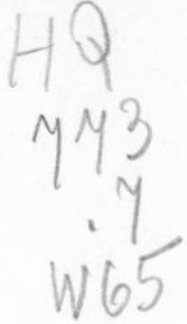

Preface

Management of the family of the mentally retarded implies to us the entry of persons or organizations in an official, or at least widely sanctioned, capacity into the lives of members of families of the mentally retarded, purportedly for the benefit of either these family members, of the retardate himself, or of the community. The activities subsumed by this definition include referral, fact finding, case evaluation, counseling, psychotherapy, guidance, tuition, education, casework, direction, supervision, and control.

In the course of discussing this book with colleagues, we have found that several have objected to the term "management" because of its authoritarian overtones. However, we feel strongly that this term is the only one that is broad enough to subsume the range of appropriate services; furthermore, we feel that the term is the only honest one to describe the realities of the field. In the American culture, individual freedom is highly valued. As a consequence, managers of human affairs have been socialized to value and maximize, at least on the verbal level, the voluntary aspects of the manager-managed relationship. Human managers have sometimes lost sight of the fact that their entry into the family, no matter how it is structured or interpreted, is likely to have powerful stimulus qualities and is therefore likely to elicit significant responses. It is true that the manager rarely exerts legal control over the behavior of the managed, but it can scarcely be denied that he exerts considerable social, emotional, or financial stimulus control over the behavior of his client. In some cases, however, his control is actually legal and physical, as when he represents the courts, institutions, etc. We have thus been deliberate in choosing our title, and hope that both the terms and the concepts of human management and family management will be widely accepted in the field.

Services for the mentally retarded are now developing at a rapid pace, and increasing numbers of professionals in diverse disciplines are assuming management roles with families of retarded individuals. Demand for services is likely to outstrip the supply of trained manpower for the foreseeable future, and many professionals will play management roles despite limited relevant training. Familiarity with the pertinent theories, issues, and facts in the area is crucial to adequate managerial performance, yet such knowledge may take years to acquire, and may be acquired in haphazard rather than systematic fashion. This book of readings was compiled in order to bring together relevant material scattered throughout the literature and over time, thus facilitating the learning process of family managers.

Specifically, the readings were selected on the basis of four criteria:

1. To present contributions which are likely to enhance practical management competency of persons working with families of the retarded. In particular, an attempt was made to include selections exemplifying the breadth of options and alternatives that are available and conceivable. While many of these alternatives still lack empirical demonstration of effectiveness, they do illustrate the creativity and flexibility desirable in a good program.

2. To acquaint the student or worker with existing writings that present issues, thoughts, or insights so uniquely, succinctly, or incisively that more effective summarization or restatement is not very likely.

3. To bring together sources that have come to be considered classics, being quoted again and again in the literature. Items in this category may or may not contain the best knowledge that we have today, but they do represent the milestones of progress.

4. To provide a sense of history and continuity. New workers in the field often do not realize how far we have come in a very short time, and how and why we have come as far as we have. They may neither appreciate the darkness in which the family of the retarded once lived—nor the darkness that could return if society decided that the benefits derived from retardation programming were not worth the social cost.

An effort was made to demonstrate a) the supradisciplinary nature of the management of the family of the mentally retarded, and b) the range and continuity of management options. Throughout, the reader will notice that alternate management approaches are not being viewed as sacrosanct, but merely as means or tools for attaining one consistent goal: responsible, dedicated pursuit of enlightened management of the families of the retarded.

In selecting the readings and excerpts, we consciously and unashamedly applied certain value judgments. Thus, an attempt was made to include heavy doses of what we believe to be the most enlightened thinking in the field. In a few instances, selections which differed from our viewpoints were included if they were well stated and reasoned, or if they constituted illustrations of an historically significant approach. Some selections that made a good point, or were the only or chief representative of their kind, were included even if they lacked somewhat in quality. While selections were heavily edited so as to minimize irrelevant, outdated, or redundant material, some elements and terms which would now be considered outdated were retained for the sake of continuity and flavor. Whenever possible, footnotes and references were omitted. When retained, they were sometimes reorganized and renumbered consecutively. A full line of ellipses (or three ellipses) was used to indicate omissions.

The organization of the book is, of course, quite arbitrary, and overlap between sections proved to be unavoidable. At times, we have taken the liberty of fragmenting an item and assigning the fragments into different but appropriate sections, and at other times we have combined content from several related publications. Frequently, a selection would have been suitable for more than one section, in which case we included it in the section to which it made its most pertinent contribution.

We view this book of readings as serving somewhat in the role of a companion volume to the recently-published review chapter "Counseling the Parents of the Retarded" (W. Wolfensberger, in A. Baumeister, Ed., Mental Retardation: Appraisal, Education, and Rehabilitation. *Chicago: Aldine, 1967). The learning value of the present book will probably be enhanced if the reader first familiarizes himself with this broad and evaluative review of the field. The rationale for including many of the selections presented here will then become much clearer. Furthermore, the empirical literature which was largely omitted from this book of readings is discussed and summarized in the review chapter.*

As mentioned previously, this is a supradisciplinary book. It is intended for all those involved in the management of the family of the mentally retarded, regardless of their disciplinary affiliation and orientation. However, it is hoped that some parents, too, will find it useful, particularly those who play leadership roles in mental retardation. It is to the parents that this book is dedicated.

WOLF WOLFENSBERGER
RICHARD A. KURTZ

Table of Contents

turmoil for which there seems to be no release.

But even the parents who can and do admit their child's limitations often find it difficult if not almost impossible to share their sorrow because their friends, neighbors and relatives are hesitant to ask about the child's welfare. In the case of severe physical illness or death, we would think it inconceivable if our friends, relatives or neighbors showed no concern for our need—yet in this case where the emotional shock is sometimes even more severe than in death, we are denied the privilege of sharing our grief with those closest to us because of a sense of embarrassment or shame. All of you know the real therapeutic value of being able to "talk out our troubles" with someone who understands. But often in the early stages of discovery of mental retardation within a family, the parents have difficulty in talking with one another—let alone with relatives or friends. Fortunately this is not the case too often, but it can and does happen.

This inability to share our problem exists through no fault of the parents, or of the general public. It is simply the result of having looked upon mental abnormalities with superstition, with fear, with ignorance of the true facts, or, perhaps with the naive belief that if we just refuse to look at them or discuss them objectively they will somehow cease to exist.

After talking with hundreds of parents it is my feeling that more real damage has been brought about by this inability to share their problem than by any other single factor. May we reiterate again and again that this is not the fault of the parents nor of society in general. It is simply a condition which exists—but one which is now crying out loud for correction.

4. The fourth problem is one which is almost totally ignored by those professional persons whom parents are most likely to consult in regard to their child, and yet it is one of the most real and vital problems they face: we refer to the *theological conflicts which arise in the minds of parents when faced with such a heart-rending situation within their own personal lives.* Death, they can accept—because death, at one stage or another, is a normal and natural part of life's history; physical illness they can accept because they have seen physical illness and deformity throughout their lives. Broken homes, loss of jobs and economical security, serious injury by accident—all these unfortunate circumstances are familiar to every adult couple and are within the realm of possibility in their thinking.

But to suddenly face the fact that their child is a mental cripple and will remain so throughout life, well—this simply places them outside the providence of God's mercy and justice, or so they often feel—if they can indeed still believe that there *is* a God.

If the parents have been reared in a somewhat puritanical concept they may possibly become so overwhelmed with a sense of guilt that it is totally impossible for them to see their problem from a rational viewpoint. *Any condition of life which destroys or permanently damages one's concept of a loving and merciful God presents a serious problem*—a problem with which he must have help lest he finally sink into a state of despair from which there is no return. For this reason we believe that our clergymen, our priests and rabbis should have competent, professional knowledge about the facts of mental retardation so as to be more able to advise and counsel wisely with the members of their parish who are faced with this problem.

5. The fifth, and probably the most heart-rending of all the many problems we face is that of *seeking a solution to the matter of satisfactory life-time care for our handicapped child, who, in many instances, will need adult guidance and care throughout his normal life span.*

We believe that it can be safely said that very few professional persons can fully appreciate or understand the intense feelings of anxiety and concern on the part of parents over this acute problem of life-time care. The professional person, by the very nature of his training is primarily concerned with finding a solution to the problem immediately at hand—and this is as it should be. The doctor endeavors to provide the small retardate with the healthiest, strongest physical body he can be given; the teacher works and thinks in terms of helping him learn to use and further develop his limited mental capacity; the social worker works in terms of helping the child and his family in making a satisfactory adjustment to his environment; the psychologist and psychiatrist endeavor to help both parent and child to an acceptance of his limitation and to a wiser understanding of their own feelings and motivations.

Professional help is not only good, it is actually imperative in meeting the problems of the moment. But the professional person must always keep in mind that with the child's parent the problem is not for "just now" but for *always*. Such an attitude of understanding about the permanence of the problem from the standpoint of the parents will enable the professional person to work more constructively with us as parents in meeting the problems immediately at hand.

In families where there are other children to be considered the problem of life-time care is intensified because we must take into consideration not only the handicapped child but the other children as well. Here again, there is no single, easy answer. Decisions must be made in the light of many, many factors—too numerous to go into at this time. But let it be said here that the decisions which must be made by parents on this one point alone are grave enough to shake the emotional, spiritual, and mental equilibrium of even the most stable personalities.

6. A sixth and final problem with which most parents have to cope at one time or another during their experience is with *inept, inaccurate and ill-timed professional advice*. Now I am well aware that such a statement as this coming from a parent contains potential dynamite! I must also confess that a sore temptation presents itself to cast all objectivity aside and give you some stories which parents have told me over the past few years—but I shall resist the temptation to do so. Instead, I would ask your permission to share with you material from several recognized leaders in the field of mental deficiency. All of their statements tend to lift up the point that we want to make here and it is this: parents can be spared much emotional damage and conflict if the professional persons they consult have two things:

a. a comprehensive knowledge of all factors concerning mental retardation so far as they are known;

b. the ability to counsel parents in a straightforward, honest but gracious manner.

To put it a bit more bluntly, the reaction of parents to their problem will depend to a great degree on the emotional and spiritual maturity of the professional person whom they consult as well as the professional person's knowledge or lack of knowledge concerning mental retardation.

The first statement we would present for your consideration is lifted from an address by Dr. William M. Cruickshank, Director of Special Education, Syracuse University. This address was presented to the Virginia Public Health Conference, May 2, 1956 in Roanoke, Virginia.

"I am concerned that in the first contact which parents have with a professional person they will be given an honest diagnosis and that they will also be given a realistic and honest prognosis. The diagnostic problem is the responsibility of the medical profession and the psychological profession. Both groups in the past have been remiss on many occasions and have frequently failed to bring to the child the best diagnostic procedure. Oftentimes this has resulted from ignorance. This situation can be corrected and is now being made the focus of attention of medical and psychological faculties.

"The problem of honest prognosis is more subtle because it is dependent on the emotional security of the professional person in his relation to the clients. Too often professional personnel simply do not have the ability to be able to tell parents the realities of a situation. Only recently, a set of parents brought a ten-year old child to our clinic. The child was markedly retarded. In the interpretive conference with the parent we asked why it was they had waited so long to seek assistance with their problem.

> "Surely you must have suspected long before this that your child was not developing properly." The mother replied: "We did suspect that something was wrong. He did not talk as soon as the other children had. He didn't walk as early as the others either. We took him to our pediatrician and he said: 'Don't worry Mrs. Jones, when Tommy is sixteen years old you'll never be able to tell him from other boys on the street.' "

"This is indeed inaccurate. It happens so frequently, however, that many of us are seriously disturbed. Educators likewise are to be criticized. I have a letter on my desk from a school principal to a mother.

> The school is recommending that her retarded child be placed in a special class. The mother objects. The principal's letter states: "I can understand your feeling about our recommendation for Stewart's placement in a special class. I wonder if we could suggest a compromise: let us place Stewart in the special class for a year or two and then we will return him to the regular grades."

"This is more than inaccurate. It is an absolute mis-statement of the facts. It implies that while the child is in the special class, educators will wave a magic wand over the child's head, cure him of mental retardation, and thus put him back in the regular grades. . . .

"Can we not be honest in our reporting to parents? Can we not be conservatively realistic? Parents may not like what we say, and their feelings we can appreciate. Nevertheless, basically they want an honest appraisal of the situation, as distasteful as that may be. They need to be secure in the knowledge that the professions are shooting straight from the shoulder and that with such realism, appropriate planning for the child can be undertaken."

The second statement is lifted from an article appearing in the *American Journal of Mental Deficiency* and comes from H. S. Storrs:

"Medicine is an art, and handling the relatives is one of the important functions of this art. In my opinion, every case is individual and should be investigated as such. I want to know all I can about the child, the family, and all situations connected with both the child and the family. . . . Doctors as a class do not seem to realize the enormity of the tragedy experienced by the parents when they find that their child is definitely defective. This should be appreciated by all doctors and they should size up the parents.

"I have always felt that it was a mistake not to tell the parents the whole truth. . . . Parents have in many instances been from doctor to doctor, spending their money, have been given evasive answers, have built up hopes over and over, only to have them dashed to the ground, finally. It always seemed to me that they should be told the truth as early as possible, with, as I have said, consideration for the individual family situation."

Other problems arise between the professional person and parents when the professional person tends to hide behind certain well-worn cliches such as the following: "These parents can't be helped because they just don't want to believe what we tell them," or, "These parents believe that this just couldn't happen to them," or—more common still—"These parents have rejected their child so there is little that I can do to help them."

Some very well-qualified persons have come to feel that the over-use of these well-worn phrases usually arises from the fact that the professional person feels his own inadequacy in knowing how to successfully counsel with parents in a constructive manner. The professional person should ever bear in mind that the wrong kind of help or advice given to an emotionally disturbed parent is often worse than no help at all.

And whether we like to admit it or not, most of us *are* disturbed to various degrees in the initial stages of our adjustment. We as parents need to have a wiser understanding of our own feelings during this period—but since many of us do not have, we must depend on you to sometimes go the second mile in trying to help us out of our emotional turmoil. However, let us hasten to add that just as we feel parents should not be harshly judged because they do not know how to handle their retarded children most wisely, we should also recognize that professional persons should not be harshly judged because they often do not know how to handle parents wisely. We simply must take into account that the primary reason that both situations exist is due to ignorance and inexperience, in most instances.

We have now considered six of the most basic problems faced by the parents of retarded children. What then, is their greatest need?

After thirteen years experience as the mother of a retarded child and having talked and corresponded with literally hundreds of other parents, I have come to the conclusion that all of our many, many needs can be covered in one sentence and it is this:

The greatest single need of parents of mentally retarded children is constructive professional counselling at various stages in the child's life which will enable the parents to find the answers to their own individual problems to a reasonably satisfactory degree.

In the early stages of our initial adjustment to life with a retarded child we need someone who can and will explain to us in lay language some of the numerous factors relating to mental retardation; we need someone to help us understand our own attitudes and feelings in relation to our handicapped child. We need someone to give us guidance in the simple, basic processes of home training. We need someone who can put us in touch with the various community and state agencies that can help with constructive management of the child. We need guidance from someone who can help us see that this thing which has happened to us, even though it may be a *life-shaking* experience does not of necessity have to be a *life-breaking* one.

Several years later we need guidance from those who can help us decide upon and provide a training program for the child. In later years we need guidance and help in making plans which will provide permanent care for our child when we are gone.

Again, we may repeat that our greatest single need is for the kind of counsel which will enable us to find the answers to our individual problems. Please note that we are not suggesting that others should make our decisions for us, or that they should bear the burden of telling us what or what not to do—only that we might be given the guidance that will enable us to make our own decisions in a way which will result in the greatest good for the child and the family of which he is a part. . . .

□ □ □

SECTION B

Through the Parents' Eyes

A competent manager in this field is sensitive to parental reaction to the advent of a retarded child. Yet in many cases, this impact may be underestimated because many parents either lack skills of expression or, in our culture, minimize overt display of their feelings. Once in a while, lest the manager become too professionally distant or complacent, he needs an intense confrontation with a reality he usually need not face himself. In "Peter Beautiful," Edith Gramm has distilled in most powerful form the feelings and experiences of many a less articulate parent. Any person reading her story without being deeply moved should examine his suitability as a manager.

The second selection is the story of a parent's experiences during a darker age. Let us remember that management so inappropriate as to be unbelievable to many newcomers to the field occurred but yesterday. W. Newland Reilly is a prototype of the early parent leader: abused, mismanaged, hurt, fighting-mad, and eloquent. In all humility, let us further recall that it was the Reillys, not the professionals, who led the field into a new day. After all, it was the professionals who headed the services and agencies, and who did such a poor job of it. It was the layman, the parent, the humanist, the journalist who labeled our institutions as the snake pits they were, while the professional was often occupied in attempts to defend the status quo.

While Reilly's story captures the flavor of the early parent movement, Weingold, a well-known parent leader, gives us a further glimpse of the movement from the days when the National Association for Retarded Children was formed. Again, his documentation of the irrational and now almost incomprehensible opposition of professionals to the parent movement carries a lesson for today. We may well ask ourselves whether there may be a trend or movement in dealing with retardation which, though threatening to us today, may be proved correct tomorrow. Which of tomorrow's realities do we consider impossible today?

Articles by Zwerling and Waskowitz remind the professional of the way parents have viewed services he has rendered, giving us further cause to be humble and introspective. In the two concluding selections, parent leaders Patterson and Bostock give the professional some wise counsel, and point the way to better cooperation and enlightened management.

PETER BEAUTIFUL: THE STORY OF AN ENCHANTED CHILD

Edith P. Gramm

(*American Journal of Mental Deficiency*, 1951)

Peter was fourteen hours old when I first saw him. I was still in pain, but excitement overrode everything else. One of those pink and blue packages being carried into the ward was for me—my prize.

Of course I had always known it would be a boy. We never doubted that. We hadn't been very intuitive, though. We didn't know it would be an emergency Caesarian in the eighth month.

Peter was the conventional pink—too tiny to be believed, and awfully unhappy. Since I wasn't allowed to nurse him, I couldn't hold him, but the nurse was compassionate; she undraped the absurd little curling limbs which she called his "fine long legs," and I touched one. It was air made palpable, too slight, too delicate. I suppose it was that first pang of almost maniacal pity that made me officially a mother.

She told me we were lucky to be alive, and when he unsquinted his eyes for a second, I caught a flash of the most incredible blue and I thought she could never know how lucky. No baby would ever be loved as I would love Peter. One day I would write a little story for him, and I would call it *Peter Beautiful.* In it he would hear all those things about himself that make each of us feel wonderful and blithe.

I would never strike him nor scream at him. Other mothers who did were harassed, but nerves would never drive me to unkindness. For one thing, don't we always say that we face life's greatest crises alone? I had been given a companion in my ordeal.

Twenty-five hours ago I last saw Peter. Almost six and a half years ago the nurse had said we were lucky to be alive. We *are* both alive. Our hearts beat and we breathe. We instinctively recoil from danger. He likes milk and cookies and I say yes enthusiastically to the suggestion of ice cream or a walk. But it ends there, and we are not lucky.

I close my eyes now and wonder how I can ever get our agony onto a page. I think "I must simply describe that picture that lies behind my eyelids when I close my eyes."

It is nothing very heroic; nothing dramatic of itself. Just a very small boy walking away from me down a long corridor. He doesn't turn back, so his father and I are, this one time, spared the look of those enormous eyes.

Peter is very wee for a six-year-old. His upper arms are thinner than his forearms, and so the elbows jut. His thighs are thinner than his thin, fine legs, and so the knees bump out toward each other.

We know what he is saying. He has a little trick of making consoling promises to himself. He has been repeating this special legend since he heard us say that we had better bring him back to his ward. It concerns cookies and chocolate raisins and Mommie and Daddy again in seven days. There is a nurse here too. I don't even remember her face, but she is someone very impersonal, and she smiles and says something about his knowing the way.

This was yesterday. We visited our baby in the *state institution.*

Last summer we were forced by our conscience, by my broken nerves (I have struck my Peter Beautiful, and I have screamed at him), and by the pressure of advising, censorious neighbors who considered this thirty-odd pounds of prettiness a menace to their stalwart young pugnacious "normals"—we were forced by all this to "put him away."

I won't pretend it was because we were advised to do so by every physician we saw. Nor can I rationalize that it was because he was becoming a very evident danger to himself. There is nothing rational about parenthood. It is primitive and emotional.

Cool reason and social awareness were stripped from us every time a stranger would stop us in the street and lecture us on how badly we were rearing our child because he would suddenly decide that the moment had come to lie down and spit artfully along the cracks in the sidewalk.

Peter's daddy, the poet, the idealist, would envision the most skillful violence against his fellow man whenever a woman, passing for an instant through our grief-stricken lives, would stop in her tracks, turn back, and corner us into an explanation of our son's sudden, spasmodic shrieking.

Peter is dear and beautiful and frail. Peter is affectionate and subtle and sensitive. Music was always his chiefest joy—and he was responsive to all beauty. If I could have obeyed my son's requests, we would have wreaths in the windows and a Christmas tree and carols playing all year through.

There were, rare as angels among us, those who saw beneath the grotesque of Peter's behavior. They felt the sad affection for him that one usually feels for a hurt child. We felt the cool distillations of their advice (which in their wisdom, they applied only to our lives and not to Peter's lawless condition), and we were revived by it. They, unknowing, have saved us from ultimate, willful isolation.

Mostly, however, I lived through a cacophony of phrases:

If he's feeble-minded, why don't you put him away?

What manners! Why don't you teach him?

You shouldn't ever take a child like that out of the house.

He's perfectly normal. All babies do that. (Peter was five.)

If you just let him run wild . . .

You must never take your eyes off him.

Maybe you don't have enough patience.

All he needs is a spanking.

And bitterest of all to hear:

If he were mine . . .

And Lord, in my weakest hours, I have wished a child like Peter to be born to each of them. With experience comes understanding.

We entered him that summer in a private institution. The woman in charge said all the right things. She promised the same extra milk and egg drinks we gave him. Oh, she understood "these wiry ones." How she promised! And we left him that bright day, with his voice grown hideous in its screaming. He wanted us. How desperately he wanted us!

Somehow, somewhere, in the dark place before birth, he had been injured. But how he loved us!

We wondered how our toppler of blocks, and chewer of storybooks would ever become like the quiet little creatures around him.

We discovered. On the twelfth day when we visited him he was beaten black and blue. There were imprints of hands, and there were furrows under his eyes that showed he had cried as no God could want His littlest ones to cry.

We took him home with us. For all we felt, we were less broken than he. Not since that time has he been totally a child. The sprigs of mischief and baby jollity that once bravely flourished through the arid places of his life have been forever choked. He moves through his toddlerhood with all the trepidation of a diplomat whose country verges on war. Armed with infantile defenses, he faces the monstrous enemies—anger, ridicule, rejection and the heavy hand.

Yes, we took him home with us. After his first and more obvious terrors had subsided, our problems began afresh. There was no clearing, no lightening, no easing in sight. There was just one specialist more.

This year Peter is in a state institution where they do their best. But he is not where there is love. His smile when he first sees us—his manliness when we leave him—these things are too intimately involved with the life functions of the three of us ever to be communicated.

Peter seems broken to me. He is too docile now. The skinny cold little wrist I held yesterday has lain against my heart all night. And that little part of me won't have to bother about dying when the time comes for the rest of me to die.

There are still the neighbors—the passers-by who remember him. Sometimes they are vocal—these women before whom I tell myself I need no longer cringe. They speak and the words are all variations of "he is better off," but they have no knowledge of the truth of this, nor the shadowy facts that modify and sometimes negate the statement.

It is in their eyes and the expressions of their mouths that they manage their shabby eloquence. It has halted me abruptly in my awareness of a baby crying pitifully in its carriage because the sun is in its eyes and its mother is unaware. It has stayed my involuntary impulse when a little one has teetered into the gutter and clearly contemplates the wonderful, forbidden width of road.

I am not of the elect. There is something very important in which I have failed. *Their* children are normal.

If they could see Peter's father when he cuddles his gangling big baby of a boy—if they could see the infinite tenderness—the ache to help—to tell his love—the sudden aging of his face when he says good-by.

Yet, in witnessing, they would not really see depths of human emotion, emotion that has never been awakened in them.

No one street, no single playground marks a neighborhood. Not for us. The world of normal children is a vast yard, fenced and gated. There is no place in the immediate here nor the far there where we might go to reclaim our lives and ourselves. There is the chance that Peter, years from now, might become docile; not negatively so from shock, as he is now, but through a series of victorious little adventures among his peers. There is that chance. But he must not waste away before he reaches it.

He is not really among his own. There is no child there who is at all like him. Peter belongs to a never-never land of frisky bunnies and blown leaves. He is the changeling child I read of long ago. He is enchanted, but the charm is ugly with reality. And love, which can work such magic, was not enough when we lived with him.

□ □ □

LET THE PARENT LIVE AGAIN

W. Newland Reilly

(American Journal of Mental Deficiency, 1942)

Ladies and Gentlemen:

To some of you, I am an unknown quantity, a missing link, as it were, for I am a member of a parent organization working for the good of children in custodial care.

I am the parent of a boy who has the mind of a baby and the body of a man, and I am here to plead with you to help spread the new doctrine of parent cooperation with custodial institutions, which has been developed by the Children's Benevolent League in the state of Washington.

We parents belong to no class, no creed, no race and to no special environment. We are just typical American men and women, who have suffered a particular type of misfortune.

Our ranks include some with wealth and position, and some who suffer from poverty and obscurity. We number some who have intelligence above the average, and some who, themselves, need custodial care.

We have one thing in common. Almost without exception, we have withdrawn from society to give special care to our handicapped child, and we have given that care until health or economic reasons have forced us to turn to the state or to a special school to take over the job.

My wife and I, as have others, moved to the outskirts of the city—to a neighborhood where we had no friends—and there built a high-board fence as a haven for the boy. We would not admit he was doomed to mental darkness, and we gave him attention twenty-four hours a day.

And then came the day, when the boy was about ten years old and I had been ill at home for six months, when we were forced to give up the fight, and ask the state to accept our boy as a ward.

We took the youngster to the school at Medical Lake, now known as the Eastern Washington Custodial school, and there we were told: "Your boy is now a ward of the state, and if you are wise, you will go home, have other children, and forget him."

Those were hard words—words that were repeated to all parents who left children at the school in those years. Needless to say, the words were held against the man who spoke them, and he has paid the price. If it had not been for those words, and for other things, he might now be superintendent at Medical Lake. I helped spike his efforts to return to the school only this spring.

After our boy had been at Medical Lake something more than a year, Mr. Charles A. Parker was named superintendent. He was a man with broad humanitarian principles, and he revolutionized methods at the school, changing it from a mere asylum to the type of institution it was designed to be.

A short time after Mr. Parker took over the work, he stood talking to a parent from western Washington when the idea was developed to create an organization of parents similar to the Parent-Teacher Association.

Mr. Parker urged me to take the lead in the organization of a group in Spokane. I refused. I might as well be honest and admit that I refused because I was so unsocial, due largely to years of isolation with the boy, that I considered myself better than other parents of retarded children in the Spokane area. I felt that my wife and I were exceptions. No others had suffered as we had suffered. Other parents, I thought, were low grade morons, who never should have been permitted to have children, whereas my wife was a college graduate and the holder of a life diploma as a high school teacher, and I had won some recognition as a newspaper man.

I was wrong, of course. I have learned since that all parents have suffered equally, and that a majority are fine people.

A group was formed in Spokane, but it was doomed to failure, partially because I and other intelligent parents refused to play ball, and partially because it lacked a proper program.

About thirty months ago, a man of vision, understanding, and leadership issued a call for the formation of a new unit in Spokane. A little group of us faced sub-zero weather one January night, and the present Spokane unit of the Children's Benevolent League of Washington came into being. Full credit for what has been accomplished belongs to one man—Mr. A. G. Naundorf, an executive of a large industrial plant, who has given of his time and money to promote the work of the league. Mr. Naundorf has taught me by his example that no man has a right to be too proud to associate with his fellow sufferers, no matter what their mental or social position.

We parents, in working with him, have found a new hope and a new life, and we have been able to do real work for the children in the school and to help each other to a degree that does not seem possible. We have ceased to be unsocial, and once more are reasonably normal citizens.

When we met first, one mother in the group was actively wrecking four lives because one of her children was retarded. She felt she was the only one who was so afflicted. All parents seem to feel that way. Later she found that others had similar grief, and she found, also, that she was able to help others bear up under it. As a result, she has acquired a new outlook. She is a charming hostess when you visit her home, and a gay guest when in yours. I might go into many other similar case histories, but I won't. The important thing here is not what has been accomplished in particular lives, but how it was accomplished.

The real upsurge in the social consciousness of the Spokane group became obvious when the first social meeting was held at a member's home after the parents had been meeting about five months. The results took the leaders by surprise. For a time there had been a feeling nothing had happened.

Finally, the facts became clear. We saw that what are parents needed was a very simple thing—nothing more than a chance to talk, without explanation or apology, about their children. We could give that, and it cost us nothing.

Each parent had a normal, deep and earnest love for his child, and each had a rational desire to chatter lovingly about the thing closest to his heart. One can not talk freely to an "outsider" about a boy or girl whose mind is not normal. It is only when we meet others who have similar problems that we can open our hearts and express our innermost thoughts. And when our parents meet on the street, in the home or at a unit meeting, they talk gaily to each other—and I mean gaily—about mentally retarded Susie or Johnny, just as other parents discuss normal children.

The real work we have accomplished in thirty months is just as simple as that. There were no prepared plans and no deep-laid psychological plots by which to accomplish the end. The result came before the planning. We merely stumbled unto something, and having found it, surrendered to its fascinating grasp.

Today, when a child is admitted at Medical Lake for the first time, the school workers advise the parents to attend meetings of the units throughout the state of the Children's Benevolent League. Usually, a member of a group calls upon the new parents and issues a friendly invitation. The new parents come diffidently—often defiantly—and are given a direct and simple welcome. We have seen them come—dozens of them—and we believe they have found in our midst a wholesome new outlook on their problems. All we do for them is to suggest means by which they can help the children at the school, and then give them an opportunity to talk rationally about their children.

I want you to see two pictures.

The first is of a dozen or so parents gathered that first January night in a barn-like public assembly room. No one smiled, and no one spoke to a neighbor. One mother expressed it this way: "I felt it was no-one's business why I was there, and I would have slapped anyone who asked if I had a child in the school."

The second picture is a typical meeting of the Spokane unit. The early birds turn on the lights in a pleasant social room at the Y. W. C. A. The room fills, and the more active move about to welcome strangers and exchange handshakes and banter with old friends. The meeting comes to order. The business of the evening, including an address on some phase of the work with mentally retarded children, is brought to a close. Little groups form and reform, and there is a buzz of happy conversation, which continues until the officers start turning out the lights between 11 o'clock and midnight.

I wish I could make you feel the happiness that is almost vocal in the room—a happiness created by nothing more tangible than giving the parents an opportunity to talk about their retarded children.

Of course, there is another side to the picture. Our work has had its faults. We have made mistakes—too many of them. We have not succeeded in cheering the lives of all parents we have contacted. We have injured a few. We've had some pretty hot fights when the good of the school was at stake, and the results have not always been happy for some parents.

I've been the political mouthpiece for the Spokane unit, and I'm hot-headed, and I say things which I regret afterward.

We staged a real fight when Mr. Parker was dismissed as superintendent at Medical Lake because of biased testimony presented to a grand jury by a state officer of our league who wanted the job, but didn't get it. We have been in another battle of wits to prevent the dismissal of our present superintendent, Mr. Lester F. Mason, who is a grand executive with a sincere feeling of responsibility for the welfare of the children. Mr. Mason's job was endangered when a new governor took office.

If I could turn back the clock six or seven years to the day when Mr. Parker asked me to organize a Spokane unit, I should start by calling together a small group of selected parents, and I'd outline to them a very simple program, based upon the opportunity to do small things for the good of the children. I'd serve refreshments and let them get acquainted, and all the time I'd try to fire them with enthusiasm. If the parents had the right stuff in them, they'd soon form a working unit.

I'd invite my group to meet again, and I'd bring in others. Perhaps, at the second meeting I'd try to have an officer present from the school to discuss some phase of his work.

The organizer of a parent group must not lose sight of the fact that talking is not enough. Talking is merely a by-product, a sort of catalytic agent, which produces results. Before a group really gets down to talking, it must have work to do.

Above all, an organizer should not present a program for the social readjustment of the parents. None of us want to be rehabilitated. The rehabilitation must come as a result, and not as an aim.

There is only one type of program which will prove successful over a long period of time, and that is the doing of small, tangible things for the happiness of children.

The various units of the Children's Benevolent League of Washington started along varying lines. There was no formula to be followed, and each charted its own course.

The first successful groups were in western Washington, and they were nothing more than political machines, organized to coerce the legislature into making an appropriation for a custodial school in western Washington. There was smart political guidance—too smart, it proved in the end—and the program of several groups was centered not so much on getting a new school as having the new school located in the particular area of each group. It was easy to get the backing of chambers of commerce and civic organizations and expand the group membership to thousands.

The vast majority of these chamber of commerce members dropped out the moment the announcement was received that the new school would be constructed at Buckley. That moment brought with it, also, a need for a new program for the western Washington groups.

It is an interesting fact that all but the smallest groups included in their parent-membership a number of keen-minded individuals, who were able to keep the units together. The one thing, however, which prevented some groups from disintegrating, if I get the picture correctly, was that they had become strong social entities, and the parents felt the need for the social life the groups provided.

One western Washington group seemed on the verge of collapse this spring, and it was the one closest to the new Buckley school—the one which, normally, should have the most incentive to keep going. Its troubles are due to the continued political activity of a single member. It will be a simple matter, however, to reform the group, should the need arise. [The group was going strong again when this article first appeared in print.]

The first unit formed in Spokane failed for want of a simple program. It tried to enter into the fight for a new school in western Washington, but a school existed twenty miles from Spokane, and there was no real incentive for the work.

When the Spokane unit was reorganized thirty months ago, it undertook a very simple routine—nothing more than encouraging the parents to co-operate with Superintendent Parker in a program of school betterment. The collection of books and magazines was added. Plans were perfected whereby each child from the Spokane area has received a birthday card each year. A program of educational talks on the problems of the mentally retarded child was presented. The parents collected prizes for Fourth of July events at the school and provided Christmas presents. All these activities were simple and natural.

It is a noteworthy fact that when a group loses its objective, it starts raising money in a big way to do big things for the children. We have steered clear of high-pressure money-raising schemes in Spokane. We have needed little money. We have no dues, and what funds we have needed have come from free-will offerings. We are having a raffle this year to raise funds to assure financial success for a state convention in 1942.

There is one thought I want to leave with you, and that is that a group of rehabilitated parents—if they are for you—can be real job insurance for you, but, if you are falling down on your job, they are equally competent to raise particular hell.

Whether you like us or not, we parents are fixed entities in your lives. We don't want to be a part of your work, but nature, in its own wisdom, has said that we must be. We in the state of Washington feel that we have pioneered a new field of work, which is of real benefit to the parents, to the children and to the school staffs, and my closing thought is an appeal to you to help spread in your own state the work that has been undertaken—more successfully than any of us dreamed—by the Children's Benevolent League in the state of Washington.

□ □ □

from PARENTS' GROUPS AND THE PROBLEM OF MENTAL RETARDATION

Joseph T. Weingold

(American Journal of Mental Deficiency, 1952)

. . . .

The amazing thing about the recent tremendous pace at which the parents of the mentally retarded have banded together into groups is not that we have done so, but that it has taken us so long to start. Surely the advent of Parents' Groups should have coincided with the awakening of social consciousness in the 19th century. Surely there were parents then and their problems, if anything, were as acute as the parents' problems today. The reasons for this failure, however, can readily be seen when we consider the difficulties involved, even today, in the formation and continued existence of Parents' Groups.

The difficulties in the path to the formation and continued existence of Parents' Groups in the field of mental retardation are many. First, and foremost, perhaps, is the emotional problem arising with the discovery that a child in the family is retarded. We need not discuss here the feelings of guilt, shame, fear and frustrated parenthood which may arise in the parents. All these tend to inhibit the admission of the problem. These are natural feelings and are not to be dismissed. They represent, perhaps, the greatest single stumbling block to the formation of Parents' Groups which bring the condition into the cold light of day and to the attention of an all-too-frequently unsympathetic and misinformed, if not hostile, society. We can readily see how difficult it is to overcome this in the ordinary parent when many well informed and educated parents of retarded children are still reluctant to publicize their condition.

Nor does this difficulty cease with the admission of this problem to oneself. The acceptance of the condition is too often identified with resignation, and there is an enormous reluctance to bring the problem into the open. We have but to read the psychiatrists on mental retardation and its relationship to the family to see how great a place this aspect has in their considerations; indeed, sometimes they are preoccupied with it to the exclusion of any affirmative action.

This brings us to a third obstacle. Having admitted the condition and being willing to bring it out into the open, how are these parents to find each other? The parents of children who are in institutions or state schools already have a common bond of interest, and here in New York the Association for the Help of Retarded Children was preceded some years ago by the Welfare League for Retarded Children composed of parents whose children were at Letchworth Village, one of the State Schools in New York. The desire of such parents to do something collectively for their particular children at a particular institution is understandable. Such a Parents' Group, however, if working alone, tends to have a limited function—the well-being of their children at the particular state school. They may also foster research in this connection, but by the very nature of their composition such a Parents' Group may be in a difficult position to press vigorously for the betterment of conditions there and for improvement of the entire system of state schools.

In large urban communities there is another group of parents of retarded children who, it would seem, should have found each other long before this. I refer to the parents of children in the special classes in the public schools. In New York City there are some 700 such classes and over 11,000 children in them. Yet, until January of 1949 no Parents' Group was formed. This is merely an extension of our first difficulty, the reluctance of parents to admit the problem. It reaches such refinement that even after the child has been tested by the Bureau of Child Guidance and placed in a special class, the parent still feels this is but a way-station to the regular classes. One could say that it is only through chance that a group large enough and persistent enough to go on finally came together. (In New York it was done through a newspaper advertisement and a following human interest story in one of the newspapers.)

You will note at the beginning that I spoke of the formation and *continued existence* of Parents' Groups. Let us consider their continued existence. Such a group is, of necessity, heterogeneous in character. It consists of the parents of very young children, school age children, adolescents, and adults, with all the degrees of retardation and all the clinical types. These must be bound together into one whole. Individual problems must be merged into the overall picture. This is not easy when each parent has at last found a place to express his individual needs so long suppressed. These pent up pressures of years burst forth to demand facilities for each. These must be channelized into a program which shall take all into consideration. It is obvious that even the most successful group cannot realize a total program at once, and the education of all of us to submerge our own immediate needs for the good of all is indeed a prime necessity for the continued existence of the Parents' Group.

Besides the parents themselves, two other groups must be won over in each community to assure the continued existence of Parents' Groups. These are the agencies in the community and the professionals in the field of retardation. By agencies I mean the departments of mental hygiene, education, health, welfare, and all the social agencies whose cooperation must be enlisted. Since Parents' Groups are not professionally led, at the beginning at least, they are viewed with suspicion as amateurs and pressure groups. I cannot present any set formula to overcome this. We in New York kept up a steady stream of correspondence with all of them and saw every one personally more than once. We presented ourselves for what we were, a group of parents of mentally retarded children for whom the community provided inadequate facilities, if any, for diagnosis, treatment where necessary, guidance, education, vocational training, job placement, or even institutionalization where necessary. It was not long before we were taken seriously and treated as equals. But it was and continues to be a most necessary step.

We encountered suspicion and hostility, moreover, from some of the professionals in the field of retardation. Parents' Groups meant apparently impossible demands to them. Furthermore, they meant demands for immediate action to implement the plans which were on paper only. We as parents came to them with a new voice of hope in place of the status quo. We were accused of selling "blue sky" when all we insisted on was that all is not darkness or penumbrous region. We overcame some of this by a realistic approach. We formed a Board of Advisors and enlisted some of our critics to help us. With their cooperation and the knowledge of our own needs we planned a program which could meet with professional approval. I will not say that we have won full confidence, but at least we can meet on common ground to discuss and work together. This is an absolute necessity. Parents' Groups need the trained minds of the professionals, but by the same token we have long been a non-existing necessity to shake loose the bonds of orthodoxy in this field and translate planning into action.

The very act of forming a Parents' Group, and its continued fight to survive and grow, must involve most of the parents personally. This in itself is important therapy and conditions the parents to face squarely the problems that arise out of mental retardation. The pooled experiences of thousands of parents can point up the needs that exist and the lack of community facilities.

The problems arising out of mental retardation differ with the various age groups, from birth to six, from seven to sixteen (the adolescents), sixteen to twenty, and the adults. What we think are the essential features of a community program for the mentally retarded takes into consideration the special needs of each of these groups and the parents. In the first place, we need not worry too much about duplicating existing facilities, that bugaboo of social agencies, because there are either no facilities in the community or, if they do exist, they are extremely inadequate. Most of us have experienced the statement, "we do not handle mentally retarded children here." . . .

In New York we are trying to use all the media possible to disseminate information on mental retardation, make existing agencies aware of the scope of the problem, and present the needs. We have had articles written for the newspapers. This has taken the form of letters to the editor, planned articles, and human interest stories. We have found the radio receptive. Many stations give us station break announcements, and we have had a number of interviews which have brought a large response from parents and others. We have helped furnish material for national magazine articles. This is of the utmost importance. A recent article by Judith Crist in "Better Homes and Gardens" which mentioned the Association for the Help of Retarded Children by name and gave its address brought us hundreds of letters from all over the country. I am sure that several Parents' Groups will result from it. The big article on Parents' Groups only is yet to be published. We have spoken before thousands of people—women's organizations, men's clubs, PTA groups. We have appeared on a television program and hope to appear on more. We publish our own monthly newspaper, "Our Children's Voice," which some of you may have seen. Our mailing list has grown to almost 10,000 throughout this country and abroad. We have not yet made movies because these are very expensive and must be carefully produced. We have circulated the names of all the psychologists and psychiatrists in the metropolitan area. We are now preparing a letter to all physicians. We are trying to make the legislators, camp directors, social service directors, and clinics aware of the needs of our children and their duty to enlarge their philosophy and base to include them in their plans.

All of this is for the following aims:

1. Make the public understand the problems arising out of mental retardation.

2. Demonstrate the needs.

3. Make the public understand that it is not only humane but good economics to have a constructive program aimed to ameliorate the conditions arising out of mental retardation.

4. Stimulate research.

5. Press for implementation of existing legislation. There are statutes on the books which are ignored by local authorities because it may mean spending money. In this connection Parents' Groups should have a legal committee to study all existing legislation and press for its observance.

6. Press for new legislation—state and federal. We in New York recently had a joint resolution introduced into the Legislature calling for a Commission to study the whole question of retardation in the state, to plan, and to report. I am sorry to have to tell you that it was killed in committee. Such legislation is a must to get a total picture of the problem and a coordinated plan instead of attacking it piecemeal. I understand that New Jersey has succeeded in having such a commission voted. There is in addition an enormous amount of legislation, state and federal, aimed to aid the rehabilitation of physically handicapped. There are now some five bills before Congress on this point alone. We must make every effort to have the mentally handicapped included in this help at all levels of government. We must tack on to any legislation for the aid of any handicapped.

7. Stimulate public giving. We learned one thing very quickly. Nothing can be done without money, large sums of money, and with our efforts at education have gone appeals for funds. It was not easy to get significant donations in the beginning, but we kept on trying and have been successful in several important instances, especially with women's groups. This effort must go on continually until such time as our education efforts have prepared the public for a full scale fund drive. Parents' Groups should get lists of all organizations of this kind in the community and try to appear before them.

I should like to point out here that this would be an excellent time for the professional group in the field, the American Association of Mental Deficiency (AAMD), to reexamine the semantics of mental retardation. We feel that we have been and are hampered in our work by the terms so long used to describe various forms and levels of retardation. Of course, Parents' Groups must be realistic. They cannot afford to build false hope, but neither should they have to face the world with a nomenclature of despair. The terms used today are those of defeatism. Idiot, imbecile, moron are no longer terms of art: they have been preempted by literature and cheap vaudeville. Their connotations are those arising from the novel and the low comedian. It is extremely unrealistic to ask Parents' Groups to do a selling job equipped with such unpalatable labels for wares which deserve better.

Another thing we have begun is the education of the parents themselves. We hold monthly meetings where some aspect of the problem is discussed by an authority in the field and the parents ask questions, and speakers don't always say what parents would like to hear.

We have also arranged a series of parent education courses, given through the cooperation of members of the Bureau for Children of Retarded Mental Development of the New York City Board of Education. This has been our first term and has been quite successful. The groups are never larger than twenty-five. These courses acquaint the parents generally with the various phases of the problem and help them enormously in adjusting to it.

As part of the task of education, Parents' Groups must evolve an overall plan. In New York, we have called it "A Proposed Long Range program" contained in a little leaflet. This program is what the Parents' Group itself must do to demonstrate concretely—Retarded Children can be Helped!—which is our slogan. We call these Pilot Projects. Their purpose is not to be self-perpetuating but to demonstrate what can be done and then to have the community take them over. The problems arising out of mental retardation can be solved by total community participation only, not by the Parents' Groups alone. This should be a function of an enlightened society.

Our program includes in addition to public and parent education 1) pilot clinics, 2) pilot pre-school-age kindergartens, 3) pilot schools, 4) pilot sheltered workshops and industrial training, 5) after-school activities and socialization, 6) research and scholarships, and 7) better state schools. In the past year we have sponsored the establishment of a Clinic for Mentally Retarded Children at New York Medical College Flower–5th Avenue Hospitals. Another clinic will be opened soon in Brooklyn.[1] All the medical services are involved in addition to social service and psychiatry. The whole child is treated there. The parents are prepared to accept and deal with the problems on an intelligent basis. Where necessary they even receive psychotherapy individually and in groups. The clinics will serve as centers for research and training in the field of mental retardation.

Within the next two months we will have established a special speech clinic for mentally retarded children, a most important area of therapy which the children have been able to get sporadically and by sufferance only in the clinics that exist. And isn't that true of all children's services?

We are planning cooperative classes this fall for those children who do not meet the qualifications of public school special classes. I believe a good deal of this has been done by other Parents' Groups.

We are now negotiating with existing sheltered workshops for physically handicapped to broaden their base to include mentally handicapped. In this connection the Bureau of Rehabilitation of New York State Department of Education, operating under funds from the federal government, is being most helpful. They may provide the funds for training these youngsters. It is the beginning of our first sheltered workshops. In this connection we are exploring the possibilities of employment in private industry on a non-competitive basis. We have already found one large national concern willing to make jobs for several of these boys and girls where they will work under supervision, with rest periods and guidance—and they will pay them seventy-five cents per hour. Where there is only the will, how much can be done.

Several of our parents have formed clubs for the adolescents and older boys and girls with the most gratifying results. It is amazing how some of these youngsters, long withdrawn from others, shy and apparently uninterested, have become social human beings, interested and alert.

The association for the Help of Retarded Children has been in existence a little more than two years. Sometimes, when I have the time to look back, the little things we have done seem like miracles, but so much, so very much, remains to be done and, for us as parents, so little time in which to do it. Suddenly as we gathered together there was tremendous urgency to the problem, an immediacy about everything. Parents who had been resigned for twenty years or more suddenly wanted everything at once. Do we initiate projects? Do we create events? It would seem that the pent up energies of many years propel us forward and we move with a motion and volition beyond our control.

This sense of inevitability must not be dissipated in local action only. Our problem is nationwide and is found in every state, city, county and hamlet. What we can do as individual groups can be multiplied a thousand fold when all Parents' Groups join together their forces. What we can then tell the nation will echo and re-echo through every community. Voltaire has said, "There is one thing greater than all the armies of the world, that is an idea whose time has come."

FOOTNOTES

1. Opened at the Jewish Hospital of Brooklyn. The Morris J. Solomon Clinic for the Rehabilitation of Retarded Children.

□ □ □

from INITIAL COUNSELING OF PARENTS WITH MENTALLY RETARDED CHILDREN

Israel Zwerling

(*Journal of Pediatrics,* 1954)

The problem of how much, when, and how to tell the patient or his family is an ever-present one in medicine. The situation varies with the diagnosis, the nature of the patient or family, and the personality of the physician. When the diagnosis is clear-cut, the prognosis favorable, the patient or family free from great anxiety, and the physician confident of his therapy, the problem of informing the patient or family either does not arise at all, or else permits of ready disposition. The concern of the present paper is with mental deficiency, a situation in which none of these favorable factors prevails. Here the prognosis is almost uniformly poor, the etiology only infrequently ascertainable, the parents regularly anxious, and the physician seldom confident of a therapeutic regimen.

The anxiety of the parents is of particular concern to the physician who must tell them his diagnosis of mental deficiency. There are a number of reasons for this anxiety. To begin with, there is an awareness of the long-term implications of the diagnosis, and of the extremely limited therapeutic outlook. Another reason is the widespread awe of the "mental" as against the "physical" in human malfunction. However far we prefer to feel we have moved from the era of demonology, an irrational fear of intellectual deficiency is still manifest precisely because it is "mental."

It must also be noted that there is seen, with extraordinary frequency, a marked guilt reaction on the part of the parents. The sources of the guilt feelings are complex and outside the scope of this paper, but their manifestations are familiar to the physician who has dealt with the parents of retarded children.

Finally, as Doll has stressed, the core of any definition of mental deficiency is social incompetence, and much of the parental anxiety reflects the social stigma inherent in severe and prolonged social incompetence. Abel has recently written: "The mentally retarded is a deviant who is perhaps treated with greater rejection and less respect by parents, teachers and the community than is any other deviant, perhaps with the exception of the person with Hanson's disease." Certainly a number of additional diseases provoke rejection and loss of respect by family and community, but it remains true that the characteristic attitude of the community to the mentally retarded child operates to heighten the anxiety of the parents of the child.

At the same time much can be done precisely at the time the diagnosis is presented to the parents to reduce this anxiety and to promote a more accepting and constructive attitude toward the child. It is the thesis of this paper that the initial counseling of the parents is of critical importance in this regard, and that appropriate handling by the physician can turn a potentially devastating experience into the foundation for a satisfactory adjustment to the problem [of mental retardation] and to the child.

Procedure

The National Association for Retarded Children initially stimulated this study and cooperated in the procedure. Members of the N.A.R.C. who were themselves parents of retarded children were asked to communicate with me with regard to the circumstances of their first learning of the diagnosis, their reaction at the time, and their feelings about whether the situation had been well or poorly handled. Eighty-five letters were received from parents scattered over twenty-three states and Canada. The contents of these communications were then tabulated and form the basis of the discussion presented below.

Several considerations render the data unsuited for normal statistical handling. These experiences are presented as reported by the parents, with no independent data available as to what the physician actually said or did. In addition to the misconceptions and distortions seen with some frequency immediately after contact with a physician, there is here the added problem of an interval of from a few months to several years having elapsed between the actual contact with the doctor and the report of this contact by the parent. Again, these are unusual parents in that they have been able to accept their retarded child at least to the extent of identifying themselves with the membership of the National Association for Retarded Children. The ability to write about the initial experience of being informed of the diagnosis of mental deficiency in their child is a further differentiating factor in this regard. One parent wrote:

> ". . . a person cannot sit down and write of this experience without opening old wounds. I think you would get more information through interviews than letters, for somehow it is easier to talk than to write."

Finally, it is likely that experiences felt by the parents to have been poorly handled by the doctor would be more likely to prompt a letter than experiences felt to have been adequately handled. It must, therefore, be stressed that the letters cited are by no means offered as reflections on what physicians generally do in handling this problem, nor is it the intent to offer a tabulation of how representative parents react to being informed of the diagnosis of mental deficiency. Rather, the reported experiences have been analyzed for their individual content, and common concerns have been extracted for discussion as suggested areas of interest to the physician faced with parents with retarded children. These are presented below, and are then compared with techniques for handling the initial counseling of parents with retarded children proposed by three recent contributors to the literature in this field.

The Attitude of the Physician

A striking number of letters (thirty-three of the eighty-five) refer to the importance of the attitude of the physician. A representative letter noted:

> "Dr. J. was superb in his telling of Steve's limitations. . . . Mainly, the points I remember were of course his gentle treatment of us, his exquisite choice of words so as to avoid the obnoxious ones. . . ."

Another wrote:

> "We shall be everlastingly grateful to our young pediatrician for his skillful, sympathetic handling of our case. He took as much interest in us as he did in our child and spared us what may have been a dreadful shock."

The converse experience is reported by another parent as follows:

> "When his prophecies failed to materialize within the allotted time, he sent us to a very distinguished neurologist-psychiatrist. This man pronounced the accurate diagnosis with a hard, cold, almost surgical economy of words and feelings. To put it mildly, he was brutal. My wife and I walked through the streets of Brooklyn, weeping openly."

The significance to the parents of the attitude of the physician is reflected not only in the frequency with which it is mentioned, but also in the degree of concern which is expressed. One parent reported that her doctor had commented about her mongoloid daughter that

> ". . . they make nice pets around the house."

Another wrote:

> "This doctor was a woman, and I didn't have my child with me at the time. She asked me many questions about her training and eating habits, then she asked me about her speech. When I said she didn't talk, she told me I should put her away and forget I ever had her, unless I wanted to limit myself to a dog's life. At least a dog could bark, she told me. . . . Every time I think about this doctor, I think how much more I have than her, and that is love for human beings."

One letter made it clear that the parent was not seeking maudlin sentimentality:

> "I was taken back to my room, and about twenty minutes later my doctor came in and the tears were running down his cheeks. He said there was something terribly wrong with my baby. He couldn't tell me at first, but finally told me that my baby was the type known as mongoloid. . . . My doctor had a compassionate heart, but it just seems to me that he did not have the right psychological approach. I was terrorized over the situation and remained so for about three years."

The concern of these parents with the attitude of their doctors is, of course, not unique to the field of mental deficiency. It is my impression, however, that few diagnoses provoke more anxiety in the physician than feeble-mindedness. A meaningful study remains to be done in defining the sources of doctors' attitudes toward mental deficiency. In any case, it is apparent that some parents react with great sensitivity to the warmth or coldness, the gentleness or harshness, the acceptance or rejection in the attitude of the doctor.

Twelve of the letters received from the parents comment upon the thoroughness of the study which preceded the announcement of the diagnosis. Several shared the direct comment of the mother who wrote:

> "I, as a thinking parent, was not content with anything less than a complete study of the child."

Another wrote:

> "Dr. B's statement on hearing my story was, 'I cannot say from this one examination just what is wrong, but if it were my child I would make certain tests.' . . . Blood tests were made and x-rays taken . . . the consensus of neurological, psychological and medical examinations agreed with her tentative diagnosis."

Another parent, reporting a less favorable experience, wrote:

> "A lot of the shopping around that doctors deplore would be avoided if doctors would take patients into their confidence and not act threatened when a consultation is requested."

A less bitter report by another parent was,

> "Dr. L. saw her for five minutes. . . . He told us gently enough that she would never be able to assume adult responsiblities and that there was a theory that the same kind of lesions as she had on her face, that Dr. B had called adenoma sebaceum, probably were inside her skull and pressed on her brain. . . . We should have accepted what he said, but we felt that he had not seen her for long enough. . . . Dr. C., a psychiatrist friend of mine, told me that one of the things he had learned with experience was

> not to give patients a quick diagnosis. Even if he knew what was wrong, he said, he went through the motions of more examinations because that gave people more confidence that he was not judging hastily."

It is, of course, obvious that not all clinical types of mental deficiency require equal investigative effort. Further, and precisely in cases in which diagnosis is immediately apparent, parents will recognize the perceptiveness of the physician and will be pleased that prolonged study was not required. Certainly, too, the suggestion that the physician who knows the diagnosis and prognosis make a pretense of thoroughly examining the child must be rejected. It remains true, however, that in many instances the special skills required for an inclusive evaluation of a retarded child exceed those possessed by the individual practitioner. Pediatrics, neurology, radiology, psychology, psychiatry, and orthopedics each may contribute. The physician should certainly be prepared, where indications exist, for consulting specialists in these and other fields, to explain the need for these consultations, and to utilize all available relevant professional resources toward the end of complete diagnosis.

Related to both the attitude of the physician and the thoroughness of the study preceding the diagnosis is the problem of the kind of information requested by the parents. In this regard, there are several interrelated problems. As is so often the case in the communication of technical information to lay persons, the problem of intelligibility is relevant. One parent wrote:

> "I feel that it is the doctor's duty to have the parents in for a discussion of what the full meaning of their diagnosis is. Instead, in their well-meaning way, they left us with a mumbo-jumbo of medical terms that I had to find a medical dictionary to look up the meaning."

Another wrote of being sent by the family doctor to a specialist, who

> ". . . gave us what amounted to me to a great deal of double talk in medical terms that were above my comprehension."

Concern with the content of the doctor's statement was more prominent. Eleven letters made reference to the fact that the doctor had stressed the negative aspects of the picture to the total exclusion of any assets in the child. One parent wrote:

> "I believe that when the doctor tells parents the child is defective he should point out the fact that it is possible to maintain a normal family life with such a child . . . and not point out the negative side so readily. . . ."

Another parent listed some of the current accomplishments of her five-year-old daughter, and added:

> "The thought has occurred to me many times, but there is no way of knowing, that it might have been a different story for me if the doctor had told me a few things like that . . . just knowing that they do act like human beings would have helped, I think."

A third parent wrote:

> "Tim is five years old now, very lovable, and he can say several words and even group a few together. He can ride a bicycle. . . . All of the doctors who saw Tim were kind, but not one of them gave one word of hope or reassurance."

A related problem was the concern of the parents for more information with regard to the prognosis and management of the child. Several expressed views similar to the parent who wrote:

> "Doctors should be supplied with more material so they could advise you . . . on the proper ways to rear a retarded child, so that you will not expect more of the child than he is capable."

Another wrote, more emphatically:

> "If I were to summarize what we would want, it is . . . an explanation to the parents of what [diagnostic procedures] has been done, . . . what positive conclusions can be drawn, what uncertainties remain, what general prognosis can be made. . . . The physician should give continuing, positive advice, well founded, and of a practical nature, on the day-to-day handling of problems."

It is here again pertinent to add that parents present a wide range of capacities for accepting and understanding the doctor's discussion. One must agree with the parent who wrote:

> ". . . when a husband is a Ph.D. and the wife a college graduate, I think the doctor should lay the books on the table. He makes himself look foolish when he doesn't."

At the same time, initial counseling must also be provided to the parent who wrote:

> "My reaction to the knowledge of my child's retardation was to lead an army, all alone if necessary, to help her live a normal life."

This parent never did get beyond the expression of her powerful feelings of protectiveness for her child to describe the actual experience of being informed of the diagnosis. No single formulation of content can hope to serve so varied a population.

A second point to be stressed in this regard is that the physician is being asked to provide information in fields in which he only rarely attains competence—child rearing and education of retarded children. A technique reported upon favorably by the parents is of providing appropriate literature at the time of initial counseling.

Several excellent pamphlets and books are available, and a bibliography for such purposes may be readily obtained by writing to the National Association for Retarded Children. An additional suggestion of even wider applicability is for the physician to direct the parents to the local council for retarded children. Most units maintain programs directed precisely toward answering these questions, and at the same time serve to integrate the parents into the wider community aspects of the problem of mental deficiency.

A theme which appeared in twenty-two of the eighty-five letters written by the parents was the positive role played by religion in their adjustment. In most instances there was only a brief reference to the role, but several parents devoted considerable emphasis to this source of help. One noted:

> "It was really through the church that I gained two important insights: one, that we looked at things as punishment which might be our own guilt feelings . . .. two, in connection with the Bible story of the man born blind, that these things were not a reflection on the parents, but could be used as a means of helpful endeavor."

In this connection it would appear that the physician might extend the collaboration with the minister, priest, or rabbi, certainly not infrequent in many areas of work, to the initial counseling of parents with retarded children when this appears to be indicated.

Institutional Care

The most bitter expression of feeling by the parents concerned their being advised to institutionalize their retarded children. This subject was approached in widely varied ways. Some, concerned with the frequency with which the advice to institutionalize the child was given, wrote on the factors within the doctor which they felt to be responsible. One parent said:

> "Medical doctors work with so much sick tissue that they think everything defective should be scrapped."

Some parents remarked on the lack of factual information concerning institutions possessed by the doctors urging this disposition. One wrote:

"... this has come up with other doctors; they do not know the institutional setup and do not take the trouble to find out what facilities are actually available and suitable for the child, nor do they refer parents to positive sources of information on these topics. One psychiatrist recommended the W. . . School [a very expensive private school] to the wife of a machinist. In our case, the recommendation of Letchworth Village [a New York State institution] to New Jersey residents was quite frustrating."

Fifteen parents commented on the attitude of the physician toward institutionalization as one of finding some place to "put away" the child, rather than as a positive procedure in the management of the child. A rather typical statement by one parent read:

"He folded his arms across his chest and without batting an eyelash said, 'You're wasting your time. The only thing to do with this child is to place him in an institution.' "

Another parent wrote:

"The doctor there . . . advised that we should put him away and forget about him. I have never in my life heard such a cruel sentence."

Five parents characterized the doctor's attitude toward institutionalization as demanding. One wrote:

"I can supply you, practically verbatim, with the interview we had with the doctor . . . and with our reactions over that weekend when we thought our boy would be snatched away to an institution in a very short time."

Twelve letters referred scornfully to advice for immediate institutionalization and then described a currently adequate home adjustment. One parent wrote:

"Each time we went to the doctor he would ask us if we had taken out the papers yet, and when we said no he would harass us further. . . . Our boy walked at three, stood up alone and walked on his birthday! Were we ever surprised! You can imagine our joy! It took us quite a time to really accept him for the child he was, and to see he would never be the child we would have liked to have him be. He is a happy, well-adjusted and self-sufficient child."

The parent quoted above as interpreting the advice to institutionalize her child as a "sentence" went on to write:

"My boy is now six years old. He goes to D. . . School. He is talking very well and can carry out all the orders I give him in the home. He is sweet, very affectionate, and I guess the dearest little soul on this earth as far as his mother, daddy, and sister are concerned."

A less frequently voiced complaint about advice to institutionalize concerned the timing; characteristic was the statement:

"I would say that a doctor should take it in easy stages in telling a parent. Tell them the child is retarded, yes, but don't go into a long talk about institutions. A parent is absolutely in no condition at the time of the initial shock to hear a verdict like that."

These statements serve to emphasize a most important area of concern to the physician who must tell parents of the existence of mental deficiency in a child. The decision to institutionalize a retarded child is complexly determined by the nature of the child, the available institutions, the parents, the siblings, and the timing of the procedure in the light of all these factors. The role of the institution in the management of the retarded child is variable; the proportion of actual training and of sheer custodial care will vary with the adequacy of the institution as well as the abilities of the children. Institutionalization is not a disposition to be cavalierly arrived at, nor one to be callously recommended.

When to Inform Parents

Among the parents who commented on the point, there was substantial agreement concerning the question of *when* they should be told of the diagnosis. Eighteen of the letters reported at least one, and generally several, experiences of being told their child would "grow out of it." Thirteen of the letters make the specific complaint that the parents should have been told earlier:

> "He [the consultant pediatrician] also told us to go back to our family doctor and not to go chasing after miracles. At the time I was very depressed and bitter toward our family doctor. Since then we have gone back to him, but there is still a little resentment because he didn't tell us himself when he first suspected the baby was retarded."

Another wrote bitterly:

> "I continually asked my pediatrician why Brian was so slow—in sitting up, in standing, in walking; if there was any chance that his physical slowness would be accompanied by mental retardation. Always I got a placating, 'No, he is just slow and will catch up.' There was no effort to refer me to a psychologist or psychiatrist for testing and advice. Do not the doctors know the signs of mental retardation and deficiency, or are they just afraid to tell us?"

Several parents described the converse experience; one wrote:

> "I'm glad I knew from the start. Worry would have been worse."

Another wrote, in a similar vein:

> ". . . learning the results of his tests was at the same time a tremendous blow and a tremendous relief from worrying and wondering just what, if anything, was wrong."

In a few instances (five letters) a stronger feeling is expressed on this matter, in terms of the feelings of inadequacy developed by the parents. One mother reported, in dialogue form, a series of conversations with various doctors in which she asked about specific developmental lags and was continually reassured that the child merely needed more time:

> ". . . until I got to the point of feeling that I was a neurotic mother—a completely inadequate one—with no one paying any attention to me, not even my own husband."

Only one letter expressed support for a delay in being told the diagnosis. This mother learned that she had given birth to a mongoloid child through a tragedy of errors in which the husband, obstetrician, and pediatrician each thought one of the others had told her, and, therefore, greeted her successively on the morning after the delivery with expressions of sympathy. She wrote:

> "I do not think a mother should be told until she has had at least two weeks to recuperate from the actual birth of the child."

In the matter of the timing of discussions and advising institutionalization, the parents contributing letters to the present study are particularly unrepresentative samples of the population with which the physician must deal. First, these *are* parents of retarded children, and one would have to raise the question of how vigorous a protest against doctors who gave incautious diagnoses of mental deficiency could be culled from parents with children who did "grow out of it." Certainly, the anguish caused by needlessly alarming such parents can equal or exceed the despair of the parents contributing to this report. Again, these are parents who have accepted their children at least to the point of joining member units of the N.A.R.C. Denial is then not prominent in their collective defenses against the impact of the diagnosis, and denials on the part of their physicians are condemned. No conclusion concerning actual practice is, therefore, warranted from the letters in this regard.

However, it may be emphasized that the letters express concerns which are central to good clinical practice. The task of the physician is to become fully skilled in developmental diagnosis, so that clear indications of mental deficiency are not relegated to the lower end of the normal range. It is likely that the anxiety of the physician, rather than a lack of knowledge concerning developmental norms or a lack of faith in the capacity of the parents to accept the diagnosis, prompts some of the counsel for waiting for the child to "grow out of it." It is the further task of the physician to recognize and avoid such motive for his counsel. . . .

There is a growing tendency to refer retarded children to special clinics for diagnostic evaluation and for treatment recommendations. In communities where such clinics are available, the problem of counseling parents will be shifted from individual practitioner to clinic staff. However, such facilities remain few in number and inadequate in staff for more than token capacities. The individual physician—pediatrician, or neurologist, or psychiatrist, or most frequently general practitioner—will continue to serve as initial counselor for the great majority of parents with retarded children, and must develop appropriate knowledge and skills for this difficult task.

The reports of the parents who contributed letters are not felt to reflect the characteristic practices of physicians. They are, however, felt to be of value in providing principles for the correct handling of the initial counseling situation, and these are seen to be in accord with the principles announced by Jensen, Doll, and Kanner in recent contributions to the field. . . .

from THE PARENTS OF RETARDED CHILDREN SPEAK FOR THEMSELVES

Charlotte H. Waskowitz

(Journal of Pediatrics, 1959)

Within the last decade [1949-59] there have been vast development and rapid progress in the total area of mental retardation—more and better resources; specialized clinical and counseling services; training, educational, and recreational facilities; medical research; and financial aid. Concomitantly, there has been widespread interest in professional circles as well as in the community, increased understanding, acceptance, and tolerance of the mentally retarded child and his family. Much of the credit for the impetus to this important movement belongs to the parents of retarded children who, because of their persistence, perserverance, and courage, have shown the way. It is parents themselves who have given us clues about their own capacity and strength to find solutions and resolutions to their problems.

Although much has been accomplished, one area that is a constant source of difficulty is that of communication between parents and professional personnel. Frequently the parents of a retarded child go away from a contact with a physician, psychologist, or social worker with a good deal of justifiable dissatisfaction. This is not an isolated occurrence but tends to be rather widespread, and, as professional persons, we must assume the responsibility and blame for these difficulties. The services that are offered can and should be improved. As a means of improving these services, the author enlisted the participation of the Maryland Society for Mentally Retarded Children and interviewed the parents in the following exploratory study.

With the approval of the officers and members of the Society, a letter was sent to every fourth member stating the purpose of the study. A questionnaire was developed as a general guide, with the full knowledge that this study would produce qualitative material of importance although not statistically impressive. In general, the guide fell into the following categories: 1) identifying data, 2) when retardation was first suspected by parents, 3) consultations by specialists, 4) counseling by professional persons and parents' reactions to counseling, and 5) value of group organization to the parents. Interviews were held by the author in the Harriet Lane Psychiatric Clinic; the average length of interview-time was approximately one hour and, with few exceptions, it was the mother who came for the interview. Of a group of fifty to whom letters were sent and follow-up contacts made, forty were seen; of the ten remaining, the majority could not be reached and only three refused to participate. It should be noted that the group was a highly selected one, and the material was based on recall; therefore, the study does not lend itself to usual statistical methods.

In general, the parents can be described as an intelligent group of young and middle-aged people, with small families of two and three children, of the white race, and the middle socioeconomic class. . . . Answers to factual questions of

> "When did you first suspect something was wrong?" "Was someone professionally consulted at that time?" "Who really told you your child was retarded?"

produced difficulty in pinpointing answers. One explanation is the time lapse and problem of recall, since this material was gathered from several months to many years after the patient was diagnosed as retarded. However, other factors that bear consideration are 1) problems in diagnosing, 2) parents' reactions to the seriousness of the problem of retardation, to their feeling of difference from other parents, and resultant feelings of fear and anxiety.

Often there is much uncertainty around diagnosis because many different factors must be weighed and evaluated such as physical, emotional, and limitations in the tests themselves and the difficulties surrounding the testing, particularly of young children. The process of considering physical factors that complicate accurate evaluation frequently involves referral to many different specialists with their variety of opinions and, certainly, their uniquely different ways of handling the parents. It was not unusual to hear such expressions as:

> "My doctor did not know whether his slowness was due to his mental condition or to his physical sickness."
> "The doctor was confused as to whether the child could hear."
> "The doctor's first impression was muscular dystrophy and then in another examination he thought he was just retarded."

Occasionally the influence of emotional factors must be considered, which necessitates intensive involvement of the parents in recapitulation of bitter life experiences. The limitations of the tests themselves, just in terms of evaluating intelligence, lend another element of doubt. Certainly the innumerable difficulties in having the child perform at his best and obtaining as much as possible from him create questions and doubts. In other words, are the test results representative of the child's intelligence? And lastly, the adequacy and skill of the tester add another problem to the welter of confusion.

Mention of retardation creates a serious impact on parents, which is understandable in view of the attitude of society and the problems of the intellectually limited child in achieving a safe, secure place in our culture. The very practical aspects of everyday living, training, schooling, recreation and, lastly, occupation and self-support have been almost insurmountable. It is no wonder then that usual responses were:

> "It's like someone came to you and told you your child was dead."
> "When we were told, it was a terrible shock—you stop living."
> "I was on the verge of a nervous breakdown."

It was not surprising, therefore, that these reactions were followed by acute feelings of "aloneness," "difference," being set apart from the rest of the world, rejection, and lack of interest in the children and their problems. This is vividly illustrated by such comments as:

> "None of the doctors said anything to me; I couldn't even get any schooling for him."
> "We got so nervous–everywhere we went nobody would help us. We then thought it was God's will and we did not go anywhere."
> "I feel the doctors brushed me off."
> "I feel that the medical profession did not want to be bothered, were impatient and annoyed." . . .

Is it any wonder then that there were expressions of anxiety, embarrassment, and guilt? As one parent said, "The doctor did not want to be bothered. I was embarrassed to go to his office. I had to sit with other people's children. I was always treated with the attitude: 'Here comes this woman with this child.' The doctor did not like him and did not mince any words about it." . . .

Of the total group of forty, in thirty of the cases studied the parents suspected or were aware of retardation in the first year of life. Of the mongoloid group of nineteen, in thirteen instances the parents were aware of and/or were told of the serious deficiency within the first month. The brain damaged and the etiologically unspecified cases of mental retardation took longer to diagnose. In the brain-damaged group, twelve were suspected of retardation under one year of age, (three of whom were known under the age of one month) and the remaining three took up to three years to diagnose. In the cases where no specific cause of retardation was known, one was diagnosed at age twenty days, one at eight months, one at one year, and one at eighteen months. In the two remaining cases, the epileptic was diagnosed at ten months and the other was diagnosed as questionable retardation due to emotional factors. Therefore, we must conclude that mental retardation was serious enough to be detected reasonably early in this group of children.

As one would expect, it was the pediatrician who was most frequently consulted first (in twenty-five instances). This was followed, in order of frequency, by the family doctor in seven instances, the obstetrician in three, the neurologist in one, and the child guidance clinic in one. In three instances the parents "just knew" and did not consult anyone at the time. "Were others consulted and at what ages?" prompted a succession of medical specialists too numerous to record. Illustrative is one parent's comment.

> "I must have had Billy to over 100 different doctors." Another replied, "I must have spent over $8,000.00 for various consultations to no avail."

Unfortunately, parents did not seem to obtain the help they needed early enough to prevent the trauma of endless pursuit of answers to their problems. Perhaps, significant is the fact that the "end of the road" seems to be the child guidance clinic, psychologist, or psychiatrist, whom the parents finally seek in desperation, usually after the child is two years of age. Also significant is the fact that one-half of these patients finally reached these specialists.

"Who really told you?" produced only one significant point, namely, many parents "just knew" or suspected serious pathology long before affirmation by specialists. The author has found that it is not an unusual occurrence in clinical work for a parent to be able to state fairly accurately the intellectual level at which his child is functioning at the time he is seen. What the parents are really asking for is not just a diagnosis, but total handling of the problem.

The question "How were you told your child was retarded?" evoked the most intense responses indicative of the traumatic experiences suffered by so many of these parents. The striking thing that permeated this section was that the different reactions to what parents considered good and poor handling varied according to their own individual needs, so that one is forced to conclude that the most important consideration is the ability of the counselor to individualize, to be sensitive to where the parents are emotionally at a particular time, in other words, to empathize with the parents.

Some parents wanted to be told directly as soon as retardation was suspected. A typical comment was:

> "The doctor was very frank about it. It was very positive and in no way abrupt. We were aware of what the situation was, and we appreciated knowing this."

Another commented:

> "I was told right at the beginning. We were always thankful to the doctor who did tell us."

On the other hand, many parents indicated their wish to be prepared gradually, as follows:

> "The doctor was very tactful. He implied things right along. At first he said she was not holding her head up, not sitting up, etc. Not until two or three years later did he really tell me the child was seriously defective and had to be in an institution. He prepared me well."

Another parent reported:

> "A pediatrician told us the child was retarded. He told us in the nicest way it could be explained. He told us it was far too early to say how much he would progress. We returned for visits frequently. As the child grew older, we were told what the future held."

Apropos of this discussion, it should be pointed out that frequently parents inadvertently mentioned the names of the doctors they had consulted (in spite of the request that no names be mentioned). It is of interest to note that one parent would condemn a doctor while another would highly praise the same doctor. This obviously casts no reflection on the doctor but emphasizes the need to individualize each situation. Another observation is that in almost every record there is an admixture of good as well as poor handling, which again emphasizes the promise to handle each situation individually.

Important to note is that, when questioned specifically, only twenty-five per cent of the parents indicated that their contact with professional people was satisfactory. The most important factor in this regard was that these parents were counseled not only sensitively and directly, but also their questions were answered, particularly those relating to implications for the future. A typical expression was:

> "Our family doctor was wonderful. He talked to us for about an hour. He said our child was a dull boy and to give him regular care, but to give him a little bit of extra love. He answered all my questions and told me just what to do. He prepared me well for the future."

Another stated:

> "A psychiatrist told me for the first time my child was retarded. It was a shock, a bitter disappointment, but it was accepted. He told us what to expect and gave us wonderful advice."

Another eight also indicated they were told directly, frankly, tactfully, sensitively, or slowly, but in most instances, questions pertaining to implications for the future were not answered. In three cases parents were not informed by anyone, "they just knew."

In sixteen instances parents clearly described how poorly they were told with such adjectives as cruel, abrupt, confused, blunt, upsetting, contradictory. The adjectives the parents used are graphically illustrative of descriptions of their experiences, and they reacted to them with such comments as:

> "They tell you your child is an idiot and everything else. There should be a nice way to tell parents. When they told us roughly, we stopped going."
> "The doctor said, 'He will never be any good to you or to himself.' I told him I was raised with the feeling where there's life, there's hope."

> "I was told my child was mongoloid without any preparation for it. I thought he was perfectly normal, and it came as a complete surprise. We had just stopped in for a checkup. The doctor said I should have him in an institution because it would be better for the child and everybody else. All I wanted was to get out; I was stunned. My husband was overseas at the time, which certainly did not help. When you think back, you can't believe anyone could be so blunt."

Two parents commented that they were told over the telephone:

> "My husband was told over the telephone that the child was a mongoloid when the child was four days of age."
> "The doctor said our child was a mongolian idiot over the telephone. He acted as though it was your problem, buddy."

Numerous references were made to examinations which were considered too hasty and careless:

> "It was an assembly line fashion."
> "The interview was not at all satisfactory. He saw us very quickly and did not even give us the results of the electroencephalogram. He sent us a note and suggested we buy a book he wrote. Good God, we still don't know whether he is epileptic or not."
> "I didn't have the feeling wherever we took her that they thoroughly examined the child."
> "The doctor gave her a three-minute examination and said she was brain injured and threw her out."
> "The mother knows first of all what the child is. She's around the child all the time. She knows him thoroughly. How can a doctor, who sees a child for one-half an hour, know about the child?"

One other complaint that was outstanding in the study was a tendency on the part of professional persons to evade the issue. As one parent said, "The doctors gave me no clue that anything was amiss. In fact, they assured me everything was going to be all right."

Other complaints pertained to complicated medical terminology.

As indicated in the preceding section, there are certain generalities that can be made, namely, that parents would want to be handled gently and warmly at all times, in language that they can understand, without evasiveness, after thorough examination and with enough time to digest the significance of such important material. This was reinforced by the parents in response to the question: "What type of service would you advise for people who are faced with this problem and are just beginning?" The material indicates that they need gentler, more sensitive handling than the usual patient. This is supported quite vividly, as they expressed intense feelings and reactions. Particularly they stressed that their "children be treated as individuals" and that the counselor be interested in their problems.

What they seemed to be expressing is the need for more responsible, integrated services in this field. Professional people are becoming aware of this, as special diagnostic centers are developing in various parts of the country. Parents are able and willing to accept the uncertainty involved in diagnosis in an area which is not clear-cut if they could depend on a centralized resource rather than to be left to shift for themselves in an endless search for answers which are not possible.

In the instances where parents indicated the wish for frank, direct diagnosis as early as possible, they felt they could accept the worst if the counselor was compassionate and respected them as parents with strength and dignity. They needed time to take in the extent of their problem, and they needed to work out solutions step by step. Questions did not arise in an organized, crystallized fashion, but gradually as the child grew. As one parent put it, "This is a lifetime thing."

Some of the comments of the parents are indicative of their keen feelings of anxiety and guilt, and it is important to emphasize that this is not resolved simply by articulating it for the parent.

One parent said:

> "I got angry at people who told me not to feel guilty. It only made me feel guiltier."

There seems little question that, for many parents, the highest degree of specialized skill is indicated in the area of counseling. If we, as professional persons, really listen to what parents of mentally retarded children say, we can take our clues from them. It was not unusual to find parents express relief as they learned their children could at least be toilet trained and could express such simple needs as to ask for water, etc. As one parent said:

> "I used to lie awake and pray that my child could say a little word like 'water' because I was so afraid he would be thirsty and could not help himself."

It is interesting to note that two parents spontaneously commented that they were relieved in "spilling over to me," although they had innumerable, previous opportunities to talk about their problem.

Two observations worthy of mention were related to terminology. One is that parents showed severe reaction to such terms as idiot, imbecile, and moron, and hoped for terminology that would avoid such negative connotation. Another is their request for simpler explanations in terms they could understand, particularly, practical, tangible suggestions relative to everyday living. Perhaps we need a greater appreciation of the little achievements of the retarded child and its meaning to their parents. Still another request was for clearer explanations, the full meaning of which they could take in. Parents often interpret such terms as "the child is slow" to mean that the child "will catch up in due time." In my clinical experience I have found that a better way of helping parents to understand what is really meant is to use "behind," connoting that the child will not catch up.

A discussion of the material would be incomplete without giving some illustrations of the continuous history of the parents' search for help. Comments taken out of context and categorized cannot possibly present the full meaning of the total impact of accumulated frustrations on the parents on the one hand, and their strength and capacity to handle their problems on the other. Only as we can appreciate and accept this can we be fully helpful in developing adequate services. Two records have been selected to illustrate this, the first one concerns a child diagnosed as mongoloid and the second one a child diagnosed as brain damaged.

> Mrs. Martin, the mother of five children, is a warm, motherly person, of limited educational background but, nevertheless of good intelligence. She is a thoughtful, sincere individual.
>
> She begins as follows: "I knew Johnny was a slow child, but I thought he was a sick child. During infancy he slept for the most part and we couldn't awaken him." Early he was taken to the clinic; however, no mention was made of retardation. "They said he was just sick. He was not a well baby, but would probably pick up, but they never gave me a reason." However, an attendant kept repeating, "If only I had your faith." Apparently this comment seemed so inappropriate at the time that it made an impression.
>
> "When Johnny was about two years of age, a doctor was called about another sibling and casually commented that Johnny was mentally retarded. The doctor referred him to the hospital where the opinion was that the child was a mongoloid, very retarded, and that the best thing for us to do was to put him in an institution because he would forget us very quickly and if we had other children, it would have an effect on the whole family, particularly that our children would be embarrassed because of Johnny." On this statement, Mrs. Martin comments, "I thought that was abrupt and cruel."
>
> Mrs. Martin continued, indicating her upsetness over this experience. She said, "After I got home, I wanted to know how retarded he was because I was too upset to ask any questions while I was at the hospital." She returned to her pediatrician because apparently she had a warm relationship with him. He dis-

agreed with the opinion of institutionalization, suggesting that it was the parents' prerogative to decide such a drastic move. His opinion was that the child needed the love which could not be received in an institution. He explained Johnny's mentality, cautioning her not to spend any money on Johnny, but to center her financial resources on the other children. The doctor's most meaningful comment, and Mrs. Martin says this with much warm feeling, was, "Remember, when your other children have left, you will always have Johnny." (In response to the question, "Who gave you the most help?" Mrs. Martin unequivocally said it was this pediatrician.)

The parents explored every school possibility without any success until he was ten years of age when he was accepted in a special class in the public school. He stayed there four years and was withdrawn when the center closed, and was then placed in another school. According to the mother, considering his limitations, he has made a good adjustment at school. He mixes well with the other children who have encouraged him in this respect. He even writes, spells, and does a little arithmetic. Mrs. Martin feels that the school has been instrumental in giving Johnny confidence, and enabling him to do some of the things normal children are doing. She glowingly describes her relationship with the teacher as "wonderful," particularly the help to the parents in allowing them to sit in class, observe, and learn.

In response to the question "Do you feel that your contact with professional people had been satisfactory?" Mrs. Martin's first point was, "Parents need all kindness you can give them."

She also felt that parents should know exactly what is wrong as early as possible. If known at birth, it should be told at that time because one can be more helpful to the child. She regretted the information being withheld from her. She described it as "not fair." "It's yours, your baby, you want to know right at the beginning." Mrs. Martin had the feeling that everyone knew that her child was mongoloid except herself. It bears emphasis that she was not informed that the child was a mongoloid until he was two.

She further emphasized that "if there is a ray of light, it should be told." When the pediatrician told her Johnny could reach the mental age of eight, it was helpful to her. "Every word we took hold of."

Still another area of importance is to handle questions pertaining to heredity. The Martins were very much concerned whether to have additional children, and it was with great relief that after repeated contacts with professional people, she finally got her questions answered.

"What type of service would you advise for people who are faced with this problem and are just beginning?" brought forth the seriously traumatic experience of first being told bluntly and insensitively. "I felt it could have been handled a little more kindly. If you can speak to anyone in the medical profession for a while, it's wonderful. If they can't help the child, maybe they can help the parent."

About institutionalization, she commented. "I think too many children like this are put in institutions. It frightens the parents to think of institutions. I don't think an institution should be mentioned at first. Couldn't it wait to see how a child progresses before it is mentioned? I am truly as proud of Johnny as I am of my boy who graduated from college."

The second record is as follows. This is one of the few situations in which both parents participated in the interview.

The Allans are intelligent, fairly young people, in their middle thirties, and have a family of three children. In spite of their struggles, their charm and zest for living comes through.

Bobby was about seven months of age when they had some vague suspicion that all did not seem quite right. They consulted their pediatrician who said that he was a little slow—not responding, not sitting up. "But the pediatrician said nothing to allay my fears, he said Bobby would be all right." Then, with much feeling, Mrs. Allan adds, "He didn't say this because he didn't know—he did know."

After much "badgering" on the mother's part, and insistence that there must be something wrong, they were referred to a neurologist. Bobby was about one year of age by this time. The examination showed that he was nearsighted.

Further consultation with two doctors indicated that there was nothing wrong. Mrs. Allan said, "I thought I would work harder and teach him more. Then began the most frustrating period of my life. Trying to teach a child when it was not possible to teach him was like knocking my head against a stone wall. My heart just aches when I think what we have been through. I pushed him. I spent a lot of time with him. I would try to feed and toilet train him and we got just no place."

The Allans returned to the pediatrician, whereupon they were referred to an orthopedic man. At that time, Bobby was about one and a half years old, and Mrs. Allan estimates his intelligence at about one year. The orthopedic man found his feet were quite flat and suggested corrective shoes. He also offered the following advice. "He will catch up, he will be all right." Mrs. Allan, however, felt all was not so rosy because she mentions that at nineteen months he was beginning to walk but "still there was not a flicker any place else."

When Bobby was two years of age, the family was referred to a psychiatric clinic. Here she describes her experience as "wonderful." The doctor spoke to her at some length and "it was almost a relief for me to hear it. At least I knew where I stood." By this, Mrs. Allan means she had her suspicions confirmed, namely, that Bobby was retarded. However, he was described as being only mildly retarded, with a good prognosis, but the years have proved otherwise. At least she knew she didn't have a normal child.

Mrs. Allan described meeting her pediatrician on the street and berated him for not telling her the truth. His comment was, "You couldn't have done anything about it anyway. I knew that you would find out soon enough." Mrs. Allan emphasized how deeply disturbed she was during that time.

Although Mrs. Allan felt she was reasonably well handled by the psychiatrist, her questions were not answered. When questions arose regarding other children, Mrs. Allan consulted her pediatrician and he advised her against having another child. Their obstetrician, however, encouraged her to have another one. She subsequently became pregnant, and describes this period as one of great fear of having another retarded child. In the sixth month of pregnancy she contracted mumps, and "nearly went crazy." "The baby was wonderful. Anyway it had a happy ending."

At about three and a half years of age, Bobby had his first convulsion, his condition was followed at the seizure clinic, where he was put on medicine for convulsions. The parents were told nothing about his condition, and were critical of the fact that he did not have a complete work-up. They ". . . were not even told what the EEG showed."

There was further pursuit of medical exploration until finally they consulted a psychiatrist. The psychiatric consultation was described as being reasonably satisfactory, although the psychiatrist was "cold, he told us the brutal facts. At least I could start living after that rather than just hoping. Even so, he was optimistic." He recommended institutionalization, but the parents indicate their disapproval of this with much vehemence. The psychiatrist also pointed out that they were concentrating too much on the retarded child to the exclusion of the normal sibling. The indications are that they could accept this.

In answer to the question, "Was your contact with professional persons satisfactory?" the response was "absolutely not." Then they added, "In fact, we have lost a great deal of respect for the medical profession; we have had nothing but frustration every place we have turned."

"What type of services would you advise for people who are faced with this problem and are just beginning?" brought the immediate response, "Gently, but the truth." Mr. Allan felt that the counselor should evaluate the type of parent and the intellectual capacity of the parent, have a few visits with them if necessary, and handle them accordingly. They both agreed that the parents should be informed just as soon as the doctor knows. He said, "The attitude is of paramount importance. If the parents sense sympathy in the professional person and willingness to understand, this has a great deal of meaning. After all, most parents want to respect their doctor."

One further comment revealed the magnitude of the burden for parents when Mr. Allen said, "After all, you have a whole lifetime to worry about this, and you can only take it by degrees."

The discussion of the questions of institutionalization produced much negative response on the part of the parents, especially when the counselor had no direct knowledge of the resources but, even more important, little understanding of the family and indiscriminately advised it as a solution. Illustrative are such comments as: "They all spoke of institutional care as though that was the only thing we could do. They acted as though we had no choice." "If the child can be cared for at home and is not a burden on other members of the family, then they should keep him. I look at the happiness Billy has given us—he is so sweet and kind. The other children in the family adore him." "I honestly think that Tommy would not have gotten anywhere in an institution. There is no difficulty in having him at home."

Without exception these parents wanted what was best for their children. They wanted to know whether the resources would help their children to achieve their capacities, however meager, and help them grow up as well as possible considering their handicaps. When necessary, they can come to terms with institutional care if that is the soundest way of helping their children. They asked whether their children need more than their share to enable them to assimilate whatever training and education are available. Also, they are able to provide the tender, loving care to make this possible. So many parents cannot be interviewed without the interviewer being greatly impressed with their love for their retarded children, and their ability to accept and handle frustration. It is important to note that in twenty-one of the cases, institutional care was recommended early, but in only one was it followed through. The obvious conclusion is that they were not ready or interested in this solution.

It is significant to note that there is important research going on in the field on the families who can best use institutional care for their retarded children. One study, still in progress, considers the effects of a severely retarded child on family integration, the results of which can be of help to counselors in evaluating the kind of family who can keep their child with them and those who might best be directed toward institutionalization.

Apparently there has been more change in the attitudes of society toward retarded persons than we realize. The prevalent assumption has been that families cannot accept too much difference and that the higher the cultural and intellectual achievement, the less possibility there is for the retarded child to be cared for at home. This is not supported by this study. On the contrary, a place has been found for these children in their families, neighborhoods, and schools. I do not believe that it is being too omniscient to say that many of these children have gotten as good a start in life as is possible under the circumstances. I should doubt that anyone would challenge the fact that the institutionalized child does not have his emotional needs met.

Needless to say, parents spoke glowingly of the local state Society for Retarded Children. They have found a way to share their experiences, to be supportive of each other, to resolve their feelings of difference, and, most important, to speak for retarded children and crusade in their interest. This has been an invaluable group therapeutic experience for many parents, an important factor in enabling families to live more comfortably with these children and to be helpful to them. They have proved parents need to be no longer isolated as individuals and families, with the serious emotional problems which set them apart from the rest of the world. These parents have paved the way for community understanding and acceptance of the problem, and have achieved an important role in community welfare by spearheading the need for specialized services in education, recreation, parent education facilities, and in programs of financial aid. They have discovered so much for themselves that they want to share their experiences and to be helpful to others.

□ □ □

from SOME POINTERS FOR PROFESSIONALS

Letha L. Patterson

(Children, 1956)

. . . .

Of all life's problems those presented by a handicapped child (and particularly a mentally handicapped child) require the utmost in teamwork within professions, among professions, and between professional and lay people, especially parents.

[Through the National Association for Retarded Children] we parents are attempting to assume responsibilities appropriate to the partnership through helping to define our separate roles and in heightening our communications in order to save other families from unnecessary trauma.

Dr. Martha M. Eliot [former] Chief of the Children's Bureau [has] said:

"When officials of public agencies ask what kinds of services should be provided for retarded children, my advice is 'ask the parents' . . . [they] are often best qualified to say *what* help they need, though professional persons will have to provide the *hows."*

Thus, we laymen and professionals are indispensable to one another in our efforts to make up for past neglect of this serious medical, emotional, social, and educational problem.

Perhaps I can bring together for the readers of this journal for professionals some of the written and spoken insights which have come my way from both professional workers and parents. These, I feel, are relevant for those of you who find it your task to help families face this heartbreaking problem—whether you are physicians, psychologists, social workers, nurses, teachers, or administrators.

Tell Us the Nature of Our Problems as Soon as Possible

When I said this to a class of students of child psychiatry at the University of Minnesota Medical School, I was asked by an alert student, "But Mrs. Patterson, what can the physician do when he is not sure himself and doesn't want to worry the parents?"

"Just be honest with us," was my reply.

It takes great sensitivity and intuition to take a mother's couched remarks and detect that they spell "worry." Often we parents are concerned just as early as our practitioner, but we are reluctant to put our fears and worries into words. However, we give plenty of hints that we want our professional counselor to help us get them into words, to lead us on the proper course—whether that means waiting a while or consulting with specialists immediately. It is a wise counselor who knows when he does not have the answers and is willing to admit it.

One of my psychiatrist friends put it this way: "When I am faced with a worried mother or father *I have got a problem.* Either there is something wrong with the child, or something wrong with the parents, or both. And if I can't identify the trouble, then I am obligated to get this family to someone who can."

Always See Both Parents

Fathers are parents, too, and all professional workers need to be reminded of this. Both parents should be present whenever possible, at least on first consultations regarding a child's handicap.

It is very difficult for a mother to go home and restate, interpret, and answer questions about a problem she does not clearly understand herself. Often the problem, with its fears, has brought about a lack of communication between mother and father. This is particularly true in a young marriage or when the retarded child is the first child. Establishing adequate communication is difficult in any marriage. Finding the words to support one another in *this* problem has been impossible for some of us. We have needed an objective person through whom to talk.

Unfortunately, all husbands (and wives) are not like the one who, when he learned that their little daughter would not progress like other children, said to his wife: "Honey, we don't know what lies ahead of us—but whatever it is, we can handle it because we are strong people." Many of us can find this strength, however, if you'll help us.

Another reason for seeing both parents is that both need to be pulled along together in their understanding and acceptance. I have seen too many mothers who realized the need for institutional care and were ready to "place" a child while the fathers trailed behind ignoring reality, not to recognize the great need for a common understanding. Sometimes it is the mother who will not admit that something is wrong and insists that her child stay in regular school classes when a special course of study is indicated, while the father suffers along in silence, afraid to precipitate the issue. If you but knew the isolation that can exist behind our four walls!

Watch Your Language

Parents need to understand the implications of their problem, but too often we are given professional gobbledegook, or at the other extreme, plain talk of an obnoxious variety. Words like "idiot," "moron," and "feebleminded" used to be excellent and descriptive clinical terms but they no longer apply to our retarded children. Unimaginative writers and purveyors of so-called humor have polluted the meanings with connotations of social or moral deficiency in the mentally normal.

On the other hand, there was the doctor at a residential institution who wrote to two parents stating that their son was ill with "cervical lymphatic adenitis." The worried family did considerable research to find that the child simply had swollen glands of the neck.

The child psychiatrist, into whose capable hands my husband and I finally could put our problem, was very sensitive in his use of words. He avoided "moron," "feebleminded" and even "mental retardation" by encouraging us to evaluate our child's developmental status. And when he confirmed our findings, we felt quite pleased with ourselves. He always referred to our boy as "your son," "your lad," or "Stephen" with a voice filled with great compassion so that we started thinking more about Steve's problem and less about our own hurt egos.

Help Us to See That This Is OUR Problem

One way, of course, is by example—by not taking the problem over for us.

Too many well-meaning professional people in the past have thought they knew what was good for us and have recommended, even insisted on, institutionalization. We know, now, that denial of the existence of the child is not the solution for either child or parent, that abandonment is not the answer, and that it is psychiatrically unhealthy to rob parents of their responsibility for planning. Only as we parents are helped to work through our problems can we find any peace of mind. If we have not planned for our child ourselves, if someone else has made the decisions, we have not really made up our own minds and so must keep going over the ground again and again. We may never be at peace with the solution which was reached for us.

Administrators of institutions tell us that the best help for families in adjusting to their child's placement is the fact that the parents themselves have decided —with adequate professional guidance, of course—that placement is best for the child in relation to the total family welfare.

There is another reason for showing us that this is our problem. You have no idea how much unprofessional, unsolicited, and untried advice we get from well-meaning people—our neighbors, relatives, friends, and even strangers standing on street corners. When, with your guidance and example, we realize that *this is our problem,* we can shut our ears to the static and rely on our own judgment. But we need your professional support in helping us to feel competent in making these decisions, your confidence that we will ultimately make the proper decision for care in our particular case, your assurance that there is no failure if we change our plan when circumstances change. Life situations and retarded children present different problems at different times. You can help us explore the possibilities for meeting our problem, support us in adjusting to our decision, act as a continuing sounding board against which we can bounce our own thinking, and give us a good, sturdy shoulder on which to lean when we get dizzy going through the maze of decisions.

Help Us to Understand Our Problem

Parents differ in the quantity and quality of information they can absorb during different phases of this problem. What they want and need depends greatly on the individual, but many of us have had to search for the knowledge we needed in order to understand our child.

[In 1950] when I began my search, a severe scarcity existed in printed material on the subject of mental retardation. Today, there are many fine and helpful publications in this field. . . .

Regardless of what we parents are able to read and absorb, we will always have questions to ask. We will continue to need support from someone, whether our child is at home or away—particularly in those days which follow the confirmation that mental retardation *is* our problem.

One medical counselor asks parents to come back several weeks after he has given them the bad news, knowing that they will have questions which could not come to the surface during the emotional strain of hearing the verdict. Moreover, he sees to it that the parents get to a social worker and he also urges them to join an association for retarded children.

Frequently he turns their names over to the local association's "parents counsel committee," requesting that some mature couple—a mother *and* a father—call on them. He has found that parents who have successfully faced their problems can offer a special kind of help to new families which transcends his professional services. Further, he has seen the therapeutic effects of parents working together in organizations to improve the lot of the retarded and their families. Incidentally, he was initially one of the "pros" who were afraid of this "lay" movement.

Know Your Resources

In referring to services, Dr. Eliot has called the retarded child "nobody's baby." Certainly there is evidence in most states that services are disjointed and uncoordinated. Rarely is there any one place which can put parents in touch with resources that *are* available.

In Minnesota, where the county social worker is the local resource for parents, a booklet, "You Are Not Alone," telling parents where and how to seek help, has been distributed to members of the state medical association, county welfare boards, clergymen of all faiths, family and welfare services, clinics, public-health nurses, associations for retarded children, and newspaper editors, in the hope that the booklet (or the information) will be passed along to parents. It was produced by the statewide Conference Committee on Mental Deficiency, a professional-lay body.

California has started meeting this problem with information centers for the parents of retarded children, set up in Los Angeles and San Francisco by the State department of mental hygiene. The psychiatric social workers assigned to this task have a variety of functions—counseling individual parents, putting them in touch with resources, providing information to public and private agencies, and serving as consultants in community planning.

Other States are developing a network

of clinics with built-in social services for the sustaining help so necessary.

Anyone who has carried a handicapped child from one waiting room to the next in an effort to gather resources into one piece will appreciate the significance of these several efforts to avail parents of the services that do exist.

Never Put Us on the Defensive

All parents make mistakes in raising children. Those of us who have a retarded child are bound to make errors, but we should not be made to feel guilty about them.

One day I said to my medical counselor: "You know, of course, that I was angry at you for a good long time for 'confirming my diagnosis,' but never once have you put me on the defensive about it or any of the mistakes that we have made in relation to Steve."

"Why should I?" he countered. "How do I know I could have done any better than you, had I been in your circumstances?"

He went on to give this definition of 'good parents': "Parents are good parents, when to the best of their ability, understanding, and circumstances, they meet as adequately as possible needs of their children." [Reynold Jensen, M.D.]

Remember That Parents of Retarded Children Are Just People

This has been *my* most amazing discovery. We are just people with a serious problem, a great sorrow—a living sorrow. We have the same strengths and weaknesses as others in the general population. We have the same problems, the same handicaps. But when the burden of mental retardation is heaped upon us, often these problems and defects are magnified and we, in turn, create problems for those of you who must deal with us. But *as a group,* I do not think we should be considered abnormal, particularly in view of the poor cultural attitude towards our problem, the lack of interest and services, and the fact that some parents have made great personal and family sacrifices to carry this "cause" to the public conscience.

You cannot generalize about parents of retarded children any more than you can generalize about retarded children. Gifted, average, or limited, any of us can find our problems complicated by our own emotional makeup. Professional people working with us must learn to appraise these variables in our intelligence and emotional stability.

Apropos of this are the technical articles which some of us read. Why do we *always* face such words as "anxieties, hostilities, frustrations, guilt-feelings," and other emotionally charged words to describe our reactions? Such pseudo-scientific certainties merely serve to make parents feel even more inadequate, it seems to me.

You should take seriously the comment of a New Jersey parent: ". . . Is not what appears to be 'guilt feelings' to professionals, merely concern with the child's welfare, mingled with grief over his handicap?"

"All parents experience some feelings of guilt about illness in their children . . ." Dr. Julius B. Richmond, pediatrician, of Syracuse University has said. If outward manifestations of these feelings persist in us after you have assured us that "no act of omission or commission" on our part has been responsible for the condition of our child, perhaps our feelings might be more aptly described as "regret." We are bound to feel regret if we have rejected this child—if we have struck out at him and created problems for him. With this regret we very likely feel anger at not having had the proper guidance at the times we needed it.

Might not some of our hostility be nothing more than righteous indignation over the neglect of our problem? Actually, if some of the pioneers in the parent group movement had not become "mad" in the early days, our problem would still be largely ignored. Who can say, on the basis of present knowledge, when anxieties are neurotic overreactions, if parents must ask: "What will happen to this child after we are gone?" "How can we pay for expensive care outside our home?" "Where can we hire a sitter so that we can take a vacation?"

Whatever labels we use for these feelings, they have added up to a great determination—you might call it "compulsion"—for some of us to see to it that new parents coming along can walk a smoother path. And there is considerable evidence that many of these new parents are avoiding some of the emotional scars which some of us bear.

Dan Boyd, a New Jersey parent, has described three stages in the growth of a parent of a mentally retarded child: 1) Why did this happen to me? (Self pity.) 2) What can I do for my own child and family? 3) What can we do for others?

These stages can be intermingled. The fact that a parent is working in an organization "to help all retarded children" does not necessarily mean that he has grown with his own problem. Some can be stage-three leaders, without having graduated from stage one. Such self-pitying parents are the hardest to help. It often takes a long wait and the greatest skill on the part of professional counselors and their parent counterparts to help them to begin to make realistic plans for their own child.

Most parents, however, mature quite rapidly under the stimulus of the group. Self-pity fades when they find that they are not alone. Soon they are seeking to learn from and emulate the parents who have met their problems successfully. And before they know it, they are experiencing the healing that goes with helping another family. Some move on to be eager for all parents to have access to the organization which has rescued them from desolation.

Even these mature stage-three parents can slip back temporarily into stage two, when a problem arises at home or when previous decisions must be reviewed. During these times we can be very difficult. Then you must support us, while feeling "nothing but plain, simple, humble reverence before the mystery of our misfortune," to use the words of John Cowper Powys.

This means that you must look at your own feelings about us and our children. If you do not have a natural feeling of concern for the mentally retarded, if you feel indifferent to or repelled by children who are not mentally normal or by parents under great stress, then you should not deal with us at all.

Remember That We Are Parents and That You Are Professionals

Some of us are becoming so well-informed in certain areas of this problem and we are associating with you in so many different pursuits that, at times, it must be difficult to remember that we *are* parents and, as such, will always be emotionally involved with our own problem and our own child, regardless of the "objectivity" we may have about the problem generally, or another family's problem, specifically. In communicating with us you must be clear as to whether you are speaking as counselor to client, adviser to organization member, coworker, or personal friend. In this we expect you to use professional judgment.

For example, don't, in front of us, belittle or countermand the opinion of one of your professional partners; make critical remarks about other parents and their handling of their child; jump to conclusions about our case without adequate clinical study or knowledge of the facts. And, of course, don't try to do a job that is outside your professional discipline.

When we see so much that needs to be done, we have little time for professional jealousies, or for the individual who uses mental retardation as a ladder to personal success. It does not take long for us to pigeonhole a "problem professional" whose own emotional difficulties are getting in the way of our efforts.

Remember the Importance of Your Attitude Towards Us

Sometimes I think your colleagues place too much emphasis on "objectivity" and not enough on "loving kindness." Certainly we expect you to be objective about our problem. But about us? Never! A really gifted professional person cannot *help* feeling—being subjective, attempting to stand in our shoes and to look out at our problem through our eyes—in the process of helping us. Psychiatrists call this "empathy." It is only through empathy that you can divine the proper words and acts to help us.

There are greater depths and breadths in helping parents of retarded children than many of you have realized in your initial attempts. It has been as exciting for some of us parents to watch professionals grow as it has been rewarding for professionals to watch some of us parents grow. We can help each other become more effective people through our partnership.

You are obligated, it seems to me, to "feelingly persuade" us, as Shakespeare said, to help us find "what we are." We have many strengths. If you can help us convert our problems into good for mankind, help us find the sweetness in the uses of our adversity, *you* will find a far more precious jewel in your professionalism than you ever thought existed.

And you will be professionals in the most noble and magnificent sense of the word.

□ □ □

from HOW CAN PARENTS AND PROFESSIONALS COORDINATE FOR THE BETTERMENT OF ALL RETARDED CHILDREN?

Norma L. Bostock

(*American Journal of Mental Deficiency*, 1956)

. . . .

In covering the first portion of my presentation, and so that you may have a clear understanding of the experiences of most parents in having this tragedy enter their lives, I am going to ask you to try to divorce yourselves, your thinking, and your reactions from all that you have learned about this subject as professional persons and to live for a short period of time through the actual experience of having borne a mentally retarded child. In my contacts with parents, this accounting of events is relatively accurate as conditions prevailed throughout our nation as short a time as five years ago, and as they exist in many areas even today. Bear in mind that you need go back no farther than five years to have had this happen to you.

This baby, just born, had been anticipated for many months by the parents. They had had all the usual dreams of the joy of seeing his first smile, his first steps, his gradual developing to and through the school ages, his companionship with them in all family relationships, even going so far as having had him finish college, marry, and produce grandchildren. Suddenly, this dream became a nightmare; a mentally retarded child had been born.

Realize too that these parents had been raised in the same generation of tradition, custom, and trends of thinking as you, which had placed a stigma on the parents of mentally retarded children. When such a child appeared as a result of a marriage of two persons, it branded both sides of the family because such a thing could only be inherited.

At first, there was the complete destruction of all the hopes and plans for the future; then there was self-condemnation, feelings of inadequacy and misery, a breaking up of family ties on both sides of the union because of accusations of deceit as to expected inheritance for the children; withdrawal from society because of the shame and stigma attached to such an incident; and finally there was the desperate seeking of—what could be done—what had to be done—for this unfortunate child. Bear in mind that this child was no limited animal nor inanimate object to the parents—this was their child whom they loved dearly and for whom they felt responsible.

In casting about in despair for guidance, the parents sought professional counseling and advice. The first contact, in most instances, was the family doctor. If he had the courage, which many did not have, he told them that their child was mentally retarded and, in the majority of cases, advised them to send the child away and "forget you ever had him." If he did not have the courage himself, he sent them to a consultant or a clinic, where, after going through similar procedures, they were told, "Send him away and forget you ever had him." Again I say, remember that this was their child whom they loved. Also keep in mind that you are now parents living and having this experience as recently as five years.

Many parents, who had extreme faith in the advice of those trained to guide them, decided to place their children in residential hospitals or schools as they had been told to do—for the good of the children, for the good of the families, and for the good of society, as well as for the benefit of the child himself.

The parents approached the institution and its staff. In the case of a state institution, it was necessary to go through a court procedure—declaring the child incompetent and thus denying themselves the right of jurisdiction over their child; they had to place him in the cold and unsympathetic hands of a governing body which would determine what was right and best for their child.

At the institution, they were met by a group of people who were just "doing a job," to whom this child was only one of a great number of responsibilities—nothing more. Being of the same generation and school of thinking as the parents, they attached to them the incompetencies and incapabilities their education had trained them to believe must be there—otherwise, they would not have produced a partial child. At best, they were in haste to discharge their duties and rid themselves of the offending and interfering factors—the parents. Because of limitation of staff and their many duties, they gave as little information as was necessary, brushing aside the natural human interests and fears of the parents for their loved ones.

Then there were those parents who, after having gone through the counseling and guidance described previously, decided that they could not bear to go through the uncertainties of separating themselves from their child and decided to keep him at home as long as possible. They too were met on all sides by discouragement, shame, criticism, and frustration. It was a constant struggle to combat public opinion, to protect the child from open ridicule, and to try by any method to provide for him some of the things to which he was entitled. Unfortunately, a rift developed even between the parents of the mentally retarded because of lack of understanding, those who institutionalized judging those who did not in relation only to their own decision—and vice versa.

True indeed—this is a bleak picture I have painted; nothing but rifts existed —rifts within the family, rifts among the parents of the mentally retarded, and rifts between the parents and the professional people, and, in addition, complete rejection by society.

Surely this points up the desperate need for parent education to the whole problem. The parents have traveled down a long road of rejection and despair, having met on all sides only antagonistic and unsympathetic attitudes. Isn't it understandable why they have built up tremendous defenses of bitterness against and suspicion of society as a whole, and of professional people in particular, for the abuse and lack of consideration which had been heaped on them and their children. Parents have had a long way to come back before they could even be susceptible to positive acceptance of and cooperation with the now progressive programs of the professional people and of other parents themselves. . . .

Better public understanding of the true picture of mental retardation and all that it implies may be attained only when professionals and parents alike have a fuller knowledge and acceptance of the entire problem ourselves. To accomplish this, we must have a unanimity of thought and action which can be produced only through an understanding by the professionals of the human element involved and a dedication on their part to guide and direct this human interest into the proper channels of productivity. One misconception which seemed to have existed in the past on the part of professionals was that it was wise to keep the parents uninformed. This has been proven unsound.

It is obvious that most parents of the mentally retarded have a tremendous human interest in the problem. The potential presented by this interested group can and will do much good providing it is properly understood, trained and directed. If parents remain ignorant of the total problem, are excluded from an education that is vital, and are stifled by the professional people in attempts to help, progress will be deterred.

Therefore, you who work in this field every day would be wise to acquire all the wisdom and understanding at your command, using it to assist in harnessing our unified forces into productive action.

Separately we can accomplish a great deal—by cooperatively combining our efforts, intelligence, and power, we can bring into actuality all the progressive programs which will improve conditions for all retarded children, wherever they may be.

□ □ □

SECTION C

The Old Way

Before we proceed to the coverage of enlightened management, we should taste just one more bitter sample of our past. As many sages have stated through the years, those who forget the past are condemned to repeat it. Although all three selections in this section are concerned with mongolism, this is purely coincidental. Their relevance goes far beyond this condition, and the term mongolism could be replaced by either "severe retardation" or "severe impairment recognizable at birth."

In the first selection, Aldrich presents a traditional management approach. While we now reject this approach, we will miss the point as to why this selection was included unless we remember that the management techniques described were once almost universally taught as appropriate to prospective managers, in the sincere belief that the relevant facts supporting such techniques were known and that the described approach served the best interest of both child and family.

Hormuth and Weingold, both parent leaders at that time, further remind us of conditions of the field in the earlier days. Each makes the critical observation that certain words in our society take on an evaluative tone resulting in stereotyping and compartmentalizing, which, in turn, predispose toward maladaptive social action. This is the case with such terms as "mongolism" and "severe retardation." One can generalize Hormuth's observation that the so-called children's bill of rights excludes mongoloids only—there is evidence that many of the handicapped are perceived as not possessing rights taken for granted by the non-handicapped.

Weingold astutely observes that the labeling of a child as "mongoloid" has many overtones, far beyond the description of a clinical entity. A diagnostic label is more than a simple word-description of a condition. The labeling process triggers into motion a host of actions on the part of people, and it sets the stage for emotionally-based decisions. Imagine a mother, lying in her hospital bed, awaiting the first glimpse of her newborn baby—a situation repeated in this country every few seconds. Then imagine the obstetrician entering her room, pulling the curtain for alleged privacy and, looking her straight in the eye, announcing: "Madam, I'm afraid that you have given birth to a mongolian idiot!"

from PREVENTIVE MEDICINE AND MONGOLISM *C. Anderson Aldrich*

(American Journal of Mental Deficiency, 1947)

Once in every 500 deliveries, the attending physician is faced with a potential family tragedy in the birth of a mongolian idiot. This incidence is true in the United States and, while I am not familiar with the actual statistics in reference to babies of other countries and races, it is a well-known fact that mongolism does occur in people of every land and of all colors. . . .

The problems presented by the arrival into a family of one of these accidents of development are many and of deep concern to the baby, his parents, physicians, social workers, and various officials of the state welfare and health departments.

From the baby's point of view several points should be mentioned. The *mortality* rate in the first two years of life is high because of the inferior musculature of these children. Infections of the respiratory tract are particularly dangerous and congenital heart disease is very common and a frequent cause of death.

From the standpoint of the child's living an adequate social life the prognosis is even worse. I have often remarked that the better they were, the worse off they were. The inadequacy which is inevitable in mongolism is not so noticeable if the child is an evident idiot and if he is treated appropriately. But when he almost "makes the grade" and tries to enter freely into the competition of civilized living, his experience is usually devastating and may lead to serious social situations, as you well know. The child is constantly being frustrated by his inability to compete and to comprehend his difficulties. The troubles met in dealing with mongols, however, would be much worse were it not for his well-known sunny disposition. I have often thought that in this world of strife and trouble mongolian idiots, of all human beings, perhaps live the most carefree and happy lives. Nevertheless, they are happiest when allowed to grow up in situations where they compete with their peers, in institutions.

The difficulties faced by the mothers of these children are, in many respects, more serious than those faced by the child. Because the mongolian is so incompetent in the ordinary techniques of living, his mother soon becomes a complete slave to his dependency. As a result, she devotes all of her time to his necessary care, neglecting her other household duties, her other children if there are such, and inevitably, her husband. The effect of all this is that all other satisfying areas of living are blotted out and that she becomes enmeshed in an almost hopeless entanglement of emotional ties to the mongol. From the practical standpoint, a potentially useful citizen is removed from social intercourse. It is a clinical fact that few such mothers have subsequent children.

In many instances, the father is

placed in a very trying situation. When the realization gradually seeps into his consciousness that all is not well with his child, he may notice also that his wife is becoming so engrossed with her baby that she is losing touch with him and all his areas of interest—that she has no time either for his affection or for the outside recreation they used to enjoy together. If he faces facts and tells her his fears, she often feels that she and *her* child are being attacked and responds with a defensive emotional storm. If he says nothing, they usually drift apart slowly. Many separations and divorces follow the birth of mongolian idiots.

The other children in afflicted families suffer from a social stigma which they and their playmates sense but often do not understand. With passing years, as the mongol becomes less and less acceptable in the neighborhood groups, his brothers and sisters refuse to bring other children into the house, of necessity play elsewhere, and are obsessed with a feeling of family shame no matter how unjustifiable it may be. Few situations are worse for household morale or for that of the children.

There is an economic element in this situation also. When parents finally realize the deficiencies of their child, they often begin a hopeless round of visits to doctors and clinics near and far, spending all of their savings and often borrowing up to their capacity in the vain hope of finding a cure. It is a sad commentary on human nature to note that not infrequently they encounter people who promise much and slowly drain the family's resources in fantastic and useless methods of treatment.

There is only one adequate way to lessen all this grief, fortunately a measure which most experienced physicians will agree to, and that is immediate commitment to an institution at the time of diagnosis. But this procedure is difficult to accomplish if the mother has had the child under her care for any prolonged period. She becomes so necessary to the child and so attached to him that she cannot give him up. Therefore, it becomes highly important to make the diagnosis as early as possible. Fortunately this can be done in more than ninety per cent of the cases on the day of birth. I am outlining here a technic which has been found successful in accomplishing separation of newborn mongols from the family, in the hope that it may help others in meeting this tragic situation.

1. When the diagnosis has been made in a newborn the mother is told that the baby is not strong enough to be brought to her at present and that he must remain in the nursery for a few days.

2. Next, the father is asked to meet the physician immediately, bringing with him any close relatives who are available in the neighborhood. At this conference, the nature of the problem is explained in detail, emphasizing its seriousness, the facts that no one is to blame, that future babies will be normal, and that immediate placement outside the family provides the only hope of preventing a long series of family difficulties.

It may be advisable, in many instances, to enlist the aid of the clergyman closest to the family. This has been of great help to me several times, for often the pastor will be familiar with the unfortunate sequence of events which accompanies the birth of a mongol and may have dealt with such disrupted families in his church. He is often eager to prevent any repetition of such tragedies.

3. If the father and close relatives of the family can be made to accept outside placement as the solution of their problem, the physician and the husband, backed up by the family decision, report the whole situation to the mother. She is asked, not to *make* the decision, but to accept the one which has already been made by the close relatives. This has the advantage of tending to prevent the quite natural feelings of guilt which

might otherwise plague her after surrendering the child to another's care.

4. Having obtained unanimous family permission, the physician must arrange for immediate placement of the infant. In some states this can be done through public agencies without delay. In others, a boarding home placement for the interval is necessary until the delays incident to commitment and finding institutional vacancies have been overcome.

This method is, of course, not infallible, but in the past fifteen years [1932-47] it has failed me only two or three times. It means that the physician must take the lead in precipitating an immediate crisis in order to prevent much more serious difficulties later on. This is preventive medicine.

I am presenting this report to you with the idea that it may stimulate interest in making available a rapid means of committing mongoloid infants to institutions. There is no doubt but that the social service load in any community could be lightened were cribs made available for immediate occupancy by newly born babies who were mongolian idiots.

□ □ □

HOME PROBLEMS AND FAMILY CARE OF THE MONGOLOID CHILD

Rudolf P. Hormuth

(*Quarterly Review of Pediatrics,* 1953)

One of the major contributions of the mid-century White House Conference on Children and Youth was the formulation of a set of principles embodying the basic needs of children. This children's bill of rights includes those things which are vital to the welfare of any child regardless of race, creed, color, or handicaps.

Concerned as we are in this symposium with the mongoloid child, it seems that the logical foundation on which to build a program of home care and the solving of family problems involved would be this bill of rights. As professional workers with children, it is our responsibility to review this bill of rights, incorporate its principles into our thinking, and evolve approaches to the mongoloid child which take these basic needs into account. Included in this formulation is the right of every child to:

The affection and intelligent guidance of understanding parents.

To be raised in a decent home in which he is adequately fed, clothed and sheltered.

To the benefits of religious guidance and training.

To a school program which offers maximum opportunity for individual development and preparation for living.

To receive constructive discipline for the proper development of good character, conduct, and management.

To be secure in his community against all influences detrimental to proper and wholesome development.

To free and wholesome recreation.

To live in a community in which adults practice the belief that the welfare of their children is a primary importance.

To receive good adult examples.

To a job commensurate with his or her ability, training, and experience, and protection against physical or moral employment hazards which adversely affect wholesome development.

To early diagnosis and treatment of physical handicaps and mental and social maladjustments at public expense whenever necessary.

No one who knows and understands children would attempt to deny the soundness and validity of these principles. All professional workers with children utilize them in their daily contacts. An exception, however, is always made, and in this case, the exception seems to be the mongoloid child. These rights are not extended to him. We seem to become blinded by the word mongoloid and forget that we are dealing with an individual who, as a child, has needs beyond food, clothing, and shelter which must be met. The very people who are most verbal in the defense of these rights for other children generally maintain a deadly silence when these rights are so blatantly denied to the mongoloid child. The mental hygiene movement as a whole has ignored aspects of the mental health of these children. Many physicians have nothing to offer except the term mongolism and institution. Some psychologists are still too busy evolving I.Q.'s, and some are still tagging the term idiot to the diagnosis of mongolism. Social workers content themselves with getting parents to "accept" mongoloid children—whatever that may mean—thus, facilitating the complicated arrangements for commitment. Perhaps taking the cue from the other professions, too many educators still absolve themselves from the entire problem by labeling these mongoloid children as "uneducable."

All of this adds up to a picture of a child to whom we deny the basic rights and privileges we automatically extend to all other children. He and his family can avail themselves of very few facilities in the community.

Few clinics will accept the mongoloid for adequate diagnosis; almost none offers any kind of help or therapy. If school facilities are made available, the mongoloid is generally segregated and placed in the lowest functioning group. The only door which opens to him is the institution.

The home care of the mongoloid child cannot be undertaken unless and until the professional persons with whom the child and the family come in contact are ready and willing to accord to him the rights of childhood. In order to explore what is involved in home care, we have to be willing to afford the mongoloid child an opportunity to live at home. We have to provide him with a family who can give him affection, understanding, and guidance, and we must have a community which is conducive to his growth and development, a community which offers adequate medical care, guidance, group experience, schooling, and the opportunity to work.

At present, many professional workers are still not thinking along these lines and are offering little or nothing. The reason basically is that as a group we continue to rely without further investigation on predictions and implied prognosis for the mongoloid, which have no basis in fact. In four out of five cases where a diagnosis of mongolism is established at birth, the recommendation for immediate institutional placement still forms a part of the diagnosis without regard to the extent of the retardation which may be involved and in spite of evidence that such children make good adjustment. Too many parents are still told that the mongoloid will probably not survive for more than six months to a year, or that if he does, will never develop beyond a two-year level. Parents are still frightened into attempting to secure institutional placement by the dire predictions which are made.

In most cases such placement is not feasible or cannot be carried out, and the child is eventually brought into a home and a community which has been conditioned by fear, ignorance, and prejudice to reject this child. The distorted parent-child relationship, which is created by such misinformation at the very beginning, is the major problem with which we have to deal in cases where home care for the mongoloid is attempted. The development and the basis of these problems can be clearly comprehended in the following case illustrations. We can see their beginnings with the obstetrician's first casual inspection of the newborn baby, and then, through the process of diagnosis, misinterpretations and misinformation grow and spread until they engulf the family and the community, leaving the child confined within the smothering overprotective walls of an isolated family.

L. was an only child born to parents who were intelligent, well-adjusted, eager and anxious to have a baby. A diagnosis of mongolism was made shortly after delivery. The parents were advised to institutionalize the child immediately and were discouraged from taking him home. They had never heard of the term mongolism before, but as a result of the interpretation which was given to them, they felt it best to avoid all further embarrassment and told all of their friends and relatives that the child had died shortly after birth. The delivery had occurred in a private hospital, and after two weeks, with the help of doctors, the child was transferred on the pretext of a physical illness to a city hospital, while the parents attempted to locate a suitable private nursing home for the child. Finding these far beyond their financial means, they proceeded to arrange for commitment and certifying examinations to a state school. After a great deal of difficulty and with considerable delay, they were successful in this, only to be told when the certifying examinations were completed that potentially this child should be able to achieve an I.Q. close to 75, and that as such he was not eligible for commitment to a state school.

By this time the child was six months old and the city hospital demanded that the parents remove the child from their ward. In order to do this and face their friends and relatives, who had been told the child was dead, the parents had to invent elaborate stories. The father explained that the child had been transferred to Johns Hopkins Hospital for an extremely delicate operation, that the heart had stopped beating, and the parents had been informed that the child was dead. They explained that a specialist by massaging the heart muscles had restored life, and now the child was coming home. Unfortunately, one of the relatives mentioned this to a reporter friend, who in trying to check and use the story found that no such case was known to Johns Hopkins Hospital. The resulting complications and embarrassment caused the family to withdraw from their social contacts, and subsequent to this had little to do with their own relatives.

This was the basis on which this child came home at the age of six months and began his relationship with his parents. This beginning resulted in an extreme overprotection of the child by his parents; they seldom took him anywhere, expected nothing from him, practically hid him in the closet, and were unsuccessful in developing most of the abilities and capacities which he had. It might be of interest also to note that when this child was examined at the Morris J. Solomon clinic several years later, the psychologic findings still indicated that his abilities in terms of I.Q. were in the seventies.

Another example is that of H., an only child, born to parents in their late thirties. A diagnosis of mongolism was made shortly after birth. The parents, previously unfamiliar with such a diagnosis, were told that the child would never develop and probably would not survive beyond six months of age. They were strongly urged to place H. in an institution and forget that they ever had a child. These parents tried to follow this recommendation. However, they were unable to locate a private facility because of their limited income and, because of existing regulations, were unable to secure placement in a state school. After two months, the hospital brought charges against the parents to remove the child from their nursery. The mother was forced to take the child home and, as she put it, "waited for her to die." The rejection created by the interpretation of the diagnosis was extreme. Like so many other mongoloid children, H. seldom cried and spent most of her time sleeping. The mother changed her once a day, never picked her up, and frequently didn't feed her. Despite this, H. survived beyond six months and by that time was beginning to show some progress and development. The mother began to take an interest and, of course, was overwhelmed with guilt at what she had done and then became extremely overprotective and smothering in her attentions to this child. H., now at thirteen years of age, attends a special class in the public school. One of the major problems encountered in the clinic was to get the mother to stop doing things for H. which the child was perfectly capable of doing by herself.

The vast majority of cases of mongoloid children seen at the Morris J. Solomon clinic present the same type of picture, with the problems which eventually confront the child developing in the same fashion. This sort of experience is also borne out by the family service agencies in this city. The following are typical of the types of problems which they reported.

In the case of W., the obstetrician

> and the hospital staff doctor told the family that they must not take their child home. They even refused to permit the mother to see her baby, despite her wishes. The family not being able to withstand the physicians' pressure, placed their baby in a private institution with the help of the hospital social service staff, who did not consider the financial burden this would create. Within a few months, the family was no longer able to meet the cost of private care and had gotten themselves so entangled in financial difficulties that they went to a family agency for help in unravelling their financial complications. The agency, of course, was not able to provide the financial help for the continued private care of the child, and shortly thereafter the child was brought home into an atmosphere which approximated that previously described in the other cases.
>
> The K. case was referred to a family service agency by the hospital social service for financial assistance for interim private placement, because the family could not bear to take their mongoloid child home. Their feelings had been enforced by the doctor in the hospital, who had suggested that they let friends and neighbors believe that the child was dead. The family borrowed money for the first month's placement rather than bring the child home and were vaguely searching for a nonexistent source in the community that would subsidize this plan until the child could be admitted to a state school in from three months to a year. This child also eventually came home, much to the embarrassment of the parents. By that time, the attitudes toward the child had become so hostile and so set that he was automatically blamed for all family problems. Finally, he was placed and forgotten by the parents, despite fairly high abilities that would have made adjustment in the community fairly easy.

In all these cases a similar pattern emerges. The problems, which eventually were encountered after home care was undertaken, had their roots in the orientation given to the parents and the misinformation that the community believed in. The frustration, guilt, and hostility created in the family tends to isolate them from everyone, and the child is isolated along with them. The distorted parent-child relationship and the resulting overprotection, which gives the child little opportunity to do anything for and by himself, are the basic factors involved in the major home problems that arise.

These problems are imposed on the mongoloid child from without. Inherently, the mongoloid as such does not present problems and difficulties that would make home care for him any more difficult than that involved with any other type of retarded child or any physically handicapped child. As a matter of fact compared to other diagnostic categories of the mentally retarded or even other handicapped or emotionally ill children, the mongoloid is probably easier to manage and can adjust more readily to home care. Almost every professional person who has had the experience of working with mongoloid children will testify that as a group the emotional development of the mongoloid child is on a fairly even level, that they are usually pleasant and affectionate, they rarely exhibit temper tantrums or behavior disorders, that they are highly imitative, docile and trainable.

If we do not handicap the mongoloid child by giving him a prejudiced family overwhelmed with guilt, fear, and ignorance, in most cases his chances of adjustment in a family care program are good. The case of J. W., an only child, illustrates this fairly well.

> The diagnosis of mongolism was made at birth. The attending physician had had a good deal of experience with mongoloid children and gave the mother a sympathetic but realistic interpretation of the diagnosis. He indicated that J. probably would be slower than other children in developing and he explained it would take him longer to learn, and that he might not be able to go through regular classes, but suggested that the parents take the child home and give him the opportunity to develop whatever capacities he had. He suggested to the mother that if at a later date problems or difficulties developed, she could always arrange placement. The mother proceeded on this basis. J. at thirteen years of age

was seen at the Morris J. Solomon clinic. On psychologic tests, he scored an I.Q. of approximately forty-five and a mental age of approximately six. He was just learning to read and write and had attended a special class in the public schools since the age of seven.

The remarkable thing in this case was the attitude of the parents who approached him as one of the family and accorded him the rights of other children. They made allowances for his limitations, but in general expected him to adhere to the family routine, participate in family activities, and to conform. Despite the mental age of six, J. was functioning on a social level close to that of an eleven year old. In self-care activities he was completely self sufficient. He bathed, dressed, and ate by himself, made his own lunch, and travelled to and from school (which involved two buses) by himself. There was no area in his community to which he could not find his way alone after he was shown the route once. He had joined the boy scouts, went on hikes with them, passed his tenderfoot tests, and on Saturdays even made some pocket money by carrying bundles for women shoppers at the local grocery store. There was no difficulty working with J.'s parents in the clinic and helping them create projects in the home which would develop this child's capacities even further.

There are many examples like this in the clinic files. They indicate that at the beginning, if the parents are not prejudiced against the child by misinterpretations stemming from the term mongoloid, and if they are given a realistic appraisal of the actual mental capacities, the family problems encountered in home care are not overwhelming. Further evidence of this is seen in those cases where either the parents were not aware of the diagnosis of mongolism, or the diagnosis was not established until after the child was two, three, or four years of age. In this group of cases, the family overprotection and anxiety are much less worked and certainly less hampering to the potential development of the child.

If we can eliminate those factors which set up a prejudiced family at the start, then the management aspects of the mongoloid child are reduced to the typical problems encountered with other retarded and handicapped children. The approaches used are the same basically as those employed for any child. They are applied to the retarded child on the basis of the mental and social levels rather than on the basis of chronologic age. They are also applied in a more concrete fashion—learning by action and example within the framework of a structured, detailed schedule and routine.

There is one other aspect that requires some consideration here, chiefly because of the importance usually attached to it by professional workers in the course of advising immediate institutional placement of the mongoloid child. This is the question of the effect which the mongoloid has on other normal siblings. In the work at the clinic as well as in the other projects of the Association, we have found this to be a problem that could be dealt with to the satisfaction of all and without necessarily having ill effects on the normal sibling. Two things must be recognized in this area. Firstly, that very young children show little or no prejudice, and, secondly, that most children take over and adopt attitudes and anxieties of the parents. If the parents show no prejudice, few of the normal siblings will. At the point where the siblings start to ask questions about their "different" brother or sister, they are given realistic answers. Armed with these, they are secure enough to handle and deal with most questions and remarks by others. The most successful cases we have had have been those where the normal sibling was invited to the clinic and actively involved as a member of the family in both the interpretation of findings and in evolving management approaches to the mongoloid child. Where the normal sibling is given a part to play in the entire process of helping the mongoloid child at home and in the community and where he can be shown how by his action he is helping his brother or sister, there are no ill effects.

This incidentally can be accomplished with the normal siblings at the point where they start to ask questions. It is interesting to note that in the Association, brothers and sisters of retarded children, who are of high school and college age, have formed a junior league where they can help each other with similar answers and approaches.

In conclusion, most of the home problems involved in the family care of the mongoloid child stem from a basic prejudice against him. The shock of the diagnostic implications, as they are generally interpreted, sets off a chain reaction which deprives the mongoloid of all rights to be considered as a child, denies to him the opportunities for healthy growth, and effectively stifles potential development. This chain reaction inevitably leads either to the doom of institutional placement or to a vegetative existence within the smothering confines of the wall of overprotection erected by the family.

Three basic facts must be faced and accepted by professional workers, by the family, and the community: 1) mongolism does not carry with it the corollary of "idiot," since the mongoloid has been found to function from very low to comparatively high levels; 2) most of the mentally retarded, including the mongoloid, can with the proper help and facilities function in the home and in the community; 3) none of the mentally retarded can realize their full potentials *unless* they are provided with the necessary opportunities for growth and development during their early years, and these include a family and a community which are conducive to such growth.

If the mongoloid child is viewed as a child and provided with the opportunities of other children, then family care and management become no different from that of any other handicapped child. On the basis of experience, the personality characteristics of most mongoloid children should make this task easier. The adverse effect of the mongoloid child on the family life and on the other normal siblings is minimal and can be dealt with constructively. The mongoloid child within the limits of his capacities can become a happy useful member of a family and a community.

□ □ □

from REHABILITATION OF THE MONGOLOID CHILD

Joseph T. Weingold

(Quarterly Review of Pediatrics, 1953)

The labeling of a child as a "mongoloid" has many overtones, far beyond the description of a clinical entity. What flows out of this unscientific name results in enormous complications of a problem that, medically, is complex enough. It is both the result and the cause of a pathetic and dangerous lack of knowledge, sympathy and understanding of a very large group of children with a handicap.

It is high time, indeed, that this problem be removed from the shadows, placed in the light of day, and examined, not only as to its medical implications, but also educational and social. In short, let us see the "mongoloid" as a child, unblinded by an unfortunate name, and unhampered by outworn prejudices.

I feel particularly qualified to speak about this, not only as the Executive Director of the Association for the Help of Retarded Children, the New York State Parents Group, where I come in contact with hundreds of parents of such children, but also from personal experience, because I am the father of a mongoloid boy.

My experiences were, perhaps, rather more fortunate than those of many other parents, because no one ever told us to "put him away"—but I did learn the diagnosis about two days after Jonny was born from a very personal friend and one of the country's leading neurologists. "I must tell you something you have to know," he said, "your child is a mongolian idiot." This was in 1943. These were two words that went together, "mongolian" and "idiot," and, unfortunately, still go together in the minds of too many professionals whom the parents consult, not to mention literature and the entertainment field. And why not the latter two? Are they not a reflection of the professional point of view?

I shall not speak of the repeated diagnoses we sought, but at last we admitted openly (secretly we had a long time ago) that we were convinced. What now? What manner of child is a mongoloid child? Where was the literature? And above all: What will be the future of such a child?

So began our search for a *prognosis,* and all we obtained was *diagnosis* again and again. We came the nearest to prognosis when my boy was about a year and a half old: "Mongoloid of the worst type, prognosis—hopeless"; and the kindest from a famous pediatrician: "Go home and love him—have other children—be kind to him."

It is easier to surrender than to fight on and the temptation is sometimes great, but a streak of stubbornness in my wife and myself made us strive to make a human being of this foredoomed child. I need not go into all the possible psychologic reasons such as refusal to admit that we could produce this, etc. Our whole focus became the training of Jonny.

Later on—much later—we met persons who understood, some of them helping today, but at every step were the misconceptions which doom so many of these tantalizing children, so near like others and yet so different.

The first teacher nurse we had came from a Pennsylvania institution. "Oh, such children die young," she said. The doctors said the same: "Such children's teeth decay early." He has had one cavity in nine years. However, the nurse did train him in good habit formation. Then came glutamic acid and the first psychometric—I.Q. in the 70's—and surprise that it reached this high level. Naturally our search carried us to the public schools and there, too, on an administrative level, we met the same lack of understanding and hopeless attitude encountered among doctors. Although he was well-qualified intellectually and socially, we were offered a low I.Q. class for him, a class for children with I.Q.'s between 40 and 50. It was only after a classic letter by Dr. Benda on the equal rights of all races, Asiatic as well as Caucasian, to public education that Jonny was admitted to a regular special class.

"Prognosis: hopeless." Yet, today, he is an altogether delightful little boy whose stubbornness we attribute to character. His future? It is not in our hands alone, but in the hands of the whole community where an awareness and understanding must be developed so that facilities will be set up to meet his needs and abilities. . . .

□ □ □

SECTION D

The New Way

One can ask the following significant question and ponder the significant answer: "What would have happened if a prestigious individual or organization had defined a sensible, realistic management approach to mental retardation ten or twenty years ago?" Speculation as to the answer can go full range from "complete rejection" to "complete acceptance." Perhaps surprisingly, the question can be answered because there were individuals and agencies that did foresee and formulate today's ideology. Thus, in 1954, the World Health Organization, certainly a prestigious organization, published a monograph entitled The Mentally Subnormal Child *which was well ahead of its time in suggesting a sensible and realistic approach. The answer to our hypothetical question is thus at hand, for the WHO monograph has been essentially ignored in the United States. Perhaps the report was too far ahead of its time,* i.e., *inconsistent with the then-prevailing value system.*

Almost a decade later, President Kennedy's Panel on Mental Retardation published its highly influential monograph in which a program for action to combat mental retardation was proposed. Clearly, the Panel monograph was consistent with the prevailing American value system, for this report was well received. It has become the basis for a vast program of social action, and is likely to continue in this role for some years. It will remain a landmark in the history of mental retardation in this country, equivalent to the arrival of Edouard Seguin in 1850.

from THE MENTALLY SUBNORMAL CHILD

World Health Organization

(Geneva, 1954)

. . . .

The general misconceptions regarding the nature and causes of mental subnormality, not only among the general public, but even among those whose work brings them into contact with families having a mentally subnormal child, show the amount that has still to be done to bring about an understanding attitude to those affected. . . .

The feeling of shame and disappointment which many parents have is in part socially determined. They can often be helped far more by association with others who also have subnormal children than by individual psychotherapy or guidance. The knowledge that they are not alone, but that their problems and difficulties are similar to those of many others like themselves, can be of great assistance to them. Parents' associations can in this way be valuable, and can enable the collective experience of a community to be passed on to those who would otherwise have to learn everything for themselves. . . .

To leave parents to struggle alone with the problems raised by a subnormal child, or to attempt to reassure them that the child is really normal or "will grow out of it," is not in the interests either of the child or the family, or of society. Even those countries which have made fairly adequate provision for children of school age have usually failed to appreciate the importance of early diagnosis and the need to make available adequate and flexible provision for children in infancy and early childhood. . . .

What happens once a condition of subnormality is suspected must depend on the services available. Wherever it is possible to do so, the case should be referred to a specialist, or team of specialists, who will examine and observe the child in different situations and from different points of view and make an assessment of its condition. . . .

To enable specialist services to be developed within the framework of existing services a reasonable proportion of funds should be set aside.

A second general principle is that the family rather than the subnormal child himself should be the unit considered from the public health and welfare point of view. This imposes on the various services the need to collaborate among themselves so as to avoid overlap or failure to make provision for the needs of these families.

Thirdly, as a general principle, economic and social conditions should be made such that parents will not be penalized by keeping their child at home, especially during infancy and childhood. This principle has far-reaching implications. It implies that the maternal and child health and welfare services should be competent to supervise the care of subnormal children at home before the age of compulsory schooling and to follow them through school and adolescence. They should also be able to deal with the problems of the family. It may mean that substantial family allowances should be paid to parents of subnormal children who keep their facilities, and nursery schools are made available, that special transport should be provided to and from school for those children who need it, and that home teaching arrangements are provided for children who cannot attend school.

A fourth principle is that social costs should form the basis of efficient planning. In deciding whether a child can be kept at home the adequacy of the maternal and child health and other services will be of great influence. Home care is in general cheaper and better than institution care; but its social cost may be much greater if the rest of the family is penalized because of the presence of a subnormal child in their midst.

The prevalence of mental subnormality is such that in all countries its social costs are high. These are often concealed when healthy adults are simply removed from productive and useful work and forced by circumstances to spend many years looking after a child who never develops out of dependency on its mother. The dislocation of normal family life, too, imposes social costs no less real because they are rarely assessed. There are therefore few societies which cannot afford to provide some services for their mentally subnormal, although in fact many fail to do so today. . . .

If early discovery and, where possible, diagnosis are to be aimed at, three further problems must be considered: referral of cases and collaboration of specialists, advice to parents, and disposal.

First, referral. Some severe cases, especially those with obvious physical abnormalities, and the majority of mongols, are discoverable at birth, and the doctor or midwife who delivers the child should know to whom to report the case and what action to take. In some cases of older infants or young children, the first person to be consulted or to observe that the child's development is not normal may be the family doctor: in others, it may be the public-health nurse (health visitor). Similar observations may be made at a child welfare clinic or nursery school, or by a social welfare agency or friend or counselor. . . .

Diagnosis or discovery is, however, not an end in itself. Indeed, there is little point in establishing a diagnosis, except to draw the attention of the authorities to the existence of the problem of mental subnormality, if nothing more can be done to help the family. But even in poorly developed countries there is usually some advice that could be given. As the level of the public-health, social, and educational services rises, so the amount that could be done increases. In highly developed countries comprehensive services can be organized.

What advice is given to parents and who is to give it are matters that can best be decided in a case conference in which all the specialists concerned take part. Two aspects must be distinguished: therapeutic discussion with the parents, and advice on planning for the care of the child, whether or not he remains with the family.

The discovery that a child is subnormal will inevitably come as a profound shock to parents. In many cases they will feel a groundless personal guilt or will, half-consciously, blame their marriage partner for the child's condition. They may need the opportunity for frank discussions with a specialist in both the field of mental subnormality and of mental health. It need hardly be added that more than one discussion may be necessary, since the parents cannot be expected to understand and face the full consequences of matters of such strong emotional significance after a single interview. At the same time, they should be given accurate information and have their questions fully and frankly answered. . . .

In addition to therapeutic discussions, continued if need be from time to time over a period of years, parents need advice on how best to treat their children. Subnormal children present problems of upbringing not found in normal children, and parents must be advised how to cope with these. They should also be told what they can expect of the child, and be helped to guard against demanding either too much or too little.

Once a diagnosis has been arrived at, a major decision which has to be taken is whether the child can be cared for at home or should be placed in an institution or foster-home. This decision need not be taken at once, and it may happen that a child can be cared for at home in early childhood even though when older he will need institutional care. In different countries opinions regarding the desirability of placing subnormal children in institutions will naturally differ according to the prevailing social philosophy and the facilities available. In some societies with strong traditions, families are not willing to give up their weak or old members to the care of others, and regard the segregation of the mentally handicapped as callous and inhuman. In Western society, as families have shrunk in size and institutional provision has become more readily available, there has been a tendency to recommend the placement of all severe cases and a number of cases of moderate subnormality in institutions. It should, perhaps, be added that, although to some parents in some societies institutional placement may be the most easily acceptable solution of a difficult problem, the general principle applies here that the mental health of the community as a whole will not be necessarily improved by the mere segregation of the abnormal, whether they be subnormal, senile, physically handicapped, or psychotic.

The committee was of the opinion that, in coming to the decision to recommend institutional placement, three aspects should be considered: the actual condition of the child; the mental health of the family, the competence of the mother, and the possible effect on the family of retaining a subnormal child in its midst; and the living conditions and financial circumstances of the family. In the discussion of the decision to be made it would seem essential that the family doctor or the public-health nurse concerned with the case should take an active part.

As a general rule, home care is to be recommended, unless the subnormality is very severe or the retention of the child in the home is likely to bring about serious maladjustment or the dislocation of other aspects of family life. Even children who are severely subnormal may be kept at home if the parents are able to take a realistic view of the situation and if they are able to make full use of comprehensive maternal and child health services. Moreover, generous financial and practical assistance to parents is still cheaper than hospital care, a point not often realized.

The committee does not look with favour on the growing practice of very early institutionalization. In many instances the parents are advised not to take the child home from the maternity hospital, a decision which constitutes a real hazard to the mental health of the family unit. It must be remembered that parents make a heavy emotional investment in all pregnancies and when an abnormality occurs they invariably experience feelings of guilt. The immediate admission of the infant to an institution not only fails to relieve the stress but may even intensify it. The placement is likely to be interpreted by the troubled parents as a confirmation of their own feelings of guilt and an irrevocable rejection of the child. No institution can provide an adequate substitute for the essential emotional interaction between parents and child, and this opportunity for interplay is of paramount importance in the case of the handicapped child whose parents can only slowly evolve a realistic and constructive attitude towards the situation. As a matter of fact, there are many instances of defective children being accepted by and thriving with their families. It can be denied categorically that all such infants should be institutionalized at once. In each instance the decision concerning the proper time for such placement must be made on the basis of the psychological needs of each individual family constellation.

Although in favorable circumstances some of the grossly subnormal can continue to be cared for at home, at least when young, the majority of cases remaining in the care of the family will be children of mild and moderate subnormality. For these children some specialist follow-up services may be required. But in most cases, especially during infancy and early childhood, much of the supervision of the general development of the child can continue to be exercised through the maternal and child health services. The home visits of the public-health nurse are particularly important in enabling continuity of supervision to be achieved. Her knowledge should be supplemented by advice and assistance of the social case-worker. . . .

The parents of a subnormal child of school age for whom some specialized form of education is recommended may need much enlightenment about the purpose of the recommendation if they are to accept it willingly. It may be difficult to convince them that their child should go to school at all, or, if he is in an ordinary class, that he would make better progress in a special class or school. It is nevertheless worth while for the case-worker to take great pains, continued perhaps over a long period, to obtain this real cooperation, so that the parents may feel that they have to some degree participated in the choice of their child's school. Many of the difficulties which children receiving special education encounter can be traced back to opposition and conflict of purposes between the home and school. The parent needs to know what is being done for his child, and why certain steps are taken in the child's own interest. Participation by the parents in the planning of school activities is a useful way of doing this.

Similar considerations apply to adolescents of school-leaving age. Vocational guidance should be carried out with parent cooperation. The attendance of the parent or parents at case conferences at all stages of the child's career is to be welcomed.

Special care has to be taken to see that the parents of a child in a residential school or hospital are kept interested in and informed about his progress. The need for continued visiting, for having the child at home during holidays where this is possible, and for sustained interest in the child should be made clear. Close liaison between social welfare services, parents, and the institution will make this possible in most cases. . . .

A point of importance is the provision of domestic and financial help to parents needing it, or during times of sickness or holiday, so that they will be able to continue the home care of the child when this seems the best course to take. It should be possible for a parent to place a subnormal child temporarily in an institution, if domestic assistance cannot be obtained at a time of crisis. A factor in favor of home care is that normal children living in the same family can be of great assistance in promoting the development of a subnormal child, if home conditions are good. . . .

□ □ □

from A PROPOSED PROGRAM FOR NATIONAL ACTION TO COMBAT MENTAL RETARDATION

President's Panel on Mental Retardation

(U. S. Government Printing Office, 1963)

. . . .

Acceptance by the parents of the true nature of their child's handicap is essential if they are to be effective in helping him. Even though the diagnosis is carefully explained in simple terms to the parents during and after the examination, they are frequently reticent in the presence of a physician, or are so shocked by the implications of the diagnosis that the questions they should ask do not come out until days or even weeks later. Thus, responsibility for the family starts with the first meeting, and it should continue through the period when the family needs it most, and indeed in some form throughout the life of the retarded person, if and as required.

The physician and other professional people dealing with the family do not always appreciate the severe crisis through which its members pass during the weeks or months following the revelation of their child's affliction. It is a crisis, however, to which the physician need not and should not minister alone. The family should be able to turn to its minister, priest, or rabbi for help in finding the new strength they will need.

Today there are religious leaders and groups in each of the major faiths who are awake to the need for this new ministry and who are imparting their interest and concern to their colleagues and to lay leaders.

The clergy and their lay assistants are urged to intensify their efforts to meet the spiritual needs of families faced with the problems of mental retardation. It is important that physicians and pastors meet to share their insights and experiences in helping families whose faith has been sorely tried and whose mental health may well be in jeopardy.

One of the pressing needs of parents in crisis is to be able to act in self-defense and even more in defense of their child. Here the constructive practical help of a physician, a nurse, a social worker, a teacher, or other counselor can serve to sustain and carry both parent and child forward.

Whenever the mother has capabilities of understanding and cooperation, she should be regarded as a major resource. She usually possesses strong motivation to provide care—a motivation hard to duplicate in any "out of home" programs. Both parents as well as other members of the family should be involved wherever possible.

No mother can be expected to carry the responsibilities of a retarded child without outside support. Not only is relief from a feeling of aloneness and "no-end-in-sightness" needed, but in addition, tangible help must come from the community. Through volunteers, public health nurses, homemaker services and other aids, assistance can be given to planning and carrying [out] certain household activities for the retarded child, and in obtaining qualified babysitters for an evening or for a weekend away from home. Although day care centers for retarded children are being developed, transportation and other problems make it difficult for many families to utilize them and thus release the homebound mother during the day.

It is difficult to maintain a proper balance between over-concern and rejection or alternating cycles of each in the family of the retarded. An effective means of allaying concern is the provision of substitute care by others in the home, thereby demonstrating on home grounds the ability and interest of others in caring for the child. Meetings of parents in groups are valuable in releasing tensions and encouraging a free exchange of experience and the development of an esprit de corps. It is heartening to parents who have been "through the mill" to help others to face reality and meet the challenge of a handicapped child.

The families of today are subject to many stresses and the rate of family breakup is alarming. This is, of course, one of the conditions in which mental retardation and other social ills thrive.

. . . .

When the first round of initial adjustment is over, the "long haul" begins. Here *social* management assumes increasing importance.

Securing the proper "continuum of care" for each retarded person at successive stages requires expert attention to planning on a long-range basis. The law provides that in our society, parents serve as the primary coordinators on behalf of their children. Education "for citizenship" includes learning to utilize the resources for education, health, safety, and the like on behalf of oneself and one's family. A citizen who is less than expert at this skill can usually negotiate a path to these resources to meet ordinary needs, with the informal advice of neighbors and relatives. It is when the ordinary individual has extraordinary needs that self-coordination—self-guidance through the maze of community services—may tax his capabilities. This is even more true when the individual's ability for self-management is impaired.

Coordination of services for the individual retardate begins, therefore, with a capable parent or other adult willing, able, and obligated to concern himself with the retardate's continuing and changing needs. But the most intelligent and dutiful parent or guardian, let alone the retarded adult, cannot be expected to have adequate knowledge of the extraordinary resources necessary to secure the requisite "continuum of care" for the retarded person. Furthermore, the lifetime duration of mental handicap—especially in those with more severe impairment of adaptive behavior—precludes the availability of the natural parent or guardian for the retardate who survives to the expected "three score and ten."

Experience has shown that barriers or breaks in the "continuum of care" often arise at points where the family of the retardate must find a new service and establish a relationship with it. At this point a "home base," a familiar face, a person to whom one does not have to rehearse once again one's "history," a person known and trusted from past experience, can make the difference between a referral which is accepted and one which is not.

There should be available in every community a "fixed point of referral and information" which provides a life consultation service for the retarded.

The "point" should be "fixed" in relation to the retardate and his ongoing needs. It could take the form of an office or a mobile service to which those in need of counsel could turn and return for authoritative advice and guidance, or for referral to appropriate general and special resources. Under favorable circumstances this service might be offered by a general community referral service, provided its staff has sufficient specific competence in this complex field.

To be truly effective, this service should have continuity and permanency, so that an ongoing relationship between the client and the agency, and more particularly a person in the agency, may be developed and used by the client on a recurring basis. To achieve the necessary continuity of care, this service should act both as broker and expediter in finding and making use of those resources which the community and state have to offer.

Where the volume of demand permits, consideration might well be given to developing such referral and consultation services for the potentially independent retardate apart from those for the more dependent person. Conversely, where needs are similar, the "point" might well accept and serve persons who have other closely related chronic handicaps with comparable social consequences. These two complementary services might be sponsored in any number of ways; for example, by a local voluntary social agency or by a state or local health or welfare department or other unit of government.

The modern concept of a community mental health center with its array of diagnostic services, outpatient and inpatient facilities, supervision of foster homes and other rehabilitation modalities, and community referral functions, might be one important locus for a life consultation service for the retarded. Cooperative planning for the mentally retarded child necessitates cooperation and coordination with the current planning and review of the national mental health program in which a large number of community mental health centers is envisaged. These centers are seen as a locus for services to the mentally retarded as well as to the mentally ill. . . .

The locus of service should be such, however, that the personnel therein have direct access to all resources their clients might need. In fact, it would be ideal if lifetime consultation service of this nature could be provided from an administrative base which was free of identification with any single type of service such as residential care or vocational guidance. From such a base the counselor might find it easier to be impartial in selecting and seeking services for the individual in need.

The person or persons staffing a life consultation service might come from a variety of professional backgrounds such as social work, nursing, rehabilitation, or education. Whatever their professional qualifications, personal characteristics would undoubtedly score heavily in their success or failure. They should be able to communicate with the retarded and with families from every walk of life, and capable of recognizing the links between counseling and referral, and the area of professional treatment into which they should not enter. They should also be flexible and perceptive in making use of the more intensive forms of counseling, such as are offered in clinics, by rehabilitation counselors, or by schools. The counselor should have direct access to expert professional advice in meeting problems which require competence beyond his preparation.

Local or state agencies having a major responsibility for the retarded should test the continuity of counseling and referral by selecting identified cases at random for checkout through retrospective interviews with parents or through cumulative records.

Several services now being offered have shown the practicality of many of the features here proposed. The Special Services Office, under the direction of the Committee on Mental Retardation of the Community Council of Caddo-Bossier Parishes in Shreveport, La., is one example. This pilot program receives a state subsidy. The office provides for central record-keeping, a central point of information and referral, and a life consultation service. It ties in closely with ongoing community planning based on identified gaps. The specialized counseling offered to parents and retardates in association with the unique guardianship program of the Minnesota Department of Welfare is another example. Similar functions will also be among those performed at some of the new regional centers, such as those being organized in Connecticut. The Parent Information and Counseling Service recently inaugurated in Rhode Island incorporates many useful features as does the Information and Referral Unit in Monroe County (Rochester), N.Y. The statewide traveling "home visitor" of Maine may demonstrate how these services can be brought to rural areas. A research and demonstration project in vocational rehabilitation just completed in Arkansas offers some insights into the effective use of professional and subprofessional personnel in one community setting. These may well be valid in the long-term service here proposed.

Information and referral units and other agencies dealing directly with the retarded should gather data systematically on the gaps and shortages in service and develop a means of communicating significant findings to those bodies responsible for planning and coordination. Such data should reflect any lack of service and the existence of real or perceived obstacles to reaching existing services. Such barriers may include lack of transportation, special eligibility or residence requirements, fee scales, and popular misconceptions about the service itself. Indeed, continuing interpretation to parents and others by information and referral centers can contribute much to better use of all services.

Parent education and counseling are related but different; both are important. Skillful counseling always provides a certain amount of education, but it is usually aimed primarily at the specific personal problems presented by an individual parent. Education is a more formal procedure intended to convey information concerning the nature and implications of retardation and a wide range of suggestions that will be useful in dealing with children. Most parents need some help and a great deal of basic information.

Sound, up-to-date information convincingly conveyed to parents is one of the best bulwarks against the exploitation of their misfortune by quacks. As the American Medical Association leaders have pointed out, quackery flourishes most readily in respect to disorders for which science has no valid cure. Thus the families of the retarded are a vulnerable group, and should be given the best defenses available. Knowledge of the nature and source of their child's condition, and of the breadth and scope of research and other forces mobilized to aid him, will strengthen these defenses.

Parent education requires special knowledge and skills; it cannot be carried on successfully as an incidental function, nor by persons inexperienced in the art of "drawing out" people who face serious problems. It is, therefore, important for parent and other groups, clinics, and community agencies to give time and thought to the preparation and training of parent-education leaders. The Child Study Association of America has had a long and valuable experience in conducting parent-training programs and has prepared a practical study plan for the training of leaders for parent education groups. It is suggested that demonstration programs be undertaken in several communities in the training of leaders. . . .

□ □ □

SECTION E

The Manager

When a parent learns that his child is mentally retarded, he frequently turns to certain persons with status-roles in our society defined as the helping professions. An individual occupying a helping-profession status should be adequately trained to play his defined role. Such is the division of labor in our society, a division which recognizes the importance of highly specialized training and expert-based decision making. Few of us can argue that the parent, when turning to the family manager, has a right to expect both compassionate and expert guidance.

Sarason cogently discusses inadequacies in the training of various specialists who are often thrust into the manager role without the proper training: "A great many of the difficulties encountered in working with the defective child and his family can often be traced directly to the previous failure of many of these professional people to recognize and handle the psychological aspects of the problem." His analysis also suggests that many professionals who now claim leadership in the managerial team cannot make such claims on the basis of the training they have received. By the same token, his analysis points to areas of training need.

Dorothy Garst Murray, a parent leader encountered earlier in this book, and Jensen, a psychiatrist, add further definition to the manager role. Mrs. Murray speaks from the vantage point of the parent, suggesting the need for constructive counseling and the desirable qualities of such guidance. Jensen discusses the strenuous, arduous, and exacting task of counseling parents at the time of first knowledge of retardation. Like Sarason and Murray, he focuses on the necessary training and attitude of the counselor.

One conclusion that might be drawn from these selections is that no disciplinary background or academic degree per se *constitutes adequate qualification to manage families of the retarded. Manager qualifications transcend disciplines and degrees, and are based on certain personal qualities which may be independent of training. Indeed, it is conceivable that a mature layman with certain personality attributes can be a more meaningful counselor for parents of the retarded than some well-trained professionals who lack these traits.*

from THE PROBLEM OF PROFESSIONAL TRAINING

Seymour B. Sarason

(Psychological Problems in Mental Deficiency, 1959)

The reader may have already concluded from a reading of the last two chapters that handling the problems posed therein requires not only knowledge of certain facts but an understanding of what is essentially a psychotherapeutically-oriented situation: a sustained attempt on the part of some trained person to understand the motivations of parents, their frustrations and hopes, and by virtue of such understanding, as well as by previous training, to enable parents to accept more realistic and satisfying attitudes.

To be of help to people in this manner requires more than good intentions and the possession of a particular professional title. The fact that one is a pediatrician, psychiatrist, psychologist, or teacher does not necessarily mean, as we shall see later, that one is equipped with the knowledge and training required for the handling of the problems posed in the last two chapters. A great many of the difficulties which are encountered in working with the defective child and his family can often be traced directly to the previous failure of many of these professional people to recognize and handle the psychological aspects of the problem. *It is the thesis of this chapter that this failure is in large part due to the kind of training which these workers received in their student days.* We may anticipate a later conclusion by stating here that mental deficiency in general and its psychological aspects in particular have suffered from "professional disinterest," an attitude which not only minimizes the complexity of the problem but perpetuates practices which raise more problems than they solve.

The following case can serve well to illustrate the significance of the statements made in this and the previous two chapters. The child, parental behavior, and professional practice are not atypical:

> ". . . I received a call from the secretary of a local organized group of parents of cerebral palsied children. It seems that one of the mothers had been trying to get her seven-year-old

> daughter into the kindergarten of one of the public schools. The school had refused admission because the child was not considered eligible. The mother, believing that the child was eligible, took her for a psychological examination to the out-patient clinic of one of the state training schools. The psychological report was sent to the secretary who was calling me and who had suggested that the mother arrange for a psychological examination in order to use it as evidence for her belief that the child should be in kindergarten. The psychological report contained the following: a) a diagnosis was deferred because the child did not talk and the suggestion was made that the child should be seen again when she had learned to talk; b) on those test items which could be given to the child her mental level seemed to be around three years; c) the child should not be institutionalized at this time; d) she should be entered into a kindergarten class if she was considered eligible by the school. The problem with which the secretary of the parent group confronted me was what should she tell the parent?

"The above situation is by no means infrequent, and in my own experience is the rule rather than the exception. In trying to understand these frequent situations we might ask this question: 'How do these situations come about?' Before trying to answer this question we first have to ask other questions: 'What is the nature of the situation here and now? What are the problems with which we should be concerned?' Briefly stated, here is what I think are the important aspects of the situation:

1. We are dealing with a parent who has certain beliefs about what her child can learn to do.
2. The mother's beliefs are not shared by school authorities.
3. It is very likely that the mother has a very hostile attitude toward the schools because she feels that they are being unfair and discriminatory.
4. It is also likely that the school authorities consider the mother to be unrealistic and aggressive—in short, a nuisance.
5. It is a fact that the schools do not consider this child to be *their* problem.
6. The psychological report does not support the mother's beliefs about the child's capacities.
7. The psychological report contains a recommendation about kindergarten which makes little sense in light of the earlier refusal of the school to admit the child.
8. The psychologist did not discuss his report with the mother.
9. No one, except the local parent group, considered the parent to be their problem, or understood, let alone tried to handle, the deep anguish she undoubtedly was experiencing.

"Let us now make one assumption: the mother has an unrealistic conception of her child's capacities. If this is so, it is difficult to see how anything done —by the school or the psychologist— was oriented toward helping this mother achieve a more realistic attitude. Telling a mother that her child is not eligible for school may be a valid statement, but in no way does this solve the mother's problem. In fact, making such a statement to a mother is evidence of the fact that the school assumes that only the child is a problem. Telling a mother that her child is not eligible for school without at the same time making concrete proposals concerning the child's training obviously does not help the child, but, just as obviously, increases the severity of the mother's problem. In the case of the psychological examination apparently no attempt was made to convey anything to the mother. The function of a psychological examination is not only to collect data about a child and his problems, but to use these data to help parents react realistically to the child. If the psychologist, for example, had only conveyed to the parent that the child was severely retarded, then he would have been as superficial in his approach to the problem as were the school authorities."[1]

One other fact about this case deserves mention: this eight-year-old child had previously been seen by numerous medical specialists none of whom considered the parents a problem or apparently attempted to insure that the parents had a realistic conception of their child's condition.

One could present case after case illustrating the failure of various specialists to handle the defective child and his family in such a manner as to reduce the strength of the anxieties associated with current problems and to prevent the occurrence of future ones. That mental deficiency is an incurable condition should not obscure the fact that many of the psychological and social problems to which it gives rise can either be prevented or greatly reduced in strength. In the following pages we shall see that the failure to recognize and handle such problems is in large part a function of the inadequate training which the various specialists have received.

In the following discussion of the training of those professional workers who come into contact with the defective child and his family *we shall only be interested in the adequacy of such training for meeting the psychological problems we have been discussing in the previous two chapters.*

Medical Personnel

Medical school and intern training. The medical student is not in any formal or systematic way exposed to the psychological aspects of mental deficiency. Much more frequently than not he learns to define mental deficiency in terms of a test score. He is not prepared for or closely supervised in his contacts with the parents of defective children, and is unaware of the psychological, familial, educational, and community aspects of the problem. What has just been said is a reflection of a more general problem which is beginning to concern some medical educators: medical education today does not train students to approach the patient as an organism which in addition to having physical symptoms also possesses a psychological system which has functioned and continues to function in a particular familial and social setting. To focus on the physical symptoms results in a narrow view of the case, making the recognition of present and the prevention of future problems difficult if not impossible. Insofar as the field of mental deficiency is concerned medical education shows the following lacks.

1. The student does not learn how to conduct an interview which has as its purpose the evocation of parental attitudes, goals, and anxieties in order to help them achieve a more realistic conception of and adjustment to their problems. To learn such interviewing techniques requires supervised experience which the student does not now receive. It is this lack which not only limits the amount of help which parents can receive from their contact with the physician but also has the effect of creating new or exacerbating old problems.
2. The student learns almost nothing about the educational aspects of mental deficiency: the relation of mental level to academic achievement, the nature and goals of special classes, and an understanding of the pedagogical-psychological problems confronting the special class teacher. Too frequently parents are led to expect a level of educational achievement from their child which is out of keeping with his capacities.
3. The student is not acquainted with the nature of community facilities or the criteria by which their quality can be judged. Physicians in general do not know whether the local school system has special classes for the educable and noneducable defective, whether there are special recreational facilities, or whether there is a local organization of parents of defective children.

When one realizes that parents frequently first learn about their child's condition from a physician, and that this initial contact is of prime importance in shaping their thinking, the significance of the lacks in medical education is clear.

Pediatric training. Although pediatric educators have become increasingly aware of the necessity for the student to become a psychologically sensitive observer and counselor, the detailed instruction and supervision necessary to achieve such a goal are seldom provided. Very rarely does the pediatrician in training learn to understand the techniques and problems involved in therapeutically-oriented interviews with parents.[2] The kind of interviewing with which we have been concerned is not of the fact-finding variety in which one person asks and the other answers questions—if it were, one could print the questions and have the parent write out his answers. The kind of interviewing which we have been discussing requires more than a superficial knowledge of personality dynamics or an earnest desire to be of help. It requires a degree of self-understanding and a knowledge of the tactics necessary to influence another person's behavior which are best learned under the supervision of a more experienced person.[3] The pediatrician is seldom exposed to such a learning experience. In cases of mental deficiency it is also necessary to be aware of the familial and educational ramifications of a case—an awareness which the pediatrician generally does not have for the rather simple reason that he has not been taught to become aware of such factors. Where the pediatrician has such awareness more often than not he does not possess the training in interviewing technique which would enable him to capitalize on his understanding. What further handicaps the physician in general and the pediatrician in particular is their lack of knowledge of the training, procedures, problems, and contributions of the psychologist or teacher. What knowledge they possess is usually based on a few lectures which by their nature are not likely to be revealing or helpful. As a result the pediatrician often does not understand a) the contributions and limitations of a psychological examination, b) the dangers involved in giving or reading a psychological report to parents, c) the psychologist's need for time to interpret and integrate his findings, and d) the importance of a detailed discussion between pediatrician and psychologist concerning the significance of the test findings in light of other knowledge of the case.

Another result of these "token" lectures is that the pediatrician is usually unaware of the pedagogical problems with which the teacher is faced in working with the defective child. Practically every special class teacher can point to several cases in which a problem arose with parents because of a pediatrician's unwarranted statement about a child's educational potentialities. This situation is probably due to two factors: the pediatrician's lack of knowledge of the relation between mental level and educational achievement and his failure, due to lack of previous experience, to effect an adequate liaison with the teacher. In more than a few cases a conference between teacher and pediatrician might have resulted in a more effective program for the child. The need for such conferences has long been recognized by the teacher but their value has not yet been adequately recognized by the pediatrician and general practitioner.

Psychiatric training. Although the psychiatrist in training receives long and supervised training in conducting therapeutically-oriented interviews, his clinical experience is only in small part with the defective child and his family —witness how much of his training is in a state hospital or other agency where the patient population is predominantly composed of neurotic and psychotic individuals. In addition, because the training experiences of most psychiatrists are largely with adults his knowledge of children in general, and the defective child in particular, is relatively meagre. His criterion of mental deficiency is usually that of a test score, and his knowledge of the practices, goals, and problems of special education is equally superficial. Although the psychiatrist could be a key person in handling the adjustment problems of the defective child and his family, his training does not give him knowledge, derived either from lecture or clinical contact, of the problems in the field. As a result, when the psychiatrist does encounter the mentally defective child and his family, it is not surprising that his contribution is usually not much greater or more comprehensive than that of the specialists already discussed.[4]

The reader should bear in mind that the criticisms which have been made of medical education were made only in terms of its adequacy in preparing the practitioner for meeting the problems raised in the previous two chapters—problems of which the great majority of medical personnel are only dimly aware and unprepared to meet. If the failure to meet these problems did not overlook old and create new adjustment problems for child and family, then the lacks in medical education would obviously not be of serious import. The obligations of medical training may be put in this way: if a particular condition (e.g., mental deficiency) brings into play familial, educational, and community problems, then it should be the aim of training to enable the student to recognize and handle such problems.

The Clinical Psychologist

Although clinical psychology as a discipline grew out of attempts to identify, educate, and train the mentally defective child, the clinical student today gets very little experience with the defective child. Psychological theory, diagnostic testing, interviewing and psychotherapeutic techniques, clinical experience with a variety of adjustment problems—these are some of the course and experience requirements which the clinical student must meet. It is the rare graduate department of psychology which has as a requirement course instruction in or clinical experience with the psychological problems in mental deficiency. Too frequently the clinical psychologist views the mental defective in terms only of psychological test scores—in light of his training there is little reason why he should adopt any other viewpoint. . . .

The Teacher

It is clearly the teacher who spends the greatest amount of time with the defective child and frequently has the most contact with his parents. That the teacher, particularly the special class one, faces more than a pedagogical problem, can be seen from the following problems which are by no means rare:

1. communicating to parents, who have not been so informed before, that their child is either mentally defective or retarded;
2. informing parents that the school has no facilities for their non-educable defective child;
3. explaining to parents why preschool predictions about their child's academic achievement were overly optimistic;
4. discussing with parents why institutionalization is preferred solution for the needs and problems of their child.

As has been indicated before, many of these problem situations would never have arisen if those who had earlier seen the child had handled the defective child and his family more sensitively and comprehensively. What frequently happens is that the parents become hostile to the school personnel: accusing them of discriminatory practices, lack of understanding, and, not infrequently, sheer ignorance and incompetence. "My doctor told me that he would be able to go to school," "Nobody ever said there was anything wrong with my child," "How will he ever learn to read and write if you will not let him in school?"—these are a few of the statements which parents of defective children direct to school authorities.

Although it is clear that the teacher comes into close contact with parents, and is in a position to be of help to them, teacher training does not prepare the student for the proper handling of such relationships. While teacher training requires supervised teaching, there is no such requirement for the handling of parental problems and attitudes, even though teachers are becoming more and more involved in such situations. Whatever is required today for becoming a skilled teacher does not necessarily fit one for appropriate handling of the kinds of problems which we have been discussing.

The Future

There is little reason for believing that professional disinterest in the psychological aspects of mental deficiency is likely to change in any noticeable way in the near future. To expect such a change it would be necessary to assume that educators in the various fields are aware of the discrepancy between the nature of training and the problems inherent in a case of mental deficiency—an assumption for which there is little justification. In order for a change to be effected the following attitudes and practices will have to be combated.

1. Working with the mentally defective individual is dull and unrewarding —a professional "dead-end."
2. From the psychological and psychiatric point of view there are no major or fascinating research problems in the area of mental deficiency.
3. To handle adequately a case of mental deficiency does not require any special knowledge or training.
4. The possession of a particular professional title or training thereby equips one to assume responsibility in program planning for the mentally defective child.
5. One can make recommendations for the mentally defective child without working with the parents or having a knowledge of educational practices and facilities.

What has been said in this chapter represents conclusions based on the writer's clinical and teaching experiences. They, therefore, represent opinions—a class of data which is not always true or convincing. *What is very much needed in this area is a systematic and objective evaluation of the adequacy of professional training for meeting the problems we have discussed.* Such a study should attempt to answer the following questions.

1. At different stages of training or specialization within a professional area, with what kinds of **facts** about mental deficiency is the student or practitioner acquainted? With how many cases does he actually come into contact?
2. What is the nature and extent of formal instruction? How much of such instruction involves a consideration of the training and contribution of other professional specialists who work with the mentally defective child? How much actual contact is there among the various specialists?
3. What does the student learn about the nature and scope of community facilities?
4. Within any one discipline what are the attitudes of the student or practitioner towards the value of working in the field of mental deficiency? What are the bases for such attitudes? What are some of the factors motivating people to go into this area of work?
5. What does the student or practitioner feel about his competency in this area? What does he feel is or was lacking in his training?
6. How are cases actually handled? Are there any differences in handling between the pediatrician, psychologist, general practitioner, teacher, etc.?
7. What are the reactions of parents to their contacts with these professional specialists?

To conduct a study along the above lines would obviously not be a small undertaking but the results of such a study could go a long way in effecting a change in the nature and goals of professional training for those who are called upon to handle the psychological problems in cases of mental deficiency.

Footnotes

1. Sarason, S. B., "Aspects of a community program for the retarded child," *Training School Bulletin,* Vineland, New Jersey, 1952, *48:* 201-207.
2. This is not to suggest that pediatricians, or any of the other personnel discussed in this chapter, should be or become psychotherapists. What is being suggested here is that these personnel should possess a sufficient

understanding of personality dynamics and the psychotherapeutic process to enable them to meet the problems which by tradition and practice are brought to them. If one maintained the position (for which there is no practical justification) that only psychotherapists can adequately handle the problems raised in chapters 11 and 12, then the future in this field, in light of the dearth of psychotherapists, is indeed gloomy.
3. The reader has undoubtedly become aware of the importance which the writer attaches to supervision. There are several reasons for this emphasis: a) students differ in the degree to which they are aware of how they strike or influence other people, b) the beginner is not the best judge of the relation between what he did and what he wanted to do, c) without some independent observer, "wrong" techniques cannot be recognized and unlearned, d) the welfare of the patient requires that the beginner's handling of the situation be controlled in some fashion. The best ways to conduct competently a psychotherapeutically-oriented interview cannot be learned from books, lectures, or even by observing an experienced person. One learns by doing under critical supervision. Without close supervision practice may result in the perfection of inadequate techniques.
4. It is sometimes overlooked that work in the area of mental deficiency requires special knowledge and training. Only educators seem to have recognized this fact and to have acted upon it, as witness the wide differences of curricula and of other aspects of training special teachers. In medicine and psychology there are no special prerequisites which the student must complete before becoming a practitioner or specialist in the field of mental deficiency. Perhaps a more correct way of describing the situation would be to say that neither the field of medicine nor clinical psychology recognizes mental deficiency as an area of specialization.
5. Sarason, S. B., "The psychology of the exceptional child," in *Proceedings of the 1952 Conference of the Child Research Clinic of the Woods Schools*, Langhorne, Pa., 1952.

□ □ □

from NEEDS OF PARENTS OF MENTALLY RETARDED CHILDREN

Dorothy Garst Murray

(American Journal of Mental Deficiency, 1959)

. . . .

If, then, constructive counseling seems to be our greatest need, what qualities do we as parents believe to be desirable in those who give guidance to us? Surely among the foremost qualities we want in those who attempt to help us in our need is absolute honesty. Perhaps some of you *think* we don't want honesty because of the parent's proneness for "shopping around" until he finds someone who will tell him what he wants to hear rather than the truth. But basically, we believe that parents *do* want honesty and in the final analysis will be deeply grateful to the professional person who has the courage to make a deep clean cut.

All of you have heard this statement from your colleagues at one time or another: "But parents don't *want* to hear the truth"—of course we don't want to hear it. Not one of us present would *want* to hear that he had TB or cancer or heart trouble, but we would think a physician sadly remiss in his duty if he refused to give us an honest diagnosis of a physical ailment just because his patient didn't *want* to hear it. It would seem that this excuse is worn somewhat threadbare by those persons who just don't quite have the intestinal fortitude to face up to their own inadequacy in dealing with parents.

On the other hand we hear from parents over and over: "If we had only found someone who would have given us an honest diagnosis from the beginning we may possibly have been able to begin constructive planning for the child years sooner." We do not believe that the word honesty implies that parents need to be informed of a child's condition in a blunt, cold or cruel manner. Surely the professional person in any area who is worthy of his calling should make every effort to develop the fine art of breaking such news in a manner which will leave at least some ray of hope and encouragement to which parents can cling during their blackest moments.

Another desirable attribute to be found in those who can most successfully counsel with parents of retarded children is that of an *understanding heart*. Please do not believe that we want sympathy, particularly the maudlin kind of sympathy which is damaging to the professional person as well as the parent. But we do need the kind of understanding personality which enables the professional person to put himself in the place of the parent.

An old Indian chief gave this saying which so aptly illustrates the kind of rapport which is necessary if parents and professional persons are to work together wisely for the good of the child —and I quote: "I cannot judge or advise any man rightfully and wisely until I have walked for ten moons in his moccasins." Surely if parents and professional persons could walk (figuratively speaking) in the moccasins of each other for ten moons, both would be more able to come to an understanding which would enable each to be mutually helpful in serving the needs of the child.

A third quality which we as parents greatly desire in those who attempt to give us help is the kind of integrity and stability of character which enables the professional person to work cooperatively with other professional disciplines for the good of the child—as well as with all those within his own particular profession. We are well aware that the question of professional jealousy is a very hot potato for one to try to juggle, and particularly so in front of an audience composed primarily of professional persons! But please forgive me if I play with this hot potato a bit to give you an idea as to what damage professional jealousy *can* and *does* do to the parents of a retarded child. In the initial stages of our problem, most of us are fairly young and very, very few have had any training or background of any type that would make us familiar with the complicated, many-sided angles of mental retardation. We come to the professional person (of any discipline) with the naive and innocent belief that he or she will surely have *all* the answers to our many questions because he or she has spent years of study about the problem.

Rather soon we discover that many of the answers we hear and much of the advice we are given does not seem to be exactly "compatible." More often than you would like to believe we find capable, conscientious professional persons expressing to parents definitely contrary opinions to those expressed by another professional person concerning the child. Sometimes these contrary opinions are expressed within the same profession, sometimes in an allied one. Teachers will sometimes disagree strongly with an opinion rendered by a psychologist in regard to [a] child; psychologists will not always agree with the efforts of a conscientious social worker; physicians will express opinions which make it difficult for the parent to have proper respect and confidence in the field of psychiatry, and the members of the psychiatric profession will sometimes in turn take unprofessional little jabs at the ignorance of the general MD in matters of the mind. Worst of all, some few professional people are not above making derogatory remarks about those within their own profession. All of this tends to create a sense of tremendous confusion in the mind of an already disturbed parent and is in no way conducive to helping him think through his problem in an intelligent manner.

We are in thorough accord with the idea that there is always room for an honest and sincere difference of opinion among professional persons in their study of the retarded child. Our deep concern is that such differences of opinion should be expressed to the parents in such a manner that will not cause them to lose respect for another professional person or discipline. Each of you have at times worked with parents who seemed very much on the "defensive," so to speak. Generally speaking, this is often blamed on a "guilt complex" (whatever that is!) but did it ever occur to you that this very defensiveness in parents may have been built up because of a former unfortunate contact with an emotionally immature and insecure professional person?

Please, please do not interpret what we have said as a reflection on professional people in general. We know that your ranks are composed of all kinds of persons—just like parents of retarded children in fact, strong ones and weak ones! We know too that sometimes an entire profession suffers because of the spiritual and emotional immaturity in a few of its members. Our only plea is that if you *do* have colleagues who suffer to a certain degree from the not so rare malady of professional jealousy, just urge them to be very cautious about exposing their symptoms before parents of retarded children. WE have enough decisions to make without trying to decide in our own bewildered minds who is right and who is wrong in a professional "tug-of-war!" . . .

Over and above all, the professional person who would be of the most help to parents of retarded children must have a dedicated desire to serve his fellowman and to help him in finding answers to the complex problems which he cannot solve alone. . . .

□ □ □

from COUNSELING WITH PARENTS AT TIME OF FIRST KNOWLEDGE OF RETARDATION

Reynold A. Jensen

(Counseling Parents of Children with Mental Handicaps, 1958)

Counseling with parents at the time of first knowledge of their having a retarded child is a strenuous, arduous and exacting task. It is a task that is not always done too well. But, in view of the many changes now occurring, it is my hope that it will be done better by more people in the future.

It is difficult not only for the parents who, for the first time, come to an understanding of their problems and are required to come to grips with the realities of the situation, but also for the counselor who must, during the process, be one with the parents in their struggle.

. . . .

To be effective, the counselor, whoever he is, must himself have worked through his own feelings about handicapped children and he too must have learned to accept and love them for what they are. This is essential in order that the counselor may bring a certain objectivity to the task at hand.

The counselor also needs to know what he can and what he cannot do. He has to be quite content in the knowledge that there are some things that he cannot do. For example, with very few exceptions the counselor can do nothing about changing the potential of the child. Therefore, accepting this fact frees him to act more directly and definitely in helping the child, through the parents.

As he moves directly toward discussions with the parents, he must enter into a process of turmoil since he must be one with them. Through it all, he must be gentle, thoughtful, considerate and yet firm in what he knows he can do and what he must do. He must never be hostile, never aggressive, never punitive. This is sometimes difficult because the counselor must accept the fact that at times he may need to be a whipping post. This role may be necessary if he is to help the parents work out their disappointments, conflicts and guilt feelings. All of it is a part of the counseling process.

Finally, he must stand ready to offer continuing support to those whom he serves. He must know the resources of the community. He must encourage parents to follow through, using help that is available. When this has been accomplished he can be reassured that his responsibilities have been discharged. In the process, the responsibility for final decision has been placed where it rightfully belongs—with the parents.

□ □ □

Part II Parental Dynamics Relative to Management

Any program designed for management of parents of the retarded will be influenced by the prevailing image of the parent and his dynamics. We have included selections on this topic on the assumption that an understanding of certain parental dynamics and an appreciation for conflicting dynamic theories are important counselor qualifications. Unfortunately, overlap with other areas, redundancy, and even irrelevancy were at times unavoidable for the preservation of the continuity or poignancy of individual styles. In choosing selections, preference was given to articles which relate parental dynamics to the management process, although this may have introduced subject matter which otherwise would have been more properly the topic of later parts of the book.

The first selection, by Begab, sets a keynote in reminding us of the diversity of parental responses: "Parents of mentally retarded children represent the total spectrum of human personality variation." With this introductory remark, Begab points out that "each set of parents is uniquely different," and that an assumption of homogeneity would be fallacious. Thus, the tendency in the literature to stereotype parents of the retarded as guilt-ridden, anxious, insecure, and emotionally traumatized probably does violence to reality since wide individual differences are found to exist. This statement, then, sets the stage for a counselor's approach: the counselor must come to understand the individual parent, couple, and family as an initial step in formulating an optimal management approach.

Kanner was an early voice of enlightenment. In article after article he presented insights into the management of parents which, even after decades, have lost none of their freshness. We sample his inimitable style in two selections in which he discusses certain aspects of parental dynamics. He points out that the examination of the child and the issuance of correct information are important, but sole concentration on the child, to the exclusion of the parents (except as message-hearers) leaves the family in a vacuum. "All of this leads to the inescapable conclusion that the study and treatment of exceptional children would be sorely incomplete if the emotional factors of family relationships were left out of consideration." To pull the child out of his meaningful social context, and to examine him without consideration of his social milieu, does not only do injustice to both the child and his family, but is also sociologically unsound.

The historical significance of the article by Sheimo should be pointed out. Published in 1951, this article was one of the earliest ones written on the dynamics of parents of the retarded. Because of its review of the relevant literature up to that time, and because of its generally progressive tone, it has been widely quoted. Sheimo also shows a great deal of insight in his case description of parents who brought their child to the physician: ". . . It also became progressively more evident that the doctor's mere presentation of clinical diagnosis and recommendation was neither sufficient nor perhaps really *what the parents were seeking." Only after assessment of parental dynamics is it possible to make realistic management decisions for both the parent and the child.*

The contributions by Mahoney, Bryant and Hirschberg, Roos, and Smith relate their own particular impressions based on experiences with parent counseling and discuss rather broad aspects of parental dynamics. Although some of these contributions are presented within a specific disciplinary framework, in most cases the terms caseworker, physician, or psychologist could be supplanted by reference to counselors or case managers in general. Mahoney reasserts the principle of individual differences among parents of the retarded, stating ". . . A recognition of these differences is of utmost importance if our counseling efforts are to be maximally realistic and beneficial to both parent and child." Nevertheless, he proposes that certain patterns of adjustment adopted by subgroups of parents can be identified. Bryant and Hirschberg provide some insights into emotional problems which might be affecting parents' judgments of themselves, the child, the community, and the professional who is attempting to help. Roos, a psychologist, discusses parental reactions to retardation in terms of loss of self-esteem, feelings of shame, ambivalence, hostility, feelings of depression, feelings of guilt and self-reproach, and masochism. Smith suggests that to many parents of the retarded, their child's retardation becomes an all-pervading frame of reference within which reality is interpreted. This dominating motif may affect all their perceptions.

The remaining selections are articles addressed to specific themes. Thus, many writers in the field hold the view that the parental response to a retarded child is largely determined by the conscious or unconscious symbolic meaning attached to the occurrence or existence of retardation. Two selections are devoted to this theme. Mandelbaum and Wheeler explore and exemplify the significance of ways in which parents may perceive a damaged child—or each other. The authors also point out that the professional himself may be subject to the same symbolizations as a parent. Ryckman and Henderson summarize six "meanings" of retardation that various writers believe they have discerned.

Beddie and Osmond (see Part IX-A) were among the first to interpret the parental reaction to the birth of a retarded child in terms of grief and mourning. Once formulated, this view gained wide acceptance. Solnit and Stark give an interesting psychoanalytic phrasing to this theme. Olshansky introduces a refinement in his paper on chronic sorrow, and further distinguishes it from the formulation of Solnit and Stark in a second article. These three papers are samples of a number of publications that propose theories as to the type of crisis or stress parents undergo.

The construct of parental rejection is often invoked by professionals in the field. In a selection which has not received the attention it deserves, Gallagher takes a critical look at the utilization of the construct, suggesting a number of distinctions and clarifications.

In the final article Boyd, a parent, perhaps over-generalizes in his formulation of three typical stages of parental growth, but this formulation has become a much-quoted classic and has been reprinted in pamphlet form by the National Association for Retarded Children. It is included here as a representative of almost two dozen articles which propound various views about the stages of feeling and growth through which the parents of a retarded child may pass.

from CASEWORK FOR THE MENTALLY RETARDED—CASEWORK WITH PARENTS *Michael J. Begab*

(The Mentally Retarded Child: A Guide to Services of Social Agencies, 1963)

. . . .

Parents of mentally retarded children represent the total spectrum of human personality variation. Most are normal, average, well-adjusted people; some are maladjusted; others are neurotic, mentally incapacitated or intellectually inadequate. They differ greatly in their degree of usefulness to the community, in their own personal adjustment, in their capacity for parenthood, and in their skill in handling life's many problems—including mental retardation.

While it is true that some parents of mentally retarded children—especially those affiliated with parents' organizations—share common interests and, to some degree, similar feelings and reactions, it would be fallacious to assume their homogeneity according to any criteria by which persons are assessed. Each set of parents is uniquely different. Casework goals and the techniques used to achieve these goals must be related to their total psychological functioning as people, not just as parents or as parents of retarded children. Whatever their differences, most need and can profit from professional casework services.

There is a regrettable tendency in much of today's literature to categorize all parents of retarded children as guilt-ridden, anxious, insecure and emotionally traumatized persons. That these symptoms are frequently observed is undeniable, but it is important to emphasize the fact that these reactions are not universal nor are they experienced with the same intensity or duration. To the extent that parental reactions are presumed or pre-judged, we run the risk of approaching each casework situation in a stereotyped manner and misdirecting treatment efforts.

The previously well-adjusted parent is generally capable of enduring the emotional hurt and anxiety of a retarded child without severe personality disorganization and readjustment. He may experience temporary situational maladjustment and need some therapeutic reassurance and support, but his primary requirements are often largely educational in nature—understanding of the child's potential, guidance in care and management, referral to appropriate resources and services. In working with parents who have not achieved a satisfactory adjustment prior to the birth of the retarded child, casework treatment of a therapeutic nature may need to be aimed *ultimately* at the parents' personal and marital conflicts rather than their feelings relative to the retarded child. Failure to diagnose the true basis for parental maladjustment may result in support of an existing neurotic pattern and help neither parent nor child. Work with culturally deprived parents involves still another set of dynamics. Here the focus of activity may be directed primarily toward a betterment of home conditions, advice and guidance in child-rearing and homemaking, and motivating the parents toward self-improvement. . . .

□ □ □

from PARENTS' FEELINGS ABOUT RETARDED CHILDREN *Leo Kanner*

(American Journal of Mental Deficiency, 1953)

There was a time when, confronted with the task of dealing with retarded children, the educator's, psychologist's, or physician's main effort consisted of an examination of the child and advice to the family. No matter how expertly and conscientiously this was done, it somehow did not take in the whole magnitude of the problem. Parents were told of the child's low I.Q. in mournful numbers and were urged to think in terms of ungraded classes or residential school placement. The I.Q. figures may have been correct and the suggestions may have been adequate, and yet very often a major, highly important and, in fact, indispensable part of the job was somehow neglected.

It is recognized more and more that professional and at the same time humane attention should be given to the attitudes and feelings of people who are understandably puzzled by the lag in their child's development and progress. Whenever parents are given an opportunity to express themselves, they invariably air their emotional involvements in the form of questions, utterances of guilt, open and sometimes impatient rebellion against destiny, stories of frantic search for causes, pathetic accounts of matrimonial dissensions about the child's condition, regret about the course that has been taken so far, anxious appraisals of the child's future, and tearful pleas for reassurance. It takes a considerable amount of cold, hard-boiled, pseudo-professorial detachment to turn a deaf ear on the anxieties, self-incriminations, and concerns about past, present, and future contained in such remarks. We have learned to take them into serious consideration and to treat them as the genuine, deep-seated, intrinsic perplexities that they are. We have learned to distinguish between abrupt, brutal frankness and a sympathetic statement of fact, between a dictatorial, take-it-or-leave-it kind of recommendation and the sort of presentation which would appeal to parents as the most constructive and helpful procedure, best for the circumstances.

I know that it is difficult to speak in generalities about a subject which entails individual sentiments. I know from experience that every couple who comes with a retarded child carries along a set of specific curiosities which must be understood and satisfied. For this reason, it may perhaps serve the purpose of this address if I were to introduce a few definite instances and, in so doing, to discuss the principal implications as they come along in the life of the retarded child and in the minds of his family.

> Johnny Jones was brought to our clinic at the age of eight years. He was referred to us by his pediatrician with the request for a psychometric evaluation. Johnny was in his third year in school, had been demoted once, and after that had been given courtesy promotions, even though he did not master the required curriculum of his grade. The psychologist's examination showed that Johnny had a test age of six years and an I.Q. of 75.

It was obvious that, with his endowment, he could not possibly be expected to do better than low first grade work. It would have seemed easy to say to the parents that Johnny should be in an ungraded class because of his low intelligence. It would have been very easy to give them the numerical result of the test and, if they balked, to offer them an authoritative explanation of the Binet-Simon or any other scale that had been employed.

However, there was one big fly in the ointment. Mr. and Mrs. Jones were both college graduate people and moved in highly intellectual and sophisticated circles. Mr. Jones was a competent representative of a pharmaceutical firm and his wife had been a librarian prior to her marriage. They could see logically that their son had not been able to accomplish the scholastic functions expected of a child his age. But for years they had struggled against the very thought that something might be amiss with their Johnny's academic possibilities. As a result, they had kept looking for interpretations of his failures other than the one interpretation which they dreaded because they could not accept it emotionally.

They had found fault with the school system. There couldn't be anything wrong with the child; the problem must lie somewhere in the *method of instruction;* Johnny's teachers were either too young and inexperienced or too old and unfamiliar with modern education. They were alternately critical of what they chose to call either old-fashioned drilling or new-fangled frills. When, in the course of time, they had been convinced that the other children in Johnny's group got along all right under the same educational regime, they tried to seek the culprit in *Johnny's body.* After considerable search, they found one doctor who persuaded them that Johnny would do better if his tonsils and adenoids were taken out. They cherished this bit of wisdom because it fitted into their emotional pattern. They could say to themselves that, after all, their Johnny was all right and would learn better after the repair of a physical imperfection. This did not work.

In order to satisfy their need for prestige, they began to pounce on *Johnny himself.* They decided that the child must be lazy. They scolded him, deprived him of privileges and sat with him for hours trying to hammer his homework into him. They pointed out to him how well his numerous cousins did without all the help such as he received from them. The child, smarting from the constant rebuff and rebuke, sat there, unable to grasp the parental instructions and, not knowing why he could not conform, came to think of himself as a wretched, miserable, ungrateful creature who let his parents down. He gave up completely. He lost all confidence in himself and, in order to find some compensation for his anguish, he took to daydreaming.

Eventually, the parents thought that Johnny's salvation stared them in the face when they came upon an article in *The Reader's Digest* which told them that a certain drug, named glutamic acid, could brighten up children and make them learn better. They obtained the drug and got him to swallow tablet after tablet. For a time, they called off the dogs of daily tutoring and pushing, with the idea that glutamic acid would do the trick. Johnny, relieved of the pressures, perked up for a while and seemed brighter. He felt that being offered the tablets, however ill-tasting they were, was better than being hovered over impatiently at the desk. The parents came to feel that the money they paid to the druggist was about the best investment they had ever made. But in the long run they realized that, as far as learning was concerned, there was no noticeable departure from the status quo. They felt disillusioned and finally decided to take the child to the clinic.

Betty Brown was a placid, likable little girl whose physical characteristics

> and marked developmental retardation had led the child's pediatrician to make the correct diagnosis of mongolism. He was able to help the parents to understand and accept Betty's limitations. The Browns were warm-hearted people and genuinely fond of their three children, of whom Betty was the youngest. Michael and Anne were healthy and bright and held out every promise of good academic achievement. They sensed their sister's handicaps, were helped by their parents to make the necessary allowances and, being secure in the warmth of a comfortable emotional climate, adjusted nicely to Betty's need for her mother's special attention. Anne, in fact, welcomed and invited opportunities to be mother's little helper in her ministrations to Betty.

This constellation of attitudes might have made for an ideal mode of family living. But a "bull in the china shop" charged into this peaceful home in the shape of Betty's paternal grandmother who lived a few doors away from the Browns. The elder Mrs. Brown stubbornly refused to acknowledge the doctor's diagnosis. She had always been a bit critical of her daughter-in-law but had found it difficult to hold on to a specific hatrack on which to hang her expressions of disapproval. Betty's failure to develop properly came to her as a godsend. She made up her mind that there was nothing wrong with Betty herself and that the whole trouble stemmed from the child's mother's inadequate methods of training. She offered no concrete suggestions. She did not substantiate her recriminations. But every morning, with clock-like regularity, she appeared at the home, looked at the child with a mien of profound commiseration, and uttered the same reproachful phrase: "When are you going to start making something of the child?"

Mrs. Brown took this as long as she could. She discarded as utterly futile her initial attempts to convey to her tormentor the reality of Betty's condition. She decided to remain silent. But eventually she could stand it no longer. It was not easy to be confronted daily with insult added to painful injury. She turned for help to her husband, imploring him to do something about his mother's stereotyped antics. All that he had to offer was the advice that she "pay no attention." After a few months, she brought Betty to our clinic. In reality, she brought herself and her misery rather than the child. She was obviously depressed and was seeking help for herself, which by that time she needed desperately.

> Alan Smith was his parents' only child. He was severely retarded in his development. The Smiths, feeling that Alan would need all of their attention, had decided to deprive themselves of further offspring. There was also the dread of a possible repetition of the tragedy. But most pathetic of all was the boy's mother's constant self-searching for some shortcomings of her own which might be responsible for her son's intellectual defect.

When she brought him to the clinic, she asked: "Doctor, did I have something to do with it? Did I do something wrong?" She eagerly gulped down the acquittal but went on: "Well—maybe before he was born—did I do something then?" When told that her child's retardation was not determined by anything that she had done, she was still puzzled. She wondered: "If it isn't what I have *done,* maybe it's what I *am* that brought it about." Again she seemed grateful for authoritative absolution. But still she went on. If she had not contributed to the fact of Alan's retardation, then she was surely guilty of not recognizing it in time, of pushing him beyond his capacity, of losing patience with him, of doing things for him which he might have learned to do for himself. Furthermore, she had been ashamed of his backwardness and tried to hide it from her friends and neighbors, and then she was ashamed of having felt shame. Of course, she could not gain peace through mere verbal reassurance, however thirstily she lapped it up. She needed many opportunities to talk herself out, more chances for this confessional type of expiation, and help in the suggested efforts to return to her previous social and communal life from which she had removed herself in sacrificial isolation because of her feelings of shame and guilt and remorse.

> Larry White was brought to our clinic at the age of seven and one-half years. His parents were distressed by his poor progress in school and by the suggestion that he be placed in an ungraded class. Larry was their only child who had come to them after eight years of married life. His birth, preceded by a miscarriage and much gynecological maneuvering, was greeted with jubilation. His mother, previously an efficient office manager, took Larry over as the biggest assignment of her career. Her feeding methods made and kept him nice and chubby. Speech development was somewhat delayed but this, she reasoned, is true of many children who later become regular chatterboxes. His faulty articulation was handled by sending him to a "teacher of expression and dramatics." He did well in nursery school and kindergarten. He was a happy, sociable, and well-mannered child.

Then the parents experienced their great shock. Larry could not do his first grade work, failed of promotion and finally was recommended for a special class. At first, the mother blamed his eyesight but three successive examinations convinced her that his vision was not at fault. The mother tried to do his homework with him, and each attempt made her more impatient. She then employed a tutor for him. When his scholastic performance showed no improvement, the parents began to transfer the blame to Larry himself. The father found comfort in the formula that Larry was "mentally lazy." The mother began to nag and punish him and deprive him of privileges. Larry became rebellious under the many-sided pressures, was increasingly restless, at times even destructive, and developed behavior ostensibly intended to get even with his critics and oppressors.

His I.Q. was 77.

The mother reported that her nephews and nieces all had superior intelligence and remarked significantly: "I can't understand. Why does this happen to me?" The father, more genuinely fond of the child, said, "I think he is perfect apart from school," and added that his wife was disturbed because Larry obviously was not a genius. Thereupon she said categorically: "I want him to go to college. We can afford it."

It is clear that one could not use a sledge hammer in dealing with Larry's parents. Merely telling them that their son was not ready for first grade work did not solve the essential problem. They had known this for some time. But they needed help in learning to accept the child as he was without a sense of personal shame and failure. Larry's mother felt ashamed and socially disgraced by having a child whom her society considers inferior. She felt guilty because the unpleasant thought must have kept obtruding itself that, after all her gynecological difficulties, she should perhaps have remained childless. She felt frustrated because her one great asset, her efficiency, had suffered defeat.

Examples such as these can be produced almost indefinitely. But even the small number of cited instances suffices to bring out a few highly important considerations. It is, of course, necessary for the expert to make the best possible use of the available test methods in order to obtain a scientifically valid assessment of a child's developmental potentialities. The application of these tests requires skill, experience, patience, and a setting in which the tested child would be at his ease and cooperate to his best ability. Many pitfalls must be avoided, such as testing a child during his regular naptime, failure to take into account an existing impairment of hearing or vision, psychometric examination immediately preceding or following a convulsion, or difficulty in allaying a child's acute anxiety which may manifest itself in speechless timidity or noisy defiance.

When a test has been completed satisfactorily and the child's intellectual endowment has been ascertained with reasonable accuracy, it is the expert's duty to report and explain his findings to the child's parents. It should hardly seem necessary to point out that such a report, if it involves the disclosure of a child's retardation, should be made tactfully, lucidly, and truthfully. But I have known parents who, without any concern for their emotional readiness, were thrown into a panic by the words feeble-minded, imbecile, or moron hurled at them as if from an ambush. I have also known good-natured doctors who did not have the heart to confront the parents with the true state of affairs and mumbled something to the effect that Johnny or Janie may "outgrow" the developmental lag or "catch up" with other children of his or her age.

> I once had a long-distance telephone call from a physician in a small town, who asked me to see a six-year-old boy who was markedly retarded. For several years, he had "played along" with Billy's parents, who were his personal friends. He minimized, if not ridiculed, their apprehensions. When Billy did not begin to talk long past the expected time, he reminded the parents of a cousin of his who had not talked until the age of four years but then made up for lost time and eventually graduated from high school and college. He advised: "If Billy won't talk, just don't give him the things he wants unless he asks for them verbally." When this method did not work and the parents wondered whether they should have Billy tested, he said some unkind words about "all that psychology stuff." But when Billy was to be enrolled in the first grade, the school authorities refused to accept him. The heartbroken parents were enraged at the physician who, they felt, had either been inexcusably ignorant or had knowingly betrayed their trust in him. When I saw them, they asked again and again: **Why** didn't he tell us?"

Adequate examination and the issuance of correct information are indeed indispensable. But they by no means constitute the whole of the expert's responsibility. The cited examples show that the mere procedure of Binetizing and Simonizing a child, the mere determination of an intelligence quotient, the mere pronouncement of the test result do not in themselves take care of the significant matter of family sentiments. It is true that each situation is unique and that different parents come with different problems. Yet it is possible to pick out from the large welter of cases several recurrent puzzlements which are voiced almost invariably. Allow me to enumerate some of the questions which are asked regularly with a great deal of feeling and to which the inquirers hope to get straightforward answers, without evasion and without hedging:

What is the cause of our child's retardation?

Have we personally contributed to his condition?

Why did this have to happen to us?

What about heredity?

Is it safe to have another child?

Is there any danger that our normal children's offspring might be similarly affected?

How is his (or her) presence in the home likely to affect our normal children?

How shall we explain him (or her) to our normal children?

How shall we explain him (or her) to our friends and neighbors?

Is there anything that we can do to brighten him (or her) up?

Is there any operation which might help?

Is there any drug which might help?

What about glutamic acid?

Will our child ever *talk?*

What will our child be like when he (or she) grows up?

Can we expect graduation from high school? From grammar school?

Would you advise a private tutor?

Should we keep our child at home or place him (or her) in a residential school?

What specific school do you recom-

mend?

If a residential school, how long will our child have to remain there?

Will our child become alienated from us if placed in a residential school?

Will our child ever be mature enough to marry?

Do you think that our child should be sterilized and, if so, at what age?

These are some of the questions asked commonly by the parents of retarded children. These questions vary, of course, depending on the degree of the child's retardation, on the presence or absence of other children in the family, on the parents' financial resources, on their ideas about social prestige, on their degree of acceptance or rejection of the child.

It is not possible to answer every one of these questions unequivocally. Science has not advanced sufficiently—and probably never will—to make omniscient persons of the consulted physician or psychologist. Aside from the fact that causes of retardation are not always the same in all instances and that there may be multiple contributing factors in the same instance, the search for an ultimate cause often runs against the barrier of our incomplete knowledge.

I have never encountered a parent who respected me less because, in answer to the question about the cause of his or her child's retardation, I made no secret of my inability to supply a definite answer. Intelligent parents usually realize fully that would-be erudite terms, such as innate, congenital, or constitutional, though literally correct, often beg rather than answer their question. What most of them hope to hear is indeed not so much a piece of etiological wisdom in words of Greek or Latin origin as an authoritative and sympathetic endorsement of themselves, of their human and parental competence, of their right not to blame themselves for what has happened.

Parents whose first child happens to be seriously retarded, are almost invariably plagued by the question whether or not they should have another child. There is a conflict between the strong desire to enjoy the pleasure of having a healthy child and the simultaneous fear that things may go wrong again. The parents always wait for an opportunity to present this question to the person whom they consult about their handicapped offspring. They are disappointed if this opportunity is not forthcoming.

It is not an easy thing to help in the solution of this conflict. For one thing, the question is not merely a desire for information. Behind it is sometimes a scheme, of which the parents themselves are not necessarily aware, to throw the whole burden of responsibility on the adviser. If the second child should also be afflicted, the parents are clear of any blame. They can point an accusing finger at the adviser who had told them what they wanted to hear. It has been my policy to remind parents that every childbirth entails a risk, that no one could possibly have predicted that their first child would be born handicapped. Though experience teaches that lightning does not usually strike twice in the same place, the risk, however small, must rest with the parents. But if they decide in favor of having another child, they should do so only if they are capable of freeing themselves of any anticipation of disaster. Such constant dread before and after the arrival of the new baby would create an attitude not conducive to a wholesome relationship even with the healthiest and sturdiest child.

There is no time to go into a discussion of all the questions which have been enumerated above. But the introductory examples show how profoundly the feelings of parents are involved in their types of curiosity, in the handling of their retarded children, and in their need for understanding and guidance. Like all human beings, the parents of retarded children react with their feelings. Their own life experiences, which have helped to shape their personalities, have contributed to the manner in which they adjust to pleasant and unpleasant realities in general, and to the presence of a handicapped child in particular.

In essence, one may distinguish three principal types of reaction:

1. Mature acknowledgement of actuality makes it possible to assign to the child a place in the family in keeping with his specific peculiarities. The child is accepted as he is. The mother neither makes herself a slave to him, nor does she take her inevitable frustrations out on him. She goes on functioning in her accustomed way. She continues her associations with her friends and acquaintances. The father shares her fondness for the child. Both parents manage to appraise the needs of their normal children as well and to distribute their parental contributions accordingly.

2. Disguises of reality create artificialities of living and planning which tend to disarrange the family relationships. The fact of the handicap is seen clearly but is ascribed to some circumstances, the correction of which would restore the child to normalcy. Some culprit is assumed in the child's character or body or in the educational inadequacy of the trainers. The child's poor scholastic progress in the regular grades is interpreted as a manifestation of laziness or stubbornness which must be exorcised with painfully punitive methods; the full burden is placed on the child himself. His low marks, his failure of promotion, the school's recommendation that he be placed in an ungraded class, are taken as a result of the blameworthy effrontery of a willfully unaccommodating child. Parental pressures to speed up his lagging speech development, to correct his indistinct articulation, and to improve his homework heap misery on the child, who finds it impossible to gain parental approval.

Instead of, or in addition to, the child himself, his body comes in for frantic attempts at correction. Tongues are clipped, prepuces are amputated, tonsils are evicted with the notion that somehow such measures will undo the reality of his handicap. Thyroid extract, caused to be swallowed by some physicians with hazy etiologic notions, and chiropractic adjustments of an allegedly misplaced vertebra are still much too frequently employed as a means of disguising reality.

3. Complete inability to face reality in any form leads to its uncompromising denial. The formula goes something like this: "There is absolutely nothing the matter with the child. Those who are anxious about his development are merely pessimistic spreaders of gloom. Some children walk or talk sooner than others, and some take their time." This is often the reaction especially of fathers who have no knowledge of children and do not wish to be bothered about them. They are away at work most of the day, have a glimpse of the child when he is asleep, hear the child's laughter on the rare occasion when they pick him up, and conclude with a shrug of the shoulder: "I can't see anything unusual."

A busy surgeon, the father of three children, could not see anything unusual about his youngest child, a severely withdrawn, autistic boy whom his mother brought to our clinic against her husband's wishes. The surgeon finally came, after several invitations. He had no idea of the child's developmental data; he left all this to his wife, he declared complacently. I tried to get an emotional rise at least by making him angry. I asked whether he would recognize any one of his three children if he met him unexpectedly in the street. He thought for a while, scratched his head, and then said calmly: "Well, I don't really know if I would." He felt that his wife's concern about the child was all nonsense but if she wanted to bring him to the clinic, that was all right, too; after all, this was her own business.

Any slightest acquaintance with the elementary principles of psychology is enough to indicate that all these different types of attitudes and resulting practices are deeply anchored in the emotional backgrounds of the individual parents and other relatives. Smothering overprotection, cold rejection, nagging coercion, or open neglect defended as proper tactics necessary to cope with the child's handicap, are in the main fundamental, dynamically evolved reactions which seize on the handicap as a readily accessible, superficial explanation.

All of this leads to the inescapable conclusion that the study and treatment of exceptional children would be sorely incomplete if the emotional factors of family relationships were left out of the consideration. In every instance, the place of the exceptional child in the family structure calls for a thorough overhauling, often with the urgent need for interviews with the parents. Frequently enough, the parents themselves beg for such an overhauling; they do so by asking seemingly specific or insignificant questions, and are most appreciative if such hints are understood and they are given an opportunity to talk themselves out before an experienced and sympathetic listener.

□ □ □

from THE EMOTIONAL QUANDARIES OF EXCEPTIONAL CHILDREN

Leo Kanner

(Helping Parents Understand the Exceptional Child, 1952)

. . . .

There is no getting away from the fact that the knowledge of an offspring's scholastic and social incompetence is a source of perpetual heartache. One cannot possibly expect unmitigated Pollyannish acquiescence. But different people react differently to the irreversibility of unpleasant realities. Some have developed a mature outlook which enables them to weather the vicissitudes of life with relative calm and with a knack for practical reorientation. Some prefer to delay the full acknowledgment of a disturbing contingency for as long as they can, and to shove away from themselves the avowal of its very existence. Some, rebelling against destiny's unexplained vagaries, make frantic efforts to dislodge unchangeable actualities by means of agitated excursions up one blind alley after another. Some, finally, feel that they must vindicate themselves by placing the blame on what they believe to be the primary cause of their misfortune. One meets with all of these attitudes in dealing with parents of exceptional children. . . .

There are parents who insist on playing ostrich and bury their heads in the sand in order to convince themselves that what they do not see does not exist. This attitude is observed most frequently in fathers and grandparents who do not have the constant care of the child. They go around assuring themselves and others: "There is absolutely nothing the matter with the child." Those who are anxious about the child's development—and this may include an acutely observing mother—are declared to be merely pessimistic spreaders of gloom. If the ostriches ever allow themselves to get close to reality, they lap up wishful-thinking wisdom, dispensed by uninformed advisers, who advise that the child "may be a bit slow," but will be sure to "outgrow" it and "catch up" later. No plans are made for the child, and when the time comes for enrollment in school and he is refused admittance because of his retardation, the forcible removal of the sand from the ostrich eyes is accompanied by dissension, disruption and emotional turmoil. One can imagine what this does to the emotions of a child who suddenly finds himself excluded from school and the center of squabbles and disharmony.

Even greater inroads on the child's peace of mind are made by those who, though aware of his limitations, try to change the decree of nature, not infrequently with the connivance of ignorant pseudo-Joshuas for whom, however, the sun does not stand still, no matter how hard they blow their trumpets. Tongues are clipped, tonsils are evicted, endocrine extracts are administered, vitamins are prescribed, glutamic acid is given—all to "make the child over." Tutors are engaged to "brighten him up," and he is generally made the victim of numerous unscientific, fruitless and useless procedures. The press of the nation reports the wonders of this or that drug, operation, or educational formula designed to change mental retardates into potential college graduates. Of late, a new cliché has been making the rounds. Parents are told that their child's retardation is caused by an "emotional block." Quite a few markedly retarded children have been referred to our clinic to have them "unblocked" with the aid of psychiatric magic. Thus the search for some miracle takes the family on an extended shopping tour among physicians, psychologists, chiropractors, and others, distrusting the truth when it is offered and grasping at any straw, however fragile and hollow. And meanwhile, the parents are making the child miserable through their constant corrective efforts to mend the unmendable. The child, finding himself in a repair shop instead of in a home, cannot help smarting from the impact of all this molding and hammering. He cannot help being crushed, defeated, unappreciated, and either pathetically unhappy over his inability to please, or clumsily rebellious against his tormentors.

There are, lastly, those parents who cannot forgive their child that he is not as they want him to be. They vent their disappointment on him. They make him personally responsible for what they regard as a betrayal of their ambitions. The child is met with hostility, open and unvarnished. He does not even have the questionable comfort of having his tonsils or thyroid blamed. It is *he* who is the culprit. He has poor grades in school because he is "lazy." He does not speak distinctly because he is "stubborn." He does not oblige because he is "mean." Insult is thus added to injury from morning till night. This hurts even more than being in a repair shop. This is tantamount to living in an enemy camp.

It would be unfair to condemn such parents as villains bent intentionally on breaking their children's spirits. Nothing is farther from the truth. The manner of dealing with their retarded offspring is an outgrowth of their own emotional involvement in the issue. They react to a gnawing sense of guilt and to a genuine and sincere desire to improve the situation. They feel a tormenting dread of the finality which is implied in acknowledging the obvious. They are confused by misleading interpretations and recommendations. And they feel compelled to erect a defense against an attitude of society which causes the intellectual "haves" to look down on the intellectual "have-nots."

□ □ □

from PROBLEMS IN HELPING PARENTS OF MENTALLY DEFECTIVE AND HANDICAPPED CHILDREN

Stanton L. Sheimo

(*American Journal of Mental Deficiency*, 1951)

The emotional conflict in which parents of mentally defective or handicapped children frequently become entangled is one with which general practitioners, pediatricians and psychiatrists are often confronted. The intense anxiety frequently aroused is manifested in many different ways, and the problems encountered in helping such parents overcome their conflicting attitudes toward their child are often difficult and time-consuming. Although there has been an abundance of material reported in the literature discussing the mentally defective child as an individual, it seems significant that relatively little has been written concerning the parental attitudes toward such a child. Even less has been written concerning the difficulties the clinician experiences in attempting to be of help to the parents.

In a review of the literature of the past ten years, there have been some who have reported and emphasized the importance of dealing with the parental attitude and anxiety. H. C. Schumacher[1] stresses the treatment and helping of the parents, the removal of the significantly disturbed persons from the child's environment, and/or transfer of the child to a more stable environment. W. Wardell[2] reports on her experiences in dealing with the anxieties within the parents of institutionalized mentally defective children. She feels that the extra therapeutic case work effort is rewarding in its help to the parent, and its contribution to a greater ease of institutional adjustment for the child. Westlund and Palumbo[3] report on the parental attitudes in parents with crippled children, and specifically those with infantile paralysis. They recognize and discuss the tendency toward increased parental rejection of the child, with the consequent guilt and anxiety in the parents as the severity or chronicity of the debility increases. They also report a case in which a mother and handicapped daughter were seen regularly by a psychiatric social worker and a psychiatrist in therapeutic interviews. E. W. Coughlin[4] reports on parental attitudes in parents with handicapped children. He feels that these parental attitudes are perhaps no different from the attitudes of parents toward so-called "normal" children. He felt, rather, the disability brought deep-seated feelings to the surface, which might otherwise have been suppressed. Marguerite M. Stone[5] dealt with this aspect of the problem in an article more recently. She too was impressed by the paucity of the published literature on this subject. She classified the parental types according to degrees of awareness of the retardation or disability, and studied the feelings of parents as recorded in the interviews in a series of 44 cases. She did this both before and following several diagnostic interviews with the parents. She discussed the parental guilt around the tendency to reject the child, and how the defective child, often quite unconsciously, becomes the pawn in the battle between marital partners. At the same time, she recognized the importance of the skill, training, and experience of the worker, and the many difficulties involved in actually helping the parents. She thought there was an evidence of growth, during the diagnostic process, in the ability of the parent to face the problem.

Others (see footnotes 6-9) speak of how parents should educate and train the defective or handicapped child, with special projects for woodworking, needle craft, weaving, and so on. They stress the importance of better facilities including expanded foster home placement programs, parent and public education, home-training under the supervision of a staff of social workers to relieve the parents of the wearing task of constant supervision of the particular child, and education to give the parents a better understanding of the child's mental capacity and thus postpone placement. Others[10] write of "unworthy parental attitudes," as evaluated by the parents' failure to visit, send letters, and give gifts to their institutionalized child. Another[11] evaluates the hereditary genetic factor and I.Q. levels of parents of retarded children.

This author's experience consists of working with several families, each of whom came to this clinic with an obviously defective or handicapped child. The ages of the children ranged from a twenty-one-month-old mongolian idiot to a fourteen-year-old mentally defective child. In one of these cases, the experience consisted of working with the mother in bi-weekly therapeutic interviews for a period of two years. The others were seen for a briefer period, ranging from four to twenty interviews. Further investigation was made in a review of 150 cases of mentally defective children in a state institution. . . .

The uncertainty as to whether or not a child is congenitally defective obviously makes it more difficult for the doctor to deal with the parental conflict. The most relevant factor at such a point is for the doctor to clinically establish the status of the child. To whatever extent he is still uncertain, a frank expression to the parents might then liberate him from a feeling that he *has to know,* thereby making him better able to deal with the anxiety of the parents.

An outstanding factor in these cases is the extended attempt of the parents to seek help from other sources prior to their referral to this clinic. More frequently than not, most professional services had concurred in their opinion that the child was congenitally defective or handicapped. The parents' inability to accept this fact seemed to be expressed by the frequent change of doctors and clinics, and the continued search for some new medication or treatment for the child. In some cases the time, energy, and great financial sacrifice that the parents had made in search of some help was very impressive. As a result of these observations, we are faced with the question of what conflict or conflicts are possibly serving as the motivating force behind such manifestations. In attempting to evaluate this further, some of the problems encountered by the professional person become more evident.

Even though there is no question as to the clinical evaluation and diagnosis of the child's condition, the parents' initial concern is, nevertheless, centered around the condition of the child, discussion of previous experiences with doctors, and doubt as to the opinion and diagnosis of these doctors. The insistence that they believed something more could be done for the child was frequently expressed in terms of requesting glutamic acid injections, endocrine therapy, etc. (referring to some current periodical they had read) and even wanting to "offer" their child for some surgical or medicinal "experimentation."

As interviews progressed and the parents began to feel free to discuss their feelings, the meaning of the abovementioned behavior became clearer. Initially they expressed self-blame, feeling they were in some way at fault and had "caused" the condition of their child. Invariably, the parents had some idea as to the intellectual level of the child, and would say, "He acts like a one or two year old child," and would almost give the exact mental age level which psychological tests would subsequently reveal. The parents would say that a part of them knew all along that this was so, but that they felt an "inner urge or force" to do everything to disprove it.

Perhaps the most striking common factor was the intense guilt and conflict in regard to the impulse to reject the child. In one of the cases, this impulse was actually of a murderous degree. In each case, with only quantitative variations, the frequent changes of doctors, the often fantastic expenditure of energy, time, and money seemed to be a manifestation of the aforementioned conflict.

It also became progressively more evident that the doctor's mere presentation of clinical diagnosis and recommendation was neither sufficient nor perhaps *really* what the parents were seeking. Advice and suggestions seemed to be of no avail and unconsciously impossible for the parents to accept and find useful. In an attempt to help these parents, it is necessary for the doctor to become more sympathetically aware of the conflicting attitudes of the parents toward such a child. The parents' denial of the child's deficiency seemed to be an important element in their defense mechanism and very necessary in the maintenance of their self-esteem. The issue of the "child's defectiveness" frequently seemed to become, quite unconsciously, as Marguerite M. Stone states it, "the pawn in the battle between marital partners."

It is felt that the attitude of the particular doctor, whether he be pediatrician or psychiatrist, becomes an integral factor in aiding these parents. To be aware that the parents usually *know* their child is handicapped and defective and that their anxiety is predominantly an expression of their own internalized conflict, increases the possibility of being of real help to the particular parents. To tell parents that they *should* institutionalize the child, should, in a sense, "get rid of him," often tends to increase the guilt and strengthen the defense against this already forbidden impulse.

The doctor fulfills his medical responsibility when he quite frankly states his clinical diagnosis—both in regard to mental and physical status of the child —estimates the probable future difficulties, and recognizes the added burden which such children are to parents.

He becomes a physician in the true sense of the word, however, when he *recognizes* and *respects* the parents' right to decide what *they* want to do in terms of their total situation, including their own ambivalence and conflict. This implies that the doctor be ready to accept whatever decision the parents make, whether it be to keep the defective child in the home or to place him outside the home. The doctor's offer to discuss some of the parents' difficulties in arriving at a decision, becomes a beginning move in the direction of a possible resolution of the conflict.

If the doctor's efforts at being of help are directed, not toward a decision, but rather toward a resolution of the conflict and consequent relief of anxiety, it begins to liberate the parents from feeling they must come to an immediate decision. Also implicit in this is that an approach on the part of the parents toward a resolution of the conflict need not necessarily mean a decision to place the child outside the home. In the doctor's sympathetic understanding of the realistic aspect of the added burden and emotional drain such children are to parents, as well as the impulse within parents to reject such a child, he actually becomes of help in reducing the intrafamilial tension. The parents may then feel easier and consequently more ready to keep this child in the home indefinitely. In the meantime, the fruitless searching for a "cure" as a manifestation of the unresolved conflict no longer becomes as necessary.

As has already been suggested, the ambivalence and uncertainty within the clinician when he is faced with the task of dealing with these parents becomes a point at which parents, perhaps quite unconsciously, test and react. Opposing attitudes are not infrequently expressed by clinicians: on the one hand, "feeling sorry," over-solicitude, and an attempt to "soft-pedal" the truth; while on the other hand, impatience, and even annoyance, that his position as an authoritative person has been questioned.

It is understandable that doctors do appreciate and are sensitive to the unpleasantness of such a situation for the parents. To some it may seem unkind or even brutal to be frank with the parents as to the truth of the situation. Yet perhaps at just such times nothing short of an honest statement is really helpful to any of the members concerned, including the child. If the doctor is able to stand firm and strong in his convictions, while at the same time he allows the parents to react with what sometimes may be even intense rage and denial by stating that they do not and will not believe the doctor, he often proves, in the long run, to be of real, integrative value to these parents. At such moments, the doctor may not even get the satisfaction of having been of help, but in the ensuing months and years the parents may either attain a greater decisiveness or return to that particular clinician for help.

For the doctor to have the attitude that it seems illogical, if not "superhuman," for parents to expect the same degree of satisfaction from a defective child that can be received from a more "normal" child, may be of help in reducing the parents' guilt and anxiety about being "unworthy" or "bad" parents.

Likewise, it is important for the doctor to be aware of the fact that the attitudes and pressures from other children and neighbors, both toward the defective child as well as toward the parents, do add to and aggravate the existing inner turmoil and sense of dissatisfaction. This is not to imply that the clinician "warns" the parents of these factors, but rather that these concepts be a part of his attitude.

In this way parents can experience simple honesty with another person, who neither has to be unsympathetic, impatient and authoritarian, nor oversolicitous and hesitant. It behooves the clinician to recognize that these parents invariably *know* the degree of the deficiency and that their intense anxiety around the child's defectiveness is the way in which their conflict is manifested. He must therefore not wittingly participate in this manifestation.

In the case of a four-year-old male mongolian idiot, the parents had spent three years searching for some "cure" for the boy. Following several sessions, the mother became more able to discuss some of her own feelings in relationship to this child, as well as toward her husband. She discussed her fears that this child might fall into their swimming pool, and then later, with much anxiety and guilt, related the impulse she once had to push this child into the pool. The significance of these feelings as related to this mother's earlier childhood conflicts in relationships with her parents and siblings was not gone into. Nevertheless, this mother subsequently was able to come to a clearer decision to place this child outside the home.

Another case was that of a seven-year-old congenitally blind, mentally defective girl. In this case the work with the mother was more intensive and prolonged, consisting of bi-weekly therapeutic interviews for two years. This family had been to ten different sources for help. Treatment had consisted of five surgical operations on the child's eyes, numerous efforts in special schools, and temporary placements outside the home. This child's father died when she was five, two years prior to beginning treatment at this clinic. During the course of treatment the mother related with much uneasiness and guilt how she had felt "initially glad" that her daughter was born blind, because then she would not have to take care of her. Because of the guilt associated with this feeling, it became necessarily suppressed and in the ensuing seven years the mother spent her time searching for treatment. After a year of regular interviews, the mother was able to come to a decision to place her daughter in a state institution. During the subsequent year of treatment, the mother related how unhappy her marriage had been, her regret in her choice of a marital partner, and the intense guilt she felt around the sense of relief she experienced at her husband's death. The fear which she felt over the years that it would "hurt" her daughter too much if she were placed permanently away from her became clearer as a manifestation of this mother's earlier experience of feeling rejected and excluded at the birth of her sister when she was four.

Perhaps these cases were those in which the parental conflict was more severe. Nevertheless, it is felt that the difference between these cases and those where some decision in regard to the child is either made earlier or more readily is quantitative rather than qualitative. The many efforts that such families make—frequent change of doctors, great financial sacrifice, etc.—is something that has been observed by many who are called upon to be of help in such situations.

In a survey of 150 defective cases in a state institution, the direction and extent in which the parental conflict was manifested seemed significant. The pressure from parents on the particular institution in regard to the type of treatment their child was getting, the food, and so on, consumed a phenomenal amount of time on the part of all professional persons concerned. This pressure often extended to local city and county resources, State Department of Mental Hygiene, and, not infrequently, to the executive departments of the state government. At times the manifestation of the conflict seemed to be of a paranoid degree. The average age of admission (thirteen to fourteen) seemed to be in part an indication of the years of struggle the parents had been going through before finally *having to* institutionalize their defective child.

It seems important to the author not to underestimate the intense repressed forces which become mobilized in parents who have mentally defective and/or handicapped children. At such times, to center one's attention on the defective child rather than toward the parental conflict might be attempting to deal with the least relevant factor in the total situation.

FOOTNOTES

1. Schumacher, H. C., "Contribution of Child Guidance Clinic to Problem of Mental Deficiency," *American Journal of Mental Deficiency*, 50:277-283, 1945.
2. Wardell, Winifred, "Case Work with Parents of Mentally Deficient Children," *American Journal of Mental Deficiency*, 52:91-97, 1947.
3. Westlund, N., and Palumbo, A. Z., "Parental Rejection of Crippled Children," *American Journal of Orthopsychiatry*, 16:271-281, 1946.
4. Coughlin, E. W., "Parental Attitudes Toward Handicapped Children," *Children*, Volume II, No. 11, May 1947.
5. Stone, Marguerite M., "Parental Attitudes to Retardation," *American Journal of Mental Deficiency*, 53:363-372, 1948.
6. Nugent, M. A., "Home Training and Teaching of Mentally Deficient Children by Parents in Home," *American Journal of Mental Deficiency*, 45:104-109, 1940.
7. Horsefield, E., "Suggestions for Training Mentally Retarded by Parents in the Home," *American Journal of Mental Deficiency*, 46:533-537, 1942.
8. Rautman, A. L., "Mental Deficiency as a Problem in General Practice," *Wisconsin Medical Journal*, 41:771-776, 1942.
9. Johnstone, E. L., "What Should We Do With the Mentally Deficient?," *Mental Hygiene*, 30:296-302, 1946.
10. Thorne, Frederick and Andrews, Jean S., "Parental Attitudes Toward Mental Deficiency," *American Journal of Mental Deficiency*, 50:411, 1946.
11. Berry, R. J. A., "Investigation into Mental State of Parents and Siblings of 1,050 Mentally Defective Persons," *Bristol Medico-Chirurgical Journal*, 56:189-200, 1939.

□ □ □

OBSERVATIONS CONCERNING COUNSELING WITH PARENTS OF MENTALLY RETARDED CHILDREN

Stanley C. Mahoney

(American Journal of Mental Deficiency, 1958)

The parents of mentally retarded children are no longer forgotten people. Professional workers concerned with the mentally retarded child have become increasingly aware of the similar feelings and reactions experienced by most parents in our society upon learning they have a retarded child. From a period when little professional attention was given to the anxiety and confusion experienced by the parents of a retarded child, we have come to a time when parental counseling is usually accepted practice. Similar psychodynamic patterns, repeatedly found, have led to a "special psychology" of counseling with parents of retarded children.

In this paper, which is an outgrowth of the author's observations and experiences in counseling with parents of retarded children, an attempt is made to further refine our understanding by pointing out some differences among parents of retarded children. It is felt that a recognition of these differences is of utmost importance if our counseling efforts are to be maximally realistic and beneficial to both parent and child. For the most part, parents of mentally retarded children have been considered a rather homogeneous group with similar feelings and reactions to a similar traumatic situation. It is the thesis of this paper, however, that unless we go beyond the similarities involved and relate the parents' attempts to cope with their feelings in this traumatic situation to their total psychological functioning as people, and not just as parents, then we will not be as effective as we might be as counselors.

First, let us look more closely at our conception of parents of mentally retarded children. Are they as homogeneous as our categorization, and our literature, might imply? It would seem that they are as normal, as average, as maladjusted, as neurotic as are all parents—before the birth of a mentally retarded child. With this latter traumatic event, they suddenly become members of a common group—they are now parents of a mentally retarded child. But in so viewing them, are we not perhaps glossing over many real differences which exist beyond a situation they share in common and toward which they might have similar feelings and reactions? There is a danger, it would seem, in relating to these people, in perceiving them, in thinking about them, solely as parents of a retarded child. In our endeavor to help them cope with the anxiety and confusion aroused in response to a retarded child, we are frequently in danger of forgetting that they are not only parents, but also individuals uniquely different from each other, despite, in many cases, similar reactions to a similar traumatic situation.

Parents of mentally retarded children, like all parents and all people, differ greatly with regard to the adequacy of their own personal adjustment to themselves and to others. Many of these people have been able to effect an adequate adjustment to themselves and to others, and have led relatively productive lives enriched by interpersonal relationships which they have found personally satisfying. They have been able to assume a responsible adult role in our society and have achieved some measure of happiness in their everyday lives. For these parents, the birth of a mentally retarded child is a traumatic and painful incident which may, in some cases, precipitate a temporary situational maladjustment.

The parents may temporarily resort to a variety of defensive reactions to alleviate the pain and anxiety they are feeling, and may temporarily be incapable of realistic planning for their child. With time, however, and perhaps with the help of a counselor, they are able to become more tolerant of their feelings and are able to do what has to be done in the best interest of all concerned. When the parents have been well-adjusted people who have been able to achieve a happy and satisfying life, the trauma of the birth of a retarded child is relatively clean-cut, so to speak, and counseling can usually proceed to a stage of rational planning. Rheingold[1] and Kelman,[2] among others, have clearly presented the general process of such counseling.

Some individuals, however, have been unable to effect a personally satisfying adjustment to themselves and to others previous to the birth of a retarded child. To varying degrees their lives have been devoid of happiness and their behavior has been characterized by a painful, fruitless search for peace and security. Frequently lonely people, who have been unable to establish satisfying interpersonal relationships, they have been unable to assume the responsibility for seeking the psychological help which they need. A very different therapeutic situation presents itself with these parents than with parents who are relatively well-adjusted people. Here, more than ever, we must be sensitive to the various meanings the retarded child may have in the individual's total psychological functioning. We must remain especially aware of the multiple determinants of behavior, and not become lulled into a false sense of security by the perception of a familiar psychodynamic pattern.

Consider, for example, the frequently encountered pattern of over-protective behavior toward the retarded child. Most often this has been found to be reflective of rejecting and hostile feelings toward the child which the parent is unable to accept or tolerate. Consequent guilt feelings are assuaged and forestalled through a leaning over backwards, as it were, to care for and to protect the child. Thus a behavioral pattern of over-protection and over-indulgence frequently serves to thwart and render more difficult the direct expression of contrary underlying feelings of repulsion and rejection. But there are tremendous differences in the degree and intensity with which this behavioral pattern is observed among parents of retarded children. The more well-adjusted parent may be consciously aware of his ambivalent feelings toward his child, and he may struggle painfully to do what has to be done. Other parents may be able to cope with their feelings and control their behavior only after seeking help from a counselor. Still other parents rigidly adhere in a self-righteous manner to unusual degrees of protective and indulgent behavior, remaining totally unaware of the implications of their behavior and becoming highly resistant to any implications that they might find counseling helpful.

As a rule of thumb, and as a working hypothesis in need of more rigorous verification, it can be postulated that the more intense the defensive reaction toward the child, and the longer its duration, the more probable it is that the retarded child has become an integral part of the parents' total psychological functioning. That is, it is more likely that the dynamics relating to the retarded child have become closely and vitally involved in the parent's total adjustment process as a person. It would seem that the parent who has effected the most satisfying adjustment before the coming of a retarded child will be most capable of experiencing the pain and anxiety aroused without severe personality decompensation and readjustment. The parent who has previously been unable to effect a stable, satisfying adjustment will be most likely to undergo severe personality disturbance and readjustment, and will more often tend to involve the retarded child in [his] total psychological functioning in a more pervasive and persistent manner.

Perhaps first of all, then, we must, if we are to be most effective as counselors, "forget" as much as possible our rational categorization of the individual across from us as "a parent of a mentally retarded child" and respond to him as an individual in his own right. Trite though it may be, we must concern ourselves with the whole person. We hear a great deal about the stereotypes held by the public toward the retarded child and his parents; let us recognize that we, also, have our stereotypes, our pre-judgments as to how these parents are feeling and reacting, our interpretations made upon previous knowledge and experience as to what it means to have a retarded child. Although our stereotypes may be more accurate, they can still become a hindrance in an individual counseling situation if we are not careful; we as counselors are human, too, and are not immune to misapplying and superimposing pre-existing frames of reference. In those cases, which unfortunately are not rare, where the parent has not been able to effect a relatively satisfying adjustment before the birth of the child, we are frequently in danger of supporting a neurotic adjustment pattern, and helping neither parent nor child, when we focus all our attention upon feelings related to the child. Let us remember that the parent is also a person, and recognize that the birth of a retarded child may have implications to the person far beyond his role as a parent.

The following case illustration will perhaps make some of the foregoing remarks more meaningful, and it will serve as a reference point for further discussion.

Mrs. A., a middle-aged woman of rather plain appearance, came for counseling as to when her eight-year-old daughter would be ready to attend public school. Her child had been seen previously by several physicians and psychologists, and there was a general consensus of opinion that the child was mongoloid and functioning in the low moron range of intelligence. Furthermore, this child appeared to be emotionally disturbed as well as mentally retarded; she clung to her mother continually in a demanding and manipulating manner, refusing to do anything for herself or by herself. Mrs. A. defiantly and defensively stated she over-protects her child, "always have and always will," knows that it is not good for the child, but "she's my only child and I just feel she's too good and too innocent to play with older children." Mrs. A. had flatly refused to consider institutionalization: "If you mention it, I'll leave at once, like I did the others." She expressed her desire to do anything for her daughter's good, emphasizing that she was prepared to sacrifice her own happiness to make life better for her daughter.

Mrs. A. described herself as having

been "the ugly duckling" among several sisters. In growing up she compared herself unfavorably to her sisters, fought openly with them, and blamed them for her difficulties. She did not complete high school, again blaming her "bad looks" and her sisters. She worked as a domestic helper after leaving school, became very shy and withdrawn, brooded about her homeliness and attributed her lack of happiness to her physical appearance. "It would have been different if I wasn't so ugly." When in her mid-thirties she married a man much older than herself, and, in his words, continued to question him as to why he married such an ugly person. Following her daughter's birth, and upon learning the child was mentally retarded, she apparently suddenly lost her concern over her physical appearance. According to her husband, "now everything is because of the child. If someone doesn't like her, it's because of the child; if someone looks twice at her, it's because they know about the child. First it was her looks, and now it's the child."

Mrs. A. is obviously a very disturbed woman who has been unable to effect a satisfying adjustment, either to herself or to others. In a rigid, bitterly self-righteous manner she avoided taking any responsibility for her own unhappiness, but successively attributed the source of her dissatisfaction to her sisters, her physical appearance, and now to her mentally retarded child. Her intense over-protection of her child, her refusal to consider institutionalization, and her expressed desire "to do anything to make life better for my child" are feelings and reactions which are not uncommon among parents of retarded children. However, in Mrs. A's case this is much more than a temporary reaction to a traumatic incident. Mrs. A. has not only been unable to accept her child as a person with limited capacities, she has not only reacted to underlying feelings of hostility and rejection, but she has also made this child a part of her own adjustment pattern. The child has become an integral part of her own defense system and has become vital to her own adjustment. The child has been rejected as a person, but embraced as a psychological crutch.

In dramatic and bold relief, Mrs. A.'s functioning illustrates a phenomenon found in many cases where the parent has been able to achieve only a marginally satisfying life in a rather neurotic manner prior to the coming of a retarded child. Namely, there is a rather sudden shift in the symptomatic behavior of the parent and the retarded child becomes the external, concrete anchoring point for a multiplicity of difficulties. In Mrs. A's case, her physical appearance served as an external referent for all of her difficulties and problems before the birth of her child. Then, after the birth of her child, her physical appearance suddenly became of relatively little importance and her child became the anchoring point for her inability to effect a satisfying life for herself. In a manner characteristic of many emotionally disturbed people, Mrs. A. avoided the more painful task of coming to grips with her own feelings by finding an external referent for her problems. The common dynamic, "It is not me, I'm doing my best, it is this other thing that stands in my way," underlies her use of her sisters, her physical appearance, and her retarded child.

The question can be raised as to why Mrs. A. would not favor institutionalization for her child if she felt her child to be the source of her difficulties. Logically this would seem to make sense, but the determinants of her behavior are psychological and not logical. Mrs. A. is a woman who needs a "cross to bear," so to speak, in order to maintain her neurotic adjustment to herself and others. The suffering involved in "bearing the cross" is more easily tolerated by her than the anxiety which would be aroused in assuming greater responsibility for her own happiness and behavior. She does not perceive the contradictions in her behavior, and she sincerely believes that she is motivated purely "for the child's best interests"; contradictions, distortions, and vicious circles leading nowhere are the price she unknowingly pays for the illusive and precarious security she has achieved.

For most all parents of retarded children, except for those who are outrightly and overtly rejecting of the child, the question of institutionalization is threatening and anxiety-arousing. For the average, relatively well-adjusted parent it is a painful step. The dynamics in such a situation have been known for some time, especially as they relate to the parents' unresolved guilt feelings and to their tendency to project themselves into the place of the child who is going to the institution. The chronically disturbed parent who has taken the child as a crutch, however, has an understandably greater burden at this point, and separation from the child is of truly traumatic proportions. The parent who has found in her retarded child "a new meaning in life," a focal point for activity and endeavor, or a straw to grasp at in her psychological confusion, has become more dependent upon her child than the child has upon her. To institutionalize the child is to threaten the parent's psychological existence, to take away her crutch, her "meaning in life." The question here is not how the child will manage without the parent, but how the parent will manage without the child. It is at this point that the chronically maladjusted parent is especially in need of support and help.

More often than not, the psychodynamics are not as sharply etched as in the case of Mrs. A. where only the main theme has been presented. The retarded child usually takes on a variety of meanings in the psychological functioning of the chronically disturbed parent in a much more subtle, complex, and insidious manner. Frequently the retarded child serves simply as a concrete focal point for attention and activity which is socially acceptable, providing a welcome relief from a vaguely dissatisfying and empty life. The retarded child may give the parent "a purpose in life," "a meaning for living," or "a cause to fight for," and thus become a crutch to the psychologically crippled parent. This would seem to occur most often when the marital relationship has become a treadmill of going through the motions and is devoid of any real satisfactions for the parents. Although a consuming interest in mental retardation on the part of the parent may sometimes have beneficial results for the child, too often the child becomes merely a pawn in the parents' defensive operations.

Again, as a rule of thumb and a working hypothesis in need of more rigorous verification, it can be postulated that the greater the shift of symptomatic behavior in the parent from previous external referents to the retarded child, the less can counseling be realistically oriented toward the needs of the child and the more the parent will need intensive treatment. That is, the more the child is used as a psychological crutch by the parent, the more the child becomes a part of the parent's total psychological functioning, the greater will be the difficulties in working with the parent toward the best interests of the child.

To recapitulate, when the parent has previously effected a relatively satisfying adjustment to himself and others, the retarded child may be temporarily experienced as a traumatic threat to one's well-being. Temporarily, and to varying degrees of intensity, a diversity of defensive behavior may be utilized to cope with this perceived threat. However, the parent gradually becomes better able to focus upon the realities of the situation and to tolerate the pain and anxiety frequently entailed in doing what is generally agreed upon as being best for the child. Here counseling of a generally supportive nature, with opportunity for the expression of feeling, will usually be effective and attention can be increasingly focused upon realistic planning for the child.

In cases where the parent has been unable to effect a satisfying adjustment prior to the coming of the retarded child, however, a very different therapeutic situation presents itself. The child, experienced at first as a threat, is later incorporated as a crutch. Here supportive counseling will generally be of little value, since the parent is unable to make effective use of it. In some cases legal action may be necessary for the child's well-being, despite the parent's protests. In all cases, the chronically disturbed parent will be in need of intensive psychotherapeutic help, and the crucial factor will be his or her capacity to make use of it.

REFERENCES

1. Rheingold, H. L., "Interpreting Mental Retardation to Parents," *Journal of Consulting Psychology,* 1945, 9, 142-148.
2. Kelman, Howard R., "Some Problems in Casework with Parents of Mentally Retarded Children," *American Journal of Mental Deficiency,* 1956-57, 61: 595-598.

□ □ □

from HELPING THE PARENTS OF A RETARDED CHILD: THE ROLE OF THE PHYSICIAN

Keith N. Bryant
J. Cotter Hirschberg

(American Journal of Diseases of Children, 1961)

. . . .

Parents express great anxiety about their inability to meet their child's needs—they are not confident about their handling of the child. If the mother is not secure in her feminine role, a retarded child will create special dilemmas for her. Some mothers handle this conflict by having another child, thus hoping to prove their adequacy. However, the mother may react in an opposite way and not have another child even though there is no reason why she should not. Having another child often stirs up guilt because it takes time away from the retarded child; not having another child may result in unconscious anger and resentment toward the retarded child, and in blaming him for the decision not to have another child. Another solution may be to adopt a child, but unless the negative feelings have been resolved, this solution also contains possibilities for further conflict and difficulty.

The parents may feel frustrated because the child's handicap itself is felt as a blow to their own success as parents. If they are parents who can love the child only by seeing themselves in the child, then they will always be discontented about what the child can never be or do. They will feel anger and frustration because of their own unrealistic demands on the retarded child, which because of his handicap he can never meet. They may feel angry and frustrated because of the dependent demands the retarded child necessarily makes on them; such parents cannot give the extra care required and they may need to deny the retardation in order to deny the need for the extra care. Or the parents may wish to place the child in an institution when such a placement would not ordinarily be indicated, except for their own feelings toward the child. Opposite emotional feelings, such as love and hate, toward the child commonly coexist and act unconsciously and independently of each other.

An emotionally disturbed mother may be so afraid of her own anger toward the child that she has to isolate herself from him. Her depression over the child's handicaps may prevent her from providing the emotional support and additional care that is required. She may make a "negative identification" with the child—that is, the child is seen as a "throwback" to a despised or unsuccessful member of the family, and this may prevent a positive relationship. The effect of the retarded child upon other members of the family and upon other children in the community is a concern of all parents, and if they view the child as the result of "bad blood," they will not be able to assess these concerns realistically. Parents who had problems with their own sexual development may worry unduly about their child's sexual development; parents who had difficulties in school or in social adjustment may exaggerate the retarded child's problems in these areas. Of course, every parent has aspirations and desires for his children and feels grieved and concerned when these aspirations can never be fulfilled.

Parents may also feel they have caused the retardation by negligence during the pregnancy, and if the child was not wanted, or if there were wishes or actual attempts to abort the child after conception, then the guilt will be greatly compounded. Their guilt feelings about producing a handicapped child will be accentuated if religious concepts of sin and suffering get intermingled in the parental attitudes toward the child. Parents with these attitudes sometimes act as though they are being punished by fate or by God; the retarded child is a penance they must do. This may cause them to devote an unrealistic amount of time and money to the care of this child to the neglect of the other children. However, one rarely achieves much change by pointing this out to the parents, since stressing the effects of this child on the others or on themselves only increases their anger because they feel this is a burden they *have* to bear. Such guilts may make them determine never to have another child, feeling they do not deserve anything better in life and that they do not have the right to a normal child.

To conceal their anger from themselves and others, parents may be unable to discipline the child, or to demand that the child do what he can adequately do. They overprotect the child and keep him close to them, not being able to have him away in special classes [or] facilities. It may be this need to "prove" they are "good parents" which prevents them from placing the child away from the home when it is obviously needed. But even the most normal parents will feel they are abandoning the child when he is sent away from home and will be haunted with doubts about whether he is being properly cared for and whether they should be doing something further. Here good relationships with the admitting institution and confidence in its staff and facilities will greatly help in handling the more conscious aspects of this problem. Unfortunately not many institutions as yet work actively with parents on a regular and continuing basis.

Parents may feel so ashamed and guilty about their child that they are unable to keep him at home even though this would be the best solution. Here the physician should try to encourage them to keep the child in the home at least for the younger years. However, the parents' needs must also be met and some may not be able to bear the burden such a child places on even the most normal and stable home. The social stigma of having a retarded child may continue to be a factor in the parents' reactions, even though they intellectually know it is something about which they should not be guilty or ashamed.

These unconscious conflicts may also make the parents deny the reality of the child's handicap, and maintain false expectations regarding the child's education or treatment. Instead of blaming themselves, which is the one extreme, they blame the community and ascribe the child's failure to the incompetence of the teacher or of the doctor, rather than to the disability. Such parents question the professional advice given them, and appear sometimes quite irrational in their views, often to the bafflement of those who deal with them. They will turn to charlatans, or repeatedly seek new sources of professional help. Then they will use the minutiae of differences in findings of one physician against the other, or will use one of the more developed areas in the child's functioning to deny the existence of greater problems in other areas. Only a careful, understanding approach will help them to obtain a more realistic view of the problem and to interrupt their costly and painful shopping pattern.

In spite of the physician's best efforts, and his spending of extra time with them, such parents may still complain of his lack of concern and accuse him of being biased and prejudiced. Thus it becomes obvious that as well as having special attitudes toward the retarded child, the parents also come to the doctor with certain unrealistic attitudes and expectations. They may have magical expectations in which they are doomed to disappointment, no matter what the physician is able to do for them. They may carry over attitudes they held toward their own parents to the physician and expect him to be critical, depriving, hostile, or authoritarian, or conversely to be all-giving and understanding, taking over and solving all the problems for them, as they believe a good parent would.

What are some of the other possible implications of the parents' coming to the doctor beyond obtaining a diagnostic study of the child? Sometimes it may be a bid for treatment of themselves, or they may come to solve a marital problem, but displace this difficulty onto the child. One parent may be using the child's problems to criticize the other; one parent may be coming for self-justification and for reassurance that he is doing the right thing for the child. An important question always is how is the child used in the individual parent's own needs and in the marriage. Occasionally a child may be used to maintain a neurotic balance in the marriage and may be what holds the marriage together, with this situation preventing the parents from taking constructive steps to help the child. In other marriages the child may be the final blow that leads to the disruption of the family, with the child representing an area of extreme disagreement between the parents and being used as a conductor of hostility between them. In some marriages, each parent competes for the retarded child's love and thus they are unable to initiate any discipline or achieve any separation from the child, because each sees this as a lack of love rather than as something beneficial for the child. Or the reverse may be true; hostility between the parents may lead one parent to refuse to send the child to a special school in order to oppose the views and wishes of the other.

Unconscious and conscious attitudes of the parents toward themselves, toward the child, toward the community, and toward the doctor greatly influence what can be done in providing them with help. Anyone who plays a role in this situation, even at the parents' request, is bound to be exposed to irrational feelings. Strong denial of defects, or great anger and resentment toward the physician, or toward others in the community, need to be understood in part in terms of their underlying origin—arising from fear, anger, guilt, disappointment, and despair. With such understanding, one can tolerate these attitudes, even though they are unjustified, and will be able to help the parents in their painful struggle with reality. . . .

□ □ □

from PSYCHOLOGICAL COUNSELING WITH PARENTS OF RETARDED CHILDREN

Philip Roos

(Mental Retardation, 1963)

. . . .

Many parents suffer a severe loss of self-esteem when they recognize retardation in their child. In our culture children are often considered by parents as ego-extensions; that is, the parent closely identifies with his child, taking pride in his accomplishments and basking in his reflected glory. A serious defect in the child tends to be experienced by the parent as his own defect. Hence, the parent may feel responsible for disappointing his mate, his own parents, and other family members by "presenting" them with a defective child. The possibility of genetic etiology leads some parents to renounce plans for having other children. Self-esteem may be further lowered by threat to the fantasy of immortality through one's children—the individual is suddenly faced with the prospect that he will leave no descendants after him. Life goals and basic approaches to the world may be abruptly and radically altered.

Closely allied to loss of self-esteem is the feeling of shame experienced by many parents. They may anticipate social rejection, pity, or ridicule, and related loss of prestige. It is not uncommon to find parents withdrawing from social participation and altering plans which might expose them to social rebuff. They tend to view their child's school years with particular apprehension, since during this time his defect will become most apparent.

Parents' feelings toward their retarded child are typically extremely ambivalent. Not only are they constantly frustrated by the child's lack of achievement, but the child's inadequate control often leads to extremely irritating behavior. Resentment and hostility generated by repeated frustrations may be expressed in death wishes toward the child and feelings of rejection. Typically such feelings arouse considerable guilt in the parent, who then tries to atone for his hostility by developing overprotective and overindulgent attitudes toward the child. The inconsistent reactions by the parent of demandingness, hostility and rejection, alternating with overprotection and overindulgence, are likely to disturb the child and thereby further reduce his efficiency, in turn increasing parental frustration. Such a self-perpetuating "vicious cycle" may further reduce the child's intellectual efficiency.

Hostility generated by frustration experienced in their interaction with the retarded child is often displaced by the parent[s] onto other relationships. Parents may present a "chip-on-the-shoulder" attitude. Their irritable, resentful demeanor tends to alienate others and leads to rejection and avoidance by friends and relatives, further frustrating the parents and thereby increasing their resentment. The counselor should be alerted to the possibility that his clients may be in the grips of such a vicious cycle. Inappropriate attacks against the counselor are more easily accepted if recognized as manifestations of displaced hostility stemming from serious frustrations.

Feelings of depression are to be expected. The absence of such feelings, particularly when realization of the child's retardation is recent, is unusual enough to raise suspicions regarding the possibility of atypical techniques of handling emotions (e.g., repression and isolation of affect). Some parents react to the retarded child as if he had died and manifest the typical grief reactions associated with the loss of a loved one. Such extreme reactions tend to be most prevalent in highly intelligent parents who tend to equate being human with the possession of intelligence. Disappointment in the child and concern for his future are appropriate reactions typically accompanied by some degree of unhappiness. Parents' ambivalence toward the child may contribute to depression, inasmuch as the hostility toward the child may be redirected toward the self.

Feelings of guilt and self-reproach may accompany depression and usually reflect internalization of hostility toward the child. It is not uncommon for parents to indicate that they feel responsible for the retardation, which may be described as a form of punishment for sins or as the outcome of transgressions. Cause of the retardation is sometimes erroneously attributed to guilt-ridden sexual activities.

Some parents adopt a masochistic position, almost welcoming the suffering they anticipate will accompany rearing the defective child. They may think of themselves as "martyrs" who will devote all their energies and sacrifice all pleasures for the child. The retardate may become the focus of a lifelong pattern of self-sacrifice and lamentation. It almost seems as if such parents "love to be miserable." They may dwell in detail on the tragic and sordid aspects of their situation and often share their unhappiness with all who will listen. Such parents are typically reluctant to institutionalize their child—no matter how severely incapacitated he might be—and may neglect siblings, relatives, careers, etc., for the "welfare" of the child. In counseling with such parents, it usually becomes apparent that the retardate plays a very significant role in the parents' adjustment patterns.

Realization that a child is retarded

often has disruptive effects not only on the parents but on the entire family unit, and possibly on friends, acquaintances, and neighbors as well. Siblings and grandparents are very obviously involved, and increased tensions typically develop within the family. Marital conflicts may be aggravated, and the retarded child may become the focus of mutual blame and criticism by the parents. It is as if the child were a catalyst activating long-dormant conflicts into overt explosion.

Ambivalence toward the child may lead to defensiveness as well as to overprotection. Parents may become acutely sensitive to implied criticisms of the child and may react with resentment and belligerence. It may be difficult in such cases to present factual information which may be interpreted as depreciating the child.

A more extreme position is found in those parents who have attempted to protect themselves against the pain of recognizing retardation in their child by failing to become aware of its existence. Human beings can become highly skilled at remaining unaware of a certain aspect of reality, even when it is thrust upon them with some force. Mechanisms of denial, repression, and selective inattention have been described in detail as techniques whereby people are able to exercise control over the extent of their awareness. It is not unusual, therefore, to find parents who claim that "there is really nothing wrong" with an obviously severely retarded child. They may attribute the child's complete failure in school to a vindictive teacher, for example, or to bouts of tonsillitis. Parents may be helped in this self-deception by relatives, friends, and at times even professionals, who have reassured them of the child's "normality." Reluctance to face a painful and irrevocable situation is not limited to parents, and it is not surprising to find, therefore, that others have likewise failed to recognize the situation.

The trauma of experiencing retardation in one's child may precipitate serious existential conflicts. Concern with religion, the meaning of life, the tragedy of death, the inescapability of aloneness, and the relative insignificance and helplessness of man may preoccupy the parents. Although these concerns are usually less obvious than the other reactions described above, their significance should not be underestimated. . . .

□ □ □

from EMOTIONAL FACTORS AS REVEALED IN THE INTAKE PROCESS WITH PARENTS OF DEFECTIVE CHILDREN *Elizabeth M. Smith*

(American Journal of Mental Deficiency, 1952)

. . . .

Many of the parents of a defective child gradually narrow their world until the term mental deficiency becomes the sounding board for all their thoughts and actions. They become aware of the neighbor's child down the street, Johnny who is not quite bright, the mother who hides her baby from questioning neighbors, the normal children whose brutal remarks serve as a constant reminder of the parental failure. These parents run the emotional gamut from terror through anxiety to guilt, and for the most part, they have not quite come to grips with the child's handicaps. They are forever seeking the new drug, the new operation, the new treatment that will cure the condition of retardation. While verbalizing their acceptance of the situation and their realization that there is no known cure, they, nevertheless, cling to a threadbare hope and they take the "Evangeline" course from doctor to doctor, book to book, and place to place, seeking the magic formula. They vaccilate from extreme hope to extreme despair, but the course they follow is a conflicting one at best. The world in which they live is one of a never-ending series of problems. The stigma of having borne a defective child is a devastating shock that places the family in the unfortunate position of hiding behind closed doors, shunning friends, and gradually withdrawing from normal, healthy contacts in the community. Complete withdrawal is often the only recourse left to the parents whose child is looked upon as a neighborhood nuisance. There are no special community facilities for such children; other youngsters will not play with them; more frequently they are the recipients of spiteful jokes or harsh unscrupulous treatment. Consequently, the mother whose hydrocephalic baby is referred to as "the big fathead" or the mother of the mongoloid child who is called "the dope," has no recourse but to hide and hope. Some parents, in their very real anxiety, related so closely to their feelings of guilt, try to resolve their emotional problems by excessive concern, over-protection, and over-indulgence. Others will go from doctor to doctor, but nowhere is there a frank answer, and so their confusion and doubt mount. There are also those parents who have been told that they should have another child immediately because a similar birth could not occur again. But witness the stricken face of the mother as she appears for her second interview for the admission of her second microcephalic baby.

The financial picture is also a source of very real anxiety for the parents, and frequently, when a diagnosis of mental retardation is made, they follow the doctor's recommendation for immediate placement, rush the child off to the first private school they hear about. Temporarily at least, the very element of sacrifice seems to relieve some of their guilt. However, the cost is generally prohibitive; and eventually, the financial picture is completely out of balance with consequent deprivation and burdens creating a rising tension and anxiety in the group. When the expense can no longer be borne, the family must face the temporary return of the baby to the home. Explanations must be given and questions answered; normal routines disappear; the family is neglected as a result of the concentration of attention on the defective child; friends are not invited in and the parents can not go out, leaving the child in someone's care. With some of these children, there may be severe convulsions or grotesque malformations which most people are not able even to look upon, much less stay with for a period of time. Obtaining a baby sitter is practically impossible, and consequently, the parents are confined to the home with little or no chance for normal social life. Misunderstandings and quarrels between the parents may increase, and this often extends beyond the parents to the grandparents who can not accept the child's condition but can still less accept the placement. They may hint at the parents' coldness and cruelty in giving up the child, thereby increasing tension and guilt and widening the areas of conflict regarding placement. Intra-family relationships are strained to a breaking point, family ties may be broken, and the parents may feel completely alone in their situation.

In the overall picture the social worker's chief concern at this particular time is not so much with the patient, but for the parents who must continue to function as responsible persons in the community.

The ultimate success of any program designed to help retarded individuals must depend in part on the parents' attitudes and thinking, but the thinking cannot be clear if based on conflicting judgments, doubts, and veiled statements. . . .

□ □ □

from THE MEANING OF A DEFECTIVE CHILD TO PARENTS

Arthur Mandelbaum
Mary Ella Wheeler

(*Social Casework*, 1960)

. . . .

Social Attitudes toward Defective Children

From ancient times societies have had some method of dealing with defective children. In some cultures, such children were destroyed when it became evident that they could not be incorporated into society in a useful capacity. Even when defective children escaped this fate, the attitudes of society toward them were still hostile and fearful. In medieval times, the mentally defective person sometimes became the court fool or jester, where he was both mocked and ridiculed and protected and shown favor. The defective person was sometimes regarded with awe and was given superstitious reverence as if he possessed magical power. Defective children were often called "les enfants du bon Dieu," while Luther and Calvin described them as "filled with Satan." Within our own recent historical past, mental defectiveness has often been confused with insanity, and the defective person has been considered a potentially dangerous criminal.

Although the extremely negative attitudes of earlier times no longer prevail in our society, certain residual feelings of anger and fear about the defective child remain in most of us—parents and professional people alike. Such feelings, rooted in our past culture, militate against acceptance of the present-day humane philosophy and produce inner conflict, guilt, and bitterness. These feelings must be recognized and understood if help is to be given to the child and his parents.

Characteristic Attitudes of Parents

Since few couples view their child's problems in the same way, it is not surprising that they seldom are united in their struggle to find a solution. An important function of the diagnostic study, therefore, is to help the parents resolve their conflicting views. When they continue to be competitive and inconsistent, they tend to reject both the child and the clinical findings. For example, if one parent wishes to place the child, the other parent, who opposes placement, may feel that he is the child's staunchest defender. This attitude may call forth resentment in the parent who seeks placement. Thus, the conflict may serve to bind the opposing parent to the child, making the other parent feel guilty and disloyal. It is in this way that a destructive cycle of feelings may be set in motion.

> Mrs. A often insisted that her husband take Ben with him when he went out, although she knew Ben's behavior was often unpredictable and likely to be embarrassing. If Mr. A protested, Mrs. A would accuse him of not loving the boy. Mr. A admitted that frequently this was true, but it no longer caused him to feel guilty. There was a time when he shared his wife's belief that a miracle might happen and Ben would suddenly become a normal boy. "But," he explained, "I no longer have that faith–only a little hope." Feeling his marriage jeopardized and lacking a shared belief in "love, faith, and hope," Mr. A proposed that his wife either place Ben or agree to a divorce. He said in effect, "Choose between us–either my son or me."

In the above example, the mother tried to use her own troubled feelings about the child to punish her husband and make him feel guilty. Quite often disagreements about a child and his potentialities spread throughout the marriage and threaten total disintegration of the family. In such cases, it is difficult to determine whether the child is the major cause of marital tension and, if so, whether the parents have enough stability and find sufficient gratification in other areas of their relationships to indicate possibilities for saving the marriage. A profound disagreement between the partners about a child—if it cannot be resolved—acts as a dangerous infection in the entire family, often culminating in a severe emotional crippling of all members.

Defense Patterns

A mother whose guilt makes her feel

she alone is responsible for the problem may carry the full burden for the physical and emotional care of the defective child. Ostensibly, she does this to shield and protect her husband, but she may actually view him as too weak and too passive to share the burden. As the responsibilities become heavier with time, she tends to become resentful of her husband's apparent indifference and he, in turn, feels excluded. Acutely sensitive to the unexpressed attitudes of his wife, the father attributes his exclusion to his weakness. He assumes that his wife is more able than he to assume the responsibility for their child.

Mrs. H assumed the major physical and emotional burden of caring for their daughter, Inge. On the basis that the husband was busy with his work, the mother rarely shared with him the daily problems created by the girl. In reality, however, she felt she was the stronger of the two and became able to deal with Inge. Although she gave care uncomplainingly, she deeply resented her husband's acceptance that she carry the burden. She interpreted his behavior as rejection of Inge and his silence as a lack of concern about the child and an inability to make decisions for the family. Although Mr. H was relieved not to have to be bothered about the care of Inge, he felt guilty about his lack of involvement and resentful of his wife's implication that he was inadequate.

In such a situation, the father's withdrawal into work may be viewed as his method for handling his grief and depression. His withdrawal, although partially desired by the mother, creates in her a fear that she has been left alone to deal with the child. She feels that her husband has deserted her and their handicapped child as well. It is hard for either spouse fully to understand this kind of withdrawal as a defense against grief. A mother has fewer environmental methods of withdrawal. She cannot easily leave the child and family to seek solace in work. Therefore, we frequently find mothers using such defenses as emotional isolation, retreat into depression, and outbursts of anger.

Some mothers try to deal with their distress by not having other children. Others want another child, hoping that they can prove their adequacy and their capacity to bear healthy children. In some instances, having another child serves as a justification for the mother's withdrawal from the defective child, since a new infant demands her central attention and activity. This solution, however, creates a conflict of loyalties and therefore adds to her guilt. During pregnancy, the mother's thoughts and energies are psychologically turned toward the unborn infant but, after his birth, the problem of the defective child returns with increased vigor; it is felt again as an inescapable reality. The mother may then view the new infant as a symbol of her rejection and abandonment of the defective child. One mother expressed fear that her defective child, who had been placed, would accuse her of having "thrown him away" and would therefore never forgive her. Her intense wish to have him visit the home was understandable only in terms of her wish that he would find pleasure in seeing his new sibling. She felt that his pleasure would relieve her guilt at having displaced him with a normal child.

Some mothers who cannot give birth to another child turn to adoption of a child as a defense against their troubled inner thoughts. Frequently the adopted child becomes the "target" for the parents' unresolved anger. Because he has talents and skills their defective child can never have, the adopted child comes to be jealously resented. The resentment directed against the adopted child, however, is often a displacement—he becomes the object of the anger the parents feel, but can never express, toward their own defective child. To be angry with their own child, who "did not choose to be born," is often seen by such parents as a cowardly, immoral act.

Another common defense utilized by parents is their frantic search for the "cause" of their child's defectiveness, with the hope that it can be attributed to heredity or family background.

> Mr. F often referred to his own siblings, each of whom in some aspect resembled his defective son George. For example, one brother in a fit of rage accidentally shot and killed another brother. One brother was always considered "stupid," although he had made a fair adjustment to farm work. Still another was "so dumb that he let himself be kicked by a mule" and later died of tetanus. Mr. F insisted he had no choice but to believe George's condition was inherited.

Frequently, one of the parents attributes the child's condition to the family background of the spouse. He may refer to the "poor stock" of the family. In other instances, a parent may point out that the child's defectiveness is attributable to too much brilliance in either his or his spouse's family, calling attention to a member who was a "genius." The implication is that [a] genius has erratic, fragile, esoteric qualities that are akin to those found in the mentally defective person.

Some parents, in speaking of their child, may suggest that he has certain grotesque qualities that are frightening to them. They may say he treats life as a joke and point to his clown-like appearance. They may also refer to the attitudes expressed by neighborhood children who view him as silly and funny. Parents who describe their child in this way are subtly conveying the idea that life has played a cruel joke on them about which they are both dismayed and angry. They may also feel that somehow the child has wilfully produced his defectiveness and is attacking them with it. They do not realize that the desperate efforts such a child makes to confabulate in order to conceal his inadequacies may give him an appearance of joking or teasing. The parents are unable to see that behind this facade the child is making desperate attempts to please them.

In another context, Schilder has pointed out that "the neurotic tendency gets a great influence from the inferior organ." In the same way, the impact of a defective child on his family influences neurotic tendencies and may call forth latent conflicts. When the child fails to achieve normal development, the parents' latent conflict may emerge at varying levels of intensity and complexity. On the simplest level, the parents will recall unconscious aggressive thoughts, frustrated dependency needs, and ambivalent wishes. These may appear singly or in combination. When they come to the surface during an evaluative study, the parents sense them as intrusive thoughts or guilt reactions, and tend to think of them as the secret cause of the child's defectiveness. In relatively mature parents, such thoughts and concerns dissolve quickly when their reality is evaluated.

> When Mrs. J was pregnant with Karl, she had an "uneasy" feeling that something was wrong either with her or with the unborn infant. When Karl was born, she was miserably disappointed because she had so much wanted a girl. As he grew and developed, Mrs. J was unable to take any delight in him; she "just knew" something was wrong. When the diagnostic findings confirmed her fear that Karl was brain damaged, Mrs. J thought that his condition was God's punishment for her acute disappointment because her child was not a girl.

On a more complicated level, parents may view their feelings of rejection as the cause of the child's damage. This reaction is common with parents who have marked feelings of inadequacy and low self-esteem. Their self-blame, hitherto latent, is likely to come to the surface during the evaluative process and become a powerful dynamic against making realistic plans. Such parents find it easier to focus on the past than on the current problem that is the cause of their immediate pain.

It has been postulated that "the more intense the defensive reaction toward the child and the longer its duration, the more probable it is that the retarded child has become an integral part of the parents' total psychological functioning." We have found, as Mahoney has observed, that parents who have achieved a relatively satisfying adjustment are likely to be able to bear the pain of having a defective child without prolonged personality disturbance. On the other hand, parents who have not been able to achieve a satisfying adjustment in their previous years tend to react with severe personality difficulties. It is these parents with pathological reactions—who involve their child in their own psychological dysfunction in a pervasive manner—who have difficulty in separating reality from unreality.

> Mrs. L stated with a smile that on this day she was coming in to see me as a "patient." Her eyes were bright and her body tense as she leaned forward to say that, even though she is a college graduate, her problems are the same as those of her defective child. She made a vague gesture as she explained that she had been a premature infant too, and that this was the reason she had never learned to think, to reason things out for herself or to make decisions. The major difference between herself and her son was that he could think and reason better than she; he can make decisions she cannot. She said she felt like a puppet on a string and she wept as she described her hatred for her mother and the maltreatment and emotional neglect she had suffered as a child. Her mother still seemed to exert control over her, even though many miles separated them. She confused the child with herself, although she knew she was trying to give things her mother had not given to her.

As some parents become aware of their own unexpressed anger toward a child who is a disappointment to them, they begin to express fear of the child's aggressiveness. Such parents are keenly aware of the difficulty they had as children in controlling their destructive impulses. Some may even speak of their own sense of confused sexual identity, relating their confusion to their child's struggles with problems of growth. They may recall memories of feeling rejected by their parents and of their fears about their bodies when they were children. Some mothers have stated that their bodies were unsuited to produce children; that they had "immature" reproductive organs or that their pelvic bones were "funnel shaped."

It is not unusual for these mothers to recall that during pregnancy they experienced an obsessive fear of giving birth to a damaged infant. Some think that their child was damaged as a result of their destructive wishes and fantasies, which the mothers still regard as omnipotent. A few mothers reported that during pregnancy they felt unusual activity in the womb—the fetus kicked and squirmed in an unusual manner. One mother stated that her unborn child had an "epileptic fit in utero." When a mother feels that her child has been magically damaged because of her forbidden wishes, angry feelings, or fantasied acts of cruelty, she may be too immobilized to assume appropriate responsibility. Such feelings may also serve as rationalizations for feelings of dependency, helplessness, and bewilderment. Sometimes a mother may insist on viewing the child as a symbol of her martyrdom and sacrifice.

On an even deeper level, a mother may be so psychologically fused with the child that she makes no differentiation between herself and the child, seeing the child as a reflection of herself. She may remember that her own parents regarded her as inadequate and damaged; thus, her child is really herself. Such closeness serves as a potent force preventing the mother from expressing angry feelings toward the child. It also serves to keep alive their intense mutual dependency on each other.

The Helping Procedures

It is presumptuous to think that within the relatively short period of the diagnostic study the totality of the parent-child interaction can be uncovered, unraveled, or resolved. It is possible, however, to identify some of the complex feelings that exist between the parents and their child and to help them understand some of their interrelationships.

Parents come to the diagnostic study with an accumulation of months, and frequently years, of pain and distress. The patterns of the interrelationship are set, as if in concrete. At the time of the study it may seem that all three—parents and child—have reached an impasse.

One of the purposes of the study is to assist the parents to take action once again, but this time with a clearer view of their individual and mutual needs. The parents' feeling of hope must be founded on reality and plans must be based on a true estimate of whatever strengths they may possess. It should be emphasized that we consider the diagnostic study only a beginning step in the helping process, although an important one. The helping process is set in motion by the caseworker who helps both parents, individually and together, to express their bitterness, their confusions, their shattered hopes. It gains direction when the parents are encouraged to observe and reflect on their thoughts and feelings, to make connections between pertinent fragments of experience, to begin to express their frustrations and bewilderment, as well as their hopes and joys, and to consider together their own needs as they examine alternative solutions. . . .

Too often, the caseworker underrates the importance of this beginning phase of help and thinks of it as a total process, to be completed within a week or ten days. He may throw aside patience, calmness, and consistency, and thereby give the parents the impression that he is more concerned, for reasons of prestige, to have them accept the recommendations than he is to have them use their own strengths to arrive at a satisfactory solution to their problem.

It is important, therefore, to examine some of the reasons why caseworkers feel such a desperate need to have parents accept the clinical findings of mental deficiency. Such feelings of desperation are often found to be linked with frustration as well as guilt if the caseworker must tell the parents that their child's condition is irreversible; he seems to be saying "there is no help." The caseworker may resist accepting the clinical findings and be angry at having to tell the parents about the child's limitations and handicaps. Caseworkers, as well as parents, may have magical wishes and deep resentment against the "senselessness of nature." Resistance may also stem from the fact that deep within all of us are feelings about the worthlessness of persons who deviate markedly from normal standards and about the futility of endeavoring to help them. We may feel deep guilt about the fact that such misfortune has happened to others and that we have "escaped" this fate. Many parents do not hesitate to mention this fact. Our frustration from being unhelpful heightens our self-doubts, and we may question our ability to be of help to parents with such a problem.

The caseworker, therefore, if he is to be of help, must be aware of the possibility that he may have many of the same feelings that trouble the parents. He should recognize the similarities in feelings, but he must also be aware of his different position and outlook. If he trusts his technical skills, he will feel less inner pressure to persuade parents to accept the clinic's diagnosis and the recommendations.

The primary aim of a diagnostic study is to assist the parents toward arriving at some resolution of their painful, conflicted feelings, of the anger and guilt that torment them, of the self-doubts that assail them, and of the distortions of reality that lead to irrational planning. If this aim is even partially achieved, the parents will experience a resurgence of whatever strengths they have and will then be able to deal with the problem as best they can. Too strenuous attempts on the part of the caseworker to have the parents accept the diagnosis or recommendations can only result in making the parents more guarded and cautious, since such an approach is viewed as an attack, both on them and on their child. If the worker has no emotional investment in a particular course of action, the parents feel free to do whatever they are able to do.

The parents of a defective child will always have difficulty with the concept of acceptance of one's problems. There are some burdens that can never be truly accepted. These parents may not accept the fact that a major portion of the child's limitations can never be reversed—that he will always have certain serious defects. Also, they may not fully accept the fact that any help provided will not accomplish all they wish.

The future, as well as the present, contains many frightening questions for such parents. Will the child be able to live as an adult without their parental care? If not, who will care for him? Will he be exploited and maltreated? Will he be able to marry? The parents deeply fear the child's physical maturation, not only because of the accompanying increase in aggression and expressions of sexuality, but also because the growing-up process exposes the child to more experiences in which he will meet defeat. Nearly all parents can tolerate the dependency needs of a child during his early years because there is promise that his dependence will diminish as the child matures. But for parents of the defective child, there is no such promise.

As we have worked with parents toward a resolution of their conflicts, and tried to consider with them healthy solutions to the problem the defective child poses for them and the family, our least successful effort has been in discussing the effect of the child on other family members. Efforts to call attention to the neglected needs of other siblings usually arouse anger and deep resentment.

Bewildered and confused by the complexity of their feelings, parents often cling to many unrealities. One parent insisted that, if he had the time, patience, and the ability to be firm with his child, he was sure the child could be taught to do many things for himself and would eventually become an independent adult. To confront the parent with the unreality of his ideas would not alter his attitude. In this instance the worker commented on the importance of the father's beliefs, his hopes, and his refusal to accept defeat, assuring him that no one would try to change his convictions. The worker then helped the father to examine the source of these feelings, to identify the pressures behind them, and to explore what they meant in his relationship to his child. Such an intellectual approach often leads into emotional channels; the worker may then, with a light touch, explore these guarded feelings.

Despite the intense resistance parents show in accepting the fact of their child's retardation, their rigid and hostile defenses often give way under the consistent warmth and empathy of the worker. Through warmth and understanding, the parents come to feel that not only they, but they and their child, are loved. Their need, therefore, to defend both him and themselves is no longer so intensively felt. They can then apply themselves in a more constructive manner to the task of securing necessary help for the child, themselves, and the total family.

As parents present a picture of their child and their relationship to him, the worker must be keenly sensitive to overt and subtle effects. He must allow sufficient time to secure details, to clarify obscure points, and to explore ambiguities and contradictions. The parents are thus led into a comfortable, supportive, and relatively deep relationship that can sustain them in dealing with the truths about the child's condition as these slowly emerge during the diagnostic study process. For example, the mother in describing her child referred to him several times as a "throwback." When the worker suggested that she seemed to see her son as a "primitive" being, the mother thoughtfully agreed. With surprise in her voice, she told with feeling that she thought her son was some kind of atavistic organism, potentially dangerous and representing an accumulation of all that was bad in the "blood lines" of her own and her husband's family. The caseworker's exploration served to turn the parent's rigid defense into a flow of feeling, in which she expressed both her suffering and her confused ideas.

Sometimes parents use the casework interviews as a form of self-punishment. They may make passive complaints about their helplessness, or they may protest their fate with quiet anger. Such parents look upon the casework contact during the diagnostic study as a means of gaining help for themselves; they hope the worker will view them as the patient and provide psychotherapy. Such parents prefer talking about their own dependency needs, their infantile conflicts, and their sexual thoughts rather than about their feelings as parents and as marital partners. It is much easier for a parent to talk about himself as weak and helpless, although his life situation and performance contradict this self-portrait, than to talk about the helplessness of his defective child. But, beneath this defense, the parent is often filled with self-doubt about the adequacy of his past care of the child. Should he accept the reality of his child's handicaps, he must then face the question as to whether he is adequate to meet this challenge and whether he can fulfill his parental role. Although the worker may offer understanding and empathy, the parent may strenuously resist a relationship with the worker because, to him, such a relationship is dangerous. To succumb to it, even slightly, may mean assuming overwhelming responsibility of dealing with the truth of his child's limitations.

Skilled casework may remove the parent's temptation to regress. The caseworker, by assuming that parents come to the diagnostic study with strengths, may provide a creative experience that will affirm the integrity of the parents and set in motion new energy to cope with the many family problems.

A final question should be raised. Is the "shopping" for a diagnosis, which many parents do, a healthy or unhealthy adaptive mechanism? Their efforts to "leave no stone unturned" may be a reflection of their strength and not, as is often assumed, an indication of their inability to face their misfortune. Their refusal to yield, their rebellion, and their conscious effort to make sense out of senselessness, are not always efforts to deny their problems. Perhaps if we had better understanding of the parents' need to leave no stone unturned, we would be more successful in curtailing futile efforts. It is important for those working with these parents to recognize that sometimes resistance and rebellion may be healthy adaptive mechanisms.

□ □ □

from THE MEANING OF A RETARDED CHILD FOR HIS PARENTS: A FOCUS FOR COUNSELORS

David B. Ryckman
Robert A. Henderson

(Mental Retardation, 1965)

. . . .

The purpose of this paper is to analyze the ideas expressed in the literature concerning the meaning of retarded children to parents and to suggest several factors which may affect the degree of parental reaction. . . .

1. *The parent views the child as a physical and psychological extension of himself.* This is either stated or implied in much of the literature. Kozier (1957, p.184) stated, "In our culture, a parent makes a great emotional and material investment in the preparation for the birth of a baby. In many ways, a child represents to the parent an extension of his own self." This concept has many ramifications to the parent, especially

when the child is defective (Cummings & Stock, 1962; Rheingold, 1945; Solnit & Stark, 1961).

The child is a physical production of the parents. He is a product of the combined characteristics inherited from the parents. Assuming for the moment that there are no environmental factors operating, the child is a combination of the positive and negative characteristics of the parents. If something is "good" about the child, it is a reflection of the "good" in one or both parents. Conversely, if something is "bad" or "wrong" with the child, it is a reflection of the same trait, overt or covert, in one or both of the parents.

Many of the authors in this area point out the almost universal feeling of inadequacy of parents when they learn that their child is retarded, i.e., that something is wrong with the child (Goodman & Rothman, 1961; Hersh, 1961; Kelman, 1953; Mayer, 1956; Stone, 1948; Willie, 1961). Dalton and Epstein (1963) specifically discuss this reaction as "well-nigh universal" among parents of retardates. If this feeling is so universal among these parents, one might speculate that this identification with the child as an extension of self may be a normal reaction of parents. Hence, this may be one relatively universal meaning of children to parents in our culture.

2. *The child is a means of vicarious satisfaction to the parents.* The parents may experience or expect to experience satisfaction of their wishes and desires through the life experiences of their children. Cummings and Stock (1962) listed some core problems of parents of retarded children which include specific mention of the disappointment, loss, and sense of bereavement associated with having a child which cannot fulfill the parents' wishes and desires. Rose (1958) discusses the deviations between the "expected" child and the "real" child and the problems inherent in separating the two.

Blodgett and Warfield (1959) refer to the "rewards" which children may offer parents as they watch their children and relive their childhood. Various authors have noted the loss which parents feel when they realize that their child cannot fulfill their hopes and desires (Begab, 1956; Michaels & Schucman, 1962; Olshansky, 1962). Auerbach (1961) makes reference to the almost universal expectation among parents that their children can fulfill these hopes and dreams. The parents of the retarded child are denied these rewards. If these expectations and desires are relatively universal within our culture and parents expect satisfaction and reward from their children, this would indicate that vicarious rewards are a second area of meaning to parents.

3. *The parents can "transcend" death through their child, i.e., derive some measure of immortality.* This area of meaning of children is not widely discussed in the literature directly but it is implied in relation to the two concepts described above. Blodgett and Warfield (1959, p. 42) state that children are highly valued in our culture, not only because of the ego-extension and vicarious satisfactions for the parents but because "they also project themselves, through their children, into a future they will not live to see."

Roos (1963) suggests the importance of this aspect in his comments on the significance of the existential conflicts of parents of retarded children, especially when they become aware of the diagnosis. He also points out that although this concept is not as readily observable in the reactions of parents to a diagnosis of retardation, it seems to have significant implications in terms of how the parents can be expected to react. Some indications that this may be relatively universal in our culture are the expressed concern that children have a better "chance" than the parent, and the hoped-for climb in status which many parents have for their children. Such things as concern for family names and traditions are also indications. All of these aspects may imply some concern of parents for achieving immortality through their children.

4. *A fourth area of meaning of children for parents is the concept of a personalized love object.* Although not directly stated in the literature, this area of meaning is implied in the widespread discussion of guilt. Dalton and Epstein (1963) describe guilt feelings of parents in terms of their inability to love the defective child wholeheartedly. Because the parent cannot do this, as he believes he should, he feels guilty. The problem of guilt becomes heightened if the parents consider institutionalization (Schipper, 1959).

Inherent in this guilt is the element of rejection, i.e., failure to love the child, accompanied by anger and frustration. There is general agreement in the literature that parents feel guilty, at least in part, because they do not love their defective child as they believe they should (Grebler, 1952; Hastings, 1948; Hersh, 1961; Zwerling, 1954). The guilt reflects their feelings that the child should be a personalized love object. The widespread reports on parental guilt in the literature suggest that it is relatively universal in our culture that a parent views his child as a personalized love object.

5. *A fifth meaning of children is the parental feeling of worth in meeting the dependency needs of the child.* Although Stone (1948) refers to this directly, it is most often expressed in terms of the overprotectiveness observed in many parents of retardates (Cummings & Stock, 1962; Grebler, 1952; Mahoney, 1958; Willie, 1961). Overprotectiveness is a means of compensating for the child's handicap, i.e., a means of achieving some satisfactions from the child. Waterman (1948) describes the "chosen people" or "martyr syndrome" in which the parents maintain some feeling of self-worth through extreme devotion to the needs of the retarded child. It is hypothesized that most parents derive some sense of worth through meeting the needs of a dependent child. This may be another relatively universal meaning of children in our culture.

6. *Negative feelings about the limitations and demands of child rearing are a sixth area of meaning of children.* Retarded children are an added burden to parents. The demands and limitations on the parents are realistically increased when rearing a retarded child (Coleman, 1953; Murray, 1959; Sheimo, 1951). When one considers the needs of a retarded child, especially a trainable or custodial child, it is not surprising that the added problems warrant attention in the literature. However, child rearing places demands and limitations on almost all parents. Thus, one might consider the negative factors of child rearing as being a relatively universal meaning of children to parents within our culture.

These six areas of meaning were extracted in reviewing the literature on the reaction of parents to their retarded children. Some of these areas were directly stated in the literature and others were felt to be implied. However, if these six areas are relatively universal, and it is hypothesized that they are, then these would have important implications in the evaluation and expectation of the parents of a retarded child.

. . . .

References

Auerbach, A. B., "Group Education for Parents of the Handicapped," *Children,* 1961, *8:* 135-140.

Begab, M. J., "Factors in Counseling Parents of Retarded Children," *American Journal of Mental Deficiency,* 1956, *60:* 515-524.

Blodgett, H. E. & Warfield, G. J., *Understanding Mentally Retarded Children.* New York: Appleton-Century-Crofts, 1959.

Coleman, J. C., Group Therapy with Parents of Mentally Deficient Children," *American Journal of Mental Deficiency,* 1953, *57:* 700-704.

Cummings, S. T. & Stock, D., "Brief Group Therapy of Mothers of Retarded Children Outside of the Specialty Clinic Setting," *American Journal of Mental Deficiency,* 1962, *66:* 739-748.

Dalton, J. & Epstein, H., "Counseling Parents of Mildly Retarded Children," *Social Casework,* 1963, *44:* 523-530.

Goodman, L. & Rothman, R., "The Development of a Group Counseling Program in a Clinic for Retarded Children," *American Journal of Mental Deficiency,* 1961, *65:* 789-795.

Grebler, A. M., "Parental Attitudes Toward Mentally Retarded Children," *American Journal of Mental Deficiency,* 1952, *56:* 475-483.

Hastings, D., "Some Psychiatric Problems of Mental Deficiency," *American Journal of Mental Deficiency,* 1948, *52:* 260-262.

Hersh, A., "Casework with Parents of Retarded Children," *Social Work,* 1961, *6:* 61-66.

Kelman, H., "Parent Guidance in a Clinic for Mentally Retarded Children," *Social Casework,* 1953, *34:* 441-447.

Kozier, A., "Casework with Parents of Children Born with Severe Brain Defects," *Social Casework,* 1957, *38:* 183-189.

Mahoney, S. C., "Observations Concerning Counseling with Parents of Mentally Retarded Children," *American Journal of Mental Deficiency,* 1958, *63:* 81-86.

Mayer, E., "Some Aspects of Casework Help to Young Retarded Adults and Their Families," *Journal of Social Work Process,* 1956, *7:* 24-49.

Michaels, J. & Schucman, H., "Observations on the Psychodynamics of Parents of Retarded Children," *American Journal of Mental Deficiency,* 1962, *66:* 568-573.

Murray, Mrs. Max, "Needs of Parents of Mentally Retarded Children," *American Journal of Mental Deficiency,* 1959, *63:* 1078-1088.

Olshansky, S., "Chronic Sorrow: A Response to Having a Mentally Defective Child," *Social Casework,* 1962, *43:* 190-193.

Rheingold, H. L., "Interpreting Mental Retardation to Parents," *Journal of Consulting Psychology,* 1945, *9:* 142-148.

Roos, P., "Psychological Counseling with Parents of Retarded Children," *Mental Retardation,* 1963, *1:* 345-350.

Rose, J. A., *Factors in the Development of Mentally Handicapped Children, Counseling Parents of Children with Mental Handicaps.* Proceedings of the 1958 Woods School Conference, May 2-3, 1958.

Schipper, M. T., "The Child with Mongolism in the Home," *Pediatrics,* 1959, *24:* July, 132-144.

Sheimo, S. L., "Problems in Helping Parents of Mentally Deficient and Handicapped Children," *American Journal of Mental Deficiency,* 1951, *56:* 42-47.

Solnit, A. J. and Stark, M. H., "Mourning and the Birth of a Defective Child," *The Psychoanalytic Study of the Child,* Vol. XVI. New York: International Universities Press, 1961.

Stone, M. M., "Parental Attitudes to Retardation," *American Journal of Mental Deficiency,* 1948 *53:* 363-372.

Waterman, J. H., "Psychogenic Factors in Parental Acceptance of Feebleminded Children," *Diseases of the Nervous System,* 1948, *9:* 184-187.

Willie, B. M., "The Role of the Social Worker," *American Journal of Mental Deficiency,* 1961, *66:* 464-471.

Zwerling, I., "The Initial Counseling of Parents with Mentally Retarded Children," *The Journal of Pediatrics,* 1954, *44:* April, 469-479.

□ □ □

from MOURNING AND THE BIRTH OF A DEFECTIVE CHILD

Albert J. Solnit, Mary H. Stark

(Psychoanalytical Study of the Child, 1961)

The study of human crisis permits the extension of our understanding of psychological health and illness and how they overlap. These opportunities become especially fruitful when the observer is also the person offering professional assistance to those whose crisis requires them to seek help.

However, these professional people require a comprehensive theory of human development to clarify and organize their observations and to make possible formulations that lead to a useful course of action. Psychoanalysis is such a theory of human psychology. In recent years the health care professions have had opportunities to integrate insights from this theory into the care of the child and his family in many different crisis situations (Bowlby et al., 1952; Burlingham and A. Freud, 1942; A. Freud, 1953; Jackson, 1942; Lindemann, 1944; MacKeith, 1953; James Robertson, 1953, 1958; Joyce Robertson, 1956; Solnit, 1960; Solnit and Green, 1959; Solnit and Stark, 1959; Spence, 1946, 1947). When a defective child is born, the pediatrician and his colleagues can make observations of the family's reactions to this catastrophic event. These observations may indicate the factors that shape the family's trauma or that lead to the family's adaptive responses.

The material on which this study is based has been collected from pediatric, psychiatric, and casework contacts with mothers and their defective children. The theoretical approach to our work is founded on the psychoanalytic explanation of the process of mourning as applied to the mother's reactions to the birth of a defective child (Freud, 1917, 1923; Bibring, 1959, 1961; Janis, 1958a, 1958b). Freud's contributions to the understanding of narcissism and its vicissitudes (1914) are essential for the study of object loss—in our case, the loss of the longed-for healthy child.

The psychological preparation for a new child during pregnancy normally involves the wish for a perfect child and the fear of a damaged child. It is very likely that there is always some discrepancy between the mother's wishes and the actual child; to work out this discrepancy becomes one of the developmental tasks of motherhood that are involved in the establishment of a healthy mother-child relationship. However, when the discrepancy is too great, as in the birth of a defective child, or where the mother's wishes are too unrealistic, a trauma may occur.

The study of pregnancy—what Ernst Kris (1955) termed a normal illness—reveals a loosening up of defenses and the more direct, and at times more threatening, access to unconscious representations, wishes, and scars (fixations). In a normal pregnancy, labor and delivery, there are psychological rearrangements and achievements necessary for the developmental advances leading to early motherhood (Benedek, 1959; Deutsch, 1945). These changes, often subtle, appear gradually over a period of time, and are best seen in the interacting development of mutuality of mother and child (Erikson, 1950). The mother's anticipation of the baby, especially of the first, is in many ways like adolescent turmoil because the adult psychic structure is gradually prepared for the birth of a new individual and the crystallization of a new unfolding within the self.

The image of the *expected baby* is a composite of representations of the self and of the love objects (mother, husband, father, and siblings). The composite representation includes the image of the expected child which has been conveyed to the expectant mother by her own mother. Each of these kaleidoscopic shifting impressions summon up for recollection and emotional review older issues, conflicts, and fears. This anticipatory process is part of the normal preparation for motherhood. As a preparation it repeats and solves again certain of the basic conflicts and identifications that the expectant mother had with her own mother.

However, this preparatory and adaptive process is abruptly interrupted by the birth of a defective or retarded child. Although the mother's reactions to her defective child are to a significant extent shaped by the type and degree of defect, they also are greatly influenced by her own past experiences with parents and siblings as well as by other significant life events. Conflicts in the woman's relationship to her own mother and in regard to her own femininity are often reawakened during the psychological work of the pregnancy (Bibring, 1959, 1961). The vicissitudes of this psychological preparation (Janis, 1958b) are outside the scope of this presentation, but an awareness of these preparatory developments in the mother will heighten the understanding of the impact of the disappointment, feeling of helplessness, and sense of failure that the individual woman experiences when the child she bears is obviously blighted.

There are many aspects of the diagnosis and treatment of defective children and their families which it will not be possible to encompass in this paper. However, the thesis of this paper will be of little value if one does not at the same time take into account specific factors, such as familial disease, previous trauma to the mother, family constellation, the genesis of the retardation, and the severity and characteristic of the defect. It will be noted that "defective" and "retarded" are used interchangeably in this paper, simply indicating that all of the children referred to are retarded and that the defect is more or less apparent.

In an experiment created by nature, the birth of a defective or deviant child, one can observe more directly the "sudden" loss of the baby that was expected; and the "sudden" birth of a feared, threatening, and anger-evoking child.

The course of motherhood, a developmental process, is influenced by the characteristics of the baby, first by his appearance and gradually by his responses. Significant deviations, such as gross retardation or obvious congenital defects, may limit or interrupt the mother's developing capacity to accept the new child who is totally dependent upon her.

In a recent article, "Is Grief a Disease?" George L. Engel (1961) has drawn attention to the importance of the mourning process in human development. Borrowing from Freud's (1917) and Lindemann's (1944) work, Engel describes mourning in terms that are useful for this presentation. "Grief is the characteristic response to the loss of a valued object, be it a loved person, a cherished possession, a job, status, home, country, an ideal, a part of the body, etc. Uncomplicated grief runs a consistent course, modified mainly by the abruptness of the loss, the nature of the preparation for the event, and the significance for the survivor of the lost object."

In the mother's mourning reaction to the loss of the healthy child, her wishes for and expectations of the desired child are crushed by the birth of the defective child. Her anxious fears of having a damaged child are realized. These disappointed, highly charged longings for the normal child may be recalled, intensely felt, and gradually discharged in order to reduce the impact of the loss of the expected loved child. This process, which requires time and repetition, can liberate the mother's feelings and interests for a more realistic adaptation. The mourning process makes it possible to progress from the initial phase of numbness and disbelief; to the dawning awareness of the disappointment and feeling of loss with the accompanying affective and physical symptoms; to the last phase of the grief reaction in which intense re-experiencing of the memories and expectations gradually reduce the hypercathexis of the wish for the idealized child.

In childbearing, the simultaneous loss of one child—the expected and narcissistically invested one—and adaptation to the deviant or defective child makes a demand that is very likely to be overwhelming. There is no time for working through the loss of the desired child before there is the demand to invest the new and handicapped child as a love object.

It is as though the work of preparing for the new child has suddenly become useless. Established libidinal pathways and attachments are abruptly terminated, and at the same time a demand for new libidinal cathexes is made. (To some extent a similar situation occurs when there is the unexpected birth of twins or of a premature child.) The unexpected aspect of the birth at a time of physiological and psychological depletion is an essential factor in the traumatizing effect of the experience.

Thus, at the time the mother is prepared to be nurtured by the satisfaction of her creative experience, and to begin nurturing her child, her adaptive capacities are sapped because she has failed to create what she intended, and feels damaged by the "new" child—the defective organism to whom she has given birth. Just as pregnancy itself is a normal crisis in which there is no turning back, so defect or retardation is a condition which cannot be undone. The irretrievable nature of the retardation adds to the mother's trapped feeling—she has failed to achieve what she has so laboriously prepared herself to create or produce. Fathers, too, will have similar or related reactions. For the purpose of this discussion, and because the mother's vulnerability is much greater, we limit our primary considerations to the mother.

Although each situation has to be individually analyzed for the highly specific considerations essential for planning and treatment, in our experience there are two extreme reaction patterns that delimit the continuum of the pathological reactions to the birth of a defective child. The manifest reaction and the underlying feelings should be differentiated. At the one extreme is the guilt feeling leading to the mother's manifest dedication of herself unremittingly and exclusively to the welfare of the retarded child. At the other extreme is the parents' manifest intolerance of the child and the almost irresistible impulse to deny their relationship to the child. The underlying narcissistic injury is intolerable. The following example illustrates the first extreme.

Jimmy, the first-born child of a young couple, was severely retarded. His mother was unable to care for her second child, Danny, who was normal, because of her "devotion" to Jimmy. Her inability to accept the reality of the retarded child began when she left her pediatrician who had advised institutionalization shortly after Jimmy's birth. It became necessary for the paternal grandmother to live with them in order to organize their household and to care for Danny shortly after he was born. The father's dissatisfaction with this plan finally resulted in a request for consultation in regard to long-term planning for Jimmy.

At the other extreme, Arnold's mother had apparently accepted the interpretation of slow development in her son soon after a difficult birth. During his first year, the parents arranged for Arnold to be placed in a foster home because they felt unable to care for him. From the many medical recommendations sought, the parents favored that one which said institutionalization at a training school would be advisable. Arnold was only slightly retarded and made good strides in his development at the foster home, eliminating the need for a training school. The parents said they could accept Arnold only if it could be guaranteed that he would be "perfectly normal." Otherwise, they feared he would "damage" their family life. Their move to another locale, which made it impractical for them to see Arnold, was to some extent determined by the father's occupation, but it also represented their effort to strengthen the denial of their relationship to their son in order to avoid the intolerable narcissistic injury evoked by their contacts with him.

There are elements of both denial and guilt involved in the reactions of parents to the birth of a retarded or defective child. However, the defenses represent the modes of warding off depression, guilt, and feelings of narcissistic injury. The defenses are selected from the interaction of the individual's characteristic patterns of defense and influenced by the predominance of the painful affect evoked by the birth of a defective child. By taking into account the parents' feelings of loss, defeat, and resentment about their defective child, and their individual ways of coping with their feelings, the interpretation of the child's diagnosis and its implications can be made more effective.

When the mother wards off her feelings of grief by establishing a guilty, depressed attachment to the retarded child she may fail to relate adequately to other members of the family because she feels she must give her life to the care of the damaged child. Conversely, the mother may identify with her defective child. In identifying with her defective offspring, the mother feels narcissistically wounded. This narcissistic injury is often intolerable, because the mother feels painfully defective as she is caring for her retarded child. The mother's withdrawal then becomes a denial of the needs of this child, which the following example illustrates.

Sally, two years of age, the second of two girls, had been examined by two doctors. When she was eight months old, a substitute for her doctor, (the family doctor was ill) told the mother that Sally was a mongol and "there would be trouble later on." This mother, aged twenty-nine, worried about the above statement for nearly a year. Her husband thought she was foolish to worry. Both parents knew Sally's development was delayed, but the father thought she would "catch up" in time. Finally, the mother was able to ask her family doctor about Sally. She had hoped that since he had not mentioned it, perhaps it was not so. He told her that he had been concerned about Sally since birth and agreed with the diagnosis of mongolism. He said he had not brought it to her attention because nothing could be done about it. He pointed out the fact that her eyes were far apart. He agreed to arrange a consultation for Sally with a specialist in child development.

The mother told the social worker, who worked with the consultant, that she thought mongolism was a strange disease, and she blamed herself for Sally's condition. As a child, the mother's poor vision required her to attend a sight-saving class in school. She associated the doctor's comment about Sally's eyes with her own visual defect. She also blamed herself for marrying a man twenty years her senior; she had read that older parents tend to produce retarded children.

Because of her painful feelings of inadequacy the mother had found herself withdrawing from Sally and spending more time with her seven-year-old daughter who provided evidence of her mother's adequacy. Sally was kept in a crib part of the day.

As this mother was given a descriptive picture of the extent of Sally's retardation (her motor development and adaptive behavior was about that of an eighteen-month-old child) and some suggestions regarding the everyday care of her child, she began to realize that Sally's future was not so hopeless. When she could talk about her disappointment and fears for Sally's future, her own poor vision, her marriage, etc., she felt less guilty. Her pent-up energies were then released to be used constructively for both of her little girls. She devoted more time to Sally, provided her with suitable toys, and began to explore nursery school opportunities that would be available when she was older.

The lack of opportunity to discuss the child's diagnosis can create a situation in which the parents feel overwhelmed and unable to gauge the reality of their child's retarded development. Denial then serves to ward off the anxiety and depression. The following vignette illustrates such a situation.

Susan, a first child, was born abroad when her father was in service. The baby was born in the seventh month of the mother's pregnancy, weighing 3 lbs., 4 oz. Three convulsions occurred on the second day of her life. Because of her prematurity, she remained in the hospital for eight weeks. No definite diagnosis was discussed with the parents. This was a difficult time for the parents because Susan was in a critical condition and fed poorly. When Susan was brought home she continued to be a source of anxiety to the parents because she failed to thrive. By eight months, she was not rolling over, and she was returned to the hospital for further studies. The parents said they would never forget the words of the physician at the time of her second hospital discharge: "You might as well put her in an institution and let her die in peace." The harshness of such words added greatly to the suffering already experienced by the parents and interfered with the mother's recognition of the reality and with her mourning reaction. The mother blamed herself for not seeking out her obstetrician a week before delivery when she was having some abdominal pains. She reasoned, if she had gone to him then, her child would not have been retarded. The thought of institutionalization caused her to cringe with anger.

It was not until there was ample opportunity to review their hopes and to discuss their fears for Susan that the parents were able to utilize a thorough evaluation and interpretation of the child's development in a continuing relationship with the pediatrician and social worker. One might say that interpretation began with what was the parents' reality, their state of grief, and then under the guidance of a skillful pediatrician they were prepared to deal with the reality of their child's condition.

In many instances the initial diagnosis has been made accurately and with adequate consultation, and has been presented to the parents in a simple, straight-forward manner, taking into account their fears and questions. However, several months later the physician is surprised to hear from a colleague or neighboring clinic that his patient is "shopping" and has presented a distorted picture of the situation. Upon reviewing this very common complication of interpretation, we have been able to demonstrate in many instances that the parents' distortion was an unwitting one that stemmed from two main sources: 1) the inability to tolerate their painful reaction to the reality of the diagnosis or to accept the first diagnosis; and 2) the lack of what might be termed follow-up. Once the physician has conveyed the initial diagnosis to the parents there is a tendency to think the interpretation of mental retardation is completed when it has only begun. The main reason for this misconception by the physician is that he has not understood the repetitive aspect of the mourning process in the mother's reaction. If the therapist has not sensed or understood the need that parents have to grieve about their tragic "loss," he will feel ineffectual and reproached by the parents when they indicate their need for repeated opportunities to review and to re-examine the past in the current "loss."

Interpretation is a continuing process which utilizes interviews with the professional person to establish a sense of confidence and trust that will promote the parents' gradual understanding of the child's defect. In this atmosphere of trust and confidence the parents are enabled to express their critical and fearful questions to the pediatrician; and the physician can describe what is known and what is not known about the retarded child in a manner that increases the parents' understanding. This understanding refers to objective and subjective components—to the comprehension of the child's condition, and to the realization by the parents of their inner reactions of disappointment, resentment, humiliation, and loneliness. Many of the subjective reactions will be experienced as repetitions of previous losses or disappointments. The pediatrician, nurse, and social worker should not make interpretations of unconscious feelings or thoughts; or attempt to make connections for the patient between past experiences of loss and the current subjective responses to the birth of the retarded child. The psychiatrist who otherwise may interpret unconscious conflicts also may avoid such interpretations because of the narcissistic involvement during the mourning period.

The medical personnel should clarify the reality of the child's condition as the parent is able to bring up each one of his questions and fears. This clarification which strengthens the reality-testing capacity of the parents will indirectly reduce the distortions responsible for unrealistic connections between past and present. In this way the dynamic interpretation of the reality aids the working through of the mourning process as one of the major avenues to the mastery of the traumatic experience.

Ideally, the parents, especially the mother, will experience what Freud (1917) described: "Each single one of the memories and situations of expectancy which demonstrate the libido's attachment to the lost object is met by the verdict of reality." It is the physician or social worker's responsibility to facilitate this process, which is gradual, repetitive, and which requires that the "verdict of reality" be offered in a useful manner. This implies that at every stage of translating the defective child's condition to the parents, the language, sequence of thoughts, and focus of the interpretation will take into account other important factors involved in the parents' reactions. These factors would include the stage of the mother's development, her current situation, and the ways in which her past experiences, cultural and personal, influence her adaptation. . . .

It becomes clear that the unexpected advent of a retarded child can have a traumatizing effect on the development of the mother and on the interactions and elaborations of family relationships. The ghost of the desired, expected healthy child continues to interfere with the family's adaptation to the defective child if the mourning process becomes fixed as the sustained atmosphere of the family.

Discussion

Interpretation of mental retardation to parents should be synchronized to the mourning reaction. In this presentation, interpretation refers to a dynamic continuing process of successive translations and clarifications, rather than to a single definitive explanation. Such interpretations are communications that facilitate the recognition of reality and promote one's adaptation to the demands of reality. The effectiveness of these communications depends upon a relationship with the interpreter that will enable the parent to express highly charged feelings and to remember the past as it relates to the present. What are referred to as interpretations for the mother with the abnormal child are also the principles upon which are based the explanations and anticipatory guidance of the mother with the normal child.

Coping with the outer reality of a child with a congenital defect and the inner reality of feeling the loss of a desired, normal child requires a great deal of mental work. Such psychic work is slow and emotionally painful, and it proceeds through the gradual and repeated discharge of intense feelings and memories. These mental and emotional reactions enable the parent to recognize and adapt to the reality, the retarded child.

The mother's reaction to a dead child is different from her reaction to the birth of a defective child (Provence, 1961), though certain aspects of these differing mourning reactions are similar. In both situations there are: feelings of loss; intense longings for the desired child; resentment of the cruel blow that life's experience has dealt; and the guilt that the dead or defective child may evoke by representing the consequences of unacceptable feelings or thoughts. The main difference between the two reactions is the persistent effect on the mother of the living defective child who realistically requires care and attention. The daily impact of the retarded child on the mother is unrelenting. Attempts to withdraw libido from the "lost," normal child are disrupted by the demands to cathect the living, blighted child. When the defective baby dies, the libido can initially be withdrawn and then become available for new attachments without the daily corrosive reminder of failure. Probably, the process of mourning cannot be as effective when the retarded child survives.

When a person is mourning, their ability to recognize, evaluate, and adapt to reality is often significantly impaired. It is for this reason that the physician often turns to the father or grandparents in the planning for the newborn defective child. Sometimes immediate planning may require this. However, from the point of view of the mother's development and the child's care, it is essential to gauge the mother's mourning reaction in order to know how and when to help her to take an active role in planning for her child's care. The continuation of mourning into a persistent, depressed, self-reproachful state may be encouraged if the mother's mourning reaction is not understood, and if the care of the child as well as the planning are carried out without her active participation. Obviously the mother needs a great deal of support and time in order to deal with her feelings of failure. The father, too, will require such aid.

The gradual investment of feeling for the child who was born cannot be hurried and will proceed along a realistic line if the mother's capacities to think, feel, and talk about her disappointment, sense of failure, and feelings of helplessness are not impaired by the atmosphere of the hospital and the attitudes of her physicians and nurses. Surely the medical personnel's feelings of helplessness and defeat in regard to the retarded child are among the important reasons that parents may fail to receive understanding support. A common obstacle to the mother's adaptation is the urgency that the physician may feel in developing a plan because of his fear that procrastination may damage the mother. One sees the exaggerated effect of the physician's anxiety in those situations in which there is the conviction that the defective child should not be seen by the mother, but should be rushed away to an institution so the mother will not form a guilt-laden attachment to the child. This attitude reflects a misunderstanding about: the precision of the prognosis; what constitutes the mother's preparation for and reaction to the newborn child; and the physician's own reaction to the situation of his patient being defective. A correct understanding of the crisis will lead to a conservative attitude toward prognosticating; an expectation that the mother will need time and help to deal with her own reactions to having a defective child; and the awareness of the physician's own feeling of helplessness and resentment that his work has failed to produce a normal child.

Often this behavior of the medical personnel to the birth of a defective child mirrors the mother's psychological state. By wishing to send the child to an institution before the mother sees the child, they are reacting partly to their own feelings of helplessness and failure; and partly they are dramatizing the loss of the normal child that the mother feels. Perhaps there is the unconscious notion that if the defective child is sent away before being seen by the mother she will have a better chance to regain the lost, normal or idealized child. It is equally wrong to insist that a mother and father see a malformed child when they wish to avoid it and express their strong opposition to the experience.

The physician and nurses can invest the deviant child realistically for the mother. This provides her with an opportunity to take an active role in planning for her child; to increase her self-esteem through the evidence that she can feed and care for the child; and to receive the satisfaction of those reactions that the retarded child demonstrates in response to the mothering care.

If the defective baby is a second or third child, and the older children are normal, the impact may be somewhat less though it follows the same pattern of mourning. If the retardation defect is not evident at birth but only gradually becomes apparent to mother and physician in the first year or two, the mourning reaction is less acute, but its structure is very similar. That is, there may be a nagging fear that the child's development is lagging, and a gradual awareness of the child's inability to respond. In this more gradually developing situation the difficulty in recognizing, identifying, and adapting to the reality of the child's retarded development may be drawn out over a long period of time. However, the gradualness of the recognition may also strengthen the denial of the reality, leading to the more tortuous and chronic mourning reaction. In a sense the parents may become fixated between the recognition of the deviation of their child and the denial of its implications. For example, the parents may steadfastly deny the child's defect or slow development, but continue to seek special help to enable their child to overcome his difficulties. In a recent discussion, Helen L. Beck (1959) stated: "The parents who come to a mental retardation clinic are as a rule quite aware of the fact that they have a problem. They may, however, deny its nature."

In order to facilitate the work of the mourning process, the mother needs: physical rest; an opportunity to review her thoughts and feelings about the wished-for child; a realistic interpretation and investment of the feared, unwanted child by doctors and nurses; and an active role in planning for and caring for the newborn child as she is able. These are the measures through which the mother can minimize or overcome the trauma of giving birth to a retarded child. The physician, nurse, and social worker will take into account these dynamic psychological reactions of the mother in order that their use of the interpretative process becomes an essential aid to the mother in mastering this crisis in her development. . . .

□ □ □

BIBLIOGRAPHY

1. Beck, H. L., "Counseling Parents of Retarded Children," *Children*, VI, 1959.
2. Benedek, T., "Parenthood As a Developmental Phase," *Journal of American Psychoanalytic Association*, VII, 1959.
3. Bibring, G. L., "Some Considerations of the Psychological Processes in Pregnancy," *This Annual*, XIV, 1959.
4. ———, "A Study of the Psychological Processes in Pregnancy and of the Earliest Mother-Child Relationships. I: Some Propositions and Comments," *ibid*, XVI, 1961.
5. Bowlby, J., Robertson, J., & Rosenbluth, D., "A Two-Year-Old Goes to Hospital," *This Annual*, VII, 1952.
6. Burlingham, D. & Freud, A., *Young Children in Wartime*. London: Allen & Unwin, 1942.
7. Deutsch, H., *The Psychology of Women, II*. New York: Grune & Stratton, 1945.
8. Engel, G. L., "Is Grief a Disease? A Challenge for Medical Research," *Psychosomatic Medicine*, XXIII, 1961.
9. Erikson, E. H., *Childhood and Society*. New York: Norton, 1950.
10. Freud, A., Film Review: "A Two-Year-Old Goes to Hospital," *International Journal of Psychoanalysis*, XXXIV, 1953.
11. ———, in MacKeith, R. and Sandler, J., ed., *Psychosomatic Aspects of Pediatrics*. London: Pergamon Press, 1961.
12. Freud S., "On Narcissism: An Introduction," *Standard Edition*, XIV. London: Hogarth Press, 1957.
13. ———, "Mourning and Melancholia," *Standard Edition*, XIV. London: Hogarth Press, 1957.
14. ———, *The Ego and the Id*. London: Hogarth Press, 1927.
15. Jackson, E. B., "Treatment of the Young Child in the Hospital," *American Journal of Orthopsychiatry*, XII, 1942.
16. Janis, I. L., *Psychological Stress*. New York: Wiley, 1958a.
17. ———, "Emotional Inoculation: Theory and Research on Effects of Preparatory Communications." In *Psychoanalysis and the Social Sciences*, V. New York: International Universities Press, 1958b.
18. Kris, E., Personal communication, 1955.
19. Lindemann, E., "Symptomatology and Management of Acute Grief," *American Journal of Psychiatry*, CI, 1944.
20. MacKeith, R., "Children in Hospital Preparation for Operation," *Lancet*, II, 1953.
21. Provence, S., Personal communication, 1961.
22. Robertson, James, Film: *A Two-Year-Old Goes to Hospital*. London: Tavistock Clinic; New York: New York University Library, 1953.
23. ———, *Young Children in Hospital*. New York: Basic Books, 1958.
24. Robertson, Joyce, "A Mother's Observations on the Tonsillectomy of Her Four-Year-Old Daughter," with comments by Anna Freud, *This Annual*, XI, 1956.
25. Spence, J. C., *The Purpose of the Family: A Guide to the Care of Children*. London: Epworth Press, 1946.
26. ———, "Care of Children in Hospital," *British Medical Journal*, I, 1947.
27. Solnit, A. J., "Hospitalization: An Aid to Physical and Psychological Health in Childhood," A.M.A. *Journal of Diseases of Children*, XCIX, 1960.
28. ——— & Green, M., "Psychologic Considerations in the Management of Deaths on Pediatric Hospital Services. I: The Doctor and the Child's Family," *Pediatrics*, XXIV, 1959.
29. ——— & Stark, M., "Pediatric Management of School Learning Problems of Underachievement," *New England Journal of Medicine*, CCLXI, 1959.

□ □ □

CHRONIC SORROW: A RESPONSE TO HAVING A MENTALLY DEFECTIVE CHILD

Simon Olshansky

(*Social Casework*, 1962)

The purpose of this article is twofold: 1) to propose that most parents who have a mentally retarded child suffer from a pervasive psychological reaction, chronic sorrow, that has not always been recognized by the professional personnel—physicians, psychologists, and social workers—who attempt to help them; and 2) to suggest some of the implications of the phenomenon of chronic sorrow for the parent counseling process. This discussion is based on the author's personal and professional experiences and on the experience of the Children's Development Clinic staff in counseling parents of severely retarded children.

The Phenomenon of Chronic Sorrow

Most parents who have a mentally defective child suffer chronic sorrow throughout their lives regardless of whether the child is kept at home or is "put away." The intensity of this sorrow varies from time to time for the same person, from situation to situation, and from one family to another. The sorrow may be more intense for one parent than for the other in the same family. Many factors, such as parent's personality, ethnic group, religion, and social class, influence the intensity of this sorrow. Some parents show their sorrow clearly; others attempt to conceal it, and sometimes they succeed. The need to keep a "stiff upper lip," especially outside the privacy of the home, is a common defense of parents. Anglo-Saxon parents in particular usually feel this need. Although chronic sorrow may be experienced by some parents of minimally retarded children, this reaction is probably more nearly universal among parents whose children are severely or moderately retarded—whose children would be considered retarded in any society and in any cultural group.

The helping professions have somewhat belabored the tendency of the parent to deny the reality of his child's mental deficiency. Few workers have reported what is probably a more frequent occurrence, the parent's tendency to deny his chronic sorrow. This tendency is often reinforced by the professional helper's habit of viewing chronic sorrow as a neurotic manifestation rather than as a natural and understandable response to a tragic fact. All the parental reactions reported in the literature, such as guilt, shame, and anger, may well be intertwined with chronic sorrow. Moreover, a parent's experiencing chronic sorrow does not preclude his deriving satisfaction and joy from his child's modest achievements in growth and development. It can also be assumed that the child's mental defectiveness has symbolic meaning, on an unconscious level, to some parents. The data that support this assumption, however, are rarely communicated by the parent except in deep psychotherapy.

The reality faced by the parent of a severely retarded child is such as to justify his chronic sorrow. When the parent is asked to "accept" mental deficiency, it is not clear just what he is being asked to do. The great stress professional workers tend to place on "acceptance" may suggest to the parent that he is expected to perceive his child from the point of view of the professional helper. This expectation may make him both resentful and resistant. In our clinical experience, we have seen relatively few parents so neurotic that they denied the fact that the child was mentally defective. We have seen relatively few parents who did not recover enough, after the initial shock of discovery, to mobilize their efforts in behalf of the child. It is understandable that some parents move slowly and erratically toward recognition of the mental defect and toward meeting the child's special needs. Some of them even "regress" to the point of denying, at certain times, the reality of the child's defectiveness. On other occasions they become unduly optimistic about the child's potentialities. In our view, such regression may help the parent to tolerate better the terrible reality that confronts him each day.

Why does the professional worker become so impatient with the parent's slowness or occasional regression and why does he feel such a great sense of urgency to do something about it? After all, the parent has a lifetime in which to learn to deal with the needs and problems of a mentally defective child. In most cases one can ask what will be lost if the parent is unable for several years to view his child as mentally defective. The parents of one of our clinic patients have told us that their child was six or seven years old before they knew definitely that she was mentally defective. Although they had sensed that her development was slow, they had failed to act on their suspicions until her subnormality became self-evident. In what way had the parents been worse off in their "blissful ignorance"? In what way had the child been worse off, since she had had the capacity to meet the parents' expectations?

The parents of a normal child have to endure many woes, many trials, and many moments of despair. Almost all these parents know, however, that ultimately the child will become a self-sufficient adult. By contrast, the parents of a mentally defective child have little to look forward to; they will always be burdened by the child's unrelenting demands and unabated dependency. The woes, the trials, the moments of despair will continue until either their own deaths or the child's death. Concern about what will happen to his child after he is dead may be a realistic concern for a parent, or it may be associated with death wishes, either for himself or for his child. Release from his chronic sorrow may be obtainable only through death.

The Counseling Process

What are some of the implications of the parent's chronic sorrow for the professional person who attempts to help him? First, the professional worker should abandon the simplistic and static concept of parental acceptance. Every parent—whether he has a normal or a mentally defective child—accepts his child and rejects his child at various times and in various situations. If both acceptance and rejection are universal parental responses, it is not clear just what the professional person is asking the parent of a mentally defective child to accept. Is the parent being asked to accept the fact that the child is defective? This the parent does, in general. Is he being asked to meet the child's needs realistically? This the parent tries to do, by and large. Is he being asked to abandon his chronic sorrow? This the parent wishes he could do but cannot.

The permanent, day-by-day dependence of the child, the interminable frustrations resulting from the child's relative changelessness, the unaesthetic quality of mental defectiveness, the deep symbolism buried in the process of giving birth to a defective child, all these join together to produce the parent's chronic sorrow. That so many parents bear this sorrow stoically is rich testimony to parental courage and endurance. (One might ask, for example, how much progress would have been achieved in the field of rehabilitation if the issue of "acceptance" had been made the primary focus of professional concern rather than the issue of managing the disability most efficiently through the use of prosthetic devices.)

Second, the professional person's perceptions of the parent will be different if he accepts the idea that chronic sorrow is a natural, rather than a neurotic, reaction. The worker's changed perceptions of the parent and his feelings may encourage the parent to discuss his chronic sorrow more openly and freely. There is danger that some workers will become overinvolved and sentimental, so that they will serve as "wailing walls" rather than as helpers. This danger, however, is always present in any helping situation if a worker surrenders the discipline, restraint, and understanding he must have to fulfill his helping role.

Although chronic sorrow is a natural, rather than a neurotic, response to a tragic fact, some parents do respond neurotically to their child's handicap and may require treatment for their neurosis. Judging from our experience, however, the number of neurotic parents is small. It is regrettable that this small number of people has received so much professional attention that the tragedy of having a mentally defective child has been viewed less as a tragedy than as a psychiatric problem.

The professional worker who learns to accept chronic sorrow as a normal psychological reaction will grant the parent a longer period of time than otherwise in which to adjust his feelings and organize his resources, both internal and external, to meet the child's needs. The worker will also plan to extend the length of the counseling process. He will alter the usual practice of telling the parent the facts about the child's mental defectiveness in as few as one to four interviews, since the worker will realize that the communication of facts is only one part of the counseling process and is not necessarily the most important part. Some parents may require months, or even years, of counseling before they can muster and maintain the strength and stamina needed to live with the tragedy of having a mentally defective child. What the parent requires, beyond a knowledge of the facts, is an opportunity to ventilate and clarify his feelings and to receive support for the legitimacy of the feelings he is expressing. In some instances the parent will need to be given this opportunity at various times throughout his life.

In addition to providing more time during which the parent can learn to face his problem, and to offering counseling at a slower pace, the worker should also make himself accessible to the parent over a long period of time. No matter how effective the counseling is, many parents need to discuss their feelings and the problems associated with a defective child on many occasions. This need for repeated counseling is natural and should not be considered a sign of either regression or neurosis. The experience of our clinic has demonstrated the importance of accessibility—an "open door" policy—for the parents of mentally defective children. A parent may telephone a staff member again and again about a recurring problem, a new problem, an emerging crisis, or his own distress.

Finally, if the worker accepts the validity of the concept of chronic sorrow, his goal in counseling the parent will be to increase the parent's comfortableness in living with and managing his defective child. In addition to providing psychological help, the worker will emphasize, more than formerly, the help the mother needs in order to learn to manage such problems as how to feed, discipline, and toilet-train the child. Use of such facilities as preschool nurseries, special education classes, day care centers, and sheltered workshops should be made available when they can be used appropriately. Moreover, the mother should be given an opportunity to be away from the child at recurring intervals. Although some workers tend to discount the value of "baby sitting" services, these services can make it possible for the mother to get much-needed relief and can enhance her sense of personal comfort. Greater comfortableness may help make her chronic sorrow more tolerable and may increase her effectiveness in meeting the child's continuing needs. Also, through increased comfortableness the parents may become more accessible to psychological help for themselves.

In summary, it has been suggested that the parent of a mentally defective child suffers from chronic sorrow. This sorrow is a natural response to a tragic fact. If the professional worker accepts chronic sorrow as a natural, rather than a neurotic, response, he can be more effective in helping the parent achieve the goal of increased comfort in living with and managing a mentally defective child.

□ □ □

from PARENT RESPONSES TO A MENTALLY DEFECTIVE CHILD

Simon Olshansky

(Mental Retardation, 1966)

. . . .

Mental deficiency is not a simple disease process that runs its course toward recovery. It is best viewed by professionals as a syndrome of diverse etiology; for parents it becomes a many-faceted symbol—of personal defeat, cruel fate, an angry God, death, marital strife, guilt, anger, despair, genetic contamination, and punishment for sexual license.

With this background in mind let us consider more concretely some possible responses of the afflicted family.

Mental deficiency is a family tragedy, and whatever one may do or say, the tragedy remains. Almost all families with mentally defective children experience what I call "chronic sorrow," which I feel is an understandable, nonneurotic response to a tragic fact. The sorrow is chronic and lasts as long as the child lives.

A somewhat different point of view has been suggested by Solnit and Stark (1961). Their view might be summarized as follows: The birth of a mentally defective child is a severe narcissistic blow similar to loss suffered through the death of a loved one, leaving the parents in a state of acute grief. Solnit and Stark hypothesize that the mother expects to have a normal child and builds up a fantasy image of it. The birth of a defective child means the loss of the normal child. The defective child is somehow equated with a dead child. When the damaged child is born, there is no time for working through the loss of the expected normal child because the "unexpected" abnormal baby requires immediate attention.

Although their hypothesis may be true for some parents, the following arguments may be advanced against its universal application. First, the death of a dream child is not equivalent to the death of a real child. Second, the hypothesis takes insufficient account of the fact that for many parents identification of mental deficiency does not take place at birth. How, for example, could we explain the response of parents whose child is not defined as mentally defective until the age of three? Third, those parents who passed the period of mourning should be free of sorrow and should be able to attend to the needs of their child. My experience is to the contrary; i.e., that sorrow continues as long as the defective child lives.

My fourth objection to their hypothesis is that it keeps the problem neatly encapsulated, within the psyche, when it is clearly both in and outside the psyche. I have gone into the Solnit and Stark hypothesis at some length because it appears to be an attempt to define the afflicted parents as neurotic, thus maintaining the tradition which has prevailed so long in the field and which has often interfered with appropriate help to these parents.

In describing chronic sorrow further, I am discussing the family of a child who would be considered mentally defective within any society. I am not talking about the intellectually impoverished slum child who becomes defined as mentally retarded and placed in special classes on the basis of an inappropriate IQ test.

Although I feel that almost all parents of mentally defective children suffer chronic sorrow, there are differences in the quality of response, depending on many variables. Some of these are social class, age of parents, religion, ethnicity, size of family, and ordinal position and sex of the defective child. Mothers respond differently from fathers. . . . Also, differences in responses appear which are not explainable in terms of the listed variables. . . .

Concurrent with all the negative feelings that draw our attention, these parents do enjoy some of the pleasures of observing some growth and some development of the child, but within the context of chronic sorrow.

In working with parents of the mentally defective, the professional should keep in mind that parents of normal children suffer varied amounts of distress and disorder in managing and living with their children. Being a parent of any child is an extremely strenuous role to fulfill, since some conflicts, heartbreaks, and frustrations are inevitable by-products. What often sustains parents of normal children is the knowledge that ultimately their children will grow up, become self-supporting, and leave home. For the parents of the mentally defective, continuing dependency is their lot.

There is much the professional can do, but his expectations will have to be modest, and his effectiveness will depend on seeing the mentally defective child within the family from a proper perspective. My own feelings are that many parents have considerable strength and stamina, and it is a mistake to view them as helpless.

I believe that parental acceptance will come in time if they are helped to deal with their chronic sorrow, and if concrete services are available to help them in managing and living with the child.

The problem and process of parental acceptance have been distorted by some professionals and given a priority which often suggests to the parents that the professionals are looking through the wrong end of the telescope. Some parents may begin to wonder whose sense of reality is out of focus.

Moreover, in working with parents, professionals should be clear about the goal. I would say that an appropriate goal would be increased comfortableness in living with and in managing a mentally defective child day by day. How can this goal be best achieved?

We should provide parents with an opportunity over long periods of time to ventilate their feelings of sorrow, of anger, and of anguish. We should reassure them that such feelings are legitimate and understandable. The suppression of such feelings, so commonly observed, is regrettable. Some parents require much time to learn to tolerate their unmending wounds. But these feelings of chronic sorrow have to be brought into awareness and legitimatized.

Further, increased comfortableness might be achieved by providing some concrete services. In our traditional concern for the intrapersonal we have tended to discount the value of such services as these:

A good clinic, which provides diagnostic services, social case work, and public health nursing services;

Pre-school nurseries to improve and accelerate the process of socialization;

Baby-sitting services so mothers may be able to go out for a change of scenery, or maybe just have a chance for a nap;

High quality institutions for both temporary and permanent care. Admission to these institutions should be based on need;

An adequate program of education which does not terminate at age 16;

Sheltered workshops for those unable to work in regular industry.

Other services might be listed, but I think that the point is clear. Parents of mentally defective children need more than psychological and case work services to make their life more endurable. More important, these services may enable the mother to respond with more vigor and more good feelings to her mentally defective child. Generally a mother needs to have a "good" and responsive child to function well. In the absence of a "good" child, the mother needs considerable help to maintain her morale.

Unhappy parents suffering a tragedy of such dimensions as having a mentally defective child need scapegoats. One of their scapegoats is the physician. Some physicians may not do a very good job in telling parents what has to be told. But it would be naive to accept uncritically all the stories repeatedly related about how blunt and brusque doctors were in "breaking the news" or in advising immediate institutionalization. *Bad news is bad news,* and it is against the bad news that parents are often protesting.

Since we are supposed to accept strokes of ill fortune stoically and as there is still a need to express anger against fate, the doctor becomes a substitute target. There is little point in disputing this matter with parents as long as we understand that it is their fate rather than the doctor against which they are protesting.

If parents use doctors as scapegoats, so some social workers, psychologists, and psychiatrists may use parents as their scapegoats. In essential terms mental deficiency cannot be reversed in the same way as we may be able to reverse some cases of mental illness. To handle our frustrations at our seeming helplessness we protest the parents' recalcitrance and ironically their inability to perceive the problem from our point of view. We accuse them of such high crimes as "denial" and "regression." We often become distressed if parents shop around for other diagnostic services.

Our way of expressing our anger and of using parents as substitute targets for our anger is to label their expression of sorrow and anguish as neurotic. In this way, we try to enhance our feelings of helpfulness and to reduce our feelings of helplessness. That is, we can do more about neurotic behavior than we can about mental deficiency. This fact may explain, in part, the attractiveness of the hypothesis offered by Solnit and Stark. Of course, some parents are neurotic and are properly so defined. What I am protesting is the more general tendency of misperception by some professionals. . . .

□ □ □

from REJECTING PARENTS?

James J. Gallagher

(Exceptional Children, 1956)

The statement, "These parents have rejected their child," has been one of the most standard cliches in the area of exceptional children. Although it is heard most frequently in the field of mental deficiency, it is a statement familiar to personnel in the entire area of education and training of handicapped children.

Psychologists have given much of value to the area of education and training of exceptional children, and it is not surprising to see psychological terms appear in the vocabulary of teachers, rehabilitation counselors, school psychologists, and other workers in the field. The purpose of the present article is to present an analysis of the meaning of the term *rejection* so that it might be used in its proper context and, above all, with its proper limitations.

A distraught and tense mother comes to a teacher and complains, "If I have to spend another moment with that child, I am just going to go out of my mind." Is she rejecting her child? An embarrassed father nervously tells a counselor about plans for the placement of his child in a distant institution for the good of all concerned. Is he rejecting his child? A mother in a burst of anger strikes her little girl and tells her that she does not love her any more. Is this *parental rejection?*

To put the question in a more general form, does parental rejection mean the holding or expression of negative values or attitudes toward their child? Such instances as described above often are used to bolster and exemplify such a diagnosis. Needless to say, every parent can be indicted at one time or another if expression of negative values is the only criterion for parental rejection, especially if the observer happens to catch the parents under conditions of stress. When we think of the problems that parents of normal children face and then consider the extra stress which is placed on parents of handicapped children, it is little wonder that the term used loosely could apply to almost any mother or father. What parent could be completely happy or positively oriented to a child who is quadriplegic, or blind, or severely mentally retarded, or, for that matter, completely normal in every respect?

It might be useful in considering this problem for the reader to picture in his mind the most emotionally mature individual he knows. Should we expect him or her to accept totally a child with these handicaps and accompanying problems with merely a calm smile or philosophical shrug of the shoulders? The *I-like-to-suffer-because-it-makes-me-feel-so-good-and-noble* philosophy occurs quite frequently in soap operas, but fortunately does not turn up too often in real life situations. Parents are entitled to a little negative outpouring without having their human response labelled as something psychologically revolting.

What actually is the definition of parental rejection? It is the persistent and unrelieved holding of unrealistic negative values of the child to the extent that the whole behavior of the parent towards that child is colored unrealistically by this negative tone. There are four general ways in which this rejection can be expressed.

1. *Strong underexpectations of achievement:* The child in this instance is considered so useless and devoid of positive attributes that the parents don't really believe that the child is capable of any useful function at all. This situation occurs sometimes when parents are so distressed to find that their child is intellectually inferior that they also consider him or her incapable of useful participation in social or self-care areas where there are goals well within reach of the child. Such underexpectations are also often revealed in the child's own feelings of worthlessness, resignation to failure, and lack of motivation to achieve. In short, the child has heard for so long that he is a worthless individual that he will start to believe it himself and act as though he is worthless.

2. *Setting unrealistic goals:* Some parents seem to set extremely high and impossible goals for their child to reach as a method for justifying their negative feelings and attitudes towards the child. This enables the parents to say that the child deserves punishment and reprimand because he didn't do what he was supposed to do. These goals are often set in the area of social and emotional maturity and when the child inevitably fails, the parents unleash negative feeling upon the child with the self-justification that their lazy or careless offspring has failed them again.

3. *Escape:* This reaction may take the form of running away from the child or the placement of the child at a great distance from the parent. Fathers who desert their families under conditions of stress or trouble fit into this category. Since our society makes it more difficult for the woman in the family to desert, mothers may take the next easiest way out and attempt to remove from them the child who is the major focus of difficulty. This tendency might be manifested by sending the child to a distant school when there are comparable facilities at or around home. Strong attempts may be made by the parents to rationalize this more on the basis of their inability to care for the child even when there is definite evidence to the contrary.

4. *Reaction formation:* In some parents their negative feelings toward their child are so unacceptable to their own total picture of themselves as loving, warm, kind individuals that they tend to adopt the psychological reaction of denying their negative feelings and presenting to the world precisely the opposite attitude of the one they actually experience. Thus, instead of saying, "I hate this child," which does not fit into their own self-concept of loving all children, they say instead, "I love this child." It should be emphasized that this is not a hypocritical stand on the part of the parents. They have taken themselves in as well as their friends and neighbors and truly believe the attitude that they are presenting to the outside world. This particular reaction takes unusual forms sometimes. One interesting manifestation that the author has seen was that of a parent who insisted upon placing a tag around her child's neck, each time he went out to play, with his name, address, and telephone number on it, plus sewing similar labels in all of his clothes. She claimed that she did not want her youngster to get lost and was protecting against that eventuality. This idea might have made good sense in a crowded city but appeared rather unreasonable in the rural community where the parents resided. Further counseling with this mother revealed what was suspected—that she really had strong desires to leave or lose the child and had to protect herself against these unacceptable desires by adopting a close attitude of possessiveness and overprotection.

This dramatic type of psychological reaction has led some people to observe that the parents are playing a game with the experts that they cannot win. If the parent says, "I don't like my child very much," he is condemned for having the temerity of openly rejecting his child. If on the other hand he says, "I like my handicapped child very much," he is labelled as manifesting reaction formation. Thus, no matter which way the parents express themselves, they find that they are neatly entrapped in the net of rejection woven by the professionals.

Actually, reaction formation in an extreme form is fairly rare in occurrence and can usually be distinguished from genuine positive feelings. For example, a parent who has a healthy emotional attitude toward his child does not usually hesitate to include in his total description of the child the negative aspects of his or her behavior. The parent who is using reaction formation as a defense against negative feelings may have a difficult time saying anything uncomplimentary or admitting any degree of irritation with a child no matter how serious or reasonable the provocation. It is almost as if an admission of any negative attitude on their part would break down the defenses of the parents that have held back the pressure of negative feeling and allow the unacceptable attitudes to come pouring forth much as flood water breaks through a rent in a dam.

Perhaps one of the greatest indictments of the use of the term, *parental rejection,* is the feeling of helplessness and apathy it engenders in the professional worker dealing directly with the child. The implications behind this reaction seem to be that such a condition in the parents cannot be changed or, at best, could be changed only if the parents underwent long term psychotherapy. This is a course of action most parents are either unwilling or unable to undertake. It is because of this reaction on the part of the professional workers that a further and very useful distinction should be made between primary rejection and secondary rejection.

Primary rejection means that the cause of the parental negative attitudes resides in the basic unchangeable nature of the child himself. For instance, we are all familiar with children who are rejected at birth because they do not turn out to be the sex desired by the parent. The father who turns his back on a baby girl because he wanted a boy reveals quite clearly that he is rejecting her on the basis of something which is not within her power to modify or change.

In primary rejection, the personality dynamics of the parent rather than the behavior of the child often determine the parent attitudes. The writer once knew a mother who rejected her mentally retarded girl to the extent of denying that the child was her own. Further investigation and counseling revealed that the mother had in her early years been burdened with deep feelings of inferiority and a sense of personal unworthiness. Although outwardly she fought against these feelings, inwardly she half-accepted them as being true. The birth of a handicapped child seemed to be the last straw, the objective proof of her inferiority. Her reasoning took the irrational but not uncommon line that inferior children are produced by inferior parents. It followed naturally from this conclusion that she would hate the child who had revealed her true weakness, just as we dislike the people who reveal our own weaknesses.

More common than the cases above is the parent whose need for children seems to stem from a need for self-extension. Since we can't all do what we would like in our short lifetime, some of us try to make up for this lack of time by having our children choose paths of endeavor that we would have chosen—if we had been given a second chance in our own lives. Thus, a father may reject a child who does not fulfill the father's secret need to be a football star, or a business man, or a physician.

Since the major difficulty of acceptance in most of these cases seems to rest in the personality of the parents, the possibility for the change in the family situation seems to lie primarily in modification of the parental attitude, probably through professional counseling.

Secondary rejection, on the other hand, represents the expression of negative attitudes based upon unfortunate behavior manifestations of the child himself. This is different in many important ways from the above described primary rejection. Many exceptional children, as the reader knows, manifest behavioral characteristics that would be difficult for anyone to love or accept. A deaf child may hoot or honk or make other unusual or unpleasant noises; a blind child may go through unusual bodily contortions; and the brain injured child may seem to be about to run up the wall and across the ceiling. Not only are these characteristics likely to evoke negative reaction from the parents because of their basically unfavorable or unsocial nature, but also because the parents react to the frustration they feel at being unable to deal successfully with the child's problems. In these cases there is considerable hope for improvement of the attitude of the parents, since most of these characteristics can be modified through training. . . .

Many examples could be cited of how the atmosphere of a family has been changed for the better as a result of reducing some particularly obnoxious habit of the child. When the pressure of immediate problems is lifted, the parents are then able to release themselves from their own charged emotionality and to take a more objective, calm, and useful approach to the child's other problems and difficulties. It is the writer's firm opinion that cases of secondary rejection far exceed the cases of primary rejection, and serious danger is done to the education program of many children by the erroneous conclusion that since the parents have revealed strong negative attitudes, nothing much can be expected from them in the way of cooperation.

It would be most convenient if parental attitudes in any case in question could be identified as either primary or secondary rejection. Frankly, the writer knows of no such easy yardstick. . . . The only way . . . to determine the true parental attitude is to modify the obnoxious behavior. If the parents continue their unrelieved negative attitudes after the central behavior problems have been eliminated or reduced, then one would be justified in saying that they have revealed primary rejection feelings. Generally, parents have to be seen over a considerable length of time before they will reveal their true emotional values and attitudes. One safe rule of thumb might be observed, however: *It is safer and more profitable to assume that the negative attitudes represent secondary rejection until the parents prove differently.* In this way, by giving the parents the benefit of the doubt, we can move ahead and constructively approach the child's behavior problems. If these problems can be modified or improved, then the chances seem fairly good that we will have added another pair of parents as allies and helpers in our training program for their exceptional child.

There is one more question that the reader should consider. Since we have discussed the emotional reactions of parents, it would be unfair if we left this article without also considering the role our own emotional reactions play in our professional dealings when we tend to over-use such a term as "rejecting parents." There are a number of possibilities which have occurred to the writer that might account for such over-use of this term and he would like to present them for what they are worth.

1. Some professional personnel seem to like to use technical terms such as rejection without being truly aware of their meaning. In mystery there is authority and power and the use of such terms seems to increase the profes-

sional's feeling of expertness or importance. We should hasten to point out that this is not a fault peculiar to professional people working in this field but can be observed in almost every endeavor. The physician, with his truly remarkable language of obscure terms, the lawyer with his Latin phrases, the engineer with his mathematics—all seem to use their specialized knowledge to overawe and impress on occasion.

2. Professional persons working with a child may sometimes feel uncomfortable in the presence of some parents. Thus, they might sometimes use such a label as *parental rejection* to free themselves from the responsibility of contacting or dealing with particularly unattractive or potentially uncooperative individuals. There seems to be more of a tendency for this kind of reaction when the teacher or professional person comes from one social class and the parent from another.

3. In some rare instances it might be used by a professional person as a means of establishing a position of superiority over the parents. The professional person in effect would be saying, "I would not treat that child that way if it were mine and, what's more, no decent individual would treat the child that way." It goes without saying that this is a statement that is easier to make for the professional person who does not have children of his own or at least does not have handicapped children.

4. The over-use of this term *rejection* may be due to a highly unrealistic view of how the emotionally healthy parent should react to his exceptional child. We are expecting too much from parents if we expect all sweetness and light and calm forbearance. Total positive acceptance of a handicapped child or any child in the absence of any negative attitudes is something this writer has never seen and does not anticipate seeing in the near future.

What then can we expect of the parents? We can hope that the parents will accept the child's handicap, even though they don't like it. We can expect that the parents will want the child to perform at the level of social and intellectual ability that the child is capable of (and the professional worker has the responsibility of providing this information to the parents). Finally, we can expect that aspirations of parents for their child's future are in line with all that is known about the child's potential skills and abilities. We should expect that these parents will harbor feelings of resentment towards other parents who have had the good fortune to have healthy children and that they will occasionally become downcast and discouraged over the special problems that have sometimes seemed to set them apart from other parents. In short, they will act like human beings. . . .

□ □ □

THE THREE STAGES IN THE GROWTH OF A PARENT OF A MENTALLY RETARDED CHILD

Dan Boyd

(American Journal of Mental Deficiency, 1951)

We have had some splendid speakers in our meetings from time to time, who have spoken to us on a variety of subjects, mostly concerned with the medical, psychological and training aspects of the mentally retarded child. But for a long time, I have felt that there was a place for a message of a different kind. I believe that we, as parents, need some message peculiar to ourselves, some comforting idea, some torch to light our way and keep us from stumbling in the darkness of our distress.

If I were to give a title to this message, it would be "The Three Stages in the Growth of a Parent of a Mentally Retarded Child."

I trust that you will not think me forward or presumptuous in trying to bring that message to you—in the last analysis, who that is not one of us can speak with authority? And so, please bear with me; I do not mean so much to preach to you, as to think aloud myself.

We have all trod the same path of disappointment and disillusionment, and so we speak in a common tongue; in a language which only they can understand, who have learned it from the lips of Life itself.

That awful moment of disclosure, when the doctor, perhaps with aching heart, told us that our child was not normal! I so often think of that blessed man, that physician who has passed on to his deserved reward, who had faced many a grim crisis with unflinching courage. He met me at the top of the stairs which led to the maternity ward, as I came bounding up two at a time in response to the attendant's, "You have a baby girl, Mr. Boyd—you can go up now." I shall never forget his face, so benign and gentle and yet so tortured with that message fraught with the finality of Fate. "You will want to kill me if this proves to be false," he said, "but I must tell you—I am afraid that your baby is not a normal child. I think she is a mongoloid." The earth seemed to rise up around me and the heavens seemed about to crash upon my head. A mongoloid child! What was a mongoloid child? I had heard the name, but my recollection was vague and tinged with horror. A thousand thoughts raced across my brain with kaleidoscopic rapidity. Was this the result of heredity? Was there no hope at all? Why did this have to happen to me? Why had God singled me out from all other men, to place this burden upon me? Why? Why? Why?

And then in the days that followed, the queer, hysterical thoughts that kept sweeping over me like an engulfing wave—that false sense of shame—what would people think?—how could I face them?—what would I say?—what did the future hold?—how could I go on living?

Oh, you know and I know, above all others, what silent agonies, what repressed hopes, what buried miseries we experienced in those dreadful days. Time passed, we knew not how, and eventually brought with it a kind of healing numbness. We went about our daily work mechanically and without purpose. There was no ray of sunshine, no relief from the piled up pain. And then one night I came to a meeting of the Parents' Group in that blessed old East Paterson Fire-house, and for the first time realized that I was not alone; that there were many others who had the same problems. "Misery loves company"; but I never fully appreciated that until I joined the Parents' Group.

That was the first stage in the growth of a parent of a mentally retarded child, the stage where one is entirely subjective, concerned almost wholly with himself and the effect that things have upon him.

Then came the second stage, when I began to think a little less of myself and a little more of the little one, of Bonnie. What did the medical profession know about retarded children? What treatments were available, what clinics, what help? What methods of education and training were being used?—In short, what resources could I tap for the benefit of my child? I was astounded and stunned to learn that the medical profession knew scarcely more than we did about causes and remedies and treatments. I knew by now that this was not a new problem; then, why had nothing been done about it throughout the years? There was no use in blaming the medical profession, or in condemning the educational authorities; if there were a fault, it clearly lay with the parents of the forgotten children of other years, who had locked their problems in their hearts and spoken about them only in whispers! The public did not know then, and does not know now, of the very existence of the situation. And only when an aroused public says, "This thing shall not be," will it cease to be.

I do not know your thoughts and your experiences, but there is a sameness about us, as people, which makes me think that we are not much different in our reactions. I believe that all of us have gone through the first stage of self-pity and the second stage of concern primarily for *our* child. And, heaven forbid, some of us may stop there in stunted growth, as did our forefathers! It all depends upon our thinking; upon whether we think that all is lost, or whether we think that a great opportunity lies before us. It was Shakespeare who said, "For there is nothing either good or bad, but thinking makes it so." I found that brooding did not solve my problem, nor Bonnie's; that bitterness and self-pity, on the contrary, were eating at my soul, impairing my efficiency in business, and undermining my chance for happiness. I knew that I must find some philosophy for living, some way to go on. And I found it! I found it in one of the oldest of books, and upon the very first page! "In the beginning, God created the heaven and the earth," it begins. Then a little farther on, "and God created man in his own image; in the image of God created he him." And then still farther on, "And God saw everything that he had made, and behold, it was very good." I thought about our little one, and my first reaction was: "It is a lie!" And then I thought about it some more.

Whatever our several religious tenets may be, we all believe in God, an omnipotent Being, allpowerful and supreme. And we all have some belief in a life after this one, despite the fact that it is "the undiscovered country, from whose bourne no traveler returns." We think of that life as an eternity, and in our poor human way, we try to prepare ourselves for it. All this passed through my mind, and then other excerpts from the great Book suggested themselves: "Behold, thou hast made my days as an hand-breadth"; and "Man that is born of woman is of few days, and full of trouble"; and, "My days are like a shadow that declineth"; and, "As for man, his days are as grass; as a flower of the field, he flourisheth. For the wind passeth over it, and it is gone; and the place thereof shall know it no more."

I was confused, for if God is perfect, then his work should be everlasting; particularly, if it is made in his image. And yet here, repeatedly, was a contradiction. And then I had my answer! My days *are* "like a shadow that declineth," when compared to that eternity of life that I believe awaits us all. I remember my loved ones as I saw them, but because I can no longer see them is no reason for me to believe that they have ceased to live. And so, it all came back to an understanding of the word "man." Now I knew what it meant—it was the spiritual, the everlasting, eternal man. That was what I wanted for Bonnie; that was the big thing that overshadowed all else. Now I knew that I need have no fear for her. I could speak for her from the lips of Whittier:

> I know not where his islands lift
> Their fronded palms in air;
> I only know I cannot drift
> Beyond His love and care.

Now, at last, I was able to look at life a little more objectively, to see more clearly, to think more rationally. When we can do that, we are ready for the third stage in the growth of a parent of a mentally retarded child. We now begin to think more of what we can do for others, and less of what they can do for us.

I was humbled and discouraged by the thought of how little I could do as an individual; but I was challenged by the realization of how much we could accomplish together! No one knows accurately how many mentally retarded children there are in the United States. Educators estimate that two percent of the school population is retarded, but the great majority of the mentally retarded children are never admitted to the schools. Considering the numbers in the schools, the institutions and at home, their numbers must run into the hundreds of thousands. And each child has two parents. Why, that is an army! Together, and with a common purpose, those parents could work miracles! They could sweep away all resistance and enlist the interest and support of the entire country! Money for research, training courses for special teachers, schools for all!

"God works in a mysterious way, His wonders to perform." There may be a reason for our affliction. Just think of it! This problem is as old as time. It has been no respecter of color, race, creed or time. And in all the thousands of years, nothing has been done about it! God's timing is always perfect. What a perfect coordination of factors for success, in the forever solution of this age-old problem! Modern medicine has made more progress in the past twenty-five years than it made in the previous one hundred. Sulfa, penicillin, cortisone, heart and brain surgery, and many other miracles of modern medicine are a reality; research has come into its own. And precisely at this time of medical progress, Parents' Groups are spreading all over the country—an army is falling in—the trumpets are sounding!

But it must be an army of individuals, each one inspired with a purpose, and the will to see it through. It will not be easy; it will not be quick. There will be many a disappointment and many a set-back. It will take courage on the part of all of us—the courage of that valiant old soldier who fell on the field of battle, and then cried out to his comrades:

Fight on, my men, cried Sir Andrew Barton,
 I am hurt, but I am not slaine,
I'll lie me down and bleed a-while,
 And then I'll rise and fight againe.

Yes, this is the third stage in the growth of a parent of a mentally retarded child. And how rewarding it can be to all of us! How it will broaden our lives and make them rich and pure and purposeful! You all remember those lines of Shakespeare that you struggled with in high school:

The quality of mercy is not strain'd,
 It droppeth as the gentle rain from heaven
Upon the place beneath; it is twice blest;
 It blesseth him that gives and him that takes.

And as we experience the rewards that can come when we forget about ourselves, when we merge the problem of *our child* into the problem of *all* mentally retarded children, we shall realize the promise:

> "Give, and it shall be given unto you; good measure, pressed down and shaken together, and running over."

And then we shall be able to look into our children's eyes and see them as they really are—God's children—and be thankful!

> "And God created man in his own image; in God's image created he him."
> "And God saw everything that he had made, and behold, it was very good."

□ □ □

Part III Management in Conjunction with the Diagnostic Process

Management of the family of the retarded can be viewed as having three distinct phases. Phase one includes the parental question-asking process, which leads to the rendering of diagnostic services. Phase two involves primarily the answering of parental questions in the feedback process. The third phase consists of a prolonged process of counseling and service provision. While Parts I and II of this book laid the groundwork for the coverage of the management process, Part III is concerned with the two initial phases of management. Most of the rest of the book will be addressed to the third phase of the management process.

Several writers have asserted that the early contact phase with a family is crucial, because it sets the tone for later management. This is the stage at which the family has its first experience with professionals who, by their very position, are symbols of hope to the parents. One must consider that many parents arrived at the decision to go to the experts after having been dominated by emotionality. If such a contact is a first experience for the family, the parents are frequently filled with a whole series of related but possibly incoherent questions. "What is wrong with my child?" and "what can be done?" are the two most general and basic questions. Many parents may have difficulty in phrasing such queries in the language of the professional, and the manager must be alert to the possibility that the presenting question may be an indirect phrasing of a more basic one.

If a contact is not the first experience for the family, i.e., if the counselor is just a step along a "shopping" pattern, the manager might be facing a particularly difficult problem, i.e., how to manage a family which has already been mismanaged by someone else, or which has not profited from past management. He would then have to determine what has taken place in previous management and plan accordingly. Family members might feel quite negatively toward professional activities, or they might feel that the entire management process is a farce.

While the manager must be alert to parental selectivity of perception during all phases of the managing process, such selection can be especially significant during phases one and two. The manager must ask himself constantly whether many of the words, phrases, and ideas he, or even the parent, uses are foreign to the parent who may superficially repeat or agree with all that is said because he is bewildered, or because he does not want to question authority or admit his ignorance.

SECTION A

General Considerations

The rapid development of numerous, often federally subsidized, multi-disciplinary specialty clinics in retardation constituted an opportunity to break with certain patterns of the past and to introduce fresh approaches, experimentation, and a healthy empiricism to the process of case evaluation and management. Surprisingly, the promise of such innovation has been largely unfulfilled. The following selection discusses how traditional and stereotyped models have limited the utility of the specialty clinic. At the same time, some suggestions are offered on how diagnostic services might be structured so as to increase their relevance and utility to the human management process.

from DIAGNOSIS DIAGNOSED

Wolf Wolfensberger

(Journal of Mental Subnormality, 1965)

. . . .

The treatment of mental retardation is primarily a problem of human management; and many approaches to human management, for a variety of historical and social reasons, are based upon a medical model. The treatment of mental retardation is one of these, and the field has inherited or derived many attitudes, practices, and, yes—even myths and lores from the medical models it has emulated. One complex of attitudes, practices, myths, and lores has to do with the role and significance of case evaluation, or, as it is called in the medical tradition, diagnosis.

Among some clinicians, particularly in the medical field, there exists what can almost be described as a diagnosis compulsion. Sometimes diagnosis seems to become more important than anything else, and once diagnosis has been achieved the clinician may behave as if the main task of case management were completed. Even among less diagnosis-oriented professionals, diagnosis is viewed as a sacred cow which has been enshrined in a mystique, and there are many superstitious beliefs associated with its worship. Let me enumerate only a few:

1. *Diagnosis is better than no diagnosis.*
2. *Early diagnosis is better than late diagnosis.*
3. *Diagnosis is essential to successful treatment or case management.*
4. *Differential diagnosis is important for differential treatment.*
5. *Extensive evaluation is better than limited evaluation.*
6. *Team diagnosis is better than individual diagnosis.*

These beliefs, we may almost call them dogmas, are widely subscribed to in medicine. You will readily note that all have been applied to retardation and are generally encountered and accepted there. Yet we can show that these beliefs are not only not always true in the human management of retardates, but are also sometimes invalid even in the best practice of medicine.

Let us take a critical look at the six dogmas, one by one.

1. Is diagnosis always better than no diagnosis? I submit to you that many cases of mental retardation would have been better off had they never been formally and professionally diagnosed. Some individuals, both professional and lay, see diagnosis as a magic solution to a human puzzle. Others, particularly service agencies, use it as an escape from responsibility. For whatever reason, diagnosis can quite often be a dead end for the family. Instead of leading to a meaningful service assignment it frequently results only in a frustrating series of fruitless cross-referrals.

> A typical case in my experience is that of a mildly retarded, homosexually inclined, moderately disturbed teenager who was referred back and forth between the following agencies: regular and special school programs, a child guidance and residential treatment centre, a state hospital for the mentally ill, two state institutions for the retarded, and the state vocational rehabilitation service. He was judged to be too retarded for the regular grades, too disturbing in the special class, too retarded for the outpatient and too old for the inpatient service of the disturbed children's center, too homosexual for the children's ward of the state hospital and too young for its adult wards, too high functioning for the first state retardation institution, not quite enough of a number of things for the special treatment unit of the second, and too effeminate for the programs vocational rehabilitation offered.

This cross-referring took place within a relatively short time span and three or four agencies ran him through their standard diagnostic mill. In the end, the boy somehow did not quite fit in anywhere and lived at home without any service whatever. On paper, however, he was a great success as far as the agencies were concerned. Since he was referred in each instance to what was considered to be an appropriate service by the agency one step ahead in the referral chain, he constituted at least six successful close-outs and will thus enter our national mental health, mental retardation and education statistics. A similar case has been recorded in the literature (Krush, 1964) where a boy was handed on between eighteen physicians, four teachers, one chiropractor, two clinics, two hospitals and seven schools. After this, the boy became "uncooperative, untidy, disturbed," and the mother stated that "not even the worst prognosis he had received in all our long years of searching for help had prepared us for this."

Many a parent has questioned bitterly what good the diagnostic evaluation did if it failed to lead to assignation to a service, or, even worse, if it actually resulted in the child's exclusion from a program previously enrolled in. A rather extreme example of this occurs in one of our states which I will not name. There, severely retarded children need not be included in public education programs, and only a very small number of local school districts have chosen to provide classes voluntarily. In addition, the definition of severe retardation was manipulated so as to include children up to IQ 60. Finally, even if a school district does decide to offer so-called trainable classes on a voluntary basis, children must be at least eight years old. My advice to parents of children who are probably near IQ 60 in that state is to avoid, by all means available, the testing or evaluation of their school-age child. They have nothing to gain and all to lose from a professional diagnosis.

Quite aside from the *question* of when diagnosis is better than no diagnosis is the *fact* that unlike in most areas of medicine, diagnosis in retardation is not always possible anyway. Even the most careful study of a case may leave many diagnostic questions unanswered. Especially etiological diagnosis is often only an educated guess and rarely has the weight of evidence behind it that usually supports medical diagnoses. ". . . The diagnostic label which is applied to an individual frequently reveals more about the orientation and bias of the diagnostician than about the causal agents responsible for the retardation" (Robinson & Robinson, 1965). Even when there is considerable evidence, there exist embarrassments. For example, a pregnant mother and apparently also the fetus suffered an infection and she delivered prematurely in a difficult birth. Is the child's retardation to be coded as due to pre-natal infection, prematurity or birth trauma? Most currently popular etiological and coding classification schemes permit only one entry.

The behavioral area has other kinds of problems. Here, we have heavy reliance on tests and techniques which have not been validated as regards predictions about retardates. The lack of concern for validating data on the part of some personnel in the applied areas is sometimes little short of shocking to those who take an empirical approach to behavior.

2. Is early diagnosis always desirable? I submit that perhaps it is in an ideal society, but that in the reality of everyday practice, early diagnosis can be a disaster. Let me give you a typical example. When a child is born into a family it is usually accepted and loved with little reservation. Should the child later turn out to be retarded, the problem may be worked out within the family because of the strong bonds that have been formed. However, a child diagnosed as retarded at or near birth may never find the crucial initial acceptance and may be viewed with conflicted attitudes which prevent the formation of deep parental love. This can lead to early and quite unnecessary institutionalization or other consequences detrimental to the child.

I have encountered many instances, numbering in the hundreds, where early diagnosis such as in mongolism exposed the family to professional management which appeared contrary to the welfare of either child, family or society. The most common counsel seems to be the stereotyped "put the child in the institution right away," often accompanied by the sincere admonition to "forget you ever had him" and perhaps the consolation to "have another one instead." This sort of advice is, by no means, the most inappropriate or callous one readily encountered and repeatedly documented in the literature. The dictum that early diagnosis is always optimal may thus need to be qualified. Early diagnosis is desirable when it leads to prevention, early treatment or constructive counseling; it is irrelevant if it is purely academic and does not change the course of events; it is harmful if, in balance, child or family reap more disadvantages than benefits.

3. Is diagnosis essential to successful treatment or management? In medicine we have many instances which illustrate that successful treatment can take place even when the nature of a condition is unknown.

> One of the classical examples is that of John Snow who was a public health pioneer during the 1854 cholera epidemic in London. Plotting the incidence of cholera on a map, he noticed that it centered around a well, **viz.** the Broad Street Pump. The mode of propagation of cholera was then not understood, but Snow did not wait for experiments and causal explanation. He noted the correlation between drinking from the well, and death from cholera, and resolutely closed the well. The epidemic promptly faded away.
>
> A more contemporary example is prophylactic treatment with antibiotics when one really has no idea what it is one is trying to prevent, or is, in fact, already treating.

I submit that in many cases where the main object of diagnosis is the identification of service needs, a brief interview with the family can sometimes even be sufficient. While the case itself may be complex, the *need* may be very simple. Thus, the need for a mother's helper, day care, trainable classes, public health nurse visits, etc., is often so blatant that an intelligent layman could render a good judgment, especially when the existence of retardation can no longer be doubted, and/or when previously obtained diagnostic data are already available. Yet some agencies, at least in this country, will blindly administer a mammoth and stereotyped dose of diagnostics to all comers, even where the needs are as obvious as the total lack of means to satisfy them. An example here is that of a clinic I know which routinely includes a speech evaluation in its "interdisciplinary" approach. To my amazement the speech pathologist evaluated a two-month-old mongoloid infant, and came up with a diagnosis of "delayed language development."

4. Does differential diagnosis really imply differential treatment? The belief in the importance of differential diagnosis seems primarily derived from the medical emphasis on etiological diagnosis. It is argued that you must know what caused a disorder before you can really treat it effectively. This argument, of course, is not even valid in medicine even though I have heard many physicians repeat it. It is even less valid in human management problems. Even in situations where it is believed that differential etiological diagnosis implies differential treatment, the evidence may be extremely tenuous or lacking, and the treatment may be chosen on the basis of current dogma only. A typical example is the virtually universally accepted belief encountered in untold texts and articles, *viz.* that a diagnosis of mental retardation in a child calls for an entirely different type of treatment than a diagnosis of emotional disturbance. If this is so—and I personally doubt it—it certainly has never been subjected to an adequate empirical test even though such a test would not be all that difficult. Another, similar claim which has been tested, and has found only very limited support, is that cultural-familial retardates need a different educational curriculum than retardates with presumed brain-injury.

Generally, practically useful prediction of outcome in various areas of disposition and treatment of *individual* retardates has been a spectacular failure. Literally hundreds of studies have unsuccessfully concerned themselves with this problem.

5. Is extensive evaluation always better than a limited one? Often it is, but sometimes it is not. Only too often diagnostic clinics or centers run every client through a fairly standard, little varying mill of tests and procedures.

They may do this regardless of what the presenting question or problem is. Sometimes a very extensive but standardized evaluation is entirely wasted because it did not address itself to the presenting question. When a client is fed into the diagnostic mill, the mill should be set to grind in a certain way and for a certain length. Not all grain needs or even should be ground the same way or else there will be waste.

Considering the costs involved, diagnosis should be rendered only in terms of the question: "Diagnosis for what?" Often detailed pre-diagnostic questionnaires and letters to previous contact agencies will reveal that the family only needs counseling, selective evaluation, or a referral instead of "the works." Yet, in my experience, pre-diagnostic screening is often very cursory and inadequate. Even when diagnosis could be rendered in a meaningful context it is only too often of low utility. Diagnostic teams in retardation are new and are still learning, and even skilled diagnosticians do not always render reports of practical utility to those who are often the only ones actually doing anything meaningful for the client, namely the family and the teaching and habilitative professions.

6. Is team diagnosis better than individual diagnosis? Ordinarily, the answer appears to be yes, but we must keep clearly in mind the shortcomings which tend to be characteristic of team evaluations, and that is lack of integration of the findings, and fragmentation of the client. The getting together of six people once a week in a staff meeting and reading six written reports does *not* constitute integration and team diagnosis. Team evaluation should add up to more than the sum of its parts, but often it does not even add up to as much as the sum, as when contradictory or puzzling findings are left unresolved and dangling in the air.

The above discussion has several implications to program development in the United Kingdom. Many times during my travels, program directors would apologize because retardates in their programs had rarely had the broad multidisciplinary evaluation which is relatively easy to obtain in this country, or because some retardates had not even been given a standardized intelligence test prior to service assignment. The program directors would tell me that this was regrettable and that they hoped that in the future more comprehensive evaluation centers or services would be developed. In other words, they viewed the sparsity of diagnostics as something which called for remedy.

Somehow, the British program directors' cry for diagnostic services reminds me of the Israelites' demand for a king. The Lord warned them that a king would lay a heavy hand on them, tax their property, possess their women and even take their lives. But the Israelites wanted a king, and kings they got who did exactly as the Lord had foretold. The British can have their diagnostic services and clinics just like we do, but such services can be, like kings, expensive, incompetent, tyrannical, unreasonable, destructive, remote from reality and the people, and even useless. I am not prepared to say that diagnostics in mental retardation is bad, should be abolished, or should not be established where it is not yet available. But just as we had (and still have) much to learn from U.K. service patterns, so I want to warn you not to fail to learn from our experiences, or, in this case, failures. Specifically, I would recommend to you that you invest your money (remember, we can waste ours, but you can't) in diagnostic services only if the conditions discussed below are fulfilled:

1. Diagnostic service development should not precede other service development but should follow it.

The best moment to activate a diagnostic center for retardates is probably when other services have reached the point where they are satisfying the bulk of that demand which can be met without sophisticated diagnostics. To operate a diagnostic center in a service vacuum is very frustrating for parents and sometimes even for professionals. Parents will have to be told what they need and then informed that, too bad, so sad, the needed service will not be developed until their child is too old for it anyway.

The state of the science being what it is, diagnosis and evaluation in retardation must quite often be based upon observation of the client's response to services, rather than precede it. For example, the prediction of vocational adjustment of moderately retarded adults is virtually impossible or meaningless unless vocational placement and habilitation training and counseling are available.

In the U.S. we have a situation where in many localities diagnostic services are greatly overdeveloped in comparison to other available resources. Indeed, of services in the field, diagnosis is often the most readily available, and is the first and for years the only resource to be developed. Curiously, this can create a manpower problem and far from stimulating other service development may inhibit it, as many professionals much prefer to render diagnosis than to offer families of the retarded the kind of help they need. There are a number of plausible reasons for this. Diagnosis is an intellectual exercise which calls upon the basic skills the professional has learned in his training and which can be carried out in his office. It gives him a deceptive feeling of accomplishment and can do so several times a week. In diagnosis, the professional can find many rewards and a good deal of security—just the opposite of what the parent typically finds in it. However, when it comes to other services, the professional finds neither security nor easy satisfaction. Particularly in mental retardation, traditional approaches used in mental health (and of questionable success even there) have not been very successful. Furthermore, the rewards of most services in mental retardation come very, very slowly as treatment is a long, drawn-out, difficult and laborious process. Reinforcement in the form of visible progress in an individual case may be apparent sporadically through the years rather than several times a week as in diagnosis. Finally, most effective services simply cannot be rendered in an office. All of this may keep professionals clinging to diagnosis and shying away from other services.

2. The diagnostic service should be tied firmly into the mental retardation service continuum.

This tie-in must be real, not just a verbal or paper one. Preferably, the same administrative body which controls part or all of a service continuum should control the diagnostic service. Agencies which have no major interest in the retardate and little if any service responsibility to him are particularly ill-suited for a diagnostic role, even if their personnel are highly skilled in their own area. The trouble with many U.S. diagnostic services is that they are provided by psychiatrically oriented agencies to whom mental retardation is a stepchild. Too often they regard the retardate as a disturbed psychiatric case, and may mumble something about his ego being impounded by the libidinal id. In such agencies, the parent of the retardate is almost always stereotyped as guilty, rejecting, unaccepting of reality, and in need of psychotherapy. The mother with three children (the oldest being the retardate) in nappies [diapers] who desperately needs the help of the public health nurse to teach her toilet training techniques may, instead, be told she needs psychotherapy to help her with her feeling about feces.

One of the big bonuses of tying diagnostic agencies into the service continuum is the exposure of diagnostic personnel to the refreshing wind of feedback, which can be both embarrassing and educational. This should, in time, result in more cautious and/or more accurate prediction.

3. Diagnostic services should be structured to offer substantial feedback and interpretation to the family.

Many diagnostic centers in the past have considered their duty done the moment the diagnostic process is completed *to their satisfaction*. Once the professional staff involved had reached a conclusion, the case was closed except for one, often hurried, impatient and perhaps patronizing, feedback session with the parents. They were given the facts as seen by the professional and told to "accept" them. More than one feedback session was felt to be beyond the scope of diagnosis, and a series of sessions was sometimes already considered psychotherapy which, being a "service," the parent was supposed to get elsewhere. Parents who were dissatisfied with this type of management were considered maladjusted, difficult, and "nonaccepting."

Professionals look askance at the parent who does not "accept" their diagnosis and who keeps looking elsewhere for confirmation or disconfirmation. It is undoubtedly true that many a child has been subjected to redundant diagnostics because of the parents' emotional maladjustments and feelings of guilt and hostility. At the same time I believe strongly that a good deal of diagnosis "shopping" has been due to inadequate feedback counseling.

As long as parents do not have diagnostic centers to go to, they cannot be dissatisfied with what they are not being told. Once such services are established, however, parents will expect feedback. If this feedback is inadequate, they will begin to go shopping from one diagnostic center to another. This is a very prevalent phenomenon in the U.S. where a large number of retardates undergo repeated and redundant evaluations which parents can obtain at relatively little cost if they are willing to expend time and effort. In my own experience, the record was held by a boy who, within five years, was subjected to eight evaluations, most of these by a full clinical team, and several at well-known clinics. Obtaining needed services, however, was another matter.

I am now deeply convinced, and more and more of my colleagues who work with parents seem to agree, that it takes a series of sessions, spread out over several months, before most parents come even somewhat to grips with the nature and, particularly, the implications of a diagnosis. Time and again one finds that not even parents with professional and mental health backgrounds, nor those who profess a verbal understanding during the first feedback session, have even made a good start in working through their conflicts. For this reason, spaced and repeated feedback counseling should be viewed not as a luxury but as an integral part of the function of a diagnostic service. Such counseling should be offered even if it necessitates case load reduction since, in the long run, it will probably conserve professional manpower.

It is penny-wise and pound-foolish to invest substantial and valuable resources into the diagnostic process only to begrudge a few additional hours of counseling. If the parents are not adequately counseled, they may not only go shopping, but perhaps even worse, their defenses may harden and may render them inaccessible to help. In the end this may cost ten, a hundred, and even a thousandfold what a few hours of counseling would have cost.

4. A program of staff training and attitude shaping should be a clearly structured element of a diagnostic center.

A significant proportion of the staff of our mental retardation diagnostic clinics are without any experience or training in the field, and some are without any awareness of a need for such training, and no compulsion to obtain it. In addition, they may not even have a deep interest in retardation. In short, they are what one might call "utilizers" who have no involvement in mental retardation and who might just as readily drift off to a psychiatric, geriatric, alcoholic, or any other kind of agency, depending on where the edge of personal advantage is to be found. Their services to the retardate are not infrequently worse than worthless as they may do more harm to a case than if it had been left alone. I have seen centers without a single adequately trained member on their staff.

Training is even more important for diagnostic center personnel than personnel in other services. Center personnel receive little verification, validation, or feedback in general about their work and they may rarely see retardates in any capacity other than diagnosis. As a result, they are more apt to grow dogmatic and careless in their judgements and prognoses. Particular care must be taken in the training or selection of parent counselors. There exists, at present, no certificate of training or academic degree which assures that a person is fit to manage or counsel parents of retarded children. Unfortunately, space does not permit a discussion of counselor qualification.

When setting up a mental retardation diagnostic service, training in mental retardation should be made mandatory. While this can be done on an inservice basis, it must not be done informally but in a structured and demanding fashion. Not even experience in the field can be assumed to be adequate, for I have seen professionals who, even after years of work in retardation, were as naive at the end as at the beginning. Quite often one will hear the objection that case load demands make an intensive and sustained training program impossible. In my experience, diagnostic centers where this argument is successfully advanced render very inadequate services. They would be much more useful if they reduced service load and improved quality. . . .

References

Krush, T. P., "The search for the golden key," *Bulletin of the Menninger Clinic,* 1964, *28:* 77-82.

Robinson, H. B. & Robinson, Nancy M., *The mentally retarded child: a psychological approach.* New York: McGraw-Hill, 1965.

□ □ □

SECTION B

Early Contact Phase

Begab delimits the problem by emphasizing the crucial significance of the early contact phase to parent and counselor. He suggests that the diagnostic process ". . . must embrace not only the many factors relevant to the child's condition and level of functioning, but also factors regarding the family and the community as well." Begab suggests the importance of bringing to the diagnostic process relevant sociological and psychological factors which are crucial to the case. Among these are an evaluation of the family as a whole and as an ongoing social system in which individuals with certain strengths and weaknesses, needs, and attitudes, etc. are interacting.

The importance of the early contact phase is underscored by Chamberlain, who defines a concept of treatment susceptibility which can be enhanced or impaired during the early contact phase. The first clinic contact in particular is seen as crucial in determining this treatment susceptibility. Thus, "the member who represents the team in the first major encounter with one or more representatives of the family . . . assumes the responsibility for maximizing this susceptibility."

Tizard and Grad present examples of mismanagement in the early contact and diagnostic phase. As part of a larger study of families of the retarded, they asked mothers to indicate when they had been told that their child was backward, how this had been done, and what advice and help they had been given. As these data are examined, one sees a discrepancy between what mothers would prefer and what was apparently done. For example, only seven of eighty mothers of mongoloid children reported that they were informed of their child's condition when it was first suspected, while sixty-five felt that this would have been the proper time for telling them. Further, in 14 percent of the cases it was felt that the manner in which the mother was informed was poor. Parents' evaluations of other past and present medical management are also discussed.

Krush movingly documents a case which illustrates the tragic situation that can ensue when the family-professional interaction gets off to a poor start. A family is pictured undergoing a search for the magic key that would restore a retarded child to normality. This search took them to eighteen physicians, seven schools, four teachers, two hospitals, two clinics, and one chiropractor—many of these progressively compounding and confounding each other's management errors. Is the cure worse than the disease?

Once in a while a parent, with experiences which professionals usually can verbalize but never really share, will, perhaps prompted by sadness or anger, formulate a problem with more insight, eloquence, and accuracy than the professional. We have had several selections of this nature in this book, and more will follow. Raech is such a parent. He states that the initial counseling interview can be "the greatest emotional crisis of a lifetime," and then describes three common but objectionable models for informing parents that their child is retarded. In this article a mirror is held before us, as professionals, and it requires some courage to take a hard look to see if we recognize ourselves.

The article by Anderson, a social worker, suggests a management technique worthy of consideration for increasing both efficiency and effectiveness of management during the early contact phase. She reports improving the service of a clinic by means of group orientation of parents during the intake phase. In addition to solving manifest problems of parental failure to understand clinic services, Anderson suggests that there may be latent gains, including staff understanding of parental interaction, and parental understanding of their own problems gained by seeing the problems of others.

from CASEWORK FOR THE MENTALLY RETARDED—CASEWORK WITH PARENTS

Michael J. Begab

(The Mentally Retarded Child: A Guide to Services of Social Agencies, 1963)

. . . .

In any highly charged emotional situation—so characteristic of the earlier phases of adjustment to mental retardation in many families—the giving of information by the parents has both anxiety-provoking and therapeutic effects. Similarly, in the treatment process or in the interpretation of diagnostic findings, the responses of parents and their ability to use the interview constructively offer additional insights into their strengths and weaknesses.

Casework with parents may be initiated by the parents themselves or upon referral from another source. Whatever the basis or motivation for agency referral, the diagnostic process—if it is to serve as the foundation for a treatment plan—must embrace not only the many factors relevant to the child's condition and level of functioning, but also factors regarding the family and community as well. The complexity of the information to be obtained, analyzed, interpreted, and used, calls for the contributions of many disciplines in *some* cases and at least a core group of the doctor, psychologist and social worker in *all cases*. The specific contributions of the major professions have been thoughtfully set forth in recent literature.

Realistically, these appropriate professional services are not available in all social agency settings, but these limitations can be minimized to some extent by effective collaboration with other agency resources and private practitioners. Unfortunately, in many settings, even where interdisciplinary services are available, they are not always used. Courts responsible for commitment to institutions often rely on medical evaluation alone and are often oriented more toward the determination of deficiency than the assessment of the individual's need for placement. In public schools and welfare agencies, except where a gross defect is apparent, medical resources are not always utilized and too much reliance is placed on psychometric examination. Perhaps only in highly specialized clinics, treatment or rehabilitation centers, and in some institutions, are the major disciplines invoked in an intimate working relationship in the diagnostic process.

Our growing understanding of sociological and psychological phenomena in mental retardation, and of the familial and environmental forces which affect intellectual and social performance, highlights the importance of the social worker's role in diagnosis. . . . It must nearly always include an evaluation of intrafamily relationships, parental strengths and weaknesses, the needs of parents and siblings as individuals, attitudes toward the retarded child and the resources of the family to meet the child's needs. Frequently, a full understanding of these diagnostic components rests upon the worker's appreciation of religious, ethnic and cultural variables. The meaningfulness of this information for diagnosis and planning depends on factors related to the child as a person —age, degree of handicap, behavior, personality, sphere of activities—and on the kind of problems and service needs presented. In some cases, certain areas of information have little bearing on the problem and their investigation would be regarded as an invasion of privacy. In other cases, the same information could be crucial in arriving at a total understanding of the situation.

Wherever possible the process of case study should be unhurried and therapeutically focused. Parents who are just beginning to be assailed with doubts about their child's normalcy—a situation first manifested in some children at school age—are in a highly vulnerable emotional state. Often they are confused and bewildered and their sense of self-confidence and adequacy are threatened. Recall of past incidents is often hazy or inaccurate. Certain events are exaggerated or vested with more significance than warranted. Under these circumstances, the information provided may not be totally reliable, and the act of sharing such emotionally laden information may stimulate intolerable feelings of self-incrimination and doubt which some parents are prone to suppress. Or the converse may be true, and the compulsive unburdening of the parents is so complete that they feel naked and exposed at having disclosed so many of their inner thoughts and torment.

In many of these instances, the substance of the story told by parents may have less diagnostic import for future planning than the emotion with which the story is related. If the handling of these emotions by the professional worker is to have positive effects and lay a groundwork for later constructive action by the parents, it is important that the parents have the opportunity to ventilate their anxieties and fears. Here the worker must strive for a delicate balance. He must learn enough to understand the problem but should be careful to avoid a premature exploration or complete revelation of feelings that may shatter the parent's defenses. This objective may be achieved by the same basic casework techniques that govern similar situations with other disturbed or anxious clients—empathy and support, redirection of the discussion to less threatening areas, reassurance and acceptance. It is also very helpful to verbalize for the parents some of their concerns and to help them see that most parents in similar circumstances feel as they do. Proper timing—a keen sensitivity to parental readiness to share inner feelings and concerns—is of the essence. As the worker-parent relationship becomes better established and mutual trust and respect is developed, disturbing feelings can be discussed with greater security.

Because the initial phase of adjustment is perhaps the most crucial, the questionnaire approach or interview, rigidly structured around causation, behavior, management or other child-focused considerations is not always fruitful. This technique does not readily lend itself to effective communication—though it does not necessarily preclude it. Often, when this approach is used parents who have little chance to express related anxieties are apt to regard the caseworker as unfeeling and uninterested in them as individuals. Lacking rapport, they will be reluctant to confide their personal concerns and conflicts and will tend to "tune out" interpretation of their child's limitations. They react with resentment to such treatment and if the caseworker should recommend their child's immediate institutionalization—a frequent occurrence, unfortunately—they will regard him as unsympathetic and abrupt. These are some of the reasons underlying parental dissatisfaction with diagnostic interpretations and discontent with professional services. Even when they have a good intellectual grasp of the situation, emotional acceptance may be lacking because they have not had the opportunity to release pent up feelings or to participate fully in the evaluation and planning process.

Professional honesty with parents is essential, for evasions are readily sensed and false reassurances only heighten the ultimate sense of disillusionment. Honesty, however, need not be accompanied by brusqueness or an impatience with parental disbelief. When the social worker displays these attitudes, it often reflects insecurity in handling painful interpretations or a feeling of impotence that nothing can be done to improve the child's condition or to remedy the problem.

The above comments are not representative of the initial casework needs of all parents of retarded children. Much depends on how long they have lived with the problem and how well they have adjusted to it, their previous experiences in seeking help and whether they are motivated to use help or it is being forced upon them. Parents seek or are referred to agencies for help for a variety of reasons. Some are looking for authoritative confirmation of their own suspicions regarding their child's slow development. Some want help with problems of behavior, training or placement and have fully accepted their child's retardation. And some are confronted with the problem of retardation for the first time when the child's failure in school is reported, or when he is brought to public attention through the pathways of neglect, dependency or delinquency.

The dynamics in each of these situations, though similar in some respects, have obvious differences as well, and these influence the focus of the casework relationship, not only in the initial period but also in later interviews. These differences are most marked between families whose child does not measure up to their expectations and those in which the child's deficiency is not recognized or he functions on a level comparable to other members of the family. In the former, particularly if conflicts have not yet been resolved, therapeutic considerations are predominant. However, where the parents are emotionally well adjusted to the situation, emphasis on the educational components of the casework process may be more meaningful. For them, answers must be found for such questions as: "How can I teach my child to be toilet-trained, to feed and dress himself? How can I control his temper outbursts and aggressive behavior? Where can I get for him the education, training, recreation and social companionship he needs? What patterns of development can I expect and what will my child's potentials be?"

The answers to these questions are of practical importance in enabling parents to handle daily problems and project future plans. But although the focus of some interviews may be primarily educational, knowledge in itself often has therapeutic benefits. To the extent that anxieties may be minimized, uncertainties dispelled, and fears removed by the sharing of factual information, parental security may be enhanced. The secure parent is better equipped to provide a healthy climate in which the retarded child may flourish. . . .

□ □ □

from MAXIMISING TREATMENT SUSCEPTIBILITY DURING THE DIAGNOSTIC PROCESS

E. R. Chamberlain

(Slow Learning Child, 1963)

. . . .

Impact by the Clinic

Once the referral is made, the family's contact with the clinic becomes crucial in determining treatment susceptibility. The member who represents the team in the first major encounter with one or more representatives of the family, therefore, assumes the responsibility for maximising this susceptibility. . . .

Venue of the Initial Impact

Impact with the clinical team need not take place within the clinic. It is no longer defensible to "investigate" people who are in the role of recipients of services which are the right of all, or to value observations made within the home solely for purposes of establishing eligibility. Nevertheless the diagnostic potential of home interviews is frankly recognized. Observation of the family in its natural setting is likely to yield at once a more complete and a more direct picture of the interactions between its members, as well as of standards of behaviour, symbols of culture, economic conditions. If an interview in the home has in the past been valued because it showed the family at its worst, it is now valued because it shows the family at its best. With the accent on assessment of family strengths which may be mobilized on their own behalf, there are strong arguments in favour of family diagnosis in the home.

Against such arguments questions may be raised about the rights and dignity of the individual. What of the right to privacy? A person's defences are perhaps essential to his social functioning and so to be accepted with respect. Is the home an area within which he should be allowed to lower his defences without fear of detection? Certainly entry into the home could not be an assured step unless the opportunity is provided for the family to protect itself.

Considerations of treatment might well enter into the decision as to venue. Apart from its diagnostic implications, an interview in the home might be regarded as a demonstration of the clinic's concern—a willingness to make effort, to reach out in order to encompass relevant ways of understanding why the child has not been able to realize his educational potential. So interpreted, the interview at home may provide opportunity for another indication of the clinic's ideal of service, another factor which may be utilized to encourage participation in the treatment process.

Sustainment of the Initial Effect

Wherever the introduction to the clinical team takes place, the member of staff involved needs to be mindful that he is functioning as part of the total team. This is one of the things he should make clear to the person he is interviewing. Acting as agent for the clinic he should attempt to initiate a constructive working relationship with the *clinic.* He should avoid at this stage a degree of intensity in the developing relationship with himself which would make it difficult for transfer and effective work with others at the clinic. Later, of course, if he takes up the case for therapy he may move into a more intensive relationship. On the other hand, it is equally important to make clear that the clinic expects to work with the family as a whole, not merely with the child, not merely with the parent who happens to be present at this interview, but with the constellation of persons whose relationship with the child may significantly affect his performance at school.

Obviously, though the initial impact may be crucial, it is merely a beginning, and readiness for treatment will be sustained only as long as promises implied are fulfilled. An impediment to follow-through in many instances is the impossibility of speedy intake when referrals exceed the immediate capacity of staff. Delays may occur at any or all of several points along the way. There may be delay after referral before any face-to-face encounter with the clinic staff. After the initial exploratory-interpretive interview there may be a waiting period before the further diagnostic procedures can be undertaken. Again after diagnosis is complete, there may be delay before treatment procedures can be put into operation. Remedial teaching may be recommended but the child may have to await a vacancy if classes are full.

Clearly treatment susceptibility is heightened to the extent that the steps on the way can be telescoped. Where this is impractical, treatment susceptibility may be sustained by interpreting the unavoidability of waiting periods and presenting them as one of the conditions or one of the limitations of services. This points to the advisability of making contact as soon as possible after referral, by way of the kind of introductory interview already discussed. At the same time various measures can be taken to help the child and his parents contain their anxiety. By a calm, objective approach to the situation, parents may be helped to see that the problem is not so urgent as they first thought—that in a few more weeks or even months the situation will not much worsen; that there is opportunity and time ahead for changes to occur. When the problem is urgent or anxiety unduly high, some parts of it might be worked on during the waiting period. Opportunities for communication with the clinic can be offered while awaiting the next step which is likely to be direct activity with the child in the form of psychometric testing and personality evaluation. Some superficial changes may be made, some more obvious procedures suggested. Wherever possible, and in accordance with their capacity to carry it, parents can be left with the responsibility to continue their personal efforts to help the child and it is likely that the hope engendered by the offer of help, even help which is not quite within grasp, will itself ameliorate the situation. . . .

□ □ □

from THE MENTALLY HANDICAPPED AND THEIR FAMILIES: A SOCIAL SURVEY

Jack Tizard, Jaqueline Grad

(Oxford University Press, 1961)

. . . .

Diagnosis and Disclosure

Severe mental subnormality may be caused by many factors and the etiology of the majority of conditions is still unknown. Moreover, apart from mongolism, by far the commonest clinical type, only rarely can one make a diagnosis at all, in the sense of distinguishing the syndrome characterizing the condition of mental defect. Especially during a child's earliest years one can often merely discover and describe abnormalities of structure and function that carry a more or less unfavourable prognosis.

The physician who is asked to say whether a baby or toddler is a mental defective thus has a difficult if not impossible task, since the possibility that considerable changes may occur in the rate of development cannot in many cases be excluded. If he is wise, the doctor will wish to be cautious in what he says, recognizing the element of doubt about the future. Parents, on the other hand, faced with the worry of a child who does not appear to be developing normally, seek a firm answer to their questions; and the most difficult task for the doctor may be to get them to accept the fact of the child's backwardness and at the same time take a realistic view of the future.

The diagnosis of mental defect may be made at the maternity hospital or at the child welfare clinic. Alternatively, the general practitioner may break the news, or in milder defect the first intimation may come through the school health service when the child is examined and deemed 'ineducable.' The child guidance service has also been widely used, especially in doubtful instances in which psychological testing is decisive, where emotional factors complicate the picture, or where the parents appeal against the child's exclusion from school. In London, suspected conditions are usually referred to a pediatrician and it is often he who first tells the parents.

In our inquiry we asked the mothers when they had been told that their child was backward, how this had been done, and what advice and help they had been given. We also tried to find out the effect of the news upon them and the family.

The information we obtained suggests that in very many instances the communication of the discovery of mental defect was handled extremely badly. Many of the stories we were told may be one-sided accounts of what actually happened. They are, for all that, important social data, since they suggest the impact of 'what the doctor told them' upon the parents; and they raise in an acute form the too little discussed question of the communication of medical information to patients and their relatives.

When Parents Were Told

Seventy-three of the mothers (31 per cent of those who gave replies) had been told that their child was backward before he was a year old, 76 (32 per cent) before he was five years old, and 88 (37 per cent) after he had reached school age. In 92 cases (41 per cent) the mothers believed that they had been informed as soon as the condition was suspected, and a further 39 (17 per cent) when full investigations had been made and the diagnosis confirmed. The remaining 94 (42 per cent) said they had been left to find out for themselves.

Examples of Disclosure at Different Ages

Told at one week. A mongol child was born in hospital. Two days before the mother was due to go home the doctor came and explained the situation sympathetically to her. He advised her to place the child in an institution.

Told at 18 months. The child had meningitis at six months. This diagnosis was not disclosed but the father saw it written on the case notes. After the illness the child returned home a helpless idiot. The mother continued to take him to the out-patient department and was told that because of the illness the child would be backward and be a lot of hard work, and that it would take time for him to pick up again. After eight months, when the child had still not improved the mother took him to another hospital where she was told that the child was spastic, blind, and mentally defective, and was advised to place him in an institution.

Told at two years. A mongol child was ill in [a] hospital for the first six months of life and then continued to attend the out-patient clinic. At one year the mother started to ask the doctor about her mental condition as she was not sitting up or behaving normally. The doctor said that they must expect some retardation because of the illness during the first six months after birth, but he said several times that there was nothing fundamentally wrong. At two years they took her to another hospital on the advice of a friend and were told that she was a mongol. These parents felt that the doctor had misled them through mistaken kindness, and that, as a result they had had two years of anxiety some of which could have been avoided. (Medical notes show that in fact mongolism was diagnosed at five days but not disclosed to the parents.)

Told at six years. From two to six years this child was taken regularly to out-patient clinics by his mother because he was not talking and had screaming fits. Mother was told by the doctor each time that nothing was really wrong and that the child's speech would come in time and to bring him back to hospital in six months' time. At six years father's employer gave them a letter to a doctor at another hospital who said to the mother that the child would never grow up but would always be like a baby and that nothing could be done to help him. The mother said, 'He was the only doctor who had ever spoken properly to me–he told me the truth. Before, I used to go nearly crazy with worry but I never felt so bad after that.'

The women were asked when, in the light of their own experience, they would recommend telling the parents that a child was mentally backward. Of the 218 mothers who gave an opinion, 194 (89 per cent) thought the doctor should talk to the parents as soon as he suspected that the child might be mentally defective, 17 (8 per cent) thought he should wait until the diagnosis was established, and only 7 (3 per cent) thought he should leave the mothers to find out for themselves.

The only common condition of mental defect that can be diagnosed at birth, and in which the limits of development can be stated with some confidence, is mongolism, in which the majority of cases function at imbecile level. We therefore contrasted the experience of the mothers of the mongols with their own recommendations, and the results are given in Table 13.1.

The data show that irrespective of the time at which the parents were told that their child was a mongol, the very great majority recommended that parents should be told as soon as possible. In our sample of 80 mongols only 44 parents had been told before the child was a year old; ten had been told before the child was two, and nine had not had the diagnosis confirmed until the child was of school age. Of those mothers who had been told before they left the lying-in hospital only one would have wished to have been told at a later date; and in this case the matter seemed to have been handled somewhat brusquely.

While therefore it may be true, as some doctors say, that whatever one does to break the news is wrong, it is evident that the parents themselves wish to know as soon as possible. The reasons given were the obvious ones. A mentally backward baby, especially a mongol, is usually frail and sick. The parents recognize that it is not as other children, and worry incessantly that they are managing the child badly. At the same time they do not know what to do to set matters right. In these circumstances to 'leave parents to find out for themselves' what is wrong (which in practice means to leave them to be told by a busybody in the street or by a well-meaning but probably woefully misinformed relative or neighbour), or unnecessarily to delay the news is to give them much anxiety which can hardly assist them to deal better with the difficult problems of management they are in any case faced with.

How the News Was Broken

The accounts of how the news had been broken were divided into four groups. In the first group, rated as *poorly han-*

TABLE 13.1
Time at which mothers were told their child was a mongol, and when they recommended telling

	When mothers were told	*When mothers recommended telling*
When condition first suspected	7	65
When diagnosis certain	11	7
Later	28	—
Left to find out for herself	29	3
No information	5	5
Total	80	80

dled, were those where the child was, in the mother's presence, demonstrated to students as an idiot, and the mother told nothing; where he was treated for a heart condition and she discovered from a medical certificate for rehousing that he was a mongol; where she was given obviously inadequate information out of mistaken kindness, or told to put him away as he was 'no good.' There were 34 such instances in this sample (i.e., 14 per cent of the sample).

A poorly handled discovery. Geoffrey was an uncontrollably excitable, destructive mongol boy, aged four, living at home with both parents and four elder siblings. He was born in hospital and was very quiet and still. When his mother asked why this was, she was told he was all right. At three weeks he was losing weight and the maternity and child welfare clinic sent the mother back to the hospital. Mother says, "There I saw the doctor with four students. They examined him and didn't say anything to me but just asked why I had brought him. I said because he was losing weight. I heard them use the word 'mongol.' When I got home, I looked up the word 'mongol' in the medical book and got very upset. Next visit I said that I couldn't see anything wrong with my baby and the doctor got annoyed and said I could go back to the clinic. Then the health visitor came round and told me not to bring him to the clinic." Later another hospital said the child was mentally backward and gave the mother a letter to County Hall. She said, "Doctors in hospitals don't tell you a thing and I don't like to ask, but wait for them to tell me. They should tell the husband and wife together as soon as they are sure the child is mentally defective, and explain about it so that you realize what you are up against. They didn't tell me at all—they only gave the impression."

In the second group, rated as having *unsatisfactory features,* were those instances where parents were told that the child was 'backward' and were left with the impression that he would improve or, where the diagnosis was deliberately concealed until the parents persisted and found out later, or where the parents complained of being told just the bare facts, given neither time nor opportunity to assimilate or discuss diagnosis or prognosis, nor advice. There were 102 (i.e., 41 per cent of the sample).

Discovery with 'unsatisfactory features.' Maisie was a restless, attention-seeking microcephalic, aged six, living with relatives who were her adopted parents. Her backwardness was noticed by her mother at nine months and she was taken to hospital. The doctor there, after examining her, is reported to have said, "Oh, she is only backward." Her adoptive mother said, "Why couldn't they have said more at the time to explain what this meant? We were given the impression that she was slow but would grow out of it in a few months. If they would tell you when they suspect that the child is mentally defective, you would know what you have to face and not go on for years in false hopes." When the child was five years old the education authorities informed the adoptive parents that she was mentally defective. At that time they wished to take the child to a specialist but the G.P. said, "Wait and see."

All other cases, including those where the information available was insufficient to make an assessment, were rated as *satisfactory*. There were 114 such cases (45 per cent) for 18 of which we had no definite information.

A 'satisfactory' discovery. Frances was a ten-year-old obstinate, aggressive mongol living at home with both parents and an elder brother. She was born at home and her mother was attended by the G.P. who pointed out her abnormal appearance, saying things like "she has very small apertures to her eyes," which the mother believed to have been hints to prepare her for the revelation made at three weeks by the doctor at the maternity and child welfare clinic. The mother said, "He told me about it in a nice way. He never let me come out of that room until he made an impression on me."

He discussed fully with the mother what the diagnosis of mongolism meant and what the child would be like. The G.P. discussed it further with the mother and she was able to ask him about her fears as to the possible cause; but he gave her the misleading impression that such children never even know their own mothers. When the child was one year old, mother asked to go to hospital for a specialist's opinion. The mother complained of the cursory way the matter was later treated by the hospital doctor and contrasted his rather off-hand manner and casual dismissal of the problem with "Don't worry, mother—they never live beyond twenty-five," with the sympathy and considerations she had received from the G.P. and the clinic doctors.

One cannot rate or assess the pain that a clumsily handled interview can cause the parents of a mentally subnormal child. We heard many accounts similar to the following in which a mother [Lancet (1955) ii, 44.] describes the way in which the news that her child was backward had been told her:

"I first became worried about the child when at the age of 2½ he still did not talk. I was referred to the children's department of a London teaching hospital, where I saw a consultant physician, who in the space of not more than a few minutes, and in the presence of a group of students, informed me quite bluntly that the child was mentally defective. He added that it was pointless for me to be burdened with him and that he would arrange for his removal to an institution, although this would take some time because of the long waiting list. I picked up the child in my arms, and quite unable to utter a word I left the hospital. To this day I do not remember how I got home; the shock was so great that I had complete amnesia for just about three hours."

One of the mothers in our sample told us that, as she left the consulting room following a similar interview with a pediatrician demonstrating his methods to a group of students she heard him say of the child, amid a gale of laughter: "The belly of a porpoise, the legs of a greyhound and the brain of an imbecile."

There was great bitterness among those mothers who had been put off with vague remarks, or told merely that there was nothing physically wrong, when they had taken the baby to the doctor because he was not progressing. The details of interviews that had occurred many years previously would be related, often with a great upsurge of emotion. We had little doubt that this particularly difficult situation was one which had been too rarely well handled.

Advice and Treatment

We asked the mothers how they felt about the medical advice and treatment they had had in the past, and about their present experience, to see if there were any common causes of complaint that might be brought to notice. In rating the accounts we used a three-point scale, of *satisfactory, unsatisfactory features,* and *many complaints.*

The parents' rating of past medical attention was often influenced by their opinion of the way in which the discovery had been communicated, but it was not confined to this. Many other

TABLE 13.2

Parents' opinion of past medical treatment of 250 defectives

Opinion	*Home group*		*Institution group*	*Total*	
Satisfactory or N.A.D.	81	(54%)	51	132	(53%)
Unsatisfactory features	43	(29%)	26	69	(28%)
Many complaints	23	(15%)	18	41	(16%)
Not known	3	(2%)	5	8	(3%)
Total	150		100	250	

problems might have arisen—for example advice on, or treatment for, cerebral palsy, bronchitis, chilblains or deafness—and it was these, as well as general medical advice about such matters as whether the child should be placed in an institution and whether the parents should have other children, that were considered here.

The results of the ratings for past and present medical treatment are given in Tables 13.2 and 13.3. There were 132 families (53 per cent of the sample) who thought the medical treatment in the past had been satisfactory, or had no specific complaints, whereas 186 (75 per cent) were of this opinion about present treatment; 69 families (28 per cent) spoke of unsatisfactory features in past treatment, and 43 (17 per cent) in present treatment. Forty-one families (16 per cent) had many complaints to make about past treatment, and 21 (8 per cent) had many complaints about present treatment.

It is an open question whether the greater satisfaction with present medical treatment might be ascribed to a more enlightened attitude on the part of the doctors today or to the fact that, as a child grows older, the hazards peculiar to infancy are passed, and one learns better how to cope with his special problems.

Much of the criticism of medical treatment related to the manner in which doctors reacted to requests to deal with complaints not necessarily associated with the child's mental defect. Mothers described, for example, how differently a normal child was treated from his imbecile brother suffering from the same complaint; they mentioned the difficulty of obtaining local clinic treatment for minor dental or eye troubles which might have to be taken to a hospital out-patient department with all the strain that that entailed, first of a journey and then of coping with a restless child during a lengthy period in a waiting-room. Some complained that they had so little time with the doctors that they did not feel able to ask questions or discuss their problems. At least two mothers reported that the lack of explanation had led them to stop treatment that might have ameliorated their child's condition.

The parents were asked whether they would welcome the introduction of special clinics which dealt with the problems of mental defectives. Sixty-two per

TABLE 13.3

Parents' opinion of present medical treatment of 250 defectives

Opinion	*Home group*		*Institution group*	*Total*	
Satisfactory or N.A.D.	118	(79%)	68	186	(75%)
Unsatisfactory features	25	(16%)	18	43	(17%)
Many complaints	7	(5%)	14	21	(8%)
Total	150		100	250	

cent of the parents with the child at home and 74 per cent of those with their child in an institution said they would welcome such clinics or would have done so in the past. (The need for these might be less if all hospitals and clinics used an efficient appointments system.)

Some of the criticism about lack of advice concerned the matter of whether or not to have other children, which is discussed in Chapter VIII.

The mothers of mentally backward children are extremely sensitive to implied criticism, and this may account for the fact that so many of them spoke of the medical profession as being distant, or uninterested in their problems. But it seemed too many parents who said that they had had no opportunity to discuss with doctors their fears about having other children, or about the defective (Would he become violent? Would he ever be able to work? Would he have to go away? Was he likely to get into sexual difficulties?) might have been describing their inability to ask these questions, which the doctors themselves had not raised. They had not liked to 'bother the doctor with a lot of questions', but felt that he should have told them the answers without prompting. Diagnostic interviews at teaching hospitals in particular had left them unsatisfied and disappointed, perhaps because they had expected too much of them, and perhaps too because consultants often confined themselves to an opinion about the child's condition and did not deal with the problems of the parents and the family. . . .

□ □ □

from THE SEARCH FOR THE GOLDEN KEY *Thaddeus P. Krush*

(Bulletin of the Menninger Clinic, 1964)

Some time ago there came to my office a wife and her husband seeking consultation regarding whether they had made the right decision when they had placed the oldest of their three children in a state institution caring for the mentally retarded. The mother had written, with great clarity and feeling, a thirty-two-page poignant narrative explaining to the younger brother and sister why Jimmy was not at home. Since this story is in some ways the story of all families confronted with the chronic after-effects of an accident, I asked for it so that it might be used to gain a better psychiatric understanding of such problems.

At the time the parents consulted me, their son was twenty-two years of age and had been a patient in a state school for more than ten years. The family were about to move from the state and this impending change had reawakened their old haunting doubts as to whether they had done everything possible for their son.

The mother's account of their search for the magical key that would restore their son, Jimmy, to them begins when the child was four years old. It records in detail their experience in the following years during which they discussed Jimmy's problem with eighteen physicians, four teachers and a chiropractor. Two hospitals, two clinics and seven schools were contacted and in all but two of the schools the boy spent varying periods of time.

In extracting material from her account, I wish to focus attention on the mother-physician relationship, with special emphasis on the explanations given the mother as they were interpreted by her.

Dr. One, on his first visit to Jimmy, commented on the "spastic gait" of the four-year-old boy. The mother's response was to point out that Jimmy had "just gotten out of bed." Dr. One, utilizing an *etiological* concept of disease, offered the first of many explanations the parents were to hear when he indicated "probable encephalitis" as the cause. Mother remembered only that Jimmy had been mildly sick once and was left with the final impression that whatever was wrong was "not permanently crippling."

Two clinic workers and several months later, Dr. One made a repeat call at a time when Jimmy "just roused from his nap, appeared to be cross and stupid." Couching his language as a candid opinion, he stated, "That child will never have a normal mind." The mother reacted to this at first with misery, and later with defiance.

The parents, now completely aroused to the idea that things were not progressing well with their first child, sought help at Hospital One where Dr. Two, a pediatrician, made a thorough physical examination. His judgment was that "It is impossible to be sure, but the findings lead me to believe your son will be all right." Naturally, the parents left in a happy frame of mind. However, Dr. Two had hedged his somewhat *stoic* concept of disease by referring the parents to Dr. Three, a psychiatrist. The question propounded by this physician—"When did he get control of his saliva?"—and her statement in response to the tuneful humming of the child—"Frequently mistaken by parents for signs of musical genius," evoked hostility in the mother who thought, "She thinks I'm lying," and "She has a cruel smile." An *anatomic* concept of disease was advanced in terms of neurologic disfunction and the parents returned to Dr. Two, who reaffirmed his stand that "Everything will be all right." The parents left confused, but at the suggestion of the first clinic they took the child for a month's period of observation to a private, physician-staffed school.

At the end of that time they had a conference with young Dr. Four who appeared to them as if he had a "distasteful job to do." He advanced a *genetic* concept of the boy's illness: "I believe him to be congenital defective," and, coupled with this, a *social* concept of disease: "He might pass socially unnoticed in an underprivileged area or a rural setting." The suggestion was made that the child might be better cared for in an institution. To all this the parental defense was that the diagnosis appeared to be based "only on negative evidence" and the mother introduced the *moral* conception of disease when she expressed the idea that these were "cruel blows" and "It seems as though fate is trying to bargain with me."

There followed a period of reaction during which the parents avoided contact with any physicians and bolstered their courage through the well-meant observations of friends and acquaintances who opined that: "Einstein didn't talk until he was four"—"An old friend of my mother's had a grandson who did not speak until he was three and a half"—"A close friend had received an almost identical opinion from Dr. Three and his son was now almost grown and perfectly normal." During the same period, such disconcerting acts as Jimmy's dashing unpredictably into the street continued to cast a pall of doubt on his future.

Eventually, with the aid of friends, the mother essayed another contact with a physician. Dr. Five was a psychiatrist who advanced a *psychological* concept of disease; she suggested that the difficulty was occasioned by "an emotional block at an early age." This was coupled with a variable assessment of the child's intelligence in that, though his "level of interest is below that which it should be," his intelligence appeared to be "good," because (as the mother reported) "many positive factors such as the relatively early age at which he had been housebroken." The use of the word "housebroken" suggests that the mother regarded her child in a somewhat different light than had she used the more common term "toilet trained."

The mother's response to the emotional deprivation gambit was to wonder "When could it have occurred?" and to feel that, if it did occur, it was certainly not profound enough to cause such behavioral repercussions.

Dr. Five stressed "learning to play" as the means by which Jimmy might find his way back to reality and also suggested the use, first, of a maid, and then a day school. A treatment relationship actively involving the mother was maintained for about a year with the doctor's final evaluation being "I see change, but not improvement."

Two subsequent attempts at teaching the child brought on a temporary collapse of toilet habits and referral to a new clinic where Dr. Six phrased the problem somewhat negatively: "Whatever his trouble is, it is not feeblemindedness." The child was now in his seventh year and the mother noted "poor coordination"—"destroys neighbor's flower bed," and "dashes into the street" which she attempted to counterbalance with, "but he knows the order of the ingredients for baking a cake."

In order for "no stone to be left unturned," the mother, on the advice of a chance acquaintance, now sought the help of a chiropractor who stated: "X-rays indicate a place at the base of the neck where the vertebrae exert pressure on the nerve cord." Following a series of adjustments, Jimmy became wilder, but this was passed off as "newly released energy."

On the suggestion of an acquaintance met in the chiropractor's office, the mother next sought Dr. Seven who was working with gland extracts. Her reaction to this *humoral* or *Platonic* concept of disease was that the physician seemed "not professionally reassuring—it seemed like taking a chance on a lottery ticket."

After this, the family returned to Hospital Two where many and varied tests were performed. There Dr. Eight's diagnostic pronouncement of "congenital defective—low I.Q." reaffirmed Dr. Four's clinical opinion, and the test suggested by Dr. Six yielded no constructive lead. The mother felt "at a disadvantage in talking to the doctor"; by the time she had finished what she wanted to say, "The doctor did not even appear to be listening."

An interested relative prevailed on the family to have Dr. Nine visit their home to see Jimmy in his own setting. This he did, making an estimate that the child was now functioning at a mental age of five, an emotional age of one and one-half and a social age of two. Jimmy's chronological age at this time was nine years. Such an assessment made sense to the parents who had also perceived the unevenness of their boy's development. The cause of the disorganization was given as probable birth injury. The offer of a period of observation at a private school, where efforts would be made to improve Jimmy's speech, gave the parents "a new lease on life."

Unfortunately, Jimmy's unpredictable running away made further treatment in this setting unfeasible. Arrangements were made to refer the boy for placement in School Three, a state institution having a reputation for working with speech problems. Dr. Ten was contacted and agreed to accept Jimmy, but first the child had to be examined by Dr. Eleven. In this somewhat bewildering shuffle of physicians, the mother was agreeably surprised to find a psychiatrist in a public institution who appeared sympathetic and did not appear surprised to hear that Jimmy would do some things for her that he did not do for others.

Sometime later, the parents consulted with Teacher Three at a privately endowed school which had a medical theory by which they taught. Because of the expense involved at this school, the suggestion was made that Jimmy be enrolled at School Four at a reduced rate. Jimmy was therefore removed from School Three and transported to the new school by his parents who were appalled by his deterioration in eating habits, since he now "glanced furtively from side to side and guarded his plate with his elbows."

At School Four, the teacher at first sent encouraging reports which were related to his gain in weight. Then she slowly, over the better part of a year, gave up hope, making the appraisal

"There's just nothing there," and asking the parents to make other arrangements. As the favorable tone of the reports had diminished, the parents anticipated a change and had visited two state schools where they had been unfavorably impressed. (At School Five, Dr. Fourteen had early in the initial interview alluded to the fact that "It is difficult to keep down the venereal disease rate because of the mixing of the sexes" and at School Six, the assistant superintendent appeared out of breath "because he had been assisting in the feeding of the children" due to a shortage of help.) At Private School Four, the teacher suggested State School Seven where Dr. Sixteen favorably impressed the parents.

Jimmy was therefore admitted to State School Seven and several years later, in response to the mother's inquiry about her son's welfare, Dr. Seventeen wrote of a "failure to continue development" which, along with no apparent height and weight gain in the report, alarmed the mother. On further inquiry, she was informed: "This is due to a number of causes" and, since there was no further elaboration, the mother felt that the attitude taken by the physician was that she was only a lay person who could not possibly understand such matters.

A later note from Dr. Eighteen apprised the family that Jimmy, at age twenty-two, was "uncooperative, untidy, disturbed and had to be spoon-fed." With the crushing realization that there was no "golden key" for her son, the mother ends her search and her narrative, with the admission that "Not even the worst prognosis we had received in all our long years of searching for help had prepared us for this." And, therein lies the greatest tragedy in this story of emotional and mental torment—"not even the worst prognosis we had received had prepared us for this." This mother felt that the medical field had failed her; not because we had not done all we knew how to do in our attempts to restore or improve Jimmy's mentality, but because we had not done that which was within our power—preparation of the parents for "the worst possible prognosis." . . .

□ □ □

A PARENT DISCUSSES INITIAL COUNSELING *Harry Raech*

(Mental Retardation, 1966)

In the past there have been a number of skillful comments dealing with the proper counseling of the parents of the mentally retarded. Many of these make recommended reading for specialists in the field. Evidently, these comments are being taken to heart, for in the experience of parents of the retarded, of which I am one, there is evidence that considerable thought is currently being given by professional counselors to the import of their words. However, whether those medical people *untrained* in counseling are as thoughtful in their approach to the parents may indeed be another matter.

Of particular importance, in my view, is the *initial* counseling experience. Usually this is given by a medical person untrained for the task. Yet, this interview is likely to be the source of the parents' greatest single emotional trauma in what is commonly a lifelong struggle. Since this is true, it is important that the experience be handled as skillfully as possible.

There are various situations in life which tend to strain the emotions severely. Some of these we experience directly, such as love, hate, or pain. There are others which are communicated to us. Among the latter are financial disaster, the death or impending death of a loved one (and we may include ourselves in this category), and, of course, the subject with which we are dealing—the advice that our child is retarded. I submit that in many cases, being told for the first time that one's child is retarded may well be the most severe shock that one may experience in a normal lifetime full of trying experiences.

As a direct consequence of this, it is my firm belief that the vast majority of parents of retarded tend to develop something less than a balanced outlook on life. I do not mean to imply from this mental imbalance. I do imply that they tend to be unable to enjoy life to the optimum degree because of their preoccupation with their problem.

What I am leading up to is a belief that the initial counseling experience is of major importance. I feel that those responsible for introducing the hard fact of mental retardation should and must do this with a skill and an empathy expressing their maximum ability. I feel that this is a moral responsibility stronger by far than any professional code that may be brought to bear.

It must be nearly impossible for even an experienced counselor to appreciate the depth of numbing shock that comes to parents in this first interview. Yet, only the counselor can buffer this shock and minimize the permanent trauma. On his shoulders, whether he wills it or not, must be borne the responsibility of starting the parents off with the proper mental attitude and with the realization that their problem, too, is truly solvable, and that time is indeed the great healer.

As with any parent of retarded, I have many friends with retarded children, and they live in widely scattered sections of the country, and come from a variety of social and cultural groups. I have had occasion from time to time to discuss this initial counseling experience with them, and, without exception, they have had their initial counseling with a physician or a clergyman. Thus, it appears that it is with these two groups that we have to deal.

While my further observations will apply to both groups, I should like to make a particular observation regarding the clergyman.

About a year ago, an association with which I am connected—The Southwest Association for Retarded Children—became very much concerned over the need for counseling of parents. We had observed emotional breakdowns, family breakups, and even a suicide resulting from inadequate counseling, so we formed what was called a "Samaritan Group." Its function was to provide parental guidance for parents newly aware of their problem, so that they could learn that they were not alone with the problem but that others had met and surmounted it. We sent over 100 letters to clergymen in the southwest section of Los Angeles, telling them about our group and offering to provide them basic information on retardation and the needs of the parents. Unbelievably, we received *not one* reply!

The initial counseling interview may be the greatest emotional crisis of a lifetime and must be treated accordingly. This means, then, that physicians and clergymen who are likely to contact new parents—and I mean all new parents, since the odds on having a retarded child are considerably better than those on winning at Las Vegas—must prepare themselves professionally and emotionally for the necessity of instructing new parents of their unfortunate situation. And I don't for a moment think that this requires a bit less preparation than that for the skill of surgery or the recognition of syndromes, or the guidance of souls. I feel that this is a solemn obligation no less binding than the more specific obligations occurred [sic] in the Hippocratic oath.

But what are the requirements of the interview? First, the truth must be expressed. No purpose can possibly be served by concealing the truth, and, indeed, a great deal of damage may be done in not stating the facts clearly yet gently.

Secondly, the truth must be expressed in terms clear to the parent, yet not patronizing nor overbearing. The tendency of some professional people to assume a superior and arrogant attitude is far from reassuring to the observer; the authoritarian approach builds neither admiration nor confidence in the listener. It produces exactly the opposite reaction from that intended. Confidence should be developed rather than dislike or disgust. Humility is one way to accomplish this.

Thirdly, wisdom must be used. Admittedly, this interview is uncomfortable for all concerned. Certainly the professional can think of a thousand things he would rather be doing. Yet, his handling of this short interview can have a major lifetime impact on three or more lives. A prayer for wisdom in his handling of the interview might not be inappropriate at this time.

Fourthly, he must use empathy in expressing himself. If ever a parent needs friendship and compassion in his life, he needs it at this time. The counselor must use all of the innate gentleness, thoughtfulness and kindness he would use to a beloved daughter or son in revealing to them a fact which will so change their lives.

Now that I have expressed my views on *how* the initial counseling interview should be performed, I would like to conclude my remarks with a few observations on actual cases. As you will see, they departed considerably from the ideal.

The usual initial medical counseling on retardation is, I believe, dividable into two approaches: (1) avoid the issue; (2) get it over with as soon as possible. This may be summed up simply: From the viewpoint of the counselor, the interview is a painful experience, therefore, minimize the pain.

My own experience fits into the first category. Our first child was very inactive after birth. She awakened reluctantly and did not desire to feed. We could not understand why she tended to cry so readily. Our pediatrician, who was also the obstetrician, refused to discuss the subject. Every time he was questioned regarding the child's strange behavior, he expressed the view that the child would grow out of it. Tiring of this evasion, we at length took the child to another physician. We eventually learned that the child's spinal cord had been crushed at birth, and that she was retarded and would probably be unable to walk or talk. I must add that neither prediction proved true—she now rides horses and talks endlessly.

There is nothing to be gained by evading the truth. Truth, like murder, will out and the sooner that it is uncovered, the sooner appropriate remedial measures can be taken.

The "get-it-over-with" school can be broken into several categories. Each of which can be illustrated by an actual case of which I am aware.

Category A is "the offhand remark." In this case I have in mind, the father was visiting the hospital the first day and encountered the attending physician. "By the way," said the doctor, "did you know that you have a mongolian idiot?" What a thoughtless, ill-conceived approach this was. Can you imagine the same doctor saying to a loving wife: "By the way, did you know your husband just died?"

By way of comparison, the attitude of the family doctor, approached by the same man for further advice, was a tower of wisdom. Carefully, using medical texts for illustrations and references, he gently built his explanation of what mongolism is, what its causes might be, and what the best treatment and handling might be for the balance of the child's life.

Category B is "the direct confrontation." The parents of the second child were aware that the child was not normal mentally, but needed interpretation and advice. Rather than build up the picture as did the wise young family doctor in the case just discussed, this doctor bluntly stated that the child was retarded and had best be placed in an institution as soon as it could leave its mother's breast. Not only was the advice abrupt and cruel, it was faulty, for the boy will be graduating from a "special" school in another year.

Category C is "the big deal." The

parents in this case were quite aware that their child was retarded but needed analysis and advice. They were instructed by the consulting physician to place the boy in the hands of a pediatrician who entered him into a children's hospital for a week's evaluation. At the end of this time, it was demanded that the father leave his work and come from the native city 500 miles away to be present with the mother for the medical report. The report was given in one brief sentence, "Mr. and Mrs. Jones, your child is retarded." This given in tones of transcendental knowledge.

Experience has led me to feel that there is considerable room for improvement in typical initial parental interviews. Too often, kindness, thoughtfulness, helpfulness and professional preparation are lacking. Not infrequently, there appear overtones of rejection, discomfort and impatience.

If I may be permitted to summarize that which I think is lacking in these initial interviews, I will do it in a single word, and that word is [love].

□ □ □

ORIENTATING PARENTS TO A CLINIC FOR THE RETARDED

Alice V. Anderson

(Children, 1962)

In the operation of a clinic for retarded children, the following questions are repeatedly raised:

How can the waiting list be cut down?

How can the interest of parents be maintained pending the beginning of the study?

How can parents be kept from breaking clinic appointments?

How can parents be best informed about the work of the clinic?

Confronted with these provocative questions, the staff of our clinic set up a system of group orientation meetings in March 1960 for parents at intake as a method for improving the service of the clinic. The problems presented by the long waiting list and failure of parents to understand the clinic's services are now handled more effectively. Broken appointments in a multidisciplinary clinic involving the team approach especially had long been a matter of grave concern, since a broken appointment affects several staff members simultaneously, thus wasting the service of the clinic and allowing fewer children to be served.

The meetings, which are held in the evening, were organized and conducted by the chief social worker for parents of children on the waiting list. These are parents who so far have not been interviewed at the clinic. They have either telephoned the clinic to inquire about the possibilities of service for their child or have come to the clinic's attention through a telephone call from a doctor or another professional person. In either case the clinic has received little information about them other than identifying data. During the meeting, each parent is given a schedule of individual appointments with the social worker, clinical psychologist, physician, child development specialist, and speech and hearing specialist.

Since March 1960, the meetings have been held at regular intervals and are now attended by the pediatrician-director who acts as a medical resource consultant to the group. The parents are seen in groups averaging about ten couples each. The individual appointments for each child and parent are spread over a six-week period, the first parent coming to the clinic with her child a week after the meeting for the beginning of the study.

The group meetings provide the staff with a chance to find out which parents are still interested in the clinic service and to obtain from them signed forms permitting the staff to send for pertinent medical and social information in advance of their individual interviews. The meetings' most important advantages for the staff, however, lie in the opportunity they afford for observing the parents and gaining insight into each couples' attitudes toward their child, toward each other, and toward other parents with a problem similar to their own.

The rationale of this approach is to meet the parent's need for service at the time of the request. The parent who has contacted the clinic has already overcome one hurdle by beginning to accept the fact that his child may be retarded. Therefore, it is vital to provide service to him at a time when he is still searching for help for his child, before he has had much of an opportunity to become resigned to the child's problem.

Parents usually find some therapeutic relief in learning about the detailed diagnostic procedure the clinic has to offer and in being assured that their child will be seen and assessed by a team of specialists in work with children. The clinic's structure begins to have some meaning for them as they have an opportunity to see and inspect the different examining, testing, and play rooms where the study of the child will take place. Often they express relief at learning that the study is not to be conducted in a hospital atmosphere and that the children will not have to stay overnight.

Nervous tension is often aggravated in a family by the presence of a retarded child. In these discussion groups, tensions are often relieved when parents learn that mental retardation is not necessarily inherited. Some parents also find relief in learning that in comparison with others their child is not so badly handicapped. Parents are also often relieved to learn that their child can acquire self-help skills even though this can be accomplished only through a slow, tedious, training procedure, requiring repetition, relaxation, routine.

We hear much about parents who shop around from one clinic to another. This is not necessarily as unwise as many persons assume. Since there is considerable variation in medical practice, a parent may want confirmation of a diagnosis of mental retardation just as he might of any other medical diagnosis. Thus our clinic serves parents who may be known to other diagnostic clinics as well as those who are making their first clinic appointment. They are also widely different in educational and economic background, although families from the low-income groups predominate.

In order to help parents sense quickly what they have in common despite their wide differences in background, the group leader always points out that each has come to the meeting because of a deep concern about his handicapped child and that it is important for them not to blame themselves for the handicap. This does not mean that the parents are regarded as a homogeneous group or that they all feel the same way about their retarded child. However, at the time of the meeting they are all expressing their concern as parents of handicapped children. Recognizing this fact creates a sympathetic feeling toward one another and creates interaction among them. Mutuality of interest is more important to the members of such a group than are differences in their socioeconomic, cultural, or educational background.

The social worker, through a permissive attitude, attempts to provide a "safe" climate for frank discussion among the parents. In the first part of the meeting she describes the clinic's services and what is expected of the parents. She also introduces some mental health concepts, pointing out that the clinic staff is as much concerned about the social adjustment of the child as with his physical condition. She also presents the concept of mental retardation as a symptom of biopsychosocial malfunction.

She encourages the parents to think of their child first and the handicap second, so that it becomes more than a difference in words when they say "my child who is retarded," rather than "my retarded child." Another point she stresses is that the mentally retarded child has the same desire to belong and be accepted by others as the nonretarded, and that in general his emotional needs for recognition, companionship, and a sense of usefulness are the same as those of the normal child.

Orientation Techniques

Many parents of retarded children deny the fact that their child is different from normal children before they finally accept reality. In these group meetings the social worker does not try to convince a parent that his child is below average for she realizes that while the discussion may be helpful in modifying the parent's attitudes, time will be the most important factor in this regard.

In describing the clinic, the social worker points out that it has been set up as part of the city's health program to provide complete diagnostic study and evaluation for any child under eighteen who is a resident of the District of Columbia, and in whom there is a question of mental retardation. The parents are given a description of what goes into the diagnostic study and followup services, and of the work of the various staff members who participate: a pediatrician-director, two social workers, a psychologist, a child development worker, a nursing consultant, and a psychiatric consultant who have at their disposal various other consultants from the health department's staff including specialists in speech and hearing, neurology, electroencephalography, physical and occupational therapy, orthopedics, ophthalmology, and cardiology.

The social worker compares the clinic team approach to a family, telling how each member contributes his particular skill in order to help the other team members to do a better job as well as to help the retarded child. She also stresses the informality and friendliness of the team members in order to help the anxious, hard-to-reach parents to become more relaxed so that they can become active participants in the study.

Focus on the Child

The second part of the meeting can be described as a group-intake interview through parent discussion. Social workers who have had responsibility over the years for individual intake interviews generally acquire considerable skill in quickly assessing the client's problem. This skill can be transferred to a certain extent to a group-intake setting. Of course, when a group is present the social worker cannot do as much interpretation of individual problems nor pick up immediately on some of the emotionally charged clues which emerge from the discussion. However, these clues often point the way to the focus of the subsequent individual interview.

What makes the intake interview so challenging, whether in an individual or a group setting, is that at this time, as the client presents his problems, the social worker is in a position to receive the full impact of his personality and his reactions to his problems. Later as the relationship continues and more detail complicates the picture, it is often more difficult for the worker to identify the trends which are significant for the assessment of the handicapped child in relation to his family.

As the parents describe their child's behavior, it often illustrates the child's social maladjustment. Problems in behavior such as short attention span, hyperactivity, temper tantrums, and a high degree of distractibility are described rather than examples of slow intellectual performance. It becomes evident that the children referred to our clinic are like the children at the Edenwald School of the Jewish Child Care Association of New York—"a group with retardation, emotional disturbance, and organicity all mixed up in a complicated dynamic pattern."

When the parents are stimulated to think of mental retardation as a cause of their child's social dysfunction, impairing his ability to adapt, their overemphasis on the possibility of a physical basis to the child's difficulties tends to diminish. For example, the chief complaint of most parents is that their child is not talking, even though he may be several years old. Often parents assume that the child has some defect in his speech mechanism which treatment would alleviate. The social worker tries to help these parents understand that slowness of speech is often one of the characteristics of retardation and that a child usually understands more than he can communicate.

Although parents listen with interest and often ask questions in the part of the meeting devoted to an explanation of the clinic's services, their participation intensifies considerably when the focus shifts to their problems with their child. The social worker refers to this second half of the session as "their" part of the meeting for it is their opportunity to introduce themselves, to tell about their child, his age, his characteristics, and his relations with his siblings, and to state what they want and expect from the diagnostic study.

To get the discussion going, the leader invites the parents to volunteer to talk or to take turns in the order of their seating arrangement, as they wish.

At this point, the parents' interest turns quickly from the group leader to each other, as each parent describes the condition and individual characteristics of his child. The parents generally relate to each other quickly, gaining mutual support and sympathy. Rarely has a parent decided at the meeting that he does not want his child to go through the clinic study, although a few have decided afterward that they would wait a while before having the study made.

Mutual Support

> The following example illustrates the way the parents find support in each other. A mother of a little mongoloid baby had brought in a picture of her child for the clinic personnel to examine. This woman had a great need to deny that her child looked like a mongoloid. As the discussion progressed, she passed the picture around to the other parents and a number of the parents reacted to it immediately. While some of the parents agreed with the mother that the baby did not look like a mongoloid and others thought they saw some mongoloid characteristics, the whole discussion seemed to develop a bond of sympathy and understanding in the group.

Often the group interaction has a more therapeutic effect than the explanations of the group discussion leader. This was true with Mrs. O, who described her six-year-old daughter in somewhat critical terms by saying:

> "Mary knows what to do but she won't do it. She will repeat what I tell her to do but will go ahead with her play and ignore what I have said. Punishing doesn't seem to help. When she is asked why, she replies, 'I don't know'."
>
> Obviously feeling irritated and frustrated at Mary's behavior, Mrs. O added, "I want this study to show me how I can make her do what I tell her to."
>
> Very quickly a father spoke up, saying, "It's pretty hard to make anybody do anything for very long. Maybe it would be better to have someone tell you what might be the reason for Mary's acting up." Mrs. O nodded at this and the discussion continued.

Sometimes the social worker gets clues to be followed through later.

> A mother described her slow child as being the smartest one in the family about getting her own way. She said her child could run circles around anyone by coaxing, demanding, or making a fuss. Some other parents agreed that they had the same trouble. The social worker made a mental note that these parents needed help in modifying their children's manipulative behavior.

The parents' feelings of guilt do not come out in a group as often as might be anticipated. However, one very articulate, uninhibited father suddenly blurted out:

> "Say, I have a sister in a mental hospital; do you suppose that's why my little girl is slow in developing? Would

it be my fault since it's on my side of the family?"

Before there was time for the social worker to answer, another parent said: "It is like the lady said earlier: it's not to your credit if your child is bright and it's not your fault if your child is slow."

There have been times in the meetings when mothers have wept as they described their retarded child, but when this has occurred the group has accepted it calmly.

One mother who was telling how difficult it is for a woman to handle a handicapped child alone said in a shaky voice: "My husband left me and now my little girl frequently runs away because she wants to find her daddy." The group was very silent as she struggled for self-control.

Another distraught and somewhat hostile mother of a retarded and emotionally disturbed 10-year-old boy said bluntly:

"I want my child sterilized because I don't ever want to be responsible for rearing any of his children." The other parents looked stunned at first, and then began talking of their own fears of what the future would hold in the way of social relationships for their handicapped children.

The social worker pointed out that many parents worried about this and that society does not provide a pat answer to the problem. She stressed the fact that each child is entitled to a thorough individual diagnostic study before any recommendation is made for his treatment.

Individual tape recordings of twelve of the parent group-orientation meetings have been made with permission of the parents. (They are available upon request to the clinic.) Demonstrating vividly the dynamic interaction which occurs as the parents discuss their children, they reflect both agreement and disagreement about suggestions made by the social worker as well as by the parents themselves, and show how the social worker uses opportunities to comment, interpret, or recommend a "let's wait and see" attitude.

Patterns and Values

Over the months we have been able to detect certain patterns in these meetings.

We find that a group of from eight to ten couples usually promotes more interaction among the parents than a larger or smaller group.

We find that fathers often take the initiative in describing in detail their child's problems. And, contrary to our expectations, we have often found that fathers are readier to accept a diagnosis of retardation than some mothers. For example, fathers sometimes attend the meeting alone, their wives having stayed home as babysitters, and when this happens such statements as the following are not unusual:

"I see this child as very different from other children in the family, but I wouldn't dare say this if my wife were here because she would hit the ceiling."

We find that parents want the support they get from other parents. Often at the end of the meeting parents ask about the possibility of having further opportunities to talk together about their common problems. These parents usually become the nucleus of further parent discussion groups to which parents are invited after the diagnostic study has been completed, the evaluation conference held, and the interpretation given.

The feeling of mutual support engendered in self-led parent groups, such as those sponsored by local parents' organizations, is partly the reason why such groups have grown so in strength and numbers during the past ten years. However, we have found that some additional advantages are provided when meetings are led by a professional staff person as part of the total diagnostic and treatment procedure of a clinic. This makes it possible for the meetings to:

be "treatment-oriented" instead of solely supportive and informative;

help parents consider their child's accomplishments and strengths as well as his limitations;

help parents, when necessary, to keep from revealing themselves too openly (when a parent begins an emotional "confession" or starts bringing family skeletons out of the closet, the leader can intervene with a comment which universalizes what has been said or otherwise puts it into an impersonal framework);

make it possible for every parent present to participate in the discussion. (The leader can, when necessary, tactfully terminate the discussion of a dominating member of the group and encourage a less articulate one to express himself);

provide for intervention when the discussion gets blocked on an emotional level that only feeds the members' self-pity;

help parents become better informed of community resources which have programs for retarded children.

Although each meeting does not result in all of these advantages, some are always achieved.

The group orientation procedure also saves considerable staff time during the diagnostic study by reducing the parents' need to ask questions at this time. We find especially that parents who have met and talked with other parents who have similar problems do not so frequently ask, "Why did this happen to my child?"

The group-intake procedure also gives the staff opportunity to observe how husbands and wives react to one another, to other parents in the group, and to the social workers, thus gaining some indication of the quality of a couple's marital relations and of their other interpersonal and community relations. It also gives the staff an opportunity to learn about the parents' attitudes toward their child.

Since the clinic recommends but does not require both parents to be present for the diagnostic study appointments, the parent group-orientation meeting often provides the staff with the only opportunity to see the father. This is true even though a visit by the social worker to the home is regularly included as part of each child's diagnostic study.

By providing a means of seeing parents more quickly, the group-orientation procedure avoids anxiety-producing delays not only for the parents but also for the staff. We find that staff morale has improved now that appointments with parents and children can be scheduled well ahead, thus permitting orderly planning and acceleration of clinic work.

However, although the parent group meetings at intake have an educational and an orientation focus, their chief goal is to increase the parents' understanding of their child's problem. Unless the family is helped, factors contributing to the child's problem remain unchanged. When parents are helped through group discussion or individual casework treatment, or both, much can be done to relieve the effect of retardation and help the child to develop to his full potential.

As the parents listen to each other talk about their children, they often gain new ways of looking at their own problems, feel less isolated, and gain emotional support. Treatment actually begins at the parent group-orientation meetings. . . .

□ □ □

SECTION C

Feedback Phase

Management during the feedback phase has been beset by a number of problems. One of these has to do with the professional's habits and modes of communication, another with his conceptualization of the use of feedback in the management process.

Parents look forward with great anticipation to the results of diagnostic studies. Often they have exaggerated notions about the ability of the professional to determine the cause of their child's condition, to devise or specify treatment, or to predict future development. At the same time, parents' needs and conflicts may be so great that they are apt to perceive, retain, and utilize the feedback information selectively. Even if parents were paragons of objectivity, the professional might fail to encode his communication adequately, perhaps by phrasing his message in terms inappropriate to the parents' education and intellectual level. This communicative problem, which has implications for all phases of the professional-parent relationship, is likely to be accentuated if the family is part of the lower class subculture. We will treat this problem further in the sections of this book dealing with the limited family.

The second problem alluded to above has been the tendency of managers to view feedback as the climax and logical conclusion of case management, instead of the beginning of an action and treatment program based on the evaluative phase. The selections in this and several other parts of the book provide an appreciation of how both problems have been identified, and how management ideology has changed over the last two decades.

Rheingold was among the first to discuss the interpretation of diagnostic findings to parents. She proved to be well ahead of her time, since most of her insights and recommendations would still be accepted as valid today, after more than twenty years—except that she did not express a strong view, now held by many counselors, that interpretation needs to be spread over a series of sessions.

Sarason's chapter on interpretation to parents should be mandatory reading for concerned professionals. Some of the points made by Rheingold are reinforced, and additional considerations are presented. It would be difficult to state certain principles and insights with greater force and clarity than was done here.

Ownby discusses certain points of interpretation that have particular significance for a clinic which is oriented toward the younger and probably more severely retarded child. While one may disagree with him on the desirability of a primarily medical interpretation, his viewpoint is well stated. There should be little disagreement about his emphasis on the need to tie interpretation into a treatment plan and program.

A miscellany of guidelines and insights are discussed by Drayer and Schlesinger. Their points are primarily relevant in cases where the child must be viewed as being, in all likelihood, severely handicapped for life. Particularly in such instances, the informing interview should be seen as only the first of a series of counseling contacts, since parents cannot be expected to work through the implications of the clinic findings all at once.

The final selection by Drillien and Wilkinson presents the results of a survey in which 170 mothers of mongoloid children were asked how they became informed of the child's condition. While the mode of informing preferred by parents may vary and while the pre-

ferred mode may not be the optimal one, the survey may help to sensitize case managers to the importance of the informing process in cases where impairment can be suspected at or near birth.

INTERPRETING MENTAL RETARDATION TO PARENTS

Harriet L. Rheingold

(Journal of Consulting Psychology, 1945)

A frequent and important task of the psychologist in the child guidance clinic is to give to the parents of a child an interpretation of his retardation. The interpretation is considered as much a part of the service rendered as is the determination of the child's retardation by examination. Often a guidance clinic's services are requested by parents solely to obtain an interpretation of the retardation, the examinations having been administered elsewhere. This suggests that school, court, and medical workers have limited their interviews with parents to reporting the diagnosis or to giving advice concerning commitment or special school placement. This practice too often injures the parents' feelings or arouses their antagonism. Neither attitude is a salutary one for the child or for his parents, for the antagonism causes them to dispute the findings, while disturbed emotions render them less able to consider the welfare of the child.

At the Institute for Juvenile Research it has been customary for the psychologist to interview the parents subsequent to the child's physical and psychological examinations. We are learning, however, that in many instances where other evidence of retardation is sufficient, we can render parents the assistance they need without complete psychometric examination of the child prior to the interview. What the parent wants is not only help in handling the child's problems, but also the psychologist's understanding of his own emotional needs; he does not always require an accurate measure of his child's mental status in years and months. Psychometric and other examinations should be administered, not as a routine procedure, but to meet the requirements of each situation, to aid the psychologist, or to satisfy the parents' needs. This should not be understood to minimize the importance of actual observation of the child's behavior.

The purpose of the initial interview should be to guide the parents toward an emotional acceptance of the child together with his mental defect, since wise planning for such a child is impossible if the parents do not accept his retardation. There is little likelihood that they will act upon the advice given them until this goal is attained. Emotional acceptance in this sense may be defined as: sufficient agreement between the subjective facts (the parents' feelings) and the objective facts (the reality situation) to make wise handling and planning possible.

Emotional acceptance of the child with his defect enables the parents not only to accept the psychologist's statements today, but also to feel a month from now that the conclusions are as wise as they appeared at the close of the interview. That is to say, they are able to change and adapt plans as the child or the situation changes. A realistic orientation of effort is a result of emotional acceptance. While this acceptance is the main purpose of the interview, the assistance rendered the parent in planning for the child is the chief by-product. The extent to which parents can utilize this assistance depends upon the success with which the primary purpose is achieved. Stating the diagnosis, answering questions about etiology and treatment, discussing habit training and educational plans are only the materials out of which the interviews are woven.

The interview, to be successful, should resemble closely any other therapeutic interview in which the gaining of insight is the objective. This means that the psychologist should not be, and should not allow himself to be, forced into the role of an authoritative person whose sole function is to give advice. As in all therapeutic interviews both persons—here psychologist and patient—must play active roles. The parent should feel not that he is being forced to accept what he has been told, but that he has worked in equal measure with the psychologist toward a solution of his problem. At least he should feel that having obtained a basis for action he can carry on independently.

This interview differs in some respects from the typical therapeutic interview. The psychologist possesses information which the parent needs. This means that the parent's questions cannot be turned back upon himself at every point, although at many points they need to be. The psychologist's role is therefore the more active one. Throughout the interview he should help the parent to clarify his own feelings about this problem, but if asked a question concerning test findings, private schools, and so forth, he should give a direct answer. The attitude of the psychologist should be that of any psychotherapeutic worker—interested, sympathetic, understanding.

From experimentation and experience we have found that a successful interpretive interview follows a sequence almost as orderly and regular as that of the psychometric examination itself. It possesses a logic of its own. Its development can be predicted. The content of the interview will vary, of course, according to the age and sex of the child, the degree of retardation, the physical symptoms, and the emotional needs of the parents, but this does not alter the sequence. Furthermore, each parent has been conditioned to some extent by the number of examinations his child has already had and by his own experiences with examiners. This, however, does not affect the orderly progression of the interview although it may increase the relative prominence of one step or reduce that of another, even to negligible proportions.

The writer finds that the therapeutic nature of the interviews can be facilitated by the character of the psychologist's opening remarks. As the first step, there should be a simple restatement of the problem: "You are worried about John's development, aren't you?" or, "I can see that Mary's care has been difficult for you." Such a beginning possesses several advantages. It assures the parent of the psychologist's understanding and sympathy from the first moment of the interview. It gives proper importance to the feelings of the parent, designates an active role for him, and makes him a protagonist.

Almost invariably the parent agrees that he has been worried about John for some time, or that Mary's care has been exhausting. Thus, at the very beginning of the interview the simple restatement has secured an exposure of the parent's recognition of the child's problem and avoided antagonism which would hinder the therapeutic nature of the interview. This admission is necessary for the steps to follow; without it the parent's full co-operation cannot be secured. In contrast, if the interview is opened by giving a diagnosis, the parent's verbal admission that the child is retarded may never be attained, even up to the conclusion of the interview.

The admission itself stimulates the parent to take the next step, a description of the child's behavior. In this the parent can be assisted by the psychologist's asking, "What concerns you about Mary's development?" or, "Tell me more about John." In their descriptions parents find it easier to begin with the less serious and less stigmatizing symptoms; this is usual and should be accepted. One parent will begin with, "What bothers me most is that Anita is so clumsy. She's always falling down." Another will say, "I can't get Tom to chew his food." Other symptoms frequently given prominence at the beginning of the interview are: inability to play with other children, enuresis, day-dreaming, nervousness, lack of concentration, stubbornness, temper tantrums, and speech defects. As the psychologist verbally, and more importantly by attitude, shows his acceptance of these complaints as worthy of concern, the parent works through the less serious symptoms and finally arrives at the most serious, the child's inability to learn at a normal rate.

If the psychologist seems to reject the first symptoms as of minor importance, and if he presses the parents to describe the more serious ones, the parent may limit his recital to the less stigmatizing and never approach the more serious. The desirable progress of the discussion is insured by the psychologist's attitude of interest and sympathy at every point. No more is required of the psychologist by way of a verbal response than, "Yes," or "I can understand that." Only occasionally a more specific comment may be needed, such as, "That embarrasses you, doesn't it?" or "That worries a mother."

Throughout this sequence runs an evaluation of the child's development in terms of the achievements of other children of comparable age or of the parent's own older children as he recalls their behavior at the patient's age. While this comparison is usually spontaneous, in the few cases in which it is not, such questions as, "Do any of your friends have a child about John's age?" or, "What was your older daughter like at his age?" serve to produce the evaluation for the steps to follow.

A few questions such as, "How was it from the time he was a baby?" or "When did you first notice his slowness?" stimulate the parents to relate a history of the child's development. The gathering of a detailed history prior to the interview possesses no especial advantage for this type of interview; history taking has then become an integral part of the interview.

At this point the psychologist becomes more active and asks, "What age child do you think Margaret resembles now?" In our experience, parents then estimate an age very close to the mental age indicated by the tests. Surprisingly, underestimation is somewhat more common than overestimation. This occasionally may be an expression of parental rejection of the child.

At this point we may review the processes of this step. The parent himself has given sufficient material for a diagnosis. Since this has been given in terms of the development of other children, he has supplied a measuring rod which has meaning for him. He has been led a long way towards an understanding of the child's retardation; he will not now reject the psychologist's diagnosis. He has been forced to accept nothing; he has been allowed to evaluate the problem himself.

The parent will usually ask the psychologist at this point, "What do you think?" This leads to the third step in the sequence of the interview. The psychologist answers the question, but refrains from discussing the child's retardation in terms of future development or present planning. One should keep pace with the parent's progress in grasping the implications of the problem and avoid giving him more information than he can assimilate at the time. The results of tests should be presented to the parents in terms of mental age. In our interviews it has always been sufficient to give the mental age, not in years and months, but as "about four years," or, "between seven and eight years." The terms, "idiot," "imbecile," or even "high grade mental defective" are never used. The psychologist from now on usually talks about the child as one who is "slow to learn"; occasionally, as a "mentally retarded child."

How far it is wise to spare the parent's feelings must be considered, for sometimes parents ask, "But he isn't feebleminded, is he?" One mother, seen at our clinic recently, decided to arrange for her son's commitment to a state school. The county clerk to whom she had to apply, asked her if the boy were feebleminded. Although his I.Q. was 50, we had not reported this to the mother or used the term "feeble-minded" in our interview. She answered, "No, he isn't feeble-minded," whereupon the county clerk replied, "Well, then he doesn't belong there." Since then we have modified our procedure. We now tell parents who are thinking of commitment that "feeble-mindedness" is a legal term used by officials.

Parents will ask next about the child's future: "Will he be able to go to school?" "Will he ever learn to talk?" "How far can he go in school?" "Will he be able to get a job?" This we have recognized as the fourth step of the interview. The parent is asking now about the implications of the mental retardation; he is attempting to translate them into terms of future development. In general, the psychologist waits until the parent asks the question, and answers only the questions asked of him. He refrains from predicting the child's entire life history. For example, if the parent is worried only about the speech development of a young retarded child, the psychologist does not add that the child will never be able to support himself. In the manner suggested, the worker keeps pace with the parent's needs and feelings.

The parent next asks questions about etiology and treatment—the fifth step in the sequence. Parents are forever seeking a specific statement of cause. There are two reasons for this desire: first, that a definition of cause will relieve them of the responsibility for the defect; second, that a discovery of cause will indicate an effective method of treatment to correct the defect. In the discussion of etiology, the psychologist should encourage the parents to review verbally their own attempts to account for the retardation. Often they have sought to relate it to heredity, to accidents of birth, to prenatal or neo-natal experiences.

If the explanation offered seems reasonable or constructive, the psychologist encourages the parent's belief. If it seems warranted the psychologist may offer a tentative diagnosis of mongolism, cretinism, or birth injury, to be checked by medical examination. More often, however, the psychologist can only point out the lack of definite etiologic knowledge, emphasizing points which tend to relieve feelings of responsibility, such as the many different causes advanced by medical science, the universality of the problem, the possibility of attributing it to fortuitous circumstances in the absence of more definite etiology. While the psychologist's statements in this area must be as accurate as possible, his attitudes and comments should be directed more toward allowing the parents an opportunity to bring out into the open their own thoughts on the subject rather than towards presenting them with a detailed review of medical knowledge.

The discussion of etiology leads directly into a consideration of treatment. Even if no specific statement of etiology is possible, parents hope desperately that somewhere a cure is available. They usually think of surgical measures first, then in order, other medical, educational, and social measures. Here again the parent should be encouraged to express the hopes he has cherished; again the psychologist should answer directly and as accurately as his knowledge and experience permits; for painful as it may be, most parents are seeking the truth.

For the most part parents of retarded children feel in some way responsible for the retardation. If the psychologist allows the parent the more active role during the discussion of etiology and treatment, the parent himself will raise the question of his responsibility. If he does not, the psychologist may say, "I suppose you sometimes wonder if you are to blame."

A sense of responsibility may stem from feelings of inadequacy or guilt, or both. Some parents feel that they are being punished for sins, real or imagined. The intelligent father of a very retarded child felt that he was being punished for his love of gambling. A mother may be haunted by her attempt to abort the child; another, by having entertained the idea; and still another fears that her ambivalent feelings about her pregnancy may have been the causative factor. A parent may feel that his own personal inadequacy as a man or as a woman is the cause of his child's retardation. Some parents blame themselves for not playing more with the child, or for not reading to him more often. In the latter instance, however, the self-reproaches usually mask more serious feelings of inadequacy or guilt. Associated with these feelings may be the fear of loss of status and prestige which seriously threatens the parent's emotional security.

The importance of encouraging the parent to express his feelings of responsibility can scarcely be overestimated, for the success of the interview may depend upon it. A parent does not parade these feelings; in fact, he struggles to repress them and hesitates to admit them, even to himself. But until he can obtain relief for feelings of guilt, inadequacy, or humiliation, he cannot view reality with sufficient objectivity to develop emotional acceptance of his child.

At some time during the discussion of etiology, treatment, and feelings of responsibility, the parent usually succumbs to an overt expression of his grief. Tears may come to his eyes; more often he weeps openly. This show of emotion need not disconcert the psychologist. It has cathartic value for the parent, while for the psychologist it is another indication of the successful progress of the interview. It requires no direct handling. Sometimes the psychologist need only wait until the parent gains control of himself; at other times he may say, "I understand how you feel." Frequently, following an emotional outburst, the parent will bring up what troubles him most: feelings of responsibility, fear of personal inadequacy, loss of status in the community. If the psychologist takes alarm at the show of feeling, or if he becomes too solicitous, the parent may retreat. Thus the psychologist may cut off an expression of the chief sources of the parent's anxiety.

At this point the parent usually returns to a consideration of the present situation. This is the sixth step. He asks, "What shall I do now?" He is attempting to express his clarified feelings in action. As a rule this question can be returned to the parent. The psychologist will ask, "What do you want to do?" or, "What do you think?" In this way the psychologist encourages the parent to plan for the child in accordance with the reorientation in thinking effected so far by the interview.

Since the purpose of this paper is to define the interview as a therapeutic process and to delineate its orderly progression, it is considered unnecessary to include here a discussion of the psychologist's thinking about the advantages and disadvantages of care at home vs. public institutional care; regular vs. special room placement; local resources; the tendency of most parents to press the mentally retarded child for academic achievement, at the same time requiring too little in social and emotional maturity; the possibilities for good personality development in spite of the mental defect. These are some of the considerations which arise at this point in the interview. The psychologist must be familiar with them for he will be called upon to answer questions. He should offer information freely; the decisions, however, must rest with the parent.

As the interview draws to its close, most parents begin to feel guilty because their objective discussion of the child seems to suggest their rejection of him. This attitude they express by an enumeration of the child's assets and especially of bits of behavior which seem to them bright and hopeful. They will say of a young child: "But he points out all the parts of an automobile," or of an older child, "But he can travel all over the city by himself." One should not feel at this point that the interview is of dubious success because this is only an expression of the parent's attempt to relieve his feelings of guilt. The psychologist in response verbalizes the parent's ambivalence. He may say, "You are afraid that you haven't been fair to your child," or, "It is natural for you to see that in some ways he is not as slow as in others."

Fear of seeming to reject the child becomes an even more serious matter when the parent considers committing the child to a state school. Moral censure arises both from within—his feelings of responsibility—and from without—his fear of community disapproval. Fear of loss of prestige and status arises here, too, for it is difficult for the parent to admit that he must resort to a state agency for the care of his child. Often a parent is unwilling to accept public assistance, and feels obliged to spend his own money on the child's care. When the parent can ill afford private care, and especially when the expense may be detrimental to the welfare of other children in the family, the psychologist should explain the meaning of this sacrifice as a compensation for the parent's feelings of guilt or inadequacy.

This type of interview leads to emotional acceptance of the problem and helps the parent plan for the immediate situation. His own personality needs, the severity of the retardation, the age of the child, the awareness and insight brought to the interview—these determine the extent of his acceptance. The psychologist may be skillful but he constitutes only half of the interview situation. While most parents can be carried through the interview with profit for themselves and the child, there are some who obtain only limited benefits. Occasionally a parent may seem to have arrived at emotional acceptance and to be able to plan more or less wisely for the child, yet at the end bring up his conviction that a tonsillectomy may still effect a cure. Sometimes this may represent no more than a temporary lapse into an earlier pattern of thought. At other times it may indicate that the parent is not yet able to plan wisely for the child's future. Occasionally one parent will leave the interview with apparent insight, but at home will be influenced by the other parent to return to the original hope that the child needs only speech therapy. These parents "shop around" from doctor to doctor, from clinic to clinic, seeking corroboration of their hopes. Some parents can only be regarded as untreatable.

Then, too, there are parents who, in one interview, achieve only partial emotional acceptance and objective insight into the needs of the child. The problem has proved too great and too damaging to the parent's ego, too bound up with feelings of personal inadequacy and guilt. For this reason we close each interview with an assurance of our interest and availability whenever the parent wishes to discuss any aspects of the problem. If the mother was interviewed, and it appears from her conversation that the father finds it difficult to accept the child's limitation, we offer an interview to the father and vice versa. Parents of young children are invited to return at six-month intervals for re-examination and interviews; parents of older children are invited to return at yearly intervals. Occasionally the parent's anxiety will appear disturbing enough to warrant our offering several interviews in succession. The general invitation is always given; more definite appointments depend upon his need and his desire for further help.

□ □ □

from INTERPRETATION OF MENTAL DEFICIENCY TO PARENTS *Seymour B. Sarason*

(Psychological Problems in Mental Deficiency, 3rd ed., 1959)

The failure adequately to communicate to parents the nature and implications of a diagnosis of mental deficiency probably causes more unnecessary problems and suffering than any other factor, with the obvious exception of those factors which originally produced the mental deficiency.[1] By the word "communicate" is meant not only the imparting of facts but, in addition, the attempt on the part of a qualified person to help parents recognize and adjust to the realities of their child's condition. The imparting of facts does not insure that parents will either recognize or adjust to the child's condition. Resistance, anxiety, despair, hostility, and frustration—these experiences and reactions are not quieted or eliminated by a recital of facts. One might even say that when the nature of the child's condition is explained to the parents, their tendencies to resist the explanation and to react in an emotional way are strengthened rather than decreased.

Before becoming specific about the handling of the interpretation of mental defect to parents, the following statements about the goals of such a situation should be made explicit:

1. The parents should be completely informed about the probable causes of the child's condition, the severity of the mental defect, and the probable course (educationally, vocationally, socially) of the child's development.
2. A specific program geared to the needs and capabilities of the child should be explained, discussed, and planned with the parents.
3. The personal problems of the parents, caused or exacerbated by the child's condition, should be dealt with in a manner so as to maximize the probability that parents and child will be able to function in a socially constructive and self-satisfying manner.
4. Provision should be made for periodic discussion with the parents and observation of the child in order to check on the nature of the child's and parents' adjustment and to re-evaluate the correctness of the initial program.

With these goals in mind, what follows is an attempt to describe in some detail the problems one frequently encounters and the ways in which one might handle them.

The Setting

In discussing here the interpretation of mental defect with parents it is impossible to take into account all the different settings in which such a problem is encountered. The physician in his office, the teacher in the school, the psychologist or social worker in the clinic—these and other professional specialists are called upon to handle the parents of the defective child. In each case the setting is different in terms of various diagnostic services, availability of case-history material, previous experience with the problem, knowledge of community resources, and time available for any one case. For the purposes of the present discussion we shall assume that the parents have brought their child to a clinic where psychological, medical, and social work facilities are available. We shall further assume that the child has been comprehensively examined, background data secured, and a diagnosis of mental defect made. The problem now is to communicate the findings to the parents.

Some Preliminary Considerations

In arranging for the interview it is extremely important to have *both* parents present. One must never assume that both parents have the same conception of the problem, the same attitudes toward the child, experienced a similar degree of frustration, or possess a similar degree of stability and maturity. By working only with the mother, as is most frequent, one may never find out, for example, either that the parents quarrel violently about the handling of their child, or that the father rejects the child, or that he now rejects the mother. One simply cannot assume that the mother's report is a necessarily valid or complete one, *even though she may be motivated to give what she thinks is an objective presentation of the facts.*

Since carrying out a recommended program successfully depends in large part on a harmonious relationship between the parents, it is imperative that at the outset one be in a position to evaluate the nature of that relationship. In more than a few cases the primary problem is not the defective child but unhappy, mutually aggressive parents who have become emotionally distant from each other. To focus on the defective child not only overlooks important influences on his behavior but increases the likelihood that a recommended program will fail completely or fall short of its mark.

Another difficulty in working with one parent, say the mother, is that she may not communicate to her husband the contents of the interview in an undistorted fashion. She may forget to relate certain aspects of the discussion, distort others, and attempt to answer questions posed by the husband which had not been discussed at all with the counselor. *The tendency to perceive and report in a selective manner is a human characteristic which appears to become increasingly operative when strongly felt, personal problems are aroused.* It is for this reason that so much emphasis has been and will be given here to the recognition and prevention (as far as possible) of selective perception and reporting by parents of mentally defective children.

Another advantage in having the father at the interview is that he is then more likely to share the responsibilities of caring for the child. In our culture the primary responsibility in child rearing falls upon the mother. One can say with no hesitation that rearing a defective child is certainly one of the most difficult tasks which can confront a mother. In many cases, especially when the child is severely defective, it is too much to expect the mother to handle the problem by herself; it can be done but with the likelihood that the health of the mother sooner or later deteriorates. A sickly, irritable, frustrated mother is not likely to be a satisfactory wife. Where such a problem exists an attempt should be made to get the father to see the nature of the situation and *to want* to share the responsibilities.[2]

One of the most obvious cautions to be observed in arranging for the interview is that the child should not be present. This caution is necessary not only to protect the child but to enable the parents to discuss the problem without the distracting presence of the child.

Structuring the Interview

In working with parents of defective children one must never lose sight of the fact that they have experienced keen frustration and hardship, have generally previously been given ambiguous or contradictory advice, and have been given little or no opportunity to unburden their anguish and disappointment. Unfortunately, there are too many professional specialists who give parents the feeling that they have little or limited time in which to discuss the problem with them, conduct the interview in the form of a monologue so that the parents are seldom given an opportunity to ask questions, communicate in a technical jargon which effectively confuses and overwhelms the parents, and in general manifest little or no interest in the personal problems or reactions of the parents.

Unless one is able to identify with the problems and feelings of the parents one is likely to conduct the interview in an impersonal, superficial, routine fashion—a fashion which may be considered "successful" by the specialist but is frustrating and confusing to the parents. In working with the parents of defective children—in fact, in working with the parents of any problem child—one must not only be able to experience vicariously the nature and strength of their frustrations but also to structure the relationships so as to enable one to facilitate change in parental attitude and practice.

The following represents the writer's way of structuring the interview:

Before we discuss in any detail the

> conclusions we have reached about your child there are a few things I would like to say by way of introduction. The first thing is that I hope that you will feel free **at any time** to ask questions or express an opinion—or disagreement. If I should say something you do not understand, please ask me about it immediately. All of us, you know, do not always say things as clearly as we should, so that if something is not clear to you I hope you will not feel that it is your fault and be afraid to ask questions. Sometimes we have found that parents have had important things they wanted to say or ask but for some reason they thought we might think them silly. The more questions you ask and we discuss the more help we can be to you.
>
> If I should use a word or phrase which you do not understand please interrupt and tell me. Sometimes we forget that words which mean something to us do not mean anything to another person. So I will look upon it as a favor if you tell me when you do not understand something.
>
> One more thing: in the hour or so we have at our disposal it may not be possible for us to go over every problem in great detail. We have found in the past that it is not always possible to discuss everything in one session. So at the end of our talk today I will be happy to make another appointment when we can talk some more. You may find that when you go home questions will occur to you which you forgot to ask, or what seemed clear to you now may not seem so clear later, or you may find yourself disagreeing with our conclusions. Whatever it is, I hope you will not feel that today is the only time you will have to discuss your problems with us. We will be eager to see you as many times as you think we can be of help to you.

The significance of the above lies not in the words employed or the order in which the statements are made but rather in the attempt to engender in the parents the following set of attitudes:

1. It is not only "permissible" for them to talk and ask questions but *it is expected of them.*
2. They are talking to someone whose manner does not suggest that he is impatient to get on to what is next on his appointment calendar.
3. Parents have something important to contribute to the discussion.

Needless to say, parroting words or phrases will not necessarily produce the desired effects. The words and phrases must reflect personal conviction and feeling—if they do not, the parents are likely to recognize the insincerity and react accordingly. The tone of one's voice, one's facial expression, and the manifestation of a genuine desire to understand and help—these are the media by which the words one utters gain their force.

Obtaining Parental Attitudes, Practices, and Goals

Having attempted to establish the kind of relationship described above, it has then been found helpful to determine parental attitudes about the etiology of their child's condition, how they have handled the problems he has presented, and goals they have set for him. *Without knowledge or consideration of these factors the extent to which the parent's personal problems and, consequently, the child's particular problems can be helped will be minimal.* It has been the failure to consider these factors which has caused so much ineffective planning, wasted effort, and continued disappointment and frustration. Advice about child-rearing, schooling, institutionalization and similar problems must take into account parental behavior and attitudes if such advice is to have a reasonable chance of success.

At this point in the interview the writer has found the following statements helpful:

> Although we have studied your child very carefully from many points of view—which we will discuss in a little while—I think you will understand when I say that our examinations do not always give us all the information we would like. In our experience we have found that at this point parents can be very helpful to us about certain questions. You know your child longer than we do and you have observed him in a way that we have not. We have learned from many cases in the past

> that by sharing our experiences and conclusions we might see things somewhat differently than before.
>
> You might have talked some of these things over before but it would be very helpful to all of us if you could do it again.[3] For example, I wonder if you might tell me what **you** have thought was the cause of your child's condition? From time to time several possible answers have probably occurred to you and I wonder if you could talk about them—even though you might have thought they were silly or, as sometimes happens, too unpleasant to think about. Whatever these were, it would be extremely helpful if we could talk about them.

It is clear that these statements are intended to get the parents to verbalize *their* conception of the etiology of the child's condition. The havoc which can be wrought by parental misconceptions about etiology has been nicely pointed out by Kanner and Tietze:

"Popular notions regarding heredity have provided a handy means of transferring the blame to some afflicted relative. If the hunt for a skeleton in the family closet did just that, it would serve a fairly useful function of absolving the parents from a feeling of personal guilt. But often enough a parent comes to believe, or is made to believe by hostile in-laws, that the present or past existence of such a relative is his or her own fault and contribution to the child's condition. The in-laws thus wash their hands of any complicity. The clan members of the accused spouse cannot remain idle. They usually manage, sometimes after considerable search worthy of a genealogist, to uncover some conjugal counterpart of the skeleton, and mutual recriminations are the order of the day. Psychotherapeutic consideration of the parents of retarded children cannot afford to disregard such bickering arising between and within families from the desire to put the stigma and odium of an ancestral culprit on either parent."

Misconceptions about heredity are not the only ones which parents may harbor. Some mothers have concluded that they were too active during pregnancy, or that they had experienced some frightening situation during pregnancy, or that they did not feed their child adequately in his early days, or that they did not obtain for him prompt or proper medical attention, or that the child had once slipped or fell from the mother's arms and had then cried most excessively. Parental explanations are many and varied but they usually have three characteristics in common:

1. They sound plausible and *may* contain a germ of truth; in other words, it would be difficult for a professional specialist to say that these factors have never been a possible factor in any case.
2. In the individual case the parental explanation usually cannot explain *their* child's condition. For example, an infant may receive a brain injury because of a fall, but when the neurological findings point unmistakably to early embryonic disfunction the parental explanation obviously loses its etiological relevance.
3. The parental explanation usually involves self-plaguings and feelings of guilt.

When one bears in mind to what extent parental misconception about etiology can adversely affect parental happiness and adjustment, the importance of determining the nature of such conceptions is clear. In order to disabuse parents of misconceptions and thereby give them a basis for relinquishing unrealistic and irrational attitudes it is first necessary for parents to verbalize their feelings.

The next area about which parents should be encouraged to talk might be indicated in the form of a question: "What are the main problems you have had to face as your child has developed and how have you coped with them?" Here one is interested in specific child rearing practices and problems: *When and how* did they try to teach their child to talk, walk, eat, and control toilet functions? When and how did they try to teach their child letters, words, and numbers? How did the parents handle the problem of their child's inability to play and compete with others? What are the attitudes of siblings toward the child? Of neighbors? Have the social activities of the parents been in any way affected by the condition of their child? One of the main considerations giving rise to these questions is the importance of determining the degree of emotionality which the parents experience in responding to the problems which their child has presented. Have the parents accepted his limitations or have they pushed him? Do they feel that other children and neighbors are unfair in their response to the child? Have the parents restricted excessively their own activities in order to devote their energies to the child? Do the parents see eye-to-eye on the handling of these problems? Are there indications that the parents have been unable to take advice offered previously by other agencies?

The last area about which parents should be encouraged to talk concerns their expectations of or goals for their child. What have they hoped that this child will be able to do? What are their expectations or hopes about his schooling? About his social and vocational activities? *It is through parental report about their hopes and aspirations for their child that one can best determine how realistic an understanding of their child's abilities the parents have. At the same time one can also evaluate the extent of one's task in helping the parents to adopt a more realistic approach.* A parent who says that he does not expect his child to go to college but would like him to finish high school reveals not only an unrealistic conception of his child but very frequently also a need to avoid accepting the child's limitations. The parent who says that he is not interested in the child's academic schooling but only wants him to be able to learn a trade and to maintain himself independently is also revealing a lack of understanding. The difficulty parents experience in accepting their child's limitations has been well described by Kanner and Tietze:

"During the past centuries our culture has put a special premium on good cognitive endowment, in an increasing degree. Our communal life is so constituted that to people with sufficiently high intelligence quotients go, of necessity, the functions of governing, the jobs with good incomes, the respect of contemporaries. They are the acknowledged inheritors of the earth. They are the cream of society. To have a child with a lower-than-average I.Q. means that his parents must from the beginning expect that he will be excluded from leadership, riches and esteem. Regardless of everything else, the low I.Q., as such, marks the child as socially inferior. Physical attractiveness, good manners, emotional stability and manual dexterity may create attenuating circumstances, but even though they are all combined in one person, if the I.Q. does not measure up to the existing requirements, they still fail to admit the bearer to a seat among the elite.

"It is, quite understandably, difficult for many parents, especially those who themselves have been blessed with a good I.Q., to accept their child's intellectual retardation as an Act of God, as something unpredictable, inevitable and unalterable. There comes often a search for the possibility of parental contribution to the child's inadequacy. The question, 'Why do we have such a child?' soon assumes the form of 'What have we done to have such a child?'

"Some parents do their best to escape the discomforts of trying to find an answer by flatly refusing to recognize the fact as such. The feeling, not ever verbalized, goes something like this: 'If my child were really retarded, I should be forced to ascribe his condition somehow to some shortcoming or transgression of my own. But I simply refuse to admit that he is retarded.' Then comes a hunt for excuses, usually looked for in the child's physical health. The child's admittedly poor performance must be based on unrecognized poor eyesight, glandular anomaly or something pressing on the brain. If the doctors could only find the somatic culprit, then the child will be all right and the parents will have reason to feel exculpated. If it is not an organ of the child's body, then it must be the teacher's lack of understanding, the crowded class, or the faulty school system. And if it isn't that, then the tester didn't know his business, or didn't know how to handle the child, or the child wasn't in the proper mood just then. It would be wrong to attribute this attitude, as is often done, to parental stubbornness, wicked and disrespectful lack of cooperation, or mental dishonesty. Such parents need the kind of guidance which makes it possible for them to express their feelings, frees them of any implied necessity of considering themselves personally responsible for the child's retardation, and thereby helps them lift their heads from below the ostrich sand pile."

The point which deserves emphasis is that parental misunderstanding and overevaluation of their child's behavior and capabilities stem not from stubbornness but from a need to avoid wounding their own pride and facing self-devaluation. The conception which a parent has of his child is a reflection of his conception of himself. To admit that his child is "stupid" is very likely to arouse in the parent thoughts of his own limitations.

The Interview to This Point

Thus far we have endeavored to engender in the parents a set of attitudes toward the counselor and the interview, and we have also attempted to get the parents to talk about themselves in relation to their child. *In the latter attempt the emphasis has been on what the parents have to report, the counselor adopting a relatively passive role in which he expresses no opinions but attempts in as nonleading a way as possible to get the parents to clarify and elaborate upon their thoughts and feelings.* Without the parental report it is difficult to identify oneself with them: to understand why they have reacted to their problem in the way they have and how their reactions have influenced their child. In addition, *by obtaining the parental report one is then in the position to utilize the diagnostic findings to help the parents achieve a more realistic basis for their conceptions, practices, and goals.*

Communicating the Diagnostic Findings

At this point in the interview the writer has said the following to the parents:

> I find that what you have told me is extremely interesting and has given me a better understanding of what you have been thinking and experiencing. Now I would like to share with you the results of our studies. As you know we have studied your child from many points of view and we have come to certain conclusions. Before telling you of our conclusions I would first like to tell you of some of our experiences with other parents. Sometimes parents are at first disappointed at what we have to say and sometimes do not want to accept our findings. **This is very understandable to us—no one likes to hear that his child will always have certain limitations which other children will not have.** It is not easy to accept the fact that your child will never be able to do certain kinds of activities. But we feel that it is our obligation to speak with you as frankly as we can—as we feel you would want us to do. Again I would like to remind you to ask questions whenever they occur to you, and to disagree if that is how you feel. And please remember that we will be glad to talk with you further—we will always be glad to make an appointment to discuss any matter that you want.

These statements are intended to achieve the following:

1. to reward parents for their participation and to reinforce the feeling that they have something to contribute;
2. to prepare the parents, in those cases where it is indicated, for what will be conflict-arousing information;
3. to facilitate for the parents the experiencing and verbalizing of feeling. Anxiety, hostility, disappointment, and despair—these are the feelings one should enable parents to express rather than inhibit. While the inhibition of such feeling makes for a more "pleasant" interview, it also reduces the amount of help that one can be to parents.

It is not possible to describe in detail how the diagnostic findings are presented to the parents because the order in which they are presented and the degree of emphasis which they receive are determined by the problems arising from the parental report. As was said before, *the diagnostic findings are used as the base for helping parents give up erroneous ideas and adopt a more realistic approach to their own and their child's problems.* For example, if the diagnostic findings offer no support for parental conceptions of etiology, then this point must be made explicit—and emphasized. It is not enough to tell parents that they are "wrong"; one must not give them the impression that their conceptions are silly. One must make parents feel that one understands why they arrived at their particular conceptions—but that the findings offer no support for their convictions. If parents have unrealistic anticipations about their child's future schooling, then this should be explicitly discussed. To parents who would like their child at least to finish public or high school it is not enough to say that this is not possible; one must state the basis for one's conclusion and give as explicitly as possible the probable lower and upper limits of the child's academic achievements.

In many cases parents have already indirectly revealed that many of the day-to-day problems which they experience in relation to their child stem from highly emotionally-tinged attitudes which in turn adversely affect their child's behavior. It is difficult for these parents to see that such attitudes defeat, or at least interfere with, the goals which they want to achieve. *In discussing this with parents one must be careful to avoid making them feel guilty. One must explicitly recognize and verbalize that what the parents had been doing, however ineffective, was based on "good intentions," as indeed it usually is.*

The Importance of a Specific Program

One of the most important functions of the interview is to offer to and discuss with parents a specific program for their child. A great deal of unnecessary unhappiness has resulted from the failure to give to the parents detailed advice about the handling of their child. Parents of defective children need guidance and emotional support. It is not enough to tell them that their child is defective and they should not expect much from him. The following is a list of questions which parents frequently ask—the questions, of course, varying with the age of the child, severity of defect, degree of physical handicap, etc.:

Should I try to teach my child to walk now? Am I teaching him the right way?

How can I get other children to refrain from teasing him?

Is there any way I can train my child to stop being as destructive as he is?

Should I punish him the way I do my other children?

When should he start school? Is there a school for him?

Should we institutionalize him? Where are these institutions? Are they expensive?

Should we have other children? Will my child be a bad influence on my other children? My other child who is normal resents him—what should I do about it?

One could list a great many more problems for which parents seek guidance. Some of the problems require a detailed knowledge and understanding of the child, parents, and family constellation. Other problems require, in addition, a knowledge of community resources: educational, recreational, and institutional. But in discussing any problem with parents one must wherever possible give specific advice and guidance. For example, if a mother is bothered because her child is frequently teased by neighborhood children, one must attempt to outline concrete steps which might be taken by the mother to cope with the problem. One should, of course, first determine how the mother has previously handled the problem: Has she "bawled out" the other children? Has she asked their parents to punish them? If the parent has reacted in this way then one must point out why such an approach is likely to be self-defeating.

One might then suggest that the mother have a talk with the children and explain to them that her child cannot do some of the things that they can, that he needs a little more consideration and protection, that he is not as able to protect or defend himself as they are, and that she is discussing the matter with them because she knows that if they understood her child better they would not tease him. Another suggestion concerns discussing the matter in a similar vein with the parents of the neighborhood children.

One should not give the parents of the defective child the impression that one's suggestions are sure to work after one application. In addition, one must avoid giving suggestions which, while correct in general, cannot be properly acted upon by the parent because of their excessive emotionality.

If the problem concerns the future schooling of the child one should acquaint the parent with the nature of local facilities, the people who administer them, and the requirements for entrance. One should urge the parents to visit the facilities and, if possible, arrange for the visit and for a later discussion of parental reactions and questions. Too frequently parents have had to find out about local facilities in a trial-and-error kind of way, during which time their feelings of frustration and helplessness have mounted.

The Interview to This Point

Thus far we have attempted to do four things: 1) engender in the parents a particular attitude toward the interview, 2) identify the nature of the parents' problems, 3) utilize the diagnostic findings in order to help the parents adopt a realistic conception of their child's condition, and 4) formulate and discuss with the parents a specific attack on their child's and their own problems.

As was indicated before, it is not always possible or desirable to achieve all the goals of the interview within one session. The availability and advisability of another session or sessions should be again pointed out to the parents, the decision about returning being left to them. In terminating the interview one must convey to the parents that the need for further visits is not due to a present lack of interview time but to the need for the parents to digest what has been discussed, raise new questions or problems which usually occur to them after an initial visit, and to give the interviewer more time to mull over the discussion and the problems raised.

Some Cautions

The reader should not conclude that by following the contents of this chapter he will always be able smoothly and painlessly to achieve the goals outlined earlier. Parents do not always say or do what we would like or expect. The fact that one attempts to get parents to talk about their conceptions of the origins of their child's condition does not mean that they will do so. One may try to make parents feel free to talk and raise questions but the attempt does not mean that they will act accordingly. In some cases it is not until the second or third interview that a parent will really feel free to talk and raise questions. In working with parents one must be ready to change one's approach and, with unusually emotional or unstable parents, even to narrow one's goals. But in these cases extreme care must be taken to insure that a change in approach or narrowing of goals is not the result of one's own emotional reactions. For example, *some parents seem so hostile or resistant that one reacts similarly to them, reactions which then enable the parents to continue to be hostile and resistant. In working with parents (as in therapeutic work with anyone) it is self-defeating to respond emotionally to the deliberate or unwitting provocations of those whom one is trying to help.* The task is to recognize the hostility and to help the parents see its lack of justification in this situation.

The subjective reactions of the counselor can be an interfering factor in those instances when he fears the reaction of the parent to what will probably be highly disappointing news—the interviewer wants and yet does not want to state the truth. As a consequence he will sometimes relate the findings in an ambiguous manner so that the parents can interpret them in any manner that they choose—the interviewer unknowingly speaks out of both sides of his mouth. The writer has spoken to physicians who have frankly said that they did not "have the heart" to tell parents that their child was defective. Others have adopted the position that ignorance is bliss and "they (the parents) will find out for themselves later on." Both attitudes reveal a need to avoid an unpleasant situation, an avoidance which may make life more pleasant for the physician but creates undue hardship, now and in the future, for parents and child.

Interpreting mental defect to parents is not a simple or pleasant task and cannot be approached in a perfunctory way.

. . . .

The "Untreatable" Parents

As has been pointed out elsewhere, there are always parents who are unable to face the problems brought up in the interview despite all of one's efforts. In such cases the counselor must neither lose patience nor take it as an affront. Terminating the relationship with such parents, however, should not necessarily be looked upon as a negative step. The following information should be conveyed to the parents:

1. That one understands that it is not easy to accept and to adjust to the problems and conclusions which have been discussed. Should the parents at any time in the future desire to resume discussion, or feel that the agency can in any way be of help to them, they should not hesitate to call for an appointment.

2. Should the parents feel that they would like to take their child to another agency for evaluation, it might be helpful if they were given a list of agencies or professional specialists who are competent to make such an evaluation.

It is clear that the last statement represents an attempt to insure that parents, if they are to "shop around," go to reputable and competent specialists and agencies. In more than a few cases shopping around among recommended agencies has helped parents to accept conclusions which were discussed with them earlier. In other cases, of course, the shopping around never has any beneficial effects.

It is sometimes forgotten that although parents may achieve new insights during the interview and may give clear indications that their attitudes are beginning to change, the crucial test of the efficacy of one's efforts is if after the interview the parents can *act* on the basis of what they have learned. It is unusual if inter- and intrapersonal conflicts can be resolved either during or because of a single interview. What is perhaps more usual is that after the interview previous conflicts are experienced in their original or increased strength.

One must remember that strongly held beliefs, unrealistic or not, are maintained because they are in one way or other satisfying to the believer. These beliefs serve the purpose of enabling the individual to defend himself against recognizing what for him would be an unpleasant or even impossible situation. It is because such beliefs serve this defensive purpose that they are not easily given up even when adherence to contrary beliefs is apparently being achieved. It is because of these considerations that emphasis has been given to the need for several interviews. In addition, these considerations contain the implication that in those cases where parents have achieved new insights the counselor should actively aid the parents wherever possible to follow through on their new insights. In some cases, for example, a visit to the home might not only reinforce more realistic parental behavior but might allow the counselor to be of more concrete help to the parents

—a suggestion which Yepsen and Cianci have shown to possess marked therapeutic possibilities.

FOOTNOTES

1. The writer cannot point to a study to support this statement. It is based on the writer's experience as well as on the fact that he has never heard any other worker deny that inadequate communication with parents is much more often than not the rule rather than the exception. . . . It is only recently that workers in the field have become aware of the "parent problem" and one can only hope that in the future systematic studies of the efficacy of various approaches to the problem will be available. At the present time we are operating in the realm of opinion. . . . It is because the handling of parents of defective children is fraught with so much danger that it is so important that our assumptions, practices, and alleged results be subjected to scientific study.
2. The words "to want" have been italicized in order to emphasize that the aim of the interviewer is to try to avoid telling the father that he should share the responsibilities with the mother, but rather to attempt to get the father to recognize that his own as well as his wife's present and future welfare require sharing of responsibilities. The distinction in technique is again between reciting facts, on the one hand, and clarifying and changing attitudes, on the other hand. The husband who is told what he should do is not likely to be as helpful as one who has decided for himself, on the basis of a discussion of the problem, what he should do.
3. In a clinic setting it is likely that the parents were initially seen by a social worker and that some aspects of the parental problem have been discussed. In the writer's experience, however, the intake history is relatively unrevealing in this initial contact. Whatever the limits of this initial contact, however, the sensitive social worker can make observations which can be extremely helpful to the counselor whose job it will be to work with the parents.

□ □ □

from THE INTERPRETATIVE CONFERENCE WITH PARENTS OF A MENTALLY RETARDED CHILD

Ralph Ownby

(In *The Report of Educational Program for Nurses in Region III of The Children's Bureau on Mental Retardation,* May, 1964)

If, during the course of contact between an evaluation clinic and a mentally retarded child and his family, there is a point in time that can be singled out and called "crucial," then that point is without a doubt the "interpretive conference." All of the examinations and tests have been done; the findings have been reviewed and correlated. The clinic staff and its consultants have discussed the problem, and have made reasonable determinations as to the probable cause of the child's difficulties, his present capacities and limitations, the outlook for the future, and the availability of resources in the community most appropriate to his special needs. Now it is time to meet with the parents, 1) to explain and discuss our evaluation and recommendations, 2) to help them to understand why their child is like he is, and what can be done for him now, and 3) what can be reasonably expected for the forseeable future.

This is the time that the parents have been waiting for since their first visit to the clinic. To find the answers to these questions is the reason for the evaluation, as far as they are concerned. For the parents to begin to achieve understanding and acceptance of the child as he is, and to be able to move positively toward filling his needs physically, emotionally, and educationally, we must be reasonably successful in the presentation of our evaluation and what it means. To a very large measure, all that has gone before and all that will follow depend upon the effectiveness of the interpretive conference—that is why it is so "crucial."

This conference—and I would prefer to think of it as a conference or discussion, emphasizing the mutual participation of the parents and the clinic—is not only the keystone to success or failure of the whole evaluation process and subsequent proper management of the mentally retarded child and his family, it is also in itself usually one of the most difficult tasks—if done well and effectively—to face the evaluation "team" during the study of a child. Although it might not appear to be the case superficially, the interpretation of a retarded child's condition and unique requirements to his parents is much more complicated than a simple recitation, "1, 2, 3" of medical diagnoses, mental age, and IQ numbers, and "1, 2, 3" of recommendations of medication, speech therapy or special education classes. Just as each child will differ in the specific cause of his retardation and the way it affects him, his adjustments to it, and his particular requirements for proper management, each interpretation will differ in depth, content and effectiveness, since each will be influenced by a number of different factors unique to each child, family and the particular problems involved.

If there is anyone among you who, upon noting the title of this morning's paper, came in anticipation of hearing the "best" way to conduct good interpretive conferences with parents, I will have to say this: I, like you, am still looking. . . . In our particular clinic the pediatrician who has seen the child and coordinated the studies has the primary responsibility for conducting the initial interpretive parental conference. We feel that this is most appropriate for us, in that we try to establish and maintain from the outset a physician-patient relationship in the diagnostic evaluation of the child, including his physical, motor, and behavioral development, as well as his specific problems. We feel that our patients are most comfortable and accepting of such a pediatrically oriented approach. We feel that such orientation is entirely consistent with, and in fact reinforces, the "team" concept of the clinic. The pediatrician, we feel, is in the best position to coordinate the many varied studies done on a child, and, working together with the other "basic" members of the clinic team, to correlate the results so that a reasonable diagnosis and treatment plan can be evolved. It is a logical extension of this, and one which parents expect, that the doctor should interpret the evaluation, particularly since much of the initial information given the parents, as well as the questions they ask, is primarily medical in nature.

The pediatrician who has the responsibility of interpretation in the evaluation clinic setting has certain advantages and disadvantages at the outset. I believe, however, that advantages inherent in the multiprofessional evaluation and its obvious thoroughness and comprehensiveness outweigh the fact that the doctor is a relative stranger to the parents, and does not have the advantage of previously established rapport, confidence, and "faith." However, these latter factors are not inconsiderable assets for the physician and other members of the clinic team to have, even to a limited extent, in dealing successfully with parents. If they can be established during the course of the diagnostic contacts, acceptance of interpretation will be made that much more likely. Certainly, every effort should be made to avoid a negative reaction in the parents, if effectiveness of the interpretation is not to be seriously compromised before it even begins.

As just stated, our pediatrician almost always conducts the initial interpretive interview. Frequently, another member of the clinic staff, usually the social worker or nurse, "sits in" and contributes to the discussion. We take a flexible attitude as to the number and identity of the clinic staff members involved in the parent conference, trying in general to adjust this to the special problems of the individual situation. It seems logical for the doctor to assume the major responsibility at this time, because so much of the interpretation involves summarization of medical, neurological, and, with increasing practical importance, genetic facts and their implications with regard to this specific child. Most of the parents expect these things to be explained to them by the doctor, and rightfully so. However, most parents also need help from the clinic in ways in which other staff members are especially well suited to provide. This help might be in the nature of moving toward a better acceptance and understanding of the child, in finding ways to make their own emotional adjustments to their particular problems and overall family situations, or in specific down-to-earth advice in how best to care for and bring up their child. . . .

Every conference of interpretation will be different, depending on the many human variables involved. We must try to understand what each parent brings to the conference in terms of these variables in order to help them most effectively. At the same time, it is of vital importance for us as professional people, individually and collectively, to maintain a good perspective of what we ourselves bring to the conference. We should examine ourselves critically and continually in a constructive way, so that we can use our inherent advantages of comprehensive team evaluation and knowledge of resources of specific help for the specific problem to the end that the family will receive the maximum benefit. Realistically speaking, it is sometimes unavoidable that parents will reject our findings and recommendations. In keeping this group to a minimum, it is especially important that we do not contribute to this ourselves by the content or method of our interpretation. . . .

In thinking about the ways of approaching the interpretive conference with parents, it is well to recall the importance of some of the variables that the parents bring with them, in terms of knowledge, understanding and acceptance of their child's condition, and of pre-formed conceptions and attitudes that they might have toward the child, themselves, and toward the evaluation process itself. Each family brings a variable level of awareness and understanding of their child's difficulty, and of what they want and need from the clinic. Because of the very nature of our services, almost all of the parents are aware of the existence of a problem, but have varying degrees of confusion about just what is wrong and what the future may hold, as well as what they should do for their child immediately. This is frequently made more complex by the fact that many parents have been given (or think they have been given) ambiguous or contradictory professional diagnoses and/or advice. In most instances, they have had little opportunity to unburden themselves of their anxiety, fears, doubts and despair. These things add to the difficulties of evaluation interpretation, not only because of the frustrations and misconceptions that the parents may feel about the diagnosis but because of the attitudes of resistance and even hostility toward the evaluation process, and those who attempt to present its meaning.

We should emphasize here that the interpretive process is not an end unto itself, and that the recitation of facts and information will not automatically insure that the parents will recognize or adjust to their child's condition. As a matter of fact, it has been well demonstrated that, when the nature of a child's condition is explained to parents, their tendencies to resist explanation and react in an emotional way are strengthened, rather than decreased. We should never lose sight of the fact that a mentally retarded child produces a crisis in a family. The stage of reaction to this in which we see the family varies, and our approach to them must be flexible enough to make adjustments in each situation tailored to that family's capacities and readiness to face specific aspects of the diagnostic findings. We must keep in mind the abilities of the individual parents to cope with the emotional assault that has been made on them, and to understand their subsequent attitudes in light of the adjustments that they have been able to make. These adjustments must be recognized and dealt with in terms of: 1) feelings and projections of guilt, 2) misconceptions about etiology, 3) family discord, 4) conscious or unconscious rejection or unreasonable over-protection of the child, and 5) the effects of the complex interaction of many other internal and external factors.

It should be stressed that our recognition of these problems in the parents should never be in the way of criticism, for this is self-defeating. On the contrary, we need to understand this background if we hope to be successful in the realization of one of the major goals of our whole evaluation: The accurate interpretation of the findings, and the effective marshaling of family participation in the acceptance of the child's handicap and its management. We need to apply the "Golden Rule," and to identify with the problems and feelings of the parents in the interview, in order to keep it from being impersonal, superficial, and routine.

Ideally, we hope to have gained a great deal of information about these aspects of understanding, feeling, and attitude prior to our interpretation. This, of course, should be an integral part of our diagnostic procedure and should be discussed in detail at our evaluation staff conference, utilizing these findings appropriately in our recommendations. However, it is important to remember that parents may show previously unexpressed feelings and attitudes at the time of the interpretive conference. We should be ready for this, and flexible enough in our approach to use it to our advantage.

It is very important that parents should be encouraged to talk and ask questions. We should be prepared to answer questions about etiology, and to answer them as specifically and objectively as possible, being careful to avoid criticism or ridicule, no matter how preposterous or weird some of the parental theories may seem to us. In this connection, we should choose our words and explanations carefully, in order not to create or reinforce feelings of guilt or blame that may be so near the surface in the parents' conception of what may have caused their child's condition.

The parents should not only be allowed to ask questions, they should be encouraged to talk freely. It is an especially good idea to ask the parents for their estimate of the child's overall developmental level. Several authorities in the field believe that this is an excellent starting point for the interpretation. (If this estimate has been asked for previously during the evaluation, as we usually do, it seems quite natural to come back to it at this point, and to use it as the springboard for the discussion of the entire problem.)

Several good studies have shown that there is a significant degree of correlation between the child's test performance and the parents' estimates of his capacities and limitations. If such is the case, it is a good beginning in establishing a rapport that will be helpful in the subsequent discussion to acknowledge in a positive way the ability of the parents to observe the child accurately and to realize his limitations. It is also helpful to refer—but gently, and with grace—to the parents' reasonably accurate estimate if later they tend to lose sight of the child's capacities when considering their immediate and future goals for him. Such awareness is more frequently sensed than understood, and without proper interpretation and management, can be converted into further confusion, guilt, and anxiety. In case the parents' appraisal is grossly over- or underestimated, it is even more advantageous for us to be aware of this as early as possible. Another question that can be helpful, both to the informant and to the parents, in bringing more sharply into focus their own evaluation of the problem, is something like "what are the main problems that you have faced in your child, and in what ways would you like most to be helped with them?"

The order of presentation and degree of emphasis on the diagnostic findings must be individually determined in each case. If we use the parental estimate of a child's developmental level as a starting point for the discussion, it is equally important that we make an adequate recognition of the parental concept of the etiology, as we have mentioned previously. If the diagnostic findings do not support this concept, we should make this explicit and well emphasized, but again with tolerance and understanding. We should be careful at this point not to overwhelm and confuse the parents with a mass of medical facts that they are unable to comprehend or assimilate. We should try to explain their own problem to them in as simple and straightforward a way as possible, and in language that they are able to understand. When we don't know the answers to certain questions, we should say so, but not in a way [that would] imply that possible things were left unchecked, and certainly not in the way—at least in most instances—of an impersonal discussion of the percentage of diagnostic probabilities of one kind as opposed to another. This is not the time for an academic discussion of etiological theory. It is not the total amount of information that we give to people that is of value in the final analysis, but what they hear and understand.

. . . .

Last but not least, we want to give the parents in the interpretive conference a specific program to suit the child's immediate needs, and, as well as we are able, an honest prognosis of the future. To do this latter well is oftentimes very difficult for several reasons. We must never forget that it is of paramount importance that we avoid misleading or ambiguous statements that would tend to give parents false hopes. This is an easy thing to do, augmented many times by a fear of the parents' reaction, the insecurity of the informant in the interpretive situation, or by a misplaced sense of compassion that would tend to "spare" the parents the "bad news." There is another side to the coin, however, that should give us pause. As we learn more about the causes of retardation and the factors that influence its valid measurement, we know that long-term predictions, at least in many instances, are just not possible with any degree of certainty. In general, the younger the child is when evaluated, the less valid are our predictive abilities. Also, parents differ in their emotional readiness as to what they are able to hear and accept, at least in the first informing session, and this must be taken into consideration in each case. Parents who are in an emotional turmoil, and who are often too preoccupied with their own questions of why, how, who or what is to blame for their sorrow rather than what to do about it, cannot be "made" to face all aspects of the situation immediately. They need to work their way through to it, and an over-aggressive approach, no matter how well meant, may add to the reaction of shock and resistance.

There are some rather obvious points about the arrangement and conduct of the conference that should be stated briefly. The parents should be seen in privacy, and without distracting interruptions. It is important, if possible, to have both parents present, at least at the time of the initial interpretation. They may have different conceptions of the problem, different degrees of maturity and stability, and different attitudes toward the child. Also, it is grossly unfair to everyone concerned for one parent, usually the mother, to attempt to interpret the interpretation to the other. Sufficient time should be allotted for it, so that the parents do not feel hurried, or sense impatience on the part of the informant. The first ingredient for a successful interview is genuine interest and sympathy for the people and problem involved. Little things like sincerity, tone of voice and personal conviction and feeling are not lost on parents, whether present or absent. Finally, if some parents are so hostile and resistant that one reacts in the same way, everyone involved is the loser. It is self-defeating to respond in this way to provocations from those you are trying to help.

I would like to discuss for a moment now a matter of particular importance to this group. That is, the place and responsibility of the public health nurse in the interpretation of mental retardation to parents. Although the nurse's formal role in this area undoubtedly varies from place to place, I suspect that she has become more and more a participant in most clinics, formally or otherwise. This is because, I think, the nurse is in a unique position of potential effectiveness in many areas of interpretation that is unmatched by any other member of the evaluation team. It is important that we recognize this potential, and arrange our programs and equip our nurses so that this potential may be utilized to the greatest advantage. Some points to consider:

1. The public health nurse is in a "strategic position" to establish good rapport with the parents of retarded children, where certain "built in" barriers may exist between the parents and other members of the clinic staff. Many mothers and fathers of retarded children have a feeling of hostility toward doctors which may or may not be justified, but nevertheless exists. Without going into the complex and many-faceted dynamics of the emotional reactions involved, this feeling may be carried through the evaluation process, and may interfere with the acceptance of the findings and recommendations. . . .

2. The nurse represents the continuity and extension of the clinic's evaluation and follow-up into the patient's home. Whether done personally, or by liaison with nurses in the field, or both, the effect of this is, again, to place the nurse in a unique position of strategic advantage for parent help and acceptance. In the Cambridge study just cited, "home training service, rendered by the public health nurse . . . was the first service mentioned when the mother was asked, 'What helps?' . . . People turned to her for help, and had the image of her being a 'helping person'."

In view of the importance of interpretation of mental retardation to parents, and in view of the problems frequently involved in the acceptance of this interpretation, should we not recognize the potential contribution of the nurse, this "helpful person," in such a critical area?

. . . .

Three things we can remember:

1. Be honest and straightforward.
2. Be tolerant, considerate, and understanding.
3. "It is not what you pour out of the pitcher, but what gets into the cup."

□ □ □

from THE INFORMING INTERVIEW

Carl Drayer

Elfriede G. Schlesinger

(American Journal of Mental Deficiency, 1960)

We have found that during the first phase of the interview, it is best if the informant conveys to the parents the findings and recommendations that were formulated at the case conference. It is not suggested that this consist of a mechanical recitation of the facts. Rather, some opportunity is given to the parents to restate their major questions and an attempt is made to focus discussion with these in mind. As the informant presents the findings, the parents must be given further opportunity to ask questions and to state their own opinion concerning the material being presented. The discusssion is, therefore, continually adjusted to the parents' readiness to deal with certain aspects of the findings.

Whatever is told the parents should be put simply, directly, and honestly. The diagnosis must be phrased in a manner which parents will understand and must include a statement of what is known as well as what is not known. The extent of the retardation should be conveyed to them. Here one "skates on thin ice." Sometimes parents have brought the child to the clinic at a point when they are first beginning to recognize the developmental lag. However, on their own they have not yet begun to recognize that this lag may handicap the child in all areas of functioning throughout life, and may simply not be prepared to deal with the possibility at this point.

The interview may serve to help them make a beginning step in this direction. Often, an attempt to have the parents themselves assess the child's level of development is useful. It is interesting how often their estimate corresponds very closely to our own. In this way the parents are themselves participating in the evaluation process. Generally speaking, we avoid giving a specific IQ score. The broad categories of mild, moderate, and severe retardation, and the concept of mental age, we find, have clarified the points raised in a more meaningful way. For example, the fact that the child has an IQ of 50 may shock and distress them, but gives them little concrete help in anticipating the general rate of development and functioning for the child either in long or short range terms. If, on the other hand, it is pointed out that at the age of five their child functions roughly like a two and a half or three year old, they can deal with this much more effectively. Examples drawn from their own accounts of the child's past rate of development as well as from the clinic's findings help them further to grasp the meaning of the findings. However, here too, we have applied no rigid, unswerving standard. Where a parent has learned to think in terms of IQ scores, and has perhaps misinterpreted previous information given, we occasionally give the results of our tests, being most careful to caution the parents against uncritical acceptance of the meaning of a mere number. The constancy and prognostic implications of test results are not unduly emphasized, especially when we deal with younger children.

In discussing the child we always attempt to evaluate him as a total individual, rather than focus merely on his intellectual development or upon his medical problems. Thus, discussion of his behavior, personality and sociability forms an integral part of these interviews. Where the child's behavior is severely disturbing and interferes with his learning capacities this is pointed out to the parents. Where possible, we stress the patient's strong points, his physical appearance, commendable behavior, or his capacity for affection. When, as often happens, a child's social development exceeds his intellectual capacity, this too is stressed particularly in relation to the more immediate prognosis. We stress the importance of demonstrating to the parents our recognition of a child's strengths for a number of reasons. The parent who is blinded to a degree to the inadequacies of the child may more readily accept our evaluation if we transmit the knowledge that we see his strengths despite the weaknesses and difficulties we have pointed out. For those parents who are too overwhelmed by the problems to see the child as a child, the demonstrated capacity of the informant to express positive feelings about the child as a person may help the parents to view the youngster in a new perspective.

Questions concerning etiology are in every parent's mind. In any discussion of this matter it must be anticipated that one or both parents may have feelings of guilt and the greatest discretion must be practiced. They may have strong suspicions about the obstetrical delivery, early nursing care, pediatric management, their own role, or hereditary factors, and the part they believe these may have played in producing the defective child. Where the cause of the retardation is definitely known, it should be told to the parents; if unclassified, then this should be explained to them. The likelihood of a similar occurrence in future pregnancies should be statistically predicted to the best of our abilities. Frank confessions of scientific ignorance, where applicable, are better than dogmatic but ill-founded statements.

We implied earlier that although we have a responsibility to convey to the parents the prognostic implications of our evaluation, at no time should anyone attempt to prognosticate a child's development too far in advance or to give the parents more than they are emotionally prepared to hear at the moment. A prognosis may be made for the near future while it is explained to the parents that this will have to be re-evaluated from time to time as the child is further observed. Thus, while we may be fairly certain that a young child lacks the capacity for becoming an independent functioning member of the community, errors can be made. It seems more advisable to concentrate on the more immediately attainable goals. In the case of very young children, these are often in the area of helping the child to achieve some independence in self-care skills or to provide opportunities for socialization. When the parents of such a child raise questions concerning the long range potential, it is perhaps more advisable to state rather frankly that the child is too young, or that it is too soon to make definitive statements.

We emphasize this point, since in our zeal to help parents avoid the pitfalls of over-estimating their child, we have on occasion incurred their hostility because of their inability to accept too devastating a prognosis all at once. Perhaps even more important in consideration of this point is the fact that we have been in error at times in our long range prognosis. Also, we have seen parents who are loath to accept any of our findings because of the mistaken, overly gloomy prognostications of others. The parents may have been informed earlier, by another center, that their child would never walk. Yet, they brought him to us because his incessant running and hyperactivity have become a major management problem. The younger the child, in general, the less certain is the prognosis.

We do not imply, however, that the informant goes along with the parents' most unreasonable hopes and expectations. Rather, he utilizes the parents' own observations of the child's current level of functioning and rate of progress to help them to come to a greater realization and understanding on their own. Ideally, the experience of being helped to assess the level of the child's development and rate of progress, both in terms of the clinic's estimate and their own observations, should help parents go through similar processes more independently at later stages of the child's development.

There are, however, specific situations which demand not only an evaluation of the child's current level of functioning and its implications for the more immediate future, but discussion of long range management. This is perhaps most true in the cases of pre-adolescents and adolescents. If the parents of a child in this age group are enrolling the youngster in a program of training for which he is obviously not suited, such as attempting to teach him a skilled trade, it is important to point this out to them. In situations of this kind, the technique of helping parents to comprehend the problem on the basis of their own observations or those made at the clinic is important. Thus, if the child has never shown any demonstrable skill in the areas required, this can be reviewed with the parents. When the child has reached the age when questions of independent functioning are pertinent, it is appropriate to discuss the child's capacities in relation to the skills required for independent living, and to help the parents to review the problems from this perspective. For example, if the child has failed to achieve the most minimal reading skills, and does not seem to be able to learn how to travel, this needs to be reviewed if they talk about his being a messenger boy. If his manual dexterity is shown to be most poor, their hopes that he might learn to work on an assembly line or do other semi-skilled work should be pointed out more realistically.

In outlining a program of management and treatment, the family's capacity to follow through on suggestions, in terms of the total family situation, must be kept in mind at all times. The mother of a three-year-old retardate whose self-care functioning is at an infant level, will view with skepticism any suggestion that she permit the child ample time at each meal to attain self-feeding skills, if she has several other young children, all requiring considerable attention. It may, therefore, be more practical to recommend that she select only one meal during the day in which to concentrate on this particular skill. It would be beneficial, where possible, to give the parents an approximate estimate of the time required to accomplish a specific learning process.

It is important to commend any successes parents may have met in the handling of their child because their confidence is often battered by the uphill course they have had to travel. The feeling that the child might have been "all right" had more time been devoted to his care must be corrected. Where the child's lags are accentuated by lack of parental understanding or attention this should of course be mentioned diplomatically. These situations often require further counseling or concrete help of some nature. If the mother has, for example, failed to help the child to attain independence in self-care skills because of lack of patience and know-how, the difficulties involved can be acknowledged. Further, the accumulated experience of staff members, and the availability of other resources can be pointed out. If other personnel, such as the clinic's visiting nurse, are called upon to aid the mother at home with a particular problem, it must remain clear that this role is purely supplementary to that of the family.

Parents often come seeking many therapies, in the hope that a specific type of treatment will improve the basic problem. Frequently, the child is not ready to benefit from these services. For instance, the parent who insists that speech therapy will help the child, may have overlooked his own observation that the youngster's general level of development is comparable to that of his one-year-old sibling. Recalling his earlier statement may help him view his request more realistically. More important, it aids him in coming to a firmer grip with the reality of the child's disability, and may refocus his thinking on those aspects of training which are more attainable at this point. Such an approach is also useful in consideration of the educational needs of the older retardate. If a special educational program is indicated it may help the parent accept such class placement, if the child's inability to cope with the skills required in the regular grade is pointed out.

While parents often request specific services which are believed unsuitable, they often make realistic requests. All too frequently, these services would be most beneficial to the child but are not available. At the clinic there may be a waiting list for a specific therapeutic group. In the community, there may be no opening in the local nursery school, or in the special classes. The temptation to deny the importance of these services in order to prevent feelings of frustration is great. However, parents can easily sense such deception and show a justifiable resentment. We have found that forthright admission of these inadequacies is appreciated by a parent. Further, a discussion of the role played by parents' organizations in regard to unmet community needs for the retarded may be of additional help. While it must be pointed out honestly that a parent's participation will not guarantee the establishment of a facility from which his child could benefit, the organizations' overall achievements can be stressed. Furthermore, parents find it easier to deal with their own problems, both on a practical and emotional level, when they come in contact with others who are in the same situation.

During the course of the interview, the informant may get the impression that the parents have many problems which they hesitate to voice. Often there is a fear that the presence of a retarded child may have adverse effects on other siblings. The placement of a child in an institution may be attended by such pangs of conscience that the parents do not want to discuss it. In general we know that parents of retarded children have questions on these matters at one time or another. How much of this is raised by the informant during the course of the informing interview is largely a matter of individual discretion. Of course, if the questions and problems in these areas have been brought up by the parent previously, they can be discussed very freely. Where this is not the case, and the parent has come to the interview primarily to gain an interpretation of our findings, a few well-placed questions or suggestive comments may make it possible for him to open such discussion. If there is a need for help in this area, it may be feasible to handle it briefly during the interview. Where the problems are more complicated the informant merely acknowledges this, and makes arrangements for further guidance.

An informing interview such as we have described deals essentially with the problems of an individual who is chronically handicapped, and whose functioning will be impaired in one or more major areas throughout life. In dealing with a problem of such magnitude, a single discussion seldom suffices to answer all of the family's questions or to deal with the complexities of the situation. Nor should it be anticipated that the parents will come away from such a discussion fully accepting or understanding the child's condition. Rather, a well conducted informing interview sets a firm and sound foundation for further contacts.

In summary, then, we view the informing interview held with parents following the diagnostic evaluation of their child as a medium for acquainting them with our findings and to establish a sound basis for future contacts. The informant who conducts such an interview must be equipped with much factual data concerning the major aspects of retardation. Sensitivity to the needs of the particular child and family together with a sound understanding of the specific problems of the child are crucial. The interview must be conducted in a leisurely manner and should provide the parents with ample opportunities to voice their fears and concerns. Positive aspects in the child's functioning and parental handling should be stressed. Long range prognosis should at all times be presented in a guarded manner, particularly in the case of young children. How much is told the parents about the future must be geared to the family's capacity to accept the implications of such a prognosis. However, every effort must be made to prevent the raising of false hopes and to help the parents to deal realistically with their child's limitations. It is not expected that a single discussion will serve to answer all of the parents' questions but rather that such an interview will help establish the basis for future work.

□ □ □

from MONGOLISM: WHEN SHOULD PARENTS BE TOLD?

C. M. Drillien, E. M. Wilkinson

(British Medical Journal, 1964)

The practitioner responsible for the care of a handicapped child or an infant with a congenital defect has to decide what to tell the parents and when. In the event of physical defect of a visible nature some explanation must be given at once. Although the mother may be newly delivered and one might wish to spare her the knowledge of her baby's abnormality, it is hardly possible to conceal the fact of such congenital defects as cleft-lip, talipes, or spina bifida. In the case of mongolism, the only common category of severe mental defect which is recognizable at birth, the situation is different in that it may not be obvious to the parents that the infant is abnormal.

There is considerable disagreement about the best time to tell the parents of a mongol that their infant will be mentally handicapped. Some hold that, since the diagnosis and prognosis are not in doubt, the parents have a right to be told at once or as soon as the mother has recovered from the immediate effects of the confinement. Others maintain that acceptance of a handicapped child and adjustment to the fact of mental defect is facilitated if, in the early months at least, the parents are left in ignorance and the mother is allowed to make a normal loving attachment to her baby. This argument presupposes that the mother herself will not recognize her child's abnormality and also that her medical attendants will be able to act in such a way that her suspicions are not aroused. In some cases there will be definite reasons, known to the obstetrician or family doctor, for delay in telling the parents, but in general whether or not the mother is told early depends on the usual practice of a particular doctor or hospital.

Present Study

A current aetiological study of severely subnormal children in Edinburgh has provided the opportunity of questioning mothers of mongols about their attitude to the time at which they were first told of their child's defect. The total group of 239 includes all those children born in the years 1950–6 with intelligence quotient levels of less than 60 whose mothers are at present resident in Edinburgh. Of this number, 71 are mongols. The mothers of 70 were visited at home and interviewed by a health visitor with considerable experience in dealing with parents of handicapped children. The one mother not visited is unmarried and at the time of the investigation was herself in a mental hospital. Most of the children were born in Edinburgh, but there was no indication that the experiences of mothers delivered in other areas of Scotland or England differed in any way.

Each mother was asked when and by whom she was first told that her child was a mongol; whether she would have preferred to be told sooner or later, with the reasons for her preference, and whether she had any other criticisms about the time or method of telling. In the case of children born in or referred to Edinburgh hospitals, we were usually able to check when the parents had been told. The information given by the mothers agreed substantially with that obtained from hospital records. In spite of the subjective nature of the information obtained, it seems reasonable to suppose that if a majority of mothers told at a certain time later express satisfaction at the time chosen, while a majority of mothers told at a different time express dissatisfaction, this is a valid indication of maternal preferences.

Table I gives the total number of mothers who were told at different times; the number who were satisfied with the time at which they were told and whether or not they had other criticisms; the number who were dissatisfied, and of these the number who still expressed strong resentment about the time when they were told. The other criticisms made by mothers are set out in Table II. Three mothers had no clear recollection about the time and way they were told.

Of the sixteen mothers told shortly after birth, three would have preferred to have been told later, when they were more fully recovered from the confinement. One of these still expressed considerable resentment at the shock she had received. Of the thirteen mothers who were glad to have been told at once, one spoke of her great distress at the time but thought that it was preferable to get over the initial shock while still in hospital. All other mothers who expressed dissatisfaction at the time they were told wished to have known earlier, although one who was not told until her child was over 4 years old made the comment that she might not have had another child if she had realized earlier that her first child was mentally defective. The proportion of mothers expressing satisfaction with the time they were told fell from over 80 per cent of those told shortly after birth to 22 per cent of those told after their child was two years old.

The mother's social status made little difference to the time when she was first told that her child was a mongol. Rather more of those in social classes I, II, and III were told before one month after birth, but by one year equal proportions in all social classes had been informed.

Mothers of firstborn infants were less likely to be told early than mothers of later-born infants. When the mother had other normal children one in three had been told before one month and only one in ten had not been told by the child's first birthday. When the mongol was a firstborn, one in four of the mothers was told in the first month and one in three not until after the first year. Only one of twelve mothers of firstborn mongols had no criticisms to make about the time or method of telling compared with 32 out of 58 mothers of later-born mongols.

Nearly one-half of the total mothers said that they realized before being told that there was something seriously wrong with the child's development. This was no less common when the mongol was a firstborn child. Five mothers recognized the stigmata of mongolism when they first saw their babies; one suspected that something was wrong because "a lot of doctors" (most probably students) seemed interested in the baby, and three others because of their transfer to a single room or special kindness shown by nursing and medical staff. One mother read her case notes.

After discharge from maternity hospital five mothers experienced considerable difficulties in management and feeding but were given no explanation of the cause; two of these were mothers of firstborn mongols and had attributed the difficulties to their own inexperience. Nine mothers stated that they could have been spared months of uncertainty and unexpressed fears if they had been told earlier. Only three complained that they had been told in an abrupt, blunt, or unsympathetic manner, which makes it unlikely that many of the criticisms voiced stemmed from resentment felt against the individual who first revealed that the child was mentally defective.

To sum up, the mothers who spoke most appreciatively about the way they

TABLE I

Reactions of Mothers to the Time at Which They Were Told That Their Child Was a Mongol

WHEN MOTHER WAS TOLD	TOTAL		SATISFIED WITH TIME			DISSATISFIED WITH TIME		
			TOTAL		OTHER CRITICISMS	TOTAL		MOTHER VERY RESENTFUL
	NO.	%	NO.	%		NO.	%	
Before 10 days . .	16	22·5	13	81·3	2*	3	18·7	1
10 days-1 month	2	2·8	1	50·0	–	1	50·0	–
1–6 months . .	20	28·2	12 (2†)	60·0	6	8	40·0	1
6–12 months . .	13	18·3	7	53·8	1	6	46·2	3
1–2 years	7	9·9	3	42·9	–	4	57·1	1
After 2 years . .	9	12·7	2 (2†)	22·2	–	7	77·8	2
?	3	4·2	3					
No information	1	1·4						
Total . .	71	100·0	41	57·7	9	29	40·8	8

*Stated that they should have been told even earlier.
†Specified that they did not wish to be told earlier.

TABLE II

Other Criticisms Made by Mothers

	OTHER CRITICISMS MADE BY MOTHERS WHO WERE			
	SATISFIED WITH TIME	DISSATISFIED WITH TIME	TOTAL	
			NO.	%
1. Told only after repeated questioning	2	3	5	7·1
2. Questioned at birth but reassured ..	–	3	3	4·3
3. Referred to hospital, reassured ..	–	3	3	4·3
4. Told on hospital admission for another condition	1	1	2	2·9
5. Told on application for emigration ..	–	1	1	1·4
6. Husband told early, wife told later ..	–	1	1	1·4
7. Given too gloomy a prognosis ("will never walk or talk")	1	3	4	5·7
8. Given too optimistic a prognosis ("may grow out of it")	–	1	1	1·4
9. Did not understand implication of "mongolism"	1	–	1	1·4
10. Not told about associated congenital heart defect	–	1	1	1·4
11. Method of telling abrupt, blunt, or unsympathetic	2	1	3	4·3
Total	7	18	25	35·6

had been told were those who, having been warned or told soon after birth, were given a full explanation at that time or within the next three months, more especially if thereafter they were encouraged to return to the family doctor or paediatrician with any further queries or problems and were given regular support and advice throughout the early years. The mothers who were still most resentful were those who had suspected that their child was not normal, sought advice, and been reassured that there was nothing seriously wrong. . . .

□ □ □

Part IV General Principles of Management and Counseling

Many selections in earlier parts of this book have already touched upon general management and counseling principles, as will many selections in later parts. Concentrated into this part will be items primarily addressed to the broader principles of management and counseling. Problems of a more specific nature will be treated later.

We are already familiar with the first two authors, having found their contributions significant in previous contexts. Jensen covers a number of general points, identifying three recurrent management errors as well as seven principles that should underlie constructive management. Although Jensen relates his points mostly to the case evaluation process, they are equally germane to management principles in general.

"With many retarded children, the problems encountered in promoting independence in self-care do not result from inadequate techniques in training, but from the growth-inhibiting attitudes and feelings of the parents." In this cogent and clear statement, Begab provides us with the essence of a general rationale for parent management and counseling. This is reminiscent of the statement previously quoted in the discussion of the article by Hastings (Part I, Section A): "The correct handling of the child usually lies in the correct management of the parents." What more general principle can be stated? Begab emphasizes that once parents are freed of inhibiting emotional factors they can be guided into rational and realistic learning situations. This theme is repeated in many different ways throughout the Begab selection, and is implied in the writings of many other authors.

Harriet Blodgett is a professional with considerable experience in parental guidance. Her analysis of parental problems and needs reveals particular insight. She points out that the average lay person and parent, lacking understanding of the role of intelligence in behavior organization and adaptation, frequently subscribe to fallacious notions. Thus, one of the most basic needs of parents is for proper and accurate information. A second major parental need is for practical help and guidance. Means of meeting these needs, as employed by a well known service-oriented agency (Sheltering Arms in Minneapolis), are described.

A miscellany of points are covered in the selections by Schild, Beck, and Hersch. These selections frequently relate management considerations to parental dynamics, and discussion is enlivened by means of instructive case illustrations. Points recurrently emphasized are that treatment goes far beyond diagnosis, and that parents need repeated and prolonged counseling if the child is to derive the best benefits from parental or agency efforts. Schild presents a theoretical model that calls for involvement of both parents in counseling. In addition to discussing general principles of management and counseling, Beck reviews some considerations that affect the choice between individual and group approaches and the duration of clinic services. Hersch considers a broad spectrum of management problems, from the case evaluation phase to the time when the children in a family are becoming adults and a retardate's institutional placement may be considered or effected.

In the two final selections, intensive case studies illustrate a range of management options and benefits. Stone presents a case employing a multi-faceted management approach to one family. The child, a four-year-old, mildly-retarded boy, received individual therapy from a psychologist while the parents passed from the evaluation phase to individual and eventually group counseling. Ultimately, the child progressed enough to enter a school program, and the entire family was felt to have achieved a higher level of adjustment. While a multifaceted treatment approach is essential in some cases, French, Levbarg and Michal-Smith discuss a family in which they worked entirely through a mother in bringing about markedly improved behavior in her child. The counselors tried to help the mother understand that the boy's improvement was the fruit of her own efforts. Perhaps the most noteworthy element in this report is the demonstration of how progress in a child can be achieved by parent counseling alone. In terms of cost-efficiency, such parent guidance often may be the optimal management alternative.

from THE CLINICAL MANAGEMENT OF THE MENTALLY RETARDED CHILD AND THE PARENTS

Reynold A. Jensen

(*American Journal of Psychiatry,* 1950)

. . . .

It is difficult to estimate the tragic suffering in a family that has a mentally retarded member. Such suffering is too often aggravated by generous advice from sympathetic relatives, friends, and even professional workers. In all probability our errors are due to 1) lack of understanding the basic issues inherent in each case, and 2) inadequate techniques in assisting parents to plan more objectively.

It seems obvious that in any program designed to help deficient individuals the emphasis must be placed on the family, for upon the family's attitudes and thinking, particularly that of the parents, depends the ultimate success of the program.

The task of helping parents who have a retarded child is complicated. It is not enough to sidestep the issue or to "tell" them that their child is "feeble-minded" and should be institutionalized. In our experience at the University of Minnesota Hospitals, the three most frequently encountered errors are: 1) delay in defining the problem early in the patient's life; 2) encouragement of parents by holding out false hopes, which naturally results in disillusionment later when the patient is not cordially received in school or becomes a social problem requiring immediate planning for his management, and 3) too much direct advice and/or urging adoption of a specific plan—too often institutionalization. We physicians sometimes assume that this alone will adequately solve the problem. However, our assumptions usually result in failure for we have not fully appreciated the strong emotional ties that most parents center in the mentally handicapped person. Our own hastily formulated plan often complicates the situation because it increases parental resistance.

Since we have become cognizant of the real and widespread need to offer help to the parents of retarded children, we have given serious thought to the development of a *workable* method of doing so. We believe the keynote is the approach to the parents. Several important factors require consideration. Unfortunately, most parents still regard mental deficiency as a stigma. In addition they have much real anxiety, usually closely related to feelings of guilt. In the majority of instances they try to resolve these emotional problems by assuming an attitude of overconcern and overprotectiveness toward the defective child. This, in a measure, may be protection of themselves. For these reasons we believe, with few exceptions, that management of the strong emotional ties that the average parent has toward the defective child is the core of the problem.

Average parents are aware that their child is retarded. We avoid, insofar as is possible, directly telling them what they already know. Parents come to us primarily for confirmation of their suspicions and doubts. Our task is to help parents define their own problems and possible solutions to them. In the process we are able to help reorient parental emotional ties with the defective child and give support and justification to the parents' knowledge.

Our approach to the *study* of any individual suspected of being mentally retarded requires acceptance of several basic principles. We try not to deviate from them.

1. Ample time is provided. If justice is to be done not only to the child involved but also to the parents, it is impossible to hurry. A frequent complaint made by many parents who have been disappointed is, "How does he know our problem? He was with him only a few moments. How does he know our problem?"

2. The study is thorough. *All* factors bearing on the case are carefully considered.

3. Care is exercised in the choice of words used during the interviews with the parents. Each word in our language has associated with it its own peculiar emotional colorings. Some are more emotionally charged than others. Such expressions as "feeble-minded," "moron," "imbecile," and "idiot" are avoided. In their places are substituted "backward," "slow," and "retarded in development."

4. Parents have not only the *right* but the *responsibility* for deciding what is to be done for or with their child. This right is respected by the physician.

5. Parents are encouraged to reveal their own questions and doubts. The success of the study depends in a large measure upon how completely and satisfactorily their questions are answered.

6. The physician's attitude in dealing with this problem is no different from that of dealing with any other medical problem. He approaches the problem analytically allowing no personal feelings to interfere with a sound, critical evaluation.

7. The orientation of the social worker and psychologist associated with the physician is also of paramount importance. Each must have a thorough knowledge of his field, and an appreciation of his own responsibilities is essential. At no point should anyone become overaggressive. . . .

[During evaluation] the parents are asked "How is your child different from others of comparable age?" This simple question yields surprising results because it enables parents to delineate more objectively their own thinking and at the same time to evaluate the child himself. As differences are elaborated, the final question, "On the basis of our discussion, how old would you estimate your child to be?" is asked. The accuracy with which the average parents estimate their child's developmental age is remarkable. Their answer helps them by more sharply bringing to focus their own evaluation of the problem. It also provides a logical focus for beginning the final interview. . . .

The fact of confirmation often yields surprising results in itself for it releases the parents of anxiety and enables them to consider plans that otherwise would not have been possible. This is well illustrated by the immediate response of one mother who spontaneously burst out with, "I've known from the time my child was but a few weeks old that she was not developing normally but I couldn't get anyone to confirm it." The child was nearly five years old when the study was undertaken. Once the mother's suspicions were confirmed, she was actually freed to "do something about it." This youngster is now satisfactorily placed in a school for backward children.

Next in order is the discussion of probable etiology. Parents want an explanation for the child's retardation. Either consciously or unconsciously they individually feel much personal guilt.

. . . .

The next step in the final interview is a full consideration of "What can we do about it?" As was suggested, no one has any right to tell a parent what he must do with or for a defective child. However, the physician has the responsibility to help the parents think through their problems. He does this by considering all possible plans of action and the effect these plans may have on all members of the family. Immeasurable suffering has been initiated by a too hasty suggestion that you "ought to put your child in an institution." Such procedure disregards completely the parents' emotional problems. . . .

Before the family finally decides on a plan that is "right" for them, further suggestions are elaborated:

1. The child will continue to grow physically. The unevenness of the total growth due to the persistent lag in social and intellectual maturation is carefully considered. In addition, parents are reminded that the differences already noted will become more marked as the child grows older.

2. No parents should undertake the responsibility of planning for one member of the family until the *total needs* of every member of the family, including themselves, are fully considered. Care is taken to speak directly to this point. Trouble usually ensues when parents have disregarded the needs of the other members of the family.

3. In consideration of the above questions, emphasis is placed on the point that all good parents consider fully the needs of each child in the family and try to the best of their ability and circumstances to meet them as adequately as possible. This point is made as it serves the dual purpose of a) compelling the parents to consider freely the child's own particular needs for deriving as much satisfaction from living as possible and b) protecting themselves should they decide on a placement plan.

The conference is ended by providing an opportunity for the parents to ask questions and bring out related problems. This is most essential as it makes possible full discussion of issues peculiar to the case and family. In addition, it is possible to deal with the parent's own emotional problems. It is during this phase of the interview that many parents deal directly with the real sources of their guilt and anxiety.

In general, this is our approach to the study and management of every problem of mental retardation. The approach is often varied to meet the emotional needs of the parents. Frequently the child's progress is checked at periodic intervals. In the interim, parents, benefiting from sympathetic understanding of the total problem, gradually develop for themselves greater understanding and more complete acceptance of the reality of the situation. Careful and considerate management on our part enables parents to deal more effectively with their own and the child's problems.

The question is often raised, "Doesn't this procedure seem to involve a great deal of time?" The answer is "yes," but by spending time on any one patient situation, in doing a thorough, careful analysis, time is actually saved. As parent's doubts and suspicions are confirmed, as their many questions are answered, they are gently freed of their own binding emotional problems. This lessens the need to "shop around," which means in itself a saving of time. But more than that, as parents develop insight and understanding, the child himself benefits by the change in the attitude toward him. Excessive pressures on him are lessened, and, being freed of these, in many instances he responds more favorably than would have been possible otherwise. Finally, if placement is eventually decided upon, parents have the pleasant feeling that their own rights and privileges have been respected.

Three important results have emerged following the use of this approach over the past five years: 1) Parents, when given a chance, do make good decisions; 2) should parents decide on a specific plan such as placement, they can use more constructively the services of the social worker and others who assist the parents in carrying out the plan they have decided upon; 3) this, in turn, has made it possible for the social worker to make a greater contribution to the total welfare of the family. Of equal importance is the feeling of comfortableness the physician has in dealing with a problem that, at best, is most trying and difficult. The confidence he has in understanding the basic problem and his responsibility is of material help in assisting parents with an unpleasant task.

As we all work toward this common end, society is benefited, for its fundamental unit, the family, will have been protected and [often] strengthened.

□ □ □

from CASEWORK FOR THE MENTALLY RETARDED— CASEWORK WITH PARENTS

Michael J. Begab

(*The Mentally Retarded Child: A Guide to Services of Social Agencies,* 1963)

. . . .

With many retarded children, the problems encountered in promoting independence in self-care do not result from inadequate techniques in training, but from the growth-inhibiting attitudes and feelings of the parents. Unless the child has a severe physical defect which does not permit him to perform certain functions, or is so limited mentally that he can neither be conditioned to nor taught a prescribed mode of behavior, he can usually learn self-care skills. Considerable repetition is frequently needed and more complicated processes need to be broken down into simple, successive steps, but the method of teaching is basically the same as would be used with normal children.

When retarded children fail to develop these skills even after allowances are made for developmental lags, the problem can often be traced to impatience, frustration, overprotection, or inconsistent handling by the parents. These attitudes and responses stem from many sources. In some cases they reflect the parents' characteristic way of handling the task of child-rearing even for their normal children. Sometimes parents take the "easy way" out; it is simpler to do for the child than to take the time to teach him. In other situations, however, the child's deficiency has activated feelings of anxiety, guilt and sometimes aversion, which color the parent-child relationship. Most retarded children usually sense how the parent feels and react accordingly. The child whose aggressive acts or temper outbursts are either rationalized or countenanced soon learns to manipulate his human environment. In many instances —despite limited intelligence—he is shrewd enough to get his own way without the compromise and conformity essential for social development.

To provide a setting conducive to learning the elements of social living, it is important that these feelings be resolved as soon as possible. If they are not too deep seated, they can often be approached by a concentration on the concrete problems of training, management, and discipline. The key to greater independence in the retarded child is patience and understanding in the parents. Sometimes this can be developed through an interpretation of the child's readiness to assume certain tasks and by demonstration of effective teaching techniques. Frequently parents need to be helped with their feelings of disappointment in the child or with problems of marital dissension before they can readjust their goals and apply child-rearing methods with telling results.

Many parents—once they are freed of inhibiting emotional factors—can be guided in the choice of play equipment and activities that will improve the child's sensori-motor coordination or better suit his level of development and thereby eliminate for him potential sources of failure and frustration. . . .

Other parents need guidance in identifying the kinds of household chores their retarded child can and should be given responsibility for. They must be helped to understand that it is not only proper to impose responsibilities upon the child but imperative that they do so in accord with his capacities to assume them. As the child experiences success in the handling of objects and in the performance of simple tasks, his ability to concentrate on other tasks is enhanced and his emotional controls are strengthened. With these gains—sometimes quite dramatic in nature—parents tend to regard the child's future with optimism. Equally important, as the child learns to do more for himself, the parents' burden of care and supervision is somewhat relieved and greater patience and tolerance on their part becomes possible.

Another objective of working with these parents is to counteract their social isolation and withdrawal tendencies—frequently self-imposed. Although some people are unthinking in their comments and unwilling to permit their normal children to play with a retarded child, generally their basic attitudes toward the parents of retarded children are sympathetic and understanding. Unfortunately, however, these parents sometimes interpret the actions of their neighbors as rejection of themselves and rather than risk these emotional hurts confine their social activities to the family circle. Constructive social outlets are vital safety-valves; their lack intensifies tensions within the home and is disruptive to family stability.

The social worker's acceptance and understanding of the parents as persons with their own needs and rights can relieve the bitterness and distrust they sometimes display. But the worker-client relationship is not an island unto itself and there may be little carry-over of positive feelings toward others if the retarded child and his parents are continually buffeted by rejecting community attitudes. In these instances, parents may be encouraged to interpret the child's behavior and condition to their neighbors and thus reduce unfounded fears and suspicions. Where the attitude of a particularly troublesome neighbor cannot be handled in this fashion, the worker may well weigh the advisability of making an interpretation to the neighbor himself.

Even where parents gain acceptance for themselves, the retarded child—especially if his handicap is severe—may have little opportunity for social companionship or may be unable to participate in the social activities of his peer group. Parental attempts to foster relationships with other children through sponsoring parties and special outings frequently do not result in enduring associations. The worker can be very helpful in this regard by bringing retarded children and their parents in contact with each other in small informal social groups as well as through membership in organized parent groups. . . .

Casework as a process of social diagnosis and treatment, then, is as diverse as the parents who need this service are different. The objectives in each case must be carefully assessed on the basis of the presenting problem, the parents' own needs and attitudes, and their capacity to profit from this service. In many instances casework is an indispensable component in work with the mentally retarded. Frequently it must be supplemented by concrete aids in health, training, recreation, and other welfare services. Seldom—where problems of social and emotional disturbance exist—can significant solutions be achieved without it.

□ □ □

from HELPING PARENTS IN THE COMMUNITY SETTING

Harriet E. Blodgett

(Counseling Parents of Children with Mental Retardation, 1958)

In considering major problems in connection with the parents of mentally retarded children, one of the first and biggest is lack of information.

Most parents have not planned on having a retarded child; they have not taken courses in school to learn how to cope with this possibility. Even professionally trained parents have not considered this as something that would be likely to affect their personal lives. Parents do not have information about the meaning of mental retardation, the meaning of degrees of mental retardation, what limitations are implied for school learning, for behavior learning, for terminal level of ability, or for ability in life adjustment.

Particularly, parents are usually not aware of the influence of intelligence on behavior organization and behavior learning. The first and most common interpretation that they receive is that the mentally retarded child will not be able to make adequate school progress. Many times, the parents will say, "Well, school isn't everything. If he can do other things, does it really matter if he cannot make an adequate school adjustment?"

What is not made sufficiently clear is the tremendously important part played by intelligence in the organization of all behavior—behavior controls, ability to adapt, ability to conform, ability to see the points of view of the other person, and to make adaptations for social living. Parents do not recognize, without some special help, the importance of intelligence in such areas as motivation, as persistence, as measuring work to be done and the importance of making an effort to do it. They may not understand that the total personality of the child is closely tied to his intellectual endowment which governs the pattern of his future development.

Therefore, the first area of parent counseling should be concerned with giving information of an intellectual sort or a factual sort, if you will, on which parents can base their own thinking about their own problems and their own child.

There is still another kind of information which parents typically lack. That is information about community facilities. Here is an area where the professional needs to be well informed concerning the facilities and also well informed as to current sentiment. At least he should know what the situation is and what it may become in the future.

Therefore, the professional has a real obligation to "keep up," to keep posted, to know what the new things are. It is not enough to say to parents: "Somewhere in town there is a nursery school that might give your child some group experience. I think the name of it is Elliot Park, so why don't you call them and see if your child might be eligible." Parents, in the early stages of educational planning, do not have the confidence or clear enough understanding to know what plans they should make. They need to know specifically if there is a chance that their child will be eligible. This means that the counselor must be informed about community facilities; about age limits and intelligence limits; who can be accepted; distribution of types that can be accepted; admission requirements; geoprahical restrictions—things that are part and parcel of the detail of running our own facilities but which, wrapped up as we are in our own work, we may not take the trouble to look into.

Parents need specific help. They need to know the name of the person to contact. It is better if you can also give them the phone number. This type of information helps the parent to move ahead. One of the problems we face in working with the parents of retarded children is to get them into suitable and appropriate programs.

We also need (and this is something that sounds like an ideal rather than a practical possibility) improved ways of correlating our efforts. Parents need to plan ahead for retarded children. This is not the usual way parents bring up a family. Normally, you do these things one step at a time and you think, perhaps wisely, that it is wrong to plan too far ahead for a normal youngster; that he should have a hand in shaping his own destiny; that many decisions as to where he might like to go to school, what course of study he might pursue should wait until maturity gives him a rightful share in decision making. Unfortunately, this is not the case with the retarded child.

While our facilities remain limited and we do not have enough of anything to go around, it is most important for parents of retarded children to plan ahead, to see where they are going, to see what might be the case in five years from now, not just for tomorrow. In order to help parents look to the future, we need to be pretty clear as to the things we can predict, the things we cannot foresee—as well as being completely honest with the parents in connection with which things are which.

It is true that we cannot always blueprint the entire future of a retarded child but, in many respects, we can draw the rough outlines of suitable plans.

. . . .

Another reason why parents may find it hard to plan ahead for retarded children is that the child very frequently makes it difficult for us to think of him as growing older. We call them "little kids" long after they have moved into the middle childhood range because that is how they act. This is also true in connection with parents—the fact that children require their care makes them seem younger, at least in the eyes of the parents.

So much for the informational area—which is detailed, complicated, and involves a continuous on-going process. It is quite an assignment but, without question, the emotional area with which we must also deal is more important, more difficult, and of greater significance to the family.

Parents have certain emotional problems in common as they face the situation of a retarded child, but we do not deal with problems in a vacuum. We deal with problems in people, and people come with all sorts of variations. They also come with all sorts of psychological traits as well as physical traits.

We see these parents at different stages of emotional maturity, with different degrees of ability to comprehend their individual problems. We see them at different stages of acceptance. In our discussions it is very easy to point out extremes of attitude—the very cooperative parent or the very resistant parent. We need to focus our attention on the range in between these extremes—the parents who are somewhat cooperative but also somewhat resistant.

We must remember that people do not stay the same, even from day to day. Their attitudes are undergoing gradual shifts. We must deal in day to day, week to week growth processes, maturational processes, attitude changes, increases in understanding. So, unless we pay attention to these differences, we will be doing our counseling job at less than full potential.

Early diagnosis of children is desirable for this long-range planning. However, it is at the earlier ages of their children that parents can be expected to have the most resistance to accepting the facts about them. They may still be hoping that there is some other explanation than mental deficiency in connection with the deviations of their child.

At the beginning of the counseling process a characteristic of parents which is most frequently mentioned is the tendency to reject an interpretation given them by either the psychologist, the medical expert, or the team of people who have studied the child. Again I think that this is over-simplification. We are not dealing with the total rejection of interpretations. We are dealing with stages of being able to accept, and these stages start at rather minimal points. It has already been pointed out that one of the basic principles which counselors have to grasp is the fact that parents come to them for help. This in itself indicates that they are confused, puzzled, and alarmed, and that they want some clarification. Therefore, a clarification of the facts, even though the initial reaction appears to be rejection, is most important.

When we look at the continuing process of reactions which parents may show, we are overwhelmed by the variety of them. Any attempt to put them into categories is artificial and may lead us further astray in our direct procedures.

We find that parents may move in the direction of intellectual acceptance of the problem but that their acceptance may be only on a factual level and not on a feeling level. If it is on a factual level, our problems are not solved. What that implies is that parents will not be able to make the attitude changes which are important if the child is to have appropriate goals set for him and appropriate techniques for helping him reach them.

The parent, who is intellectually accepting but emotionally unaccepting, cannot honestly see the child the way he is. Emotional acceptance for many parents takes a long time but it must remain one of our primary counseling goals.

One reason for being concerned about emotional acceptance is that many of the practical management problems which children present are created by parents, certainly not on purpose, but out of their efforts to move the child along into a more acceptable behavior pattern.

Another major reason for early work with parents is that the parents themselves are growing and changing, as we also hope we are. For all of us the life process is a process of change and hence must be viewed in a time framework.

One thing that may happen to parents, who do not receive early counseling attention, may be described by what we call "circular dependency." Normally, parents expect that they will take total care of their baby because that is what the baby needs. Normally, however, the babies themselves call a turn on this procedure by their own development, their growth and independence, their ability to get around by themselves, to communicate, to assume charge of some aspects of their own lives. However, with a retarded child, this does not happen. He stays in the dependency stage longer and he grows out of it unevenly. Parents, in the very course of taking care of the child, continue to meet needs on an infant level much longer than they do with their normal children.

We suspect that the only way parents can do this without too much frustration is to force themselves to enjoy it. In the process of forcing themselves to enjoy it, they may become dependent on this need.

I think that this is a background for many of the reactions that we see. For example, when a youngster is placed in an institution at the age of twelve or thirteen, the child has little trouble adjusting to his new environment. However, the parents may have a great deal of trouble adjusting to his absence. They find that they and the child were linked together by bonds tighter than were intended.

These are major problems. I fear that they have somewhat of a theoretical slant. We are talking about long-range plans. We are talking about long-range attitudinal changes. We are talking about emotional growth. And now, I think, we should turn our attention to some of the day-to-day essentials.

As far as parents are concerned, the things which are a source of anxiety to them are the daily behavior problems which must be handled as they happen. The questions parents ask, either openly or hiddenly, are like these: "What do we do with this child who is so hyperactive? What do we do with this child who is so destructive, who cannot communicate, who cannot seem to get toilet trained, who cannot get along with other children, who cannot sleep at night, who has temper tantrums and aggressive outbursts—what can we do? How can we cope with it all? How do we manage him?" Unless we can look at these problems from the point of view of the parents, I feel that this mutual rejection of each other as resources will widen.

Tied to these behavior-management problems, there are many less visible but perhaps equally important aspects of family living. There is concern for normal children in the family. What price are they paying for having the handicapped child at home? There is the concern for family living patterns. There is the concern for the social, professional and personal contributions that the parents, as adult citizens, make to the life of their own community. In what ways is this jeopardized or even completely destroyed?

We have to be concerned about the neighborhood situation. How are other children being affected; what about the attitudes of other adults in the community?

We have to be concerned about all of these problems. However, there has been relatively little scientific study of them because it is difficult to generalize about such situations. This is an area where individual differences are many—and important.

All of which brings us to the processes of parent counseling. We think that the emphasis in such counseling should be put on content rather than on method.

Our own parent group, which meets once a month, has made use of every technique we could think of for imparting information. We have used lectures, discussions, panel discussions, questions and answers, parent panels, and occasional outside speakers. We also invite written questions from parents which we look up in reference books in order to report back to them. We are beginning to use our own research material to make information more clear to parents.

We have used teacher-parent conferences, social worker-parent conferences, home visits, psychologist-parent conferences. We have used all three of our professional people, plus information from our medical consultants, in order to convey as many aspects of the problem as possible. We have also made use of a social hour following our serious meetings. We find this is a time when parents can let down the bars a bit, talk with each other, exchange experiences, and talk with the staff.

We have made use of classroom meetings, in which parents have an opportunity to see the work their children have done and to compare it with that of the other children.

It is one of our basic rules that each one of us must, in every conversation with a parent, be aware of the possibility of holding out unrealistic hopes without intending to do so. When you are working with retarded children you also become involved with them. You become proud of each bit of progress that is made and, subjectively, the accomplishment of the child is very much tied up with your efforts. So, it is very easy for the teacher to say that the child is doing well. It is equally easy for the parent to read into this the fact that the child is going to turn out to be normal.

This, we must truly guard against. We must say that he is doing well—for his present mental capacity. We must explain it further, in specific areas—he is doing well in contact with other children; he is less aggressive, more friendly, a little more cooperative. It requires more work to be specific but it is far more rewarding.

In our group meetings with parents, we have attempted to give them as much information as we have available. In our meetings we have discussed causation, state facilities, community programs, why we think a research approach is important—in fact, our parents now think that research is just as important as we do and they are pushing us for results of our most recent medication study.

We have also tried to discuss behavior development and behavior problems; what to do and what not to do.

In short, our content has been everything that you might hope to find in a fairly complete, up-to-date and thorough textbook on mental deficiency, but that is not all. We think that it is basically important for parents to reach a better understanding of themselves.

We rarely have a meeting without something coming up about feelings of guilt, responsibility, self-punishment, attitudes of other people—either on the surface or not very far hidden. We have discussed these things quite openly in our parents' meetings. We have tried to help parents feel that we not only understand those feelings, from the book approach, but that we share them from our own experience.

We are quite open in admitting to parents that we have problems with their children. School is not a bed of roses. We have many difficult situations and many bad days. We also have many good days. In discussing these things with parents, we believe we can take away some of the separation of the professional-parent barrier which may otherwise operate.

I am quite sure our parents do not think that we think we know all the answers. They do think, I hope, that we are willing to work on their problems with them.

We feel that a sense of humor is pretty important. We laugh at our children and with them, and they laugh at us and with us. We try to help parents take a slightly lighter point of view—this is a retarded child; this is a life situation—it can be met and handled as we handle other life situations.

To all of this, there is no standard answer. There is no standard solution, nor should there be, because there are no standard people. And, certainly, there are no standard retarded children. However, these problems can be tackled openly, honestly, without too much influence of guilt and punitiveness. And parents can be helped toward a better state, a more mature state of acceptance and problem-solving attack.

We feel we must also turn the attention of our parents to the welfare of their normal children. We do this in a number of ways. One way is by studying the brothers and sisters of our retarded children. Sometimes because they too have problems and sometimes because they do not.

If they do not have problems, we want to know why, so that we can pass on this delightful information. We occasionally ask a parent to write us a weekend diary about a normal child instead of the routine one in connection with the retarded child. We encourage all-family participation to help diminish the excessive involvement that the parent may feel with the retarded child alone.

We try to neutralize the parents' feelings of protectiveness. One step in the right direction, of course, is having the child come to school. The parent who can let his child be away from home for several hours a day has taken an important step toward both his and the child's emancipation. By having a child away for part of each day, the mother, for instance, has time to think a thought or two apart from the child.

Certainly, too, a measure of objectivity results from comparison with other children at the school. As parents come to know each other and come to understand something about the other children, they are bound to make comparisons which help in the more realistic viewing of their own youngster.

We think that parents also benefit through observing the relationship which is developed between children and staff. We are fond of our retarded children; we are tolerant of them. We accept them as they are and we are affectionate with them. At the same time, however, we are realistic about them. We do not expect things from them which they cannot do. We try them out in many things but our expectations are guided and modified by the child's performance. This is something that parents, in watching and observing, often carry back into the home in order to modify their own feelings and expectations and standards.

Further, all of us must recognize that families have other problems than the retarded child. Many times, in thinking about counseling processes, we forget about unhappy marriages. We forget about poverty and emotional conflicts between the marriage partners; we forget difficulties with other children; we forget school failures, neighborhood rejections—all of which may not have anything to do with the retarded child. We may also forget unemployment, salary problems, the cost of living, difficulties of housing, even the minor but irritating effect of families not having a telephone. If we are not able to take a broad view of counseling and look at the family situation broadly, then much of our pin-pointed effort is going to be wasted since it does not take into account all the problems that may be involved.

As far as possible, we try to give help that is practical. Parents come to us and say, "What shall I do with Johnny?" "What shall I do with Bill for he will not go to sleep?" "What shall I do with Susie for she will not eat her vegetables?"

These are things of concern. You can say, "Don't worry about it, it is unimportant. This is one stage and it will go away." But this is not very helpful.

We make our suggestions; we make them honestly, realistically and with no guarantee of success. We usually make more than one suggestion so that the parents can select the one that seems to fit their own situation the best. If it is a discipline problem, we say isolation works in some situations, that sometimes there is nothing like a good spanking to clear the air. Further, to deprive a child of privileges which are important to him will sometimes help. We ask them to try one of these suggestions and see what the results may be.

Part of the problem parents have is in wanting very specific answers to a particular difficulty. Part of the professional problem is having enough strength of ego to admit that there are lots of answers that we don't have and probably lots of answers that we may never develop.

To try to sum up our philosophy, I suppose you might call it "a philosophy of individual realism." We attempt to take into account differences not only among children but among parents. We say that we try to meet the children as they are, particularly in their emotional reactions. We try to do the same thing with parents, without establishing a preconceived level which they must reach before we accept them into our group. We try to have something to meet their needs at any level of development. We believe that the general principle of "facing up" to life problems applies to problems of retarded children as well as to other life situations.

We attempt to help parents find these principles, to understand them and to apply them to their own lives. We also attempt to help parents make compromises because the long-range view of mental retardation is a process of successive compromises in many ways.

We also do not expect that parents can be completely successful in one week. Change takes time. We try to comprehend and visualize the family pattern and to appreciate what the problem means to each family. A major goal of parent counseling, in our view, is to assist parent understanding and adjustment in as many ways as we can so that life for all our families may turn out to be generally more satisfying. . . .

□ □ □

from COUNSELING WITH PARENTS OF RETARDED CHILDREN LIVING AT HOME

Sylvia Schild

(*Social Work,* 1964)

Enormous ambivalence of feeling is evoked in a parent when he learns that his child is retarded. Feelings of rejection, dejection, and disappointment collide with anxious hopefulness, doubt, anger, and self-pity. Strong emotions of guilt mix with protective parental reactions; resentment, confusion, and insecurity become pervasive. It is this ambivalence that characterizes initial work with families of retarded children. These conflicting emotions are never completely resolved, as the long-term aspect of the problem and the repeated crises that stem directly from the fact of the child's handicap stirs up the ambivalence from time to time. To help the parent, it is necessary to ferret out the positive aspects of the ambivalence and help him to build on these so as to find some answers to the problem immediately at hand. Thus, ambivalence is dealt with in relation to the immediate crisis situation on a reality basis and by focusing on the areas that are conducive to meeting the needs of the family. The following case illustrates this point:

> A young couple had just heard the diagnosis of retardation for the first time. In the hostile tirade the mother loosed on the social worker, she vehemently denied that this catastrophe could be true, attacked the doctors, blamed herself. Toward the end of the outburst, she cried out, "Nothing I ever do is perfect. How will I ever be able to raise this child?"
>
> In this plea for help the social worker recognized the mother's immediate fear and denial of the diagnosis as resulting from her shaken confidence in being able to successfully handle her mothering role with the defective child.
>
> The positive aspect of the ambivalence, underlying the fear of inadequacy, was her intense desire to be a good mother. This was an area that could be worked with realistically in counseling, since she was indeed performing successfully in her mothering role with her two older children. The husband's support to his wife was encouraged. With help and attitudinal change, this mother was enabled to depend again on her own inner strengths and resources in coping with the child; this in turn paved the way toward better understanding of the child's limitations and freed her to work on other aspects of the problem.

A factor accounting for sustained ambivalence toward a retarded child is that the parents are deprived of the opportunity to project any blame for the problem onto the child himself. It is too difficult in any rational way to blame the child for his own defect. This differs from situations in which, when social pathology exists and becomes reflected in disturbed parent-child relationships (for example, in emotional disturbance and delinquency), the parent realistically is able to hold the child partially responsible for a share of the problem. This serves to alleviate some parental guilt and lowers resistance to accepting help. In the area of mental retardation the self-accusatory parent, who feels that he alone is in some way accountable for his child's limitations, is very well known.

It is an accepted fact that part of the resistance of the person seeking help stems from his feeling of responsibility for the problem. When guilt is intensified, the resistance to help will be proportionately increased. Because of this, those endeavoring to help parents of retarded children must be aware that heightened resistance is usually due to the inwardly projected guilt of the parent. In counseling, this guilt needs to be alleviated and an emphatic understanding of the problem area imparted to lower the parent's resistance, freeing him to benefit from the offered help. Most parents hope to hear an authoritative and sympathetic endorsement of themselves, of their human and parental competence, and of their right to blame themselves for what has happened.

One way of ameliorating the guilt of parents is to counsel them together in joint interviews. This helps to focus on the mutuality of feelings and responsibility shared by each parent, and aids to shift away from individual parents the assumption of self-blame for the problem. The joint interview technique often may help to restore the marital balance around the mutual concern for the child so that the parents are better able to mobilize all their strengths to handle crisis situations. Although mothers are generally entrusted with the major care of the child, management is a joint responsibility of both parents. Too often the father's role and share of responsibility are overlooked, especially when it is the mother who assumes the task of taking the child for his medical care and transmitting the medical information and advice to her husband. Joint interviewing frequently serves as a device to engage the father actively and to give due consideration to his concerns and attitudes, as well as to those of his wife. Counseling parents together is supportive and enables them to concentrate their energies, not as much on the fruitless searching for why this has happened to them, but more productively on how they can better perform in their parental roles in order to benefit their child.

The hard reality that needs to be faced is that with the presence of a retarded child the family is no longer the same and it cannot be reconstructed as it was before the arrival and impact of the defective child. Perhaps the area of greatest difficulty that needs to be resolved in the counseling process is the changes required on the part of the parents to meet the special needs of the retarded child. These often conflict with parental functioning that heretofore was considered satisfactory.

Often the management of the retarded child is perceived by the parents as being no different from their performance with their normal offspring. Counseling needs to be directed toward helping parents to see that their attitudes and feelings relative to mental retardation per se have indeed shifted their own parental behavior.

> One mother complained constantly of her child's temper tantrums. The disturbance the child was creating was upsetting to the entire household and the mother felt at her wit's end. The parents were beginning to feel that to keep the child in the home was almost impossible. The mother stated she was handling the problem behavior exactly as she had in the past coped with similar behavior in an older child.
>
> Closer examination revealed that in reality the mother, caught up in her disappointment and her attitude that a mentally retarded child was totally worthless, considered the child not worth bothering to discipline. Also, the father was unsupportive, leaving all discipline to his wife. Hence, the mother responded to the tantrums with anger and helplessness, and was permitting herself to be manipulated by the child. The youngster, having no external controls put on his behavior, became increasingly infantile and difficult. This gave validation to the low value placed on him by his mother.
>
> When the mother gained some insight and understanding that she was reacting differently to this child than to her normal offspring, she began to cope with the problem. Her self-esteem increased with her more effective management of the child. In addition, the father was helped to participate more meaningfully in the child's discipline, thereby giving his wife emotional support. As the child's behavior improved, the parents acquired a new appreciation of him. This in turn helped them to evaluate better the considerable potential latent in their mildly retarded son and to enjoy a more favorable relationship with him in the home situation.

The resistance and ambivalence of the parents in counseling are amplified also by the nature of the new stresses encountered merely by virtue of being the parent of a retarded child. The problem of keeping the retarded child at home is determined by a number of factors, such as sibling relationships, social status, family attitudes, the degree of deficiency in the child, and so on. These are all potential problem areas and the ability with which problems that might arise in these areas are handled and solved [varies] from family to family, situation to situation.

The new stresses arising from the presence in the family of a retarded child are not pathological as such, but should be viewed as a normal complement of problems for the situation that may affect the parent-child relationship and to which adjustments need to be made. When a pathological situation (i.e., divorce) is imposed on a family and is disruptive to family functioning, the focus in counseling must be directed toward the realistic problems that occur as a result of the pathology. It has been pointed out that the presence of a retarded child in the home is often a precipitating factor in individual or family maladjustment or breakdown. The family that is able to adjust satisfactorily to the impact on it of a retarded child has also to deal adequately with the many normal problems that occur in relation to the situation. Their attitudes, feelings, care and management of the child, and the like must all be taken into account.

These normal problems attending the presence of a retarded child in the home must be dealt with on a reality basis to permit the best possible solutions to be effected. Some of these problems are met often in other handicapping conditions of childhood: the increased dependence of the child on the parent, confusion and lack of finiteness in medical diagnosis, crumbling of parental aspirations for the child, rehabilitation and training problems, and the like. However, there are some conditions that occur uniquely in the case of the mentally retarded child and his parents.

One solution, which is culturally sanctioned, is often freely available to parents of the severely and moderately retarded. This is the opportunity to relinquish responsibility for care of the child to an institution if, considering the degree of his intellectual impairment, the child is eligible. Granted that placement holds the parents to a modicum of responsibility and is indeed an appropriate solution in many situations, there still is a need for recognition that this alternative presents conflict for the parents and may impair efforts to effect a successful adjustment in the home. From the time that parents are told that their child is eligible for institutionalization, the ambivalence about the child and the problem increases. Again, this ambivalence needs to be handled in counseling, with the focus geared to the positive aspects inherent in the successful fulfillment of parental roles and responsibilities.

One difficulty occurring in counseling with parents is that the resistance of the parent is sometimes insidiously supported by the behavior of the child himself. The parents may move well initially in shifting to more positive attitudes and methods of handling the child only to be thwarted by the slow movement of the child in responding to improved parental functioning. Although intellectually the parents can relate the slow pace to the child's mental limitations, they often become frustrated emotionally and can react by feeling that the counseling is unproductive. This can cause reversion to easier, more familiar patterns of behavior. The counselor, too, can become uneasy and impatient by the slow pace of the child's response and may fail to support the parents' efforts adequately or project blame on the parents for failure to utilize the counseling.

The most immediate help, consequently, occurs when the parents are having critical emotional distress and help can be directed toward easing their personal difficulty rather than being geared to change in the child himself. Casework for this latter goal, which is focused around the management and behavior of the child, can perhaps be best provided when spread out over proper and widely spaced intervals to give the child an opportunity to react and develop at his own speed.

A review of the reactions of forty parents to diagnosis and counseling emphasized that the parents needed time to take in the extent of their problem and solutions needed to be worked out step by step. Also, parental questions did not arise in an organized, crystallized fashion but gradually, as the child grew. When the element of time is taken into consideration and work with the family is structured over appropriate intervals, the parents are able to bring into counseling some growth on the part of the child that might not otherwise have been apparent if counseling around the child had been sustained on an intensive basis. In other words, parents need intensive casework help at times of crisis situations but, in addition, they need a continued contact. The latter can be less intensive and made available to them over a longer period of time. Such counseling should be properly spaced and educationally focused to help the parents with the practical problems of daily living with their retarded child. This help is often crucial in determining if the child can live in his own home and in strengthening and sustaining the mental health of the total family unit.

Counseling related to everyday living experiences with the retarded child helps to sustain the parents' motivation to continue in a program designed to improve the child's behavior and to develop his potential. Parents need to deal with concrete situations—the success they achieve in such common daily experiences tends to ameliorate the problems of living with a retarded child. For this kind of approach, the caseworker must have a keen knowledge and awareness of normal growth and development. To help the parents understand their child's behavior, it is important to assist them in relating behavior to normal functioning and expectations of children as well as to comprehend the limitations in their own child and the implications.

In summary, this paper has discussed some aspects of helping parents who have retarded children living at home. The following points were suggested:

1. Professionals counseling parents to keep their retarded child at home assume an additional responsibility to learn how to help the parents achieve this goal comfortably. This implies not only increased understanding of the problems faced by the parents, but also better awareness and skill in involving and sustaining parents more effectively in the counseling process itself.

2. The key factor to be dealt with in the counseling process is the ever present ambivalence of the parents about their retarded child. Movement toward satisfactory solution of problems is more easily attainable when the positive aspects of the ambivalence are used constructively to meet feelings and to free parents for changes in attitudes.

3. Guilt feelings of the parents are enhanced by the fact that they cannot rationally project any responsibility of blame for the problem on the child himself. These guilt feelings heighten the resistance to meaningful participation in counseling. Involvement of both parents in joint counseling is one way of alleviating the inwardly directed guilt and of helping parents to focus on more rewarding functioning in their parental roles with the retarded child.

4. The presence of a retarded child changes the structure of existing family relationships. One area of great difficulty is that former parental functioning may prove to be inadequate in meeting the needs of a retarded child. Parents need help in seeing that their attitudes

and feelings relevant to mental retardation *per se* affect their parental behavior.

5. There are many new stresses affecting families of retarded children that should be viewed as normal problems for the situation and that need to be dealt with on a reality level. Some of these, such as the easy access to shifting responsibility of the child through institutionalization and the slow reaction of the retarded child to parental teaching and management, are unique and may hamper counseling efforts.

6. Parents are best helped at times of crisis, but counseling geared to improvement of the child's behavior and to daily living can be structured over spaced intervals planned to compensate for the slow movement and the maturation of the child and to offer sustained support to the parents. . . .

□ □ □

from COUNSELING PARENTS OF RETARDED CHILDREN

Helen L. Beck

(Children, 1959)

. . . .

In contrast to other medical conditions, treatment of the retarded child's condition rests primarily with the parents rather than with a professional worker, even if the youngster attends school or a day care center. It usually consists of helping the child to achieve optimal development and maximum use of his capacities. To do this effectively parents need help in working through their own feelings and adjustments as well as practical advice in regard to their everyday problems.

Development of a good professional relationship is one of the main prerequisites for successful work with parents. Parents tend to reject painful information that comes from a seemingly uninterested or unfeeling source. If the diagnostic process in the clinic is an unhurried one, parents have time to understand step by step what the clinic personnel are attempting to do, to prepare themselves to accept the diagnosis and a treatment plan, and to develop a workable two-way relationship with the clinic personnel based on trust and respect. Much of the frantic "shopping around" in connection with chronic conditions may be caused by attempts on the part of clinicians to shortcut the diagnostic processes. The team approach in diagnosis gives the parent an opportunity to work through negative feelings that emerge in one or the other contact and to clarify interpretations. "Shopping around" can often be avoided by permitting parents to use the various team members for comparison of opinions.

Parents' previous experience with other facilities have to be dealt with directly at the time of first contact. If the new clinic does not want to be just one of a growing list of clinics in the parents' experience, client and workers must clearly understand the reasons for dissatisfaction with the previous agencies and what the clients' present expectations are.

At the Mental Retardation Unit of St. Christopher's Hospital for Children the diagnosis may extend over several weeks. The clinic is staffed by a team representing a variety of professional disciplines. Cases are screened for admission by the pediatrician and most of the team members are involved in the diagnostic work-up. This is terminated by a team conference in which plans are worked out with full consideration of the child's needs, family wishes, and available facilities. The team delegates discussion of such plans with the family to the person who has developed the most workable relationship with the family and who will have to carry the main responsibility for helping them carry out or modify the suggested plans. This is frequently the social caseworker.

In regard to mental retardation, there is sometimes a strange notion that establishing diagnosis is identical with giving treatment. Diagnosis is an essential step toward understanding treatment needs, but it is not treatment. The parents' expectancy and readiness for help is necessarily being aroused during the diagnostic process. If this is not followed up promptly with an actual treatment plan, their readiness to involve themselves in a treatment process may be lost.

The parents' most crucial need for service occurs at the time when they first learn of the diagnosis. It is then that they need support in handling their emotions, help in clearly understanding the diagnosis and its implications, and assistance in planning for their child.

Considerable anxiety is usually aroused by a diagnosis of mental retardation. If this is not handled promptly, parents may develop rigid defenses which are not easily amenable to change. A caseworker can help parents set up the kind of defenses that will cushion reality adjustment rather than paralyze functioning. Even the most stable parents have to cope with a certain amount of personality disorganization in reaction to severe stress and shock. Professional casework services at this point work as a "catalyst" for helping parents to recognize their thoughts and reestablish ability to function.

The parents who come to a mental retardation clinic are as a rule quite aware of the fact that they have a problem. They may, however, deny its nature. Parents should clearly understand the findings of the clinicians in regard to their child's difficulty. However, they need not accept these findings immediately and fully in order to work toward relief of their problem. Diagnosis of mental retardation is not likely to change, and the parents' acceptance may come gradually as a result of treatment.

If a parent persists in calling his child "slow" instead of retarded, the worker may do the same. If the parent continues to express conviction that the child will eventually "catch up," or does not belong in this "terrible" special class, the worker need not contradict him but can patiently help him face the truth. Parents can be helped gradually to see the diagnosis not as a "dead end" verdict, but as a starting point from which to approach much of the problem.

Parents often spend considerable effort in trying to prove to the worker that the child is normal. If they really believed this, they would not continue with the clinic. They often try to push the worker into an argument in order to convince themselves. The worker does well not to be drawn into such an argument. In time the parents draw their own conclusions.

We found most of the parents seen at our clinic very eager to find and use services. Many cooperate far beyond their own need and show good grasp of the value of their contributions to the understanding of the problem. However, as in any clinic setting, some parents withhold information or try to manipulate clinic personnel and time. Such behavior has to be discussed quite directly with the clients, and limits should be set.

Service cannot be effective without the full and voluntary participation of parents. The parent who cannot respond to efforts to help him and who continues to try to manipulate the clinic will manipulate treatment goals. Neither he nor the child will in the end profit from treatment. However, the amount of responsibility for initiation and continuation of contact that can and should be put on the client should be determined on the basis of the psychosocial diagnosis rather than on rigidly established clinic procedures.

Through social-casework counseling, parents of retarded children can be helped to develop:

1. some understanding of the meaning of the term "retarded" as it applies to their child;

2. understanding of the degree of their child's handicap and what this will mean in the future;

3. ability to understand their child's assets, his needs, and his difficulties;

4. appreciation of the effect the presence of a handicapped child has on family life in general, on their other children, on themselves as parents, and and on adjustment of the family within the neighborhood;

5. understanding of the fact that the child's retardation and his behavior are separate entities and that behavior can be influenced at least to a degree by educational approaches;

6. ability to judge whether neighborhood reactions are caused by the child's behavior, appearance, or mental ability;

7. techniques to use such understanding constructively in order to help the handicapped child, the entire family, and the community;

8. knowledge of available resources relating to their own situation and to the problem of retardation in general.

While needs differ, time for consideration of these areas has to be provided in planning. The "one shot" approach is rarely helpful.

Patterns in Counseling

In spite of the uniqueness of each case, definite patterns emerge that may serve to guide program planning. Contacts fall roughly into four phases: 1) *the initial period,* encompassing the diagnostic process, clarification of the situation and needs, establishment of treatment goals, and selection of treatment methods; 2) *treatment,* consisting of more or less intensive counseling, individually or in groups; 3) *tapering off,* a time when, goals being achieved, contact becomes less frequent and is eventually stopped; 4) *followup,* consisting of occasional contact either as needs arise or as children are brought to the clinic for other appointments.

Initial period. It is neither feasible nor necessary to offer counseling services to all parents who come to a clinic for diagnosis of their child. By the end of the diagnostic period it should be possible to estimate fairly accurately the parents' need for counseling services, their amenability to this type of service, and the feasibility of intermediate as well as long-range goals.

Selection of appropriate treatment methods should be made after consideration of a number of factors:

1. *Ego strength*—the parents' maturity; emotional stability; capacity to accept their roles as parents, as marital partners, as members of their community; their intellectual endowment and the use they make of it.

2. *Family strength*—the quality of interrelationships between the different members of the family, and the kind of emotional and practical support parents can count on from other family members.

3. *Environmental and cultural influences*—the presence or absence of other irritants in the home or in the neighborhood and the influence of cultural and religious factors on the family's acceptance or rejection of the problem.

4. *Degree of handicap*—and the parents' understanding of it. It is considerably more difficult for the parents of a moderately retarded child who is physically healthy and attractive to accept the diagnosis than to see him as plain stubborn, lazy, or spoiled. The parent of a severely retarded child with external stigmata is less able to avoid the problem.

Treatment goals. In mental retardation, treatment is aimed at increased comfort of all people concerned with a trying situation.

Problems have to be analyzed so that partial solutions can be found as the need arises. Tension and frustration in parent and child may be reduced by cathartic experiences for the parents, and by help with practical problems such as learning ways of handling unacceptable behavior, and planning for school or other types of placement. If problems are met as they occur, many retarded children can live happily within their own family groups and make their contributions to family living, at least during their childhood years. Where placement away from home is indicated, the parents can be helped to see that this has advantages for the handicapped child as well as for the rest of the family.

Level of Treatment. In general, the level of treatment remains in the area of reality adjustment, ego reintegration, and development of techniques for daily living. Intensity and depth of treatment vary greatly within the range of clinic function. If the parents have prominent personality disturbances, or many problems in addition to their child's retardation, they may have to be referred to more appropriate agencies.

Treatment Techniques. Treatment techniques most often used are clarification, supportive counseling, and environmental reorganization. This does not preclude the use of insight therapy, but where such therapy is of paramount importance, referral becomes necessary. Though the counseling focuses on the problem of mental retardation, parents may be enabled by treatment to translate the help they get for one problem to others as needed. This happened in the case of the A family.

The A's were referred by their family physician, who was struck by the intensity of the negative parent-child relationships. The oldest child, Tim, retarded because of an organic condition, was extremely hyperactive and lacked concentration. The parents' severity in trying to control his behavior had led to violent negativism on his part. The younger brother, Don, considerably brighter than Tim, got vicarious enjoyment out of teasing his older brother into temper outbursts resulting in actions for which Tim eventually was punished.

During the contact here, explanation as to the organic basis of some of Tim's behavior was given to both parents. They were helped to evaluate their own approach to the children, to consider the differences of their children's needs, and to try new ways of meeting these needs.

The parents became aware of the teasing of the younger child and of the effect on both children of their own impatience and high standards. They also became aware of their own strained relationships and how these resulted in their undercutting each other's effectiveness with the children. Gradually the whole family situation calmed down. When a new baby was born, both parents were able to avoid many of the mistakes they had made at Don's birth which had created such intense jealousy and difficulties between the boys.

Treatment Methods. The caseworker may counsel either in individual contact or in groups. It has been hoped that the development of group techniques might prove more economical of the worker's time than individual contacts. This has hardly been the case as far as economics of time and professional efforts are concerned. The economy lies in the fact that the more appropriate treatment is the more effective one.

At the St. Christopher's clinic individual counseling has been offered to the parent with highly individualized needs, strong emotional dependency, intense masochism with certain types of passive-aggressive adjustment, or clearly psychotic tendencies. We found such parents poor group risks, since they tend to be disruptive to group processes because of their urgent need for attention, the intensity of their relationships, or their need to act out. In individual contact the worker can adjust the process to the individual and can control the gratification of his particular needs. This was the method used in the B case.

The B's had accepted the diagnosis of their only child's retardation before coming to the clinic, but they felt strongly resentful of the doctor who had given the diagnosis. They interpreted his statements as meaning that no limits could be set for the boy's behavior. They joined a parents' organization and used the group to project their anxiety about their own problem.

In individual contact, the B's were brought back again and again to their own problem of handling their child's behavior. They were helped to face their misinterpretations of what they had been told. They also came to realize how much they acted out their own discouragement by proving time and again that they were not able to set limits for their child, while other people were able to do so. As it became necessary, the caseworker allowed them to forgo discussion of the child and his problem and focus on their general discouragement and disappointment, of which the child was only one factor.

The caseworker saw the parents in separate interviews and helped them work through some of their rivalry in their positions within the family so that a common approach could be established.

In group counseling we are not concerned with intensive group therapy, but with casework counseling in groups. Goals are: personality reintegration and adjustment to reality. Group processes and teaching methods are combined to afford the individual relief from tension, understanding of children's behavior, and techniques for handling specific problems.

Group processes are helpful to basically mature parents whose functioning is temporarily impaired by the overwhelming nature of their problem; to parents with a tendency toward projection and intellectualization; to parents with pronounced though well-controlled feelings of hostility, who can find relief through limited acting out; and to parents with dependency needs which may be met through group identification and support.

In selecting members for groups at St. Christopher's we have not found it particularly necessary to strive toward homogeneity of social strata, intellectual capacity, personality makeup, or degree of defect in the members' children.

Groups soon develop a homogeneity of their own, the members becoming quite supportive of one another.

The case of Mrs. C. illustrates several of these points.

Mrs. C. was unable to make effective use of individual contact when it was offered. She covered up her intense feelings of hostility by complete denial and adopted an attitude of submissiveness. In the group she quickly assumed a certain amount of leadership, which the group kept from going beyond bounds. She used the group constructively to gain better understanding of her own problems, to learn from other parents' techniques of handling situations and to get gratification for her need to dominate.

After the series of group sessions ended, a second attempt at individual counseling, made at Mrs. C's request, was no more effective than the first. But in another series of group sessions she again used the group experience constructively.

Length of time necessary to achieve intermediary or long-range goals varies greatly, depending on the kind of emotional or reality problems to be worked out and the complications encountered in the process. Length of contact may be in inverse ratio to the severity of the actual handicap. An obviously severe handicap often allows for clearer diagnosis, less parental resistance, and fewer alternatives. On the other hand, parents of a more salvageable child may be in need of longer periods of service to achieve an acceptance of the retardation and evaluate a variety of possibilities for the child.

At the St. Christopher's clinic, cases that receive *short-term services* only fall roughly into three groups.

Group 1 includes parents who during the diagnostic process or previously have learned to understand and accept their problem and are basically able to handle it on their own. Usually only one interview following the diagnostic period is needed to clarify that the clinic stands ready to help them whenever necessary. Such parents use the clinic as needs arise.

Group 2 includes parents who are not accessible to continued treatment even if they are in need of it. They either have not accepted the diagnosis or are unable to mobilize themselves sufficiently to involve themselves in treatment. The caseworker alerts other team members to these problems so that the parents may receive some help when they bring the child in for followup visits to the physician or the psychologist and may be referred to the caseworker at a later date if feasible. In the interim the caseworker seeks opportunities for casual contact with parents in clinics.

Group 3 includes parents already known to community agencies, which usually continue service to the family, often in collaboration with clinic personnel.

Intensive casework treatment over a longer period is offered parents with complex problems either of their own personalities, environmental situations, or difficulties with the child. We have found it most economical and helpful to offer intensive, frequent interviews at the very beginning of the treatment period and then to gradually decrease contacts as parents become able to manage on their own.

Recently we have begun to experiment with a more extensive than intensive approach consisting of a cooperative effort between the public health nurse and the social worker. Two groups of parents have been included in this program: 1) basically stable parents whose problems of child management are caused by the child's severe handicap; 2) immature, anxious parents who have management problems with their children caused at least in part by their own insecurity. No attempts are being made with either group toward too strong involvement in the parents' own problems. Explanations are given for the child's behavior and new approaches to handling are suggested. The public health nurse visits the more immature parents to demonstrate ways of handling the child. It is too early to say how helpful such an approach may be. However, considerable relief of upset has been achieved in a few of the families in this experiment.

All tapering off of long-term treatment should be on a planned basis. Unplanned "fizzling out" devaluates the treatment received and may leave the parents with a feeling of dissatisfaction. As treatment goals are gradually realized, parents themselves usually begin to express a lessened need for contact. Increase in problems and anxiety may occur as wider spacing of interviews begins. If the caseworker permits the parents to set their own pace, the frequency of contacts will decrease.

One advantage of casework at a clinic is that cases can be followed over extended periods of time without maintaining intensive or regular contact. Parents often use scheduled followup visits to the pediatrician, psychologist, or speech pathologist as opportunity to bring the caseworker up to date with their present stage of affairs. The caseworker also may schedule followup interviews at certain stages in the child's life, for example when he is getting ready for a nursery school experience, camp experience, or school placement.

Parents' organizations such as the Association for Retarded Children should be used as a resource in planning with parents of mentally retarded children. These organizations provide such parents with strong emotional support and valuable outlets for the constructive channeling of their anxieties, frustrations, and tensions. However, referrals to such groups should be made on the basis of diagnostic considerations, and should include preparation of the client and the organization as in any agency referral.

The timing of such a referral is important. These organizations properly expect their members to promote understanding of the problem of mental retardation. To do this effectively and without harm to themselves parents have really to understand and accept the nature of their own problem and they have to be ready to identify with a large group. Otherwise they may use activity in the organization to avoid facing their own problems and working through their own anxieties and difficulties. We have found that parents who have joined large organizations of parents without preparation often accept mental retardation as a community problem, but do not really acknowledge their own problems in relation to their own mentally retarded child.

Parents who are well prepared for group membership can offer a great deal to these organizations in their work to spread understanding of the needs of the mentally retarded.

However, this type of activity cannot substitute for the emotional and practical help needed by parents at crucial points to maintain their own and family stability in facing the problems presented by the fact of their child's retardation. In offering such help, the goal of casework counseling, whether to individuals or groups, is to help parents achieve their optimum functioning to meet their own responsibility for the treatment of their child.

□ □ □

from CASEWORK WITH PARENTS OF RETARDED CHILDREN

Alexander Hersh

(*Social Work,* 1961)

It seems to be a sign of the times, a good omen perhaps, that most parents of retarded children are eager to have help for their child, and similarly, for themselves with their own feelings about the child. Like the remainder of the community, however, they feel the need to control the help they receive. They seek it when they want it, take as much or as little as they desire, and focus their use of help in areas which present the greatest concern to them, though these may not be the areas we see as most problematic. As a natural reaction against the intense and interminable quality of their problem, they frequently want to resolve their anxiety precipitously. They seek a simple or comfortable solution. One's first reaction might be to agree with them—agree that their problem is too great and their feelings should be spared. This attitude is a reflection of the feelings of the larger community, which finds the total impact too hard to bear and surrenders to it. This may be exemplified in the "put him away and forget about him" prescription.

These observations are offered because the writer believes that in developing service for the retarded and their parents, one must look at the degree of parental and community responsibility to be borne. Compare, for instance, a service for retarded children to the family, adoption, or child guidance services. Where will you find the degree and duration of such dependency problems, except possibly with severe mental or physical illness? In the outpatient service at the Woods Schools,[1] we are always struck by the inevitable question that is asked at the end of a session when we have interpreted the results of our evaluation of the child. "When do you want us to come back?" they ask. Inherent in this powerful question is the hope that maybe next time we will see improvement, as well as the expressed need to have support in carrying the burden.

In our experience, "one-shot" evaluations are of little value. Results are too often denied or distorted by the parents and signal a start on the dreary rounds of looking for someone who will speak the hopeful words they want to hear. A service that carries with it the sincere wish to share the burden of the long-term problem will enable parents to accept a current interpretation of their child's problem. This is not a conscious withholding of information. It is a realization that the true and final expression of a child's handicap and potential cannot be predicted, but must evolve out of the parents' use of our definition of the problem given to them, as well as the climate which they may provide for him. A two- or three-year period, with planned or periodic follow-ups, allows parents time to work on their own feelings, with the specific directions and help given them through the service. The shortcoming of the one-shot evaluation is that it frequently blocks the positive parental feelings from the fullest expression.

Our own philosophy attempts to transcend direct "counseling" of parents. By this I refer to the oft-used precept of counseling: to diagnose the problem and then divulge it to the parents, together with a specific bit of advice such as "He will always need supervision." This is fine as far as it goes, and represents an important medical responsibility to parents and child. A more meaningful and skillful counseling, however, is directed toward helping parents to use this information, but with sympathetic understanding of their need to develop certain natural defenses such as denial or avoidance. One must recognize the traumatic quality and endless ramifications of their problem. These need to be seen and dealt with one by one as they emerge out of the child's daily life. In this way parents can, with a caseworker's support, organize their feelings to give positively to the child, creating a parent-child relationship that supports the child's growth and development as a person, however handicapped he may be. . . .

Casework counseling of parents of retarded children seems to be a relatively recent innovation, and until now emphasis in the literature has been on the establishment of a diagnosis with its interpretation to parents, generally given with a specific recommendation. . . . It has been our experience—and hence philosophy—that the thorough working through of parental feelings toward a retarded child is a lengthy task demanding both persistence and skill. . . .

What are some of the specific or unique problems of the parent of a retarded child? Unique, in this sense, means problems that are quantitatively the same as those present in all families but occur with unusual intensity in the families of retarded children. They constitute core problems in virtually every instance where there is a retarded child. They include disruption of normal ego functioning of parents and therefore disruption of normal family life routines; development of excessive and unusually intense feelings of guilt and personal inadequacy; excessive and long-standing dependency burdens that cause emotional draining in parents; friction in connection with siblings because of stigmata and untenable goals which the family has set for itself; distorted perceptions of the child; and finally, distorted projections on the child. Unfortunately, space will not permit discussion of the latter two categories.

The blow of having a retarded child, or learning later that one's own child is retarded, is severe. Whatever the parents' personality organization, the delivery of a severely retarded child is a terrible shock and disappointment. The disruption to normal ego function in parents, and particularly in the mother, is clearly evident and to be expected.

. . . .

Most parents go on to organize some kind of defense lest the pain become completely unbearable. With or without skilled help they mobilize themselves to make some kind of plan for their child and themselves.

Probably the largest number of parents feel at the time of the birth of their child that he is normal. It is only later, as his development lags, that he is seen as not normal. Still later, however, in recapitulating, many mothers admit that they suspected rather early that their child was different. Statements such as "He was just different," "He was too still," and "He was like a lump of clay" are common and express the extra burden that mothers carry for their closeness to their child. We have known some mothers who fought the world on behalf of their child, almost because they knew too soon that the child was different. They had a secret that acted as a bond between self and child. The invasion of the outer world and its harsh realities could be climaxed in no other way than a pitched battle in which their struggle to maintain the cherished secret was waged.

In attempting to understand these parents, one becomes aware of a number of recurring factors. First of all, it is most often the mother who is most threatened; second, it is the mother who may later develop the self-isolating and martyr-like tendency that often identifies the extreme stereotype concept of a parent of a retarded child; and third, the mother usually acts as though she has been insulted by life—as if she could no longer be fulfilled. Whatever the exact nature of the threat to the mother in having such a child, in extreme cases it seems that nothing anyone can do will remove this feeling of mutilation to the self. One mother we know spoke of the "sobering effect"—that she could never look on life in the same way as before. And countless mothers comment on the bitter frustration and their feelings of lack of fulfillment because so much of their love seems to be for naught. Some of them tend to force their mothering on the child because they refuse to be denied this pressing need of their own. It is paradoxical that in one instance a mother may place her child when he is very young and forever feel a sense of emptiness, while another says, "I know I'm being selfish but I'm keeping him at home until I die. I don't care what happens after I'm gone." At the Woods Schools we are more apt to be in a counseling relationship with the former, who feels left out of her child's life. We encourage these mothers to visit and share in their child's care and planning in any way that is practical and psychologically sound. We know of many such mothers who achieve some fulfillment by working for programs for retarded children and by supporting other parents in gaining perspective on their situations. These are important outlets if recognized as giving temporary stop-gap results.

This threat to one's feeling of wholeness that comes from having a retarded child is a difficult thing to work with or even to generalize about. The feelings of guilt and inadequacy are extreme and intense. Much has been written about the parents' feelings of guilt at having borne a retarded child, but little is known about how to relieve these feelings. It is as though this guilt became a part of the parents' character. After a period of time there is no available thread for helpful unraveling. From the caseworker's standpoint one needs to work something through for oneself to develop acceptance of parents who may not be able to see the true nature of their child's handicap and are self-punishing as a result. When a caseworker can do so, parents are less threatened and can come to see him as helpful and supporting.

The point of view of the writer, as well as his predecessor at the Woods Schools (and others), is that not every parent can be expected to "accept" the handicap in his child. Perhaps it seems too passive to say that some parents should not accept the degree of handicap because to do so might endanger their mental health. Yet I know of one such case where the child came to be a way for the mother to avoid being grown up and taking on the roles of wife and mother. She and the child are virtual siblings, to the exclusion of the father. The strength of these feelings is evidently great, for many well-intentioned people have been ignored when they have given her "advice."

. . . .

A caseworker can be of infinite help to parents in this dilemma by being clear as to which parents are motivated for change and can use active help and which must proceed in the darkness, always warding off anyone who seeks to help them change. However, there are many parents who, though severely handicapped by their own guilt, can use the support and warmth of another person. Over a period of time they can come to a greater realization that their role as parent to their handicapped child may always be a partial one, never completely fulfilling, yet with potential for satisfaction, depending on the degree of the child's handicap.

A case in point is a mother who described her own anxiety and terrible disappointment at having her child away from home, but at the same time expressed full realization and acceptance of the fact that he would undoubtedly need to be away all his life. As she spoke she evolved her own plan, which the caseworker supported, that the child should spend part of every summer with the family as long as it was practical to do so. We agreed that this would serve several purposes. It would enable both parents to feel more fulfilled and take away some of the awful feeling that they were withdrawing from their child or doing little for him. It would give the whole family a chance to interact, out of which each could develop his own relationship to the child and his problem. Finally, it would give the child a feeling of membership in the family and the support he needed in using the school placement from year to year.

Just as mothers are concerned and responsive, fathers may be equally so. It would seem that, because of the closer biological tie, the mother suffers the more intense feelings. In our own setting we find fathers more removed, less emotionally involved, more objective, and less expressive of their feelings. It is always harder to understand fathers because we do not see as much of them. We have made some interesting observations about fathers who appear extremely guilty. They have been, for the most part, overtly warm people, nearer to the maternal role than usual; they are more apt to turn their hurt into aggression because of their inability to tolerate strong feelings, or to resist stubbornly a working through of these feelings.

One such father harbored a deep resentment against his child for almost ten years. His own shame at having the child, and fear of his own strength associated with the child's negative strength, was very great. It was only after he had expressed much of this deep feeling to the caseworker that, in his words, he "became a different person." The child felt the difference and responded almost immediately. Whereas in the past the boy had always detoured around his father, he now began to share many of his thoughts with him, tested and accepted his strength, and began to identify with him as his father and as a man. Later, in describing the change, this father said he could not figure out what had happened—in the past he had not missed his boy while he was away at school, but suddenly he did!

It is a moving experience to share with a father the moment when he allows himself to feel the deep emotion of having been tragically struck by having a severely handicapped son. One father was recently bringing out his wife's question of whether she should continue to visit their boy, a severely defective child who has been a student in the school for a few years. The parents visit faithfully, but the visits have no apparent meaning to the child. The father was saying that he hoped his wife would want to come in to talk to me too, because as we spoke many questions were raised which needed to be explored. He was particularly concerned about what the other children at home would feel if they stopped visiting. Then, as if it were too much for him, he said he would not want to come just once every five years—the shock of seeing the boy physically changed might be too great. He liked to come for reassurance. He felt better when he came, even if the visits did not mean anything to him or to the boy. When the caseworker suggested that he came because Jimmy was his son, tears welled in his eyes and he could hardly get the words out as he repeated, "Yes, Jimmy's my son; that's why I come to see him." The affirmation, as he acknowledged his son, was in his voice as he spoke.

Fathers also appear to have a particular problem with their retarded child when they have not yet achieved, or are currently working through, their separation from their own fathers. As with mothers at a similar point in development, the ability to carry through in their own role depends a great deal on how liberated they are and feel. It is interesting, for example, to note how often fathers have a problem merely in relating on a level at which the retarded child is comfortable. It seems that the retarded son may create a real puncture in the male ego unless the father is well established as father and husband. This problem is often expressed in aggressive and disapproving action. More subtle and difficult to help is the father who smothers and denies the boy his own manhood. Adolescence is particularly stormy, but affords some basis for confrontation and identification between father and son.

The excessive and long-standing dependency problem presented by having a retarded child may take different forms for each parent. It is usually the mother who seems caught up in the day-to-day burden and the father who presents the greatest challenge in holding to the present in working through areas of feeling. Parent after parent expresses concern and question about "what will be later." We attempt to support the parent in concentrating on the present, but also to respect the problem of the future because it is very real. The relative helplessness of the handicapped child causes much concern about how much emotional and economic investment can be risked and made available at one time or on a sustained basis. Those who have been engaged in long-term foster care will recognize the similarity here. Again, note the interminable quality of the dependency and how deeply it affects parent reaction to responsibility.

Concerning the problems that occur in connection with siblings, we have noted clinically that parents frequently give this as a reason for putting the child into an institution. A mongoloid child is quite acceptable in the home until his sister starts dating, but then becomes a major focus of concern. In many cases families handle this kind of problem by institutionalizing the child, which then stirs much guilt. On the whole, we believe that parents should take things as they come, little by little, year by year. Some problems, however, can be predicted. Casework done with foresight will help families plan accordingly, so that they do not set their total family goals without realizing their full implications. There is thus less guilt and more meaning to steps taken later.

Most parents have a hard time allowing siblings to have their own relationship with the retarded child who is away at school, and supporting them in it. Often, this is because of parental concern with what will happen after they die. It is especially hard for parents to keep from becoming controlling—frequently an expression of their own ambivalence. That is, they unconsciously put the sibling to work carrying their negative feelings. Inevitably, and contrary to conscious parental expectation, this ends up in estrangement rather than healthy compassion between the children.

It takes a unique form when the child has been placed in an institution at an early age—before five, for example. Because the parent has often not had sufficient connection or bond with the child, the separation takes on an absolute quality and the placed child does not view his parent as a parent but merely as a visitor. A parent in this situation is unable to help the sibling with the relationship because his own is so unsatisfactory and unfinished. This, together with the unnaturalness of visits with an institutionalized child, makes it extremely difficult to sustain without guilt and strain.

There is an interesting contrast between parents' use of residential care for their child and their use of outpatient help. Work with both is equally challenging and deeply satisfying. The family whose child is being cared for in a residential school strives to find a part-time relationship in which they and the child can derive satisfaction from one another. The family whose child is at home presents the sharper need for help because their problems are more immediate. They come to identify their community outpatient service as a source of support and direction in understanding their child and his behavior and helping them to meet his needs.

Work with both groups is rewarding and represents to all engaged a challenge to be met as we develop more resources to deal with the needs of the retarded child and his parents.

FOOTNOTES

1. The Woods Schools are a private residential school for 400 children with mental, social-emotional, physical, and academic handicaps. Children are placed within the school according to chronological age, mental age, social-emotional age, degree and nature of problem. Comprehensive care is given, including special education, diagnosis, psychotherapy, and lifetime care.

□ □ □

CLINICAL TEAM TREATMENT OF A MENTALLY RETARDED CHILD AND HIS PARENTS: CASEWORK WITH THE MOTHER

Nellie D. Stone

(American Journal of Mental Deficiency, 1959)

This presentation of the treatment of the parents of a four-year-old, mildly retarded boy, Teddy T., illustrates the use of casework and group counseling as part of a total plan for family help provided through the community guidance clinic operated by the Essex Unit of the New Jersey Association for Retarded Children in East Orange, New Jersey. This professional diagnostic and counseling service has been sponsored and developed over the past eight years by the associated parents and friends of mentally retarded children as the focal point around which community programs for dealing with this handicap have been built. It is significant that only within this short time have there become available specialized treatment resources for the mentally retarded child and his parents within their home community. Whereas much of the work in the past has been pioneered within the institutional setting, we are now able to report on current efforts to assist parents and child in their own home and community setting. It is to be hoped that impetus will be given to the broadening and strengthening of general community welfare services to include adequate attention to the needs of parents and children affected by the handicap of mental retardation along with those facing other social problems. A further aim is to add to the professional understanding of social workers and other counselors so that more effective helping techniques may be developed.

The Guidance Clinic for the Retarded functions under the supervision of a multi-discipline advisory committee, with a neuropsychiatrist as medical director, and is administered by a psychiatric social worker. Its staff includes pediatric, psychiatric, neurological, speech and other specialists, as well as a clinical psychologist and caseworker. The clinical team approach, integrating medical, psychological and social casework disciplines, is used both in the basic diagnostic evaluation and in subsequent treatment services. The focus of this case presentation is the coordination of efforts with parents and child through individual and group treatment as carried out by the caseworker and psychologist in the clinic setting. The team approach is used throughout in the process of diagnosis, treatment and reevaluation from stage to stage in the helping process.

Initial Diagnostic Evaluation

Teddy, age four, was referred by his pediatrician for clinical evaluation to determine the extent of his suspected mental retardation. His parents, who are attractive and responsible young people, were felt to need counseling in understanding Teddy and their own reactions to his problem. The mother, in particular, was experiencing difficulty in accepting Teddy's slowness in speech and learning, which contrasted markedly with his baby brother's rapid development. There were problems in Teddy's toilet training, and in handling of discipline. He suffered from a chronic skin rash which did not respond to medical measures.

Medical history revealed prolonged and difficult labor due to the mother's small pelvic measurements; and oxygen had been required during Teddy's first day of life. He was an unusually quiet baby, and his early development was slow. Physical examination showed an eczematous rash on face and legs, strabismus, poor lacrimation, marked salivation, slightly protruding tongue, malocclusion of teeth, undescended testicles with inguinal hernia, and slightly hyperactive reflexes as positive findings; other physical findings were negative. The diagnostic impression was of congenital mental retardation, possibly due to cerebral injury at birth.

In the psychological evaluation, Teddy did not cooperate well, and his test performance was inconsistent, so that it was questionable whether test results represented his true intellectual potential. He was found to be functioning at about two-thirds of his age level capacity. Observations of Teddy's negativism, and of the mother's overconcern and ambivalence in attitudes and handling, suggested that emotional impediments might well be affecting Teddy's performance and relationships. Speech evaluation showed repetition of words and short phrases, along with slow development of speech. Prognosis for continued development seemed good.

In the social casework study, the parents were found to be concerned about the outlook for Teddy's training and development and anxious for clarification and guidance. The father was able to be fairly objective about Teddy, and appeared to be both stable and intelligently concerned about increasing his own understanding and helping Teddy. The mother displayed considerable anxiety through her constant talking and projecting of fears about Teddy's future, worrying about whether he would ever become self-sufficient.

Both parents were eager to secure special training for Teddy through the Association's pre-school class as soon as he was ready for this group experience. Teddy's retarded appearance, with his short, squat stature, his drooling and open mouth, was embarrassing to the mother, who constantly nagged at him to keep toys and fingers out of his mouth. Parental pressure for conformity to their standards of performance and behavior was felt to be a probable contributing factor in Teddy's present regression from early attempts at toilet training, and in his confusion and negativism in response to directions and questions. It was felt that both parents could benefit from further examination of their feelings about Teddy, and that the mother needed guidance in her handling of Teddy's training at home.

Exploratory Treatment Plan

After consideration by the entire clinic staff of the above factors, the following plan for further observation and exploration was suggested: Teddy was to be seen weekly by the psychologist during a three-month period for play observation in order to gain additional data which might define more clearly the child's ability and needs. At the same time, the mother would have weekly casework interviews to explore and clarify her feelings about Teddy and herself, and to discuss training problems. It was thought that the father could add to his understanding and perspective through participation in a parents' counseling group which would meet for ten weekly sessions under the psychologist's leadership. At the end of three months, the situation would be evaluated and the treatment plan redirected as indicated.

The family physician, who would be continuing his medical treatment of Teddy, was informed of the findings and plan, which he felt would be helpful to the family. The tentative impressions and recommendations of the clinic study were reviewed with the parents, who were receptive to the suggested plan of exploration, which was then put into effect.

Casework with the Mother

The mother came regularly for the eleven interviews, in which she participated freely and constructively. The final interview in the exploratory series was held jointly with the father and psychologist to review conclusions and suggestions for a revised treatment approach.

Mrs. T. is an attractive, expressive woman with a strong need to verbalize her concerns. From the first, she showed a willingness to examine her feelings and reactions, although she also revealed, indirectly and subtly, her reluctance to face them squarely. During the initial interviews, she wore a tense expression and constantly fixed smile, which was not at all appropriate to the anxieties which she was detailing. Also, during this beginning period, the mother suffered from persistent laryngitis, which made it very hard for her to speak, yet she forced herself to do so. It is the caseworker's feeling that these defenses were necessary for Mrs. T. during the time that she was getting to know her worker, and finding out to what extent she could relax and trust me. I saw my role with Mrs. T. to be that of an understanding, non-judgmental mother person, who would facilitate Mrs. T.'s understanding of herself, and offer support, reassurance and suggestions as appropriate and helpful. My goal was to encourage her to examine and evaluate her patterns of reaction, trying to trace their roots, as she was able, to her earlier experiences. It was hoped that clarification and possibly some change in attitudes might be brought about by the understanding thus achieved.

We focused first on Mrs. T.'s concern about Teddy's regression in toilet control. After the mother was given an explanation of the complex nature of the physical controls required of a child in toilet training, and the differing rates of emotional and neurological readiness to achieve such controls, she herself concluded that she had been premature in pressing Teddy to conform in this area at nine months of age. His subsequent rebellion, through refusing to inform her of his toilet needs or of not responding at her suggestion, was seen as related to Teddy's lack of readiness and inability to conform, rather than purely as stubborness or stupidity. The reassurance that toilet controls would develop as the child was able, both physically and emotionally, to assume responsibility for his own bodily functions relieved the mother of feeling that she was a total failure. She then could examine her own methods of handling Teddy's training, and become aware that she had been pressing him too much, and not allowing him to develop self-reliance in this area. As she was able to understand that accidents would occur as part of the learning process, the mother did not feel that each failure was solely a hostile expression directed toward her. When Mrs. T. was able to give up her punishment and berating of Teddy after each toilet accident, he was able to feel more relaxed and began to indicate his needs.

While Mrs. T. was gratified by Teddy's progress, she could not believe that the gains would be sustained. She was surprised that the improvement continued, and was not able to feel any sense of personal achievement because of her better handling of Teddy's toilet training. It was at this point that the mother's pessimistic outlook and low self regard began to be apparent. She could not believe that life could hold any happiness for her, yet she had tremendous needs and expectations. The worker's reassurance regarding the future for Teddy and concerning the mother's own capacities seemed so false to Mrs. T. that her anxiety was actually increased. As a defense, she tended to deny that there was any difficulty with Teddy and expressed her own great needs through unrealistic expectations for his future development.

With the worker's encouragement, Mrs. T. began to examine the basis for her pessimism. She revealed that she felt quite responsible for Teddy's handicap, both because his skin condition is similar to the skin problem she experienced in her childhood, and also because of his difficult birth due to her own physical build. Mrs. T.'s skin condition had been a traumatic factor throughout her life, but had diminished considerably in severity following her marriage five years ago. She characterized herself in infancy, as a "naughty little baby" who caused her mother lots of trouble by not feeding properly. From the age of one year, she was subject to a breaking out on her hands and arms which practically incapacitated her. Since her hands needed to be bandaged, both parents and teachers had to do many things for her. While she enjoyed this dependence to some extent, she also felt ashamed and unlovable because of her condition. Because she was different, she felt that no one could really like her. Feeling thus unworthy and unloved, as well as helpless, she was unable to express her hostile feelings satisfactorily. When her parents were frequently harsh and restrictive toward her, she felt helpless and as if it were useless to express her protest, even though justified. She would cry in secret or else just not say anything, and suffer in silence. Mother was able to point out that frequently at such times of suppression of feeling, her rash would break out in renewed vigor, and then her mother or father would have to feel sorry for her and take care of her. It seemed thus to serve the dual purpose of self-punishment as well as retribution on her parents, ending up in dependent gratification based on suffering and helplessness.

This pattern of reaction was seen by the worker to be of rather deep and marked nature, and to be reflected in the mother's current reaction toward Teddy. Teddy's skin difficulty and slowness seemed to reactivate the mother's early feelings about herself. Even though she would become angry at Teddy because he could not measure up to her standards for him, she felt very guilty about expressing her negative feelings. As she put it, she realized that Teddy was helpless, even as she had been helpless as a child, and therefore she became uncomfortable in punishing him. On the other hand, she saw in Teddy's difference and slowness an uncomplimentary reflection of her own self-image, which was hard to accept. She was thus caught in the conflict between her high wishes for herself and her essentially low self-esteem. Through casework discussion, Mrs. T. gained some conscious awareness of how this inner conflict pressed toward opposite extremes of reaction, resulting in contradiction and inconsistency. To a limited extent, she was able to stabilize her expressions toward increased freedom and relief for herself, and at the same time let up her pressure on Teddy. This change was facilitated by Mr. T.'s encouragement and acceptance of Mrs. T. within the family relationship, while the caseworker was giving professional acceptance of Mrs. T. as a person through casework support and clarification.

Despite improvement in her overt manifestations, Mrs. T. continued to reflect severe doubts about her own capacities and what the future might hold for Teddy. In reality, she had made a good marriage, and her life had improved since her childhood sufferings. Yet Mrs. T. could not believe that she deserved any good out of life, despite her very great longings for excessive reassurance. She found it hard to accept the smaller, realistic gains which were at hand. Unless she could be guaranteed that Teddy would turn out to be completely adequate, she was unable to accept the capacities which he really had. The persistence of such fluctuations and doubts was seen to be an indication of the deep-seated nature of Mrs. T.'s difficulties, which lay beyond the scope of the casework treatment planned with her. And yet, Mrs. T. was able to absorb some greater understanding of Teddy and his condition, at least intellectually. Also, by the end of the casework series, she was herself questioning whether things were really as bad for her as she felt they were.

In relation to Teddy's sessions, the mother showed the tendency to attempt to talk with the boy's worker at the conclusion of the hour. In this way she seemed to be expressing fear and apprehension about what Teddy might be revealing about her, as well as diverting the focus of her own efforts away from self-evaluation. This resistance to self-involvement seemed also related to her recurring unrealistic concepts of herself and Teddy. The consistent channeling of information about Teddy's progress to Mrs. T. through the caseworker was not sufficiently satisfying or reassuring to her, since it was not possible to give her the specific answer and extensive reassurance which she wished to have. In facing with Mrs. T. this implication, we were again made aware of how difficult it was for her to achieve a realistic acceptance and understanding of herself and Teddy.

Evaluation of Casework Treatment

As the material and process growing out of the eleven interviews were reviewed, certain conclusions and indications emerged. Through exploration, interpretation, and support afforded by the casework approach, Mrs. T. had gained some awareness of her own patterns of reaction, and had been able to modify them to a limited, yet significant extent. The result was more constructive handling of Teddy, and a stabilization of the mother's overt expressions. While her basic underlying conflicts remained largely unchanged, Mrs. T. had become aware to a certain extent of their existence. The fact that she was able, toward the end of the exploration, to question the validity of her extreme reactions, indicated the possibility of still further modification, even if only in external expression.

The relationship between the caseworker and the mother proved to be helpful within the limitations of the exploratory period. Through acceptance and professional understanding, Mrs. T. was enabled to explore her earlier experiences and see how they related to her present discomforts. The level of treatment and relationship was purposely kept close to reality functioning, although based upon deeper understanding of human dynamics. While it was apparent that intensive psychotherapeutic effort would be required to bring about a major change in Mrs. T.'s firmly fixed personality patterns, this possibility was not considered to be available or appropriate for Mrs. T. Instead, it was thought best to help her sustain the gains she had made, and obtain a truer perspective regarding herself and Teddy.

In view of the mother's resistance to self-involvement which had been indicated by her tendency toward interjecting herself into the sessions with Teddy, it was doubtful that she would be willing to continue individual sessions, without Teddy's being seen. Instead, it was felt that the mother was ready for and could benefit from group association with other parents in a counseling program. Such participation would afford her the opportunity for gaining perspective from other parents, and the support and reassurance which such a group could provide. Having achieved some gains and awareness from the casework exploration, Mrs. T. was felt to be better prepared to use the kind of help which the counseling group offered.

Redirection of Treatment

By the end of the play sessions, the psychologist had confirmed his original impression of Teddy's capacity as lying close to borderline capacity. Since Teddy's functioning had improved with the mother's use of casework counseling, it was decided that he was ready for nursery class experience, as a stimulation toward further development. Mr. T. had participated constructively in the counseling group, clarifying his own understanding through discussion with other parents, and was found to be operating helpfully within his own family.

A joint conference to implement this redirection of treatment for the mother and Teddy was planned between workers and parents. At this time the conclusions and suggestions growing out of the work with father, mother, and child were shared. Despite positive assurances regarding Teddy's outlook, the mother's basic doubts were again brought out. This time, however, it was the father who dealt helpfully with the mother's extreme points of view. She was quite eager to enter the counseling group, both because of Mr. T.'s enthusiastic reaction, and because of her preparation through casework exploration. The parents were pleased that Teddy would be able to attend class, and it was apparent that both of them had acquired a better understanding of Teddy and of themselves through the counseling help made available through this clinic.

□ □ □

from PARENT COUNSELING AS A MEANS OF IMPROVING THE PERFORMANCE OF A MENTALLY RETARDED BOY: A CASE STUDY PRESENTATION

Anne C. French
Morrison S. Levbarg
Harold Michal-Smith

(American Journal of Mental Deficiency, 1953)

. . . .

The case described is that of a fourteen-year-old boy who is under care in the Clinic for Mentally Retarded Children at Flower and Fifth Avenue Hospitals, New York. He is presented because of marked improvement in his behavior and adjustment during a one-year period in which his mother received guidance and supportive therapy. This service to the mother was on a counseling basis, directed toward helping her evolve better methods of training and discipline.

The good results obtained in this case are ascribed to our Clinic policy of integrating the findings of pediatricians, psychologists, and other personnel who may deal with the child, and having all of the services involved collaborate in planning for handling the case.

The case is offered as an illustration of the value of parent counseling as a means of securing improved functional efficiency in mentally retarded children.

. . . .

Two considerations prompted the decision to work intensively with Perry's mother. The first was a change noted in the mother's attitude toward the boy, in which what had originally appeared as very good general acceptance was replaced by acute anxiety relating to his temper tantrums and general lack of control. The second indication for intensive work was the psychologist's impression that Perry's potential was substantially better than the test scores indicated, and that his poor test showing was due to a capriciousness, which suggested lack of proper training. It was therefore decided to schedule additional counseling sessions to help the mother develop a management program which would guide Perry toward increased self-control.

When the treatment goal was outlined to Perry's mother, she rejected it as unrealistic and impossible and sought to prove her point by a lengthy description of his tantrums. She revealed that the violent manner in which he tore at his clothing and threw himself about so frightened her that her own self-control would be lost, making Perry the inevitable victor. Since the boy was reported to have shown tantrum behavior throughout his childhood, reasons were sought to explain the mother's sudden anxiety regarding behavior which she had been able to accept formerly. Mrs. S. then disclosed that when marked pubertal changes became apparent in the boy, the trantrums which she had previously disregarded as "childishness" took on a new significance. Her son's uncontrolled behavior now appeared to her as a forecast that he would become an adult maniac, beyond social tolerance and institutionalized under restraint.

The first step in handling these fears was to make the mother understand that the boy had not in fact changed or deteriorated, and that it was her own attitude which had changed. This served to allay her fear that he was becoming worse. The next step was to help her understand the reasons for tantrum behavior in general, and to have her see that tantrums are not characteristic of the retarded, but can occur in all children. When this point had been made, Mrs. S. herself asked what measures could be used to prevent and control tantrums, indicating a shift from her original attitude that the situation was beyond remedy.

Perry's tantrums were then discussed as a device used by the boy to attain his own ends. This was followed by a discussion of the role of firmness and habit training in building the frustration tolerance needed to help Perry attain self-control. It was suggested that the mother and father collaborate on a program in which tantrum threats would be ignored, while demands for cooperation in areas of common family interest, such as choice of television programs, be enforced with a new firmness. It was further suggested that the boy be given specific incentives to demonstrate his capacity to share in the family responsibility and meet his need for successful achievement. Three specific suggestions were made: 1) that Perry be made responsible regularly for making his own bed, a chore which he enjoyed but performed on a sporadic basis; 2) that he be given a regular allowance weekly, instead of ten cents per day; 3) that his father regularly find ways to utilize his services in making stock arrangements in the family's stationery store, a job which Perry enjoyed but was seldom allowed to share because of his inefficiency.

The program as outlined above was instituted and enforced by the family over a three month period. At the end of this time, Mrs. S. reported what she characterized as a "miraculous change in the boy's character," with a cessation of tantrums and development of general social cooperativeness. The improvement noted by the mother was confirmed by observation of the boy, who was quieter, more tractable, and had increased in cooperation enough to score thirteen points above his previous high on the intelligence test, due to better concentration and motivation.

At the time of this interview, Mrs. S. appeared calm and self-possessed, in marked contrast to the picture of panic anxiety which she had presented three months earlier. In reviewing with her the improvements which she reported in Perry, care was taken to emphasize the fact that they had resulted from a change in her own attitude and manner of handling, rather than from any magical character transformation. A return was then made to the subject of the mother's original anxiety, namely Perry's future, and the change which he had already shown was used as a demonstration of the role which training and management would play in determining it. A plan was discussed with the mother for extending the areas of the boy's self-sufficiency, by giving him responsibility for covering hair cuts and small personal necessities from an increased allowance, giving him more opportunity to work with his father in the store, and encouraging him to think and act more independently regarding amusements, etc.

At a conference one month later, the mother reported that Perry's school teacher had sent for her to comment on marked improvement in school attention and achievement. Mrs. S. also reported that Perry was showing a new awareness of his own social role and said that on one occasion, when the family had had company, he came to her after the departure of the guests and said, "See, tonight I didn't babble at all, did I?" This report was made the basis of discussing ways to aid Perry in social integration. It had been noted that his attempts at conversation were never bizarre, but had the empty content which reflects lack of experience. It was suggested that the boy be taken on trips about town and given a better opportunity to enlarge his experiential background, so that he would be able to contribute in some measure to general conversation without feeling that he was "babbling."

At this interview Mrs. S. also reported that she and her husband had been so heartened by the boy's improvement that they had determined to explore possibilities of sending him to a summer camp with a work training program. While no camp of this character was located which was operated to serve retarded children, one camp had been found which would accept a few retarded children who appeared to be able to profit by the program. Perry had been interviewed by the director of the camp and accepted. The program is one of outdoor activity, centering around forestry and lumbering, so that the individual child may work at his own speed and still remain within the framework of the general program. Both Perry's parents and the camp director felt that such a program would have great value for the boy, as a means of showing the practical values of cooperative action in a setting which would also give him an opportunity to enlarge his social experience through associations with boys of his own age.

The fact that Perry's mother had been able to initiate and carry through this camp placement was interpreted as evidence that she had overcome the anxiety crisis which she had shown at the beginning of treatment. Every effort was made to have her understand that Perry's improvement was the fruit of her own effort, and to make her feel that his progress was something which she could view with justifiable pride and a sense of achievement. . . .

□ □ □

Part V Special Management Techniques

The remainder of the book will focus primarily on an exposition of the more specific options available in case management. In this particular part, we will present and discuss techniques involving some kind of group management of parents and ways of carrying assistance to the home. Both these techniques constitute alternatives to individual management, and each appears to have specific utility with particular family or problem types. Home management programs have been very rare, and while group management has been more widely employed, it has been utilized in a haphazard and chaotically rationalized manner. Indeed, group techniques with families of the retarded are only now coming out of a period of trial and error.

Office-centered management has the appearance of efficient utilization of professional manpower. However, it also has certain inherent shortcomings. For instance, some families cannot or will not respond to office-centered management, and if they are to be helped, they must be helped where they are. Further, office management by itself may fail to provide a manager with a necessary appreciation of family variables. It may require a visit to the home to observe a family in its milieu to bring about an understanding on the part of the manager. Perhaps the home management option has been under-utilized because it is atraditional to some professions engaged in management, or because it takes the professional out of the security of his office.

Group management has been much more widely employed than home management, but neither management alternative has been adequately studied. While there is a priori *reason to believe in the effectiveness of these techniques, empirical and objective studies of effectiveness and efficiency are almost completely lacking. Most writers simply report their experiences, indicate that their techniques appeared to have had desirable results, and assume that the evidence "is in." This is most unfortunate. There is a crying need for empirical investigation under stringent conditions to evaluate the utility of specific techniques and the optimal matching of management structures to specific problems and target groups. Until this is done, we will continue to read anecdotal accounts of writers' personal experiences. These accounts may make good reading, but they do not make good verification.*

As the reader examines the specific items in this section, he may notice a certain peculiarity. When some of the writers refer to parents of the retarded, they do not mean parents at all—they mean mothers to the exclusion of fathers. Frequently in our society, mothering and parenting are taken as synonymous, with fathering included only as an afterthought, if at all. This could well be a significant blind spot which can result in inadequate management. One can hypothesize that the mother is more significant in the socialization of the normal child (a hypothesis, by the way, that receives more support from logic than from empirical evidence), but will the same hypothesis hold in the case of the retarded child? The evidence is not at hand.

SECTION A

Group Approaches

When group therapy methods were first introduced in adult psychiatric services, it was the efficiency *of treating several persons in a given amount of time available to a professional that was emphasized. Soon, however, certain unique* social treatment advantages *of group over individual methods came to be valued. In an article taken as the keynote to this section, parent leaders Weingold and Hormuth present a well-stated rationale which indicates why group techniques may be the best way of working with many parents of mentally retarded children. They refer to community pressures as a source of parental attitudes and then make the following statement: "If these parental attitudes are a result of community group pressures, then the utilization of further group approaches which are organized, directed, and channelized for therapeutic ends should logically offer some effective means of changing these parental attitudes and relieving some of the family pressures." This reasoning is consistent with sociological precepts about group effects and individual attitude-formation.*

To date, about fifty publications have appeared that have reported experience with some kind of group management of parents of the retarded. The next seven selections sample various group approaches, rationales and techniques, ranging from therapeutic (Blatt; Yates and Lederer) to educational (Popp, Ingram and Jordan); from open (Goodman and Rothman; Sternlicht and Alston) to closed (Sternlicht and Alston; Yates and Lederer); from large (Popp, Ingram, and Jordan) to small (Blatt; Yates and Lederer); from short term (Yates and Lederer) to long term (Sternlicht and Alston); from socially or intellectually homogeneous (Blatt; Nadal) to heterogeneous (Blatt); and from all mothers (Blatt; Mandelbaum; Nadal) to mixed structures (Blatt; Mandelbaum; Popp, Ingram, and Jordan; Sternlicht and Alston; Yates and Lederer). Groups with special types of parents (Goodman and Rothman; Popp, Ingram, and Jordan; Yates and Lederer) and with very loosely selected members (Nadal); groups for non-English speaking minorities (Goodman and Rothman); and the combined use of group and individual counseling (Nadal; Weingold and Hormuth) and of parents' and children's groups (Goodman and Rothman; Nadal; Weingold and Hormuth) are also illustrated. Additional uses of group techniques are encountered in other parts of this book.

Mandelbaum discusses processes that he feels are likely to occur in groups of parents of the retarded and relates how group process and content may evolve over time. He illustrates how the grief motif, covered in earlier selections on parental dynamics, may come to expression in the group. Mandelbaum recommends that group workers focus on the resolution of inner conflicts of parents rather than on parental concern about facts.

In both the Blatt article and the paper by Yates and Lederer, we find descriptions of therapeutically-oriented groups for parents of the retarded. These authors indicate that the common problem of the parents encourages them to speak freely, and to share experiences and feelings. The therapeutic goal is to help these families understand themselves and their attitudes and feelings toward the retarded child. According to the authors of these articles, group sessions were eminently successful in helping parents on the road to good adjustment.

Sternlicht and Alston detail the evolution of a group of parents of the retarded, with focus on the dynamics involved in creating and maintaining the group. After a year of sessions in which parents discussed the problems they were having with their retarded children, the group took an evolutionary turn toward discussion about themselves. At this point the leader suggested that the members think in terms of a therapeutic situation in which focus would be upon self-understanding, a suggestion which was endorsed by the group as a whole. According to the authors, the group then took on a new therapeutic flavor with emphasis on understanding of one's self.

While Nadal covers ground similar to some of the other authors, he discusses one significant innovation. In his group counseling program for mothers he identified the members who, in his estimation, were unprepared and unsuited for the group experience because of a high level of anxiety and conflict. Nadal felt that these mothers were better suited for individual counseling. Although they were not excluded from his group, they were provided with the additional individual counseling they appeared to need. It should be noted that several of the other authors in this section would probably disagree with Nadal's rationales.

Goodman and Rothman report that they selected two categories of mothers for group counseling: those with young children who had just completed a clinic evaluation, and those whose children were in or entering adolescence. Popp, Ingram, and Jordan set up an educationally-oriented and largely didactically-conducted group of parents of retarded children under ten years of age who had been excluded from school. In both groups the authors were quite enthused about the potential of group techniques with parents of the retarded.

The seven selections discussed above (excluding Weingold and Hormuth) have many shortcomings. Some were included not so much as examples to be emulated, but as typical examples of work done to date. It is hoped that in the future, group rationales and structures will be selected more thoughtfully on the basis of pragmatic and empirical determination of effectiveness with different groups and problems. To this end, objectified and carefully designed outcome studies are needed. To date, only about two or three such studies have been conducted.

Dybwad, the former excutive director of the National Association for Retarded Children, concludes Part V with a review of the field of group management of parents. He sees an urgent need for systematic efforts toward a) a clearer conceptualization of various group approaches for parents, b) clear recognition of appropriate training of managers of group problems, and c) the development of research designed to assess the effectiveness of such programs.

We have noted in the introduction to this section that there has been a shift in emphasis away from consideration of the efficiency of the group approach in management, and toward the use of this approach because it possesses unique social treatment advantages. However, the utilitarian aspects of group treatment should not be minimized. For instance, some parents have such a high commonality of needs and problems that group management techniques add an element of efficiency to the social treatment advantage. Examples of conditions with such high commonality will be presented in Part VIII.

GROUP GUIDANCE OF PARENTS OF MENTALLY RETARDED CHILDREN

Joseph T. Weingold
Rudolf P. Hormuth

(Journal of Clinical Psychology, 1953)

In a discussion of this kind it would be well to state at the very beginning what is so often posed in theory and neglected in practice: that no child stands alone; a child is part of a family and a community; what happens to the family affects the child and certainly the child affects the family. This interaction of strong forces must always be remembered and dealt with if we are to help the mentally retarded realize potentials to the maximum. To deal in isolation with the child on an "individual" basis would, of course, be unthinkable. Work must be done with the parents, too, who play so important a role in this problem.

It is just as unrealistic to deal with the parents in isolation or "individually." They, too, do not stand alone. They are part of the child's life and difficulties. Together with the child, as a family, they are part of a community life—and even more important, members of groups of individuals who, because of the presence of the retarded child in their midst, have special interests and problems.

It seems axiomatic that successful group guidance depends on at least two factors, both of which are necessary, i.e. a group to be guided and somewhere to guide them. Until recently, except in an institutional setting, there were not enough parents of mentally retarded children asking for guidance at the same time to make group work feasible and, furthermore, there was no frame of reference in which to work—nowhere to guide many of them except to institutions.

A factor which probably changes the whole emphasis in dealing with the parents of mentally retarded children has been the quite recent formal organization of these parents into associations or parents groups. Now we find large numbers of parents asking for help in a community setting. By the very act of organizing into groups the parents themselves supply the first frame of reference and even create a loose form of group therapy, lacking until now. In commenting on this phenomenon, Sarason says, "These parents, by virtue of becoming a group, have done more for their own happiness and stability than the professional or specialist has ever done for them."[1]

It now becomes necessary for the professional to reexamine old ideas and formulate new ones, even in advance of the parents' groups, or he will find himself engulfed and submerged. If he is to help the parents, "It seems important," writes Sheimo, "not to under-estimate the intense repressed forces which become mobilized in parents who have mentally defective and/or handicapped children. At such times, to center one's attention on the defective child rather than toward the parental conflict might be attempting to deal with the least relevant factor in the total situation."[2]

Previously, probably the most difficult and at times frustrating problem when trying to guide the individual parent of a mentally retarded child has been what Sheimo aptly terms the "intense repressed forces." This may have taken the form of intense resistance on the part of the parents to any realistic recognition of the limitations or even capacities of the retarded individual. Parents have insisted, on the one hand, that the child could do this, that, or the other thing if only given a chance. On the other hand, there has been intense overprotection of the child so that even in areas where the child has capacities, they are not developed because the parents are afraid to let the child do things. Johnny may get hurt, may be made fun of, etc. Families with retarded children seem to be beset much more intensely with problems of sibling rivalry, marital conflicts, etc. The presence of the retarded child seems to accentuate any personality difficulties which exist in members of the family. And indeed why shouldn't it? Here is a problem which has been the subject of community ridicule and rejection, that has to be dealt with by the parents twenty-four hours a day, without relief and often without hope of any kind.

The attitudes of the parents were a reaction to a very real rejection and non-acceptance by the community group within which the family with a retarded child found itself. The family as well as the child were ridiculed, "stared at" or avoided. The community approached them with a mingling of pity and suspicion. "Are idiots really born to intelligent people who lead a normal life?" "Johnny should not play with a 'moron', because a 'moron' may lead Johnny into delinquent acts of sexual perversion." "Aren't all mentally retarded better off in institutions?"

The professionals themselves have not helped the situation. Research still being in the "pre-fact finding" stage, there were too many unknown and unexplored facts. Too many pediatricians and obstetricians had routinely recommended immediate institutional placement whenever a mongoloid child was born. Educators have told many of these parents that their children are "uneducable." The doors of mental hygiene clinics, recreation centers, industry and community facilities were closed to the retarded and his family. For these reasons individual approaches were much too threatening to many of these parents and an unusually large proportion were found inaccessible to individual guidance or casework.

It seemed to us that these group pressures basically had forced the family of a retarded child to withdraw from normal social contacts and isolate itself with the child. In turn, the family's attention was focused more sharply on every action of the child; the resulting frustration accentuated not only the personality difficulties of the parents, but to a large extent created feelings of guilt, shame, rejection and overprotection of the retarded child. Since the latter have the same needs as the normal with regard to family life, social acceptance, etc., adequate adjustment is made infinitely harder because of the increased personality problems and difficulties of the parents. Non-acceptance by the community and the family groups is translated to the individual parent and then the child. The attitudes of the groups must be influenced and changed, and it is not only logical and feasible, but imperative to work with parents while the parents' organizations are working with the larger group—the community.

Group Guidance for Parents

If these parental attitudes are a result of community group pressures, then the utilization of further group approaches which are organized, directed and channelized for therapeutic ends should logically offer some effective means of changing these parental attitudes and relieving some of the family pressures. The organized parent groups have effectively mobilized these "intense repressed forces" towards the organization of clinics, recreation groups, schools, and other direct services for the retarded. These projects supplied the frame of reference necessary for successful group guidance—somewhere to guide the parents.

It is interesting to note the parent attitudes towards the clinic services as found by Galiboff. In analyzing these attitudes he chose twenty parents, half of whom were members of the Association for the Help of Retarded Children, which supported the clinic. "The feeling of belonging to a group of parents whose problems are being handled by their own means has a great therapeutic value. . . . The parents who were members of the association were more accepting of their children and expressed their satisfaction toward services that the clinic provided them. Those parents who were not members were mostly dissatisfied with the services of the clinic and rejected their children."[3]

We might add that this was the result of the impact of the whole parent association and not because of work done with small groups in the frame of reference of a specific service. The parents themselves recognized the need for more intense specialized group participation and guidance. They organized the Parent Education Courses, a series of lectures in the general area of mental retardation dealing with such topics as "Definitions, Kinds, and Causes of Mental Retardation," "Trends and Problems in the Medical Study of Mental Retardation," "Psychological Testing and Its Implications," "The Retarded Child in the Home," etc. (See Appendix at end of article.) A further refinement of this approach is the School for Mothers, a series of lectures and discussions dealing with specific management problems and activities of daily living for parents with retarded children under five. (See Appendix following article.) These courses are fulfilling the tremendous thirst of the parents for knowledge from which comes a significant change in the parents' attitudes to the child and the problem.

Because of the large numbers of parents involved in these courses, and the fact that the group leaders have been unfamiliar with specific problems of individual children involved, some readers may consider these programs to be parent education rather than group guidance as such. Although we do not wish to become involved in controversy, we believe that no constructive purpose is served in drawing fine distinctions which often become vague and confused in differentiating between group guidance and parent education.

Pattern of Organization

The important thing to bear in mind is that these groups were a natural consequence of a situation, a frame of reference, if you will. They started with the large group of the whole organization, then became smaller in the parent-education course and school for mothers, and finally formed into tightly knit small groups according to particular services extended to children through efforts of the parents.

From the base of the general Parent Association, the group guidance approach has been vitalized effectively and on different levels throughout the various projects organized by the Association for the Help of Retarded Children. Probably the most refined and most specialized use has been in our clinics. Typical of this use was a group of eight mothers of mongoloid children organized at the Morris J. Solomon Clinic for the Rehabilitation of Retarded Children at the Jewish Hospital of Brooklyn. These children ranged in chronological ages from three to seven (mental ages from ten months to four years eight months) and had received complete diagnostic workups at the clinic.

These evaluations made it quite clear that all the children had abilities which were not being utilized and that all could be helped to function better if several things could happen in the family group. In the first place, the tremendous anxiety, hostility, guilt, shame, and rejection which had built up in the parents had to be relieved. All of these families were more or less isolated. They had withdrawn from practically all social contacts and had to be reintegrated as functioning and participating members of the community. Further, all of them were at a complete loss in terms of management of the child at home. They were struggling with such questions as: Would their child learn to talk? How could they cut down hour-long feeding sessions? How and when could they get the child to drink from a glass, feed himself, start to dress himself, etc.?

The group of mothers had been carefully selected from a large clinic list of their children, who were at various stages within the age range. This arrangement permitted us to use the knowledge of the parents themselves about the developmental process. Thus, the phases through which one parent had gone with her child were available as information for the assistance of other group members. The mothers had also been selected to some extent to form a balanced group ranging from extremely withdrawn to very aggressive.

The psychiatric social worker, who was familiar with all the cases and had interpreted the clinic findings to these parents, acted as the group leader. Twelve weekly sessions of approximately one and one-half hours each were set. Supervision was offered for the children during the sessions. The topics covered ranged from very specific aspects of mangement in activities of daily living to discussions of their own feelings of guilt, frustration, and shame about the child, family attitudes, explanations to siblings of the mongoloid child, etc.

Group Dynamics

Things happened rather swiftly in the group. Through the support gained from the leader and the others in the group, there even was a danger at times that these parents, previously afraid of making any move, would go too fast. They began to permit the children to do things without the parents' help and thus proved to themselves that the children had capacities (which they could not see or accept when this was interpreted individually to them). When a specific management problem had been discussed and steps outlined, it became a matter of personal pride for each individual to report back at the following session what she had been able to accomplish with her child. Even the mother who for five years had spent three hours on each feeding succeeded in cutting this down by forty-five minutes by the end of the sessions. (Interestingly enough, two pediatricians had previously spent several hours with this mother on the feeding problem and had gotten nowhere. The mother refused to follow any of their instructions, expressing the fear that if she followed their advice, her child would starve to death.)

At the end of the sessions all were offered the opportunity to continue with individual guidance sessions. Only three felt they needed this. The others felt that for a time they could manage on their own and were anxious to see how far they could get before they needed additional help. This was a remarkable change for a group of parents who previously had been so isolated and confused that they were completely immobilized. At the end of the twelve weeks we noted many changes in parental attitudes. We also were able to see the beginnings of the effect of changed handling at home as it was reflected in better adjustment and improved behaviour of the children.

Guidance for Older Groups

Group guidance for parents has also been utilized effectively in the social activity program for retarded individuals from eighteen to twenty-five years of age. These individuals meet for club group activities in six centers throughout the city. Each group has approximately fifteen members, boys and girls meeting one evening a week under the direction of two professional leaders.

In organizing this program we were also faced with the kinds of problems outlined above, particularly parental attitudes which hampered and interfered with whatever progress could be achieved with the club groups. To cope with this obstacle, we set up a parent discussion group for parents whose children were participating in a particular club group. The parents met at the same time that their children did, but in a different part of the center. We utilized the services of psychiatric social workers as discussion leaders.

In this program we could not achieve the high degree of selectivity or balance which was possible in the group organized in the clinic. The grouping this time had been done in terms of the children rather than their parents. This fact presented greater difficulties in some groups overbalanced with very aggressive, dominating, or very disturbed individuals and showed itself in different rates of development in favor of more evenly matched parents. However, the discussion groups had the advantage of being formed within the realistic framework of a project for the children.

The parent-discussion groups were utilized not only to consider the recreational clubs for adolescents and young adults and to attempt to transfer insights into home life, but also went into general considerations of the problems of retardation, parental attitudes and specific management questions.

For example, the discussions over a ten month period with one group covered such areas as the parents' lack of confidence in their children and the parents' fears of permitting the retarded individuals to assume responsibility; behavior problems and how to handle them; problems of sex; goals which could be achieved, etc. The discussions were permitted to develop from the kinds of problems the parents were struggling with and out of the "new" problems which arose as a result of the club program and the new and different stimuli to which the children were exposed.

All the discussions were approached from individual problems or questions and sessions were ended with a general conclusion or summary drawn from the discussion. In this way each member of the group had some part in formulating the conclusion and felt much more personally involved in it. As a result, it was possible to take such "risks" as permitting a twenty-two-year-old retarded son to travel on the subway alone or to go to a movie in the evening with a friend. Such steps could never have been accomplished with these parents on an individual guidance basis, even though their children had long been ready for this and were capable of it. They had to have the support of other parents and—most important—a program for the children as a frame of reference and hope.

The amount of insight gained by the parents and their success in assimilating and carrying out management techniques can roughly be judged from the manner in which the kind of problems they raised refocused themselves in the course of the sessions. For example, the initial questions of discipline and control changed to questions of how can we get the children to travel alone, handle money, manage an allowance, find and hold a job. In certain areas there was a danger of the parents moving too fast and suddenly expecting too much as they began to see some further social development in their children for the first time in many years. All their repressed and forgotten hopes were reactivated. Typical of this is the whole question of sex. Whereas in the initial phases there were intense fears about permitting any of the children to be unsupervised at any time or to travel alone for fear of someone "taking advantage of them" sexually, these problems gradually were refocused on areas such as: "Could these children understand about sex?", and finally, after several months, to questions of "Should we allow them to date?" and "Is marriage feasible?"

Probably the best criterion for evaluating the effectiveness of group guidance for parents within this program is the manner in which discussion material was translated into changed attitudes and improved handling of the children. This development reflected itself very clearly in the improved adjustments of the children and their very marked and rapid progress in social adaptations.

One of our first club groups, for example, started with twenty retarded boys and girls ranging in age from 18 to 27 with I.Q.'s approximately 50 to 75. There were various diagnostic categories, and a number of individuals had been institutionalized at one point or another. At the start only three members of this group were working and only five knew how to travel by themselves. By and large, they were completely dependent upon their parents, showed very little interest in their surroundings, had no friends and had a great deal of difficulty getting along with others (one of the chief reasons why many were not working). After one and one-half years, all but two of this group were working, all were travelling by themselves, managing allowances, conducting their own business meetings, electing club officers, publishing their own club paper, dating club members of the opposite sex, meeting each other for card games, theatre parties, etc.

Admittedly, part of this development was due to the club program with the young adults themselves. It is clear, however, that even this factor could not have operated unless the parents were involved and permitted their children to assume responsibilities and effectively implement the two-hour weekly club sessions with changes of their own during the remainder of the week.

A third program which involves group guidance with parents centers in our schools (organized for children who are not eligible for the special classes in the public schools, i.e., children with I.Q. below 50). Because of the newness of our school program this phase of group guidance has not yet been fully developed, but it seems to offer tremendous possibilities. . . .

Our work with the parents of the mentally retarded has definitely established the value of group guidance for parents of mentally retarded children as one of the most effective tools to bring about a more adequate adjustment of the family to such a child, as well as more effectively reintegrating the family into the community. Our experience indicates that such group guidance is a prime necessity if the child is to get the maximum benefit from his family life or services set up to help him develop his or her capacities. In fact, the advent of Parents' Groups and their own tremendous drive makes such group guidance not only feasible, but indispensable to the success of any program.

Footnotes

1. Sarason, Seymour, "The Psychology of the Exceptional Child," Proceedings of the Annual Conference on Education and the Exceptional Child. The Woods Schools, Langhorne, Pa., May, 1952, 16-20.
2. Sheimo, S. L., "Problems in Helping Parents of Mentally Defective and Handicapped Children," *American Journal of Mental Deficiency*, 1951, 56: 42-47.
3. Galiboff, Zwi, "Parent Attitudes Toward the Services of a Clinic for Retarded Children," New York School of Social Work, Columbia University, August, 1951.

Appendix

PARENT EDUCATION COURSES ON MENTAL RETARDATION

The Help of Retarded Children, Inc.

This is a series of lectures followed by question and answer periods to acquaint parents with the various aspects and implications of mental retardation. It is an educational course to help parents understand their children's problems and, through understanding, handle them intelligently, as well as with love. The schedule of lectures is as follows:

1. Definitions, Kinds and Causes: Nature and needs of mentally retarded children; definition; causes; types and classifications of mental retardation.
2. Trends and Problems in the Medical Study of Mental Retardation.
3. Psychological Testing and its Implications: Nature of intelligence and personality; aims and objectives of the psychological examination; procedure of the examination; the examination battery; its findings and implications and relationship to mental retardation.
4. Child in the Home, Recognition, Impact and Acceptance: Methods in early detection of retardation; mental growth and personality patterns of the child; the impact of the child's retardation on the whole family; acceptance of the child as a person and his place in our society.
5. Speech for the Retarded: A definition of language and speech; the development of language and speech; preparation for language and speech.
6. Implications—Personal and Vocational: Training of the whole child with special attention to what the home and family can do to help the child grow towards his full potential in the various elements of his total personality.
7. The Older Retarded Child—Social Implications in the Home and the Community: Impact upon the home life; duties and obligations in the home towards the older retarded child and the need for community education to insure better understanding, acceptance and respect for the older mentally retarded child.
8. The Older Retarded Child—Vocational Training and Employment: What the older retarded child can do; what jobs are available to him and what training he needs.

SCHOOL FOR MOTHERS OF CHILDREN UNDER FIVE

Topics for each class:

1. Causes of Mental Retardation.
2. Self-care Activities: Feeding, dressing, toilet training.
3. Behavior Problems.
4. Speech Problems.
5. Meaning and Value of Psychological Tests.
6. Choice of Games, Toys and Crafts.
7. Healthy Parental Attitudes. How to accept your Child as a person.
8. Medical Treatment of Retardation (an evaluation of various drug therapies).
9. Role Diagnosis of Difficulties and Agreement between Parent and Child.
10. Planning the Future of the Retarded Child.

□ □ □

from THE GROUP PROCESS IN HELPING PARENTS OF RETARDED CHILDREN

Arthur Mandelbaum

(Children, 1967)

One way found to be effective in helping parents of retarded children come to terms with themselves is to bring them together in small selected groups under the leadership of a professional person who can help them share common educational, social, and emotional experiences in a way beneficial to each member of the group.

The following analysis of the process that takes place in such groups is based on my experience as a social caseworker who has worked with several small groups of parents of retarded children in the past seven years—some made up of mothers and fathers, some of mothers only. The groups met once a week for one and one-half hours each session. Some groups ran for six sessions; some for ten or twelve sessions; some, even longer. The members of the groups themselves determined how long they needed to continue meeting together.

The group process is used to help each member to bring forth his concern, anger, and thoughts so that gradually his strength comes to the fore and he can use it more creatively and independently in handling the social and emotional problems stemming from his child's retardation. If the group members can express both their positive and negative feelings, and the leader is not critical, hostile, authoritative, or judgmental and is skillfully able to ease communication, then each can grow through the experience. As each member gradually gains more knowledge of himself and of the others in the group, he expresses himself with greater freedom and spontaneity. He learns his wife has feelings he did not know she had and had not recognized in himself. He also learns that she and others have feelings that he thought existed only in himself. He begins the difficult task of learning to listen to *others* talk about *their* feelings, not only to himself. He listens to ideas expressed in a continuous, evolving process and gradually becomes aware of the intense feelings behind them and of how little he knew of this before. He may then come to understand some of the sources of his own angry feelings and to sense that they are rooted in irrationality, disillusionment, and failure to realize his dreams.

Perhaps the most significant aspect of a group process is the opportunity it gives the parent to further resolve his grief. This is necessary before the parent can release his capacity for profound understanding. As Solnit and Stark have said: "Coping with the outer reality of a child with a congenital defect and the inner reality of feeling the loss of a desired normal child requires a great deal of mental work. Such psychic work is slow and emotionally painful, and it proceeds through the gradual and repeated discharge of intense feelings and memories. These mental and emotional reactions enable the parent to recognize and adapt to the reality of the retarded child."

In many young or comparatively young parents who have the major part of their lives still ahead, the trauma they experienced when they first learned of their child's mental defect remains a raw wound.

> Mrs. A. spoke dramatically of a dream she had several months before the birth of her child. In the dream she climbed up to a balcony and then dropped the baby over, shattering him to bits.
>
> Several persons in the group gasped, and several other mothers said quickly that they too had premonitions of disaster before the birth of their children.
>
> Mrs. A. said that while she was pregnant she had seen a TV program concerning the mercy killing of a mongoloid baby. She recalled being greatly upset and thinking, "How dreadful if my baby would be like that." She described her feelings when she learned that her baby was "like that": "I was in shock, I couldn't believe it, I couldn't think."
>
> Mrs. E. told of an experience her sister-in-law had with an impersonal and busy doctor. His way of letting her know of her misfortune was to remark casually as he left her hospital room, "You have a retarded child." A shocked silence followed. Mrs. F. said softly, "I imagine it must be hard for the doctors also."
>
> After some moments of further discussion, the worker asked whether the parents thought it was hard for a doctor to tell parents they had a retarded child.
>
> Mrs. G. said her doctor had tried to tell her a little every day about her baby's condition. She thought he was afraid she might not be able to take it. Finally one day she said to him, "For goodness' sake, tell me the truth." He did. Her husband, who already knew, brought her books on the sub-

ject. But that proved to be the wrong thing to do. Her husband meant well, but some of the books contained wrong information.

Mrs. B. said she also read books about retarded children; some of these books were sentimental and phony, but, "I did learn a little about the subject."

Mrs. C. shrugged, "I was in shock, but I got over it right away."

Mrs. G. laughed in a challenging, anxious, skeptical way. Mrs. C. insisted, "But I did. I realized it was not too bad to have a blind child because they can do many things for a blind child. I didn't know then he was also retarded."

Mrs. D. said that for a long time her doctor did not know about her child's condition because "doctors still don't know many things."

Mrs. G. described how hard it was for her to tell her mother about her child's condition. Tears came to her eyes as she related how both she and her mother wept. This led her to talk about how the child cried almost incessantly. She said she needed to keep faith in God.

Some parents express their fear of having more children and their envy of other parents:

Mrs. A. said that when she sees other couples having healthy babies, a pain hits her; she thinks she is jealous. Mrs. B. said she is jealous, too, but that she knows it is wrong to have such feelings.

The discussion then turned to parents who have normal children and complain about them or abuse them. The feeling that "they do not know how lucky they are" was expressed vehemently and often.

Some themes, common to all discussion groups of parents of retarded children, are introduced with insistent force early in the group process: feelings of isolation, of loneliness, and of inability to communicate with others are quickly recalled.

Many parents tell about how impossible they found it to speak to anyone after the shock of learning about their child's condition. It seemed to them then that there was no one available to listen, at least no one capable of understanding. Professional people could not understand—they seemed, in a sense, like the parents themselves, human, fragile, fearful, lacking the courage to face the problem, to speak about it, to talk honestly, directly, and kindly. As outsiders, they could not *really* understand.

Then the parents begin gradually to bring up their feelings of anger and frustration, forbidden, dreadful feelings that produce a sense of guilt they have tried to control or deny. Some parents think that perhaps the angry feelings within themselves have a magical power and may have impaired the fetus at conception or during gestation. Some wonder whether their child's retardation is not a punishment from God because of their past sins, or whether God has not blessed them by giving them a retarded child as a symbol of innocence, purity, and holiness.

Parents always express these thoughts about God, tentatively, with awe toward mysterious, seemingly irrational forces and at the same time with bitterness, irony, and doubt. The question persists: "What did I do to have had this happen to me?"

Feelings toward the retarded children gradually emerge. Some parents see the children as grotesque objects to be hidden from public view and from friends and relatives. As such feelings come to light, they become attached to the parents' self-image. The parents feel inwardly grotesque and are afraid of being regarded as genetically imperfect, contaminated, and inextricably identified with the damaged child.

Mrs. Z. said angrily that before her retarded child was born, her mother-in-law boasted that among her fourteen grandchildren there was "not one crooked finger."

Mrs. Z. said with a laugh that she thought there was a little of the mongoloid in all of her other children too, as several of them had the simian line and blunted fingers. After the birth of the retarded child, her mother-in-law would not go near him. She suggested that the Z.'s place the child in an institution and was disappointed when they took him home. Once when the father was going to visit a relative, she urged him to take one of the normal children along so that "they could see you are capable of having normal children."

As the parents describe the cruelty of others toward them in their misfortune, many reveal their own harsh and punitive views of themselves. These are gradually modified by the gentle, kind, perceptive judgments offered by other members of the group.

Mrs. S., in an angry voice, told about taking her retarded daughter to a party and, after leaving her side for only a few minutes, being accused by the child of trying to abandon her. Mrs. J. described her embarrassment when she took her retarded son to get a haircut and he tried in his jumbled speech to talk with the barber. Mrs. V. told how her son had run excitedly into the living room speaking incoherently when the family was entertaining company. When she tried to calm him down, he had become so excited that she had to send him to the basement. Mr. and Mrs. F. admitted rather shamefacedly that they never took their daughter anywhere because she was so obviously retarded. Mrs. S. confessed that when she took her daughter anywhere she had a strong impulse to shout, "She's a retarded child!" and had real difficulty in controlling it. The group, shocked, fell silent.

The worker pointed out that all the parents apparently had these feelings of embarrassment and discomfort and asked what understanding, what thoughts they had about them.

Mrs. F. said "shame and humiliation." She said she felt like hurling something at them, those who looked at the child, those who thought she was different; she wanted to attack them and defend her child. Mr. V. said "resentment and anger" for having such a child. Mrs. E. said, "I want to say to them, well, what are you looking at?" Mrs. T. said, excitedly, "I used to do that, think that. I used to stare at them, but now I avert my eyes." Mr. F. said, "I am guilty of that, too. Inside you feel inferior, ashamed."

Mr. T. said they had left their daughter Betty at a party that night with great apprehension, for they had never left her at a party before. "My mind is there while I am talking," he said. "Betty talks, talks, talks. The people we usually leave her with when we come here are out of town. It is important to come here; we have never talked about our feelings about her with anyone else before, never even with relatives or friends." Mr. F. said, "We come here for the child as well as ourselves."

Mr. E. said he wondered whether all these feelings we were talking about were not due to the hurt inside the parents. The child, he thought, does not suffer so much as the parents. Mr. T. agreed, "It is because you feel there is something wrong with you that you should have a retarded child."

Mrs. F. spoke of knowing a nineteen-year-old retarded boy whose parents take him everywhere. "Maybe it is our fault when our child embarrasses us. Maybe he picks up our feelings about him."

Eventually, the group enters a period of alternating grief and solace: themes of loss and death alternate with themes of how gentle and lovable retarded children are and the solace they offer the family. The parents' fears that the children might die are based on reality, for many retarded children have other congenital defects that add to the difficulty of caring for them and fill their parents' days and nights with apprehension.

The parents praise each other's children, and during the expression of such positive feelings they slowly venture to speak of their anger and fright at the persistent intrusion of intense death wishes. Many say in effect, "Having a retarded child is like having a death in the family, only worse; at least you can get over a death, but this is never behind you. You have to live with this—for the rest of your life."

When the group members become aware of the intense feelings this theme arouses, they move away from it. Many indicate they do not want to look ahead very far. Groups are often quite free from expecting false assurances and are quick to challenge platitudes. The retarded child is an inescapable reality. The future is feared because the child must surely present more difficulties as he grows; his faults and defects will be magnified. Some parents express the wish that the child will remain an infantile love object to be cuddled and pampered, of whom little need be demanded. Conversely, some parents note that in remaining like an infant the child will be an ever-increasing burden, tyrannical in his need for attention and care.

Each parent in a couple seems to fear that the other will be drawn to the retarded child so strongly that all others in the family will be neglected. This leads to anger and a sense of guilt in an alternating repetitive cycle.

Parents often screen their doubts and misgivings about the extent to which they might express their innermost thoughts in the group with expressions of concern about what to tell their other children, relatives, friends, and other persons in the community. However, parents frequently say they feel both relieved and surprised after they *have* expressed a strong negative feeling or fear. They wonder that they have been able to say things in a group that they had never been able to say to a husband or wife or a best friend. Their feeling of relief, however, is soon followed by further doubts and fears of revealing deeper feelings.

So great is the need among such parents to protect their self-esteem that a group sometimes subtly divides into sections: one, parents of children who are only mildly or moderately retarded and have only slight or no physical defects; the other, parents of children who are severely retarded or whose retardation is also apparent in their physical appearance, as with mongoloid children.

Each member of the group feels defeat, but many have also had experiences that have given them a sense of victory —moments of small triumph whose import they feel the "outside world" is not equipped to understand. For example, a parent may say, "Our retarded children are different; we can shed tears together. But we are alert to and take pride in every sign of small improvement in them. Every slight step forward, which would be unnoticed in our normal children, is a major triumph in the handicapped child."

The group members usually identify with one another in an intense and binding fashion. They seem to feel that since their children are unusual, they themselves are unusual also and belong together. Sometimes they are united against the "outside world"; sometimes against the leader of the group, a representative of the outside world.

Mrs. T. said that for two years she would not admit to herself that her child was retarded. She recalled the first doctor she had consulted about the child, and she said she hated him. Mrs. N. suggested that perhaps Mrs. T. hated the doctor because he was the first person to tell her about her child's retardation. Mrs. T. agreed. The discussion then became heated as the group members spoke of doctors, how they were told about their child's handicap, and their need for someone to talk with.

For the first time, two or three parents spoke at once. The worker, raising his voice slightly to be heard, pointed out that the parents were saying three important things: first, that the doctor, by giving them the diagnosis, had hurt them; second, that the doctor had failed to help them in the way they had wanted at the time of their first deep shock; third, that they had found consolation in talking with others with the same kind of problems through the parents' association and that outsiders did not understand and could not help very much.

The parents agreed to this. Then the worker pointed out that several times previously he had tried to get into the discussion but that they had been so intent on getting their points across that he had not been able to do so. He asked whether they were aware of this and, if so, whether they could understand why.

Mr. P. quickly said, "You are an outsider, too." The worker said he thought this was an important point. Mrs. T. pointed out that one of the "professionals" on the staff of the parents' association was supposed to attend a meeting of the school board but had been "too busy" to do so. If he were a parent of a retarded child, he would

> have been there, she added, but professionals did not have the same kind of concern as parents. Mrs. N. said that the man's absence probably had nothing to do with his being a professional person; even some parents had to be pushed to attend meetings.
>
> When the group session ended, the parents remained standing outside the building as the worker drove away. Mrs. S. waved goodbye, saying, "You see, we are going to continue outside in the cold."

As the discussion explores the labyrinth of feelings, the parents grope toward mature ways of viewing behavior in an attempt to find a value system that is right for them, one that will sustain and nourish them. They support one another, bring out feelings for the scrutiny of the group, question irrational ideas, point up the inefficiency and dubious value of certain kinds of behavior, and gradually increase the ability of each person in the group to look realistically at the problems presented by his retarded child and ways of dealing with them. The worker must have faith in the inherent ability of the individual parent to release his capacity to do this—a capacity previously blocked by anger, conflict, and fantasies. If he does not have such faith, he will intervene hastily in the group's discussion and become authoritative and didactic, and in doing so dilute the emotional intensity of the experience for the parents.

Using the group process to help parents is an increasing clinical practice in service to the mentally retarded. The worker who attempts the process must be skilled in dealing with persons in one-to-one interviews, *preferably before* he attempts to deal with them in groups. If he chooses the group method because he is discontent with the one-to-one method, he should know that in trying to help individual parents through the group process he takes on a task of greater complexity, one requiring an understanding of the dynamics not only of individual behavior, both normal and abnormal, but also of the behavior of groups. If he is discontent with the slow, cautious movement in the one-to-one process and expects a more rapid progress in working with a group, he will be disillusioned. In either method the worker must be aware of the recurrent nature of grief in parents of retarded children and of the adhesive quality of their inner conflicts. He must know that he will win the group's confidence and trust only after repeated trial and error and that each member of the group grows at his own pace.

It is tempting to use the group meeting to teach parents facts about mental retardation, to answer their questions about their children, and to discuss at length the reasons for their children's slow development. Listening and observation, however, will quickly show the worker that many parents in the group are very well read on the subject of retardation and that some have become learned on specific aspects of the problem and are much closer to being masters of the subject than the worker. Instead of teaching, the worker helps the parents deal with their inner problems by using his knowledge that sorrows can be borne if they can be put into words or into a story; can be absorbed or dissolved if they can be expressed in words to those who face the same inescapable adversity and who wish to examine that adversity as it affects their inner selves. His task is to help the parents see the import of what they are saying and feeling as the discussion weaves back and forth between the way individual members feel about being parents of a mentally retarded child and how and what they understand about their world, themselves, and each other.

To the group the worker is an outsider. As the parents speak about professional people not understanding, about their treating parents abruptly and harshly and not helping in the way parents want and expect, the worker must use the strictest self-discipline to control his anger, for it becomes clear that the parents also consider him an outsider incapable of helping them and unable to understand their feelings because he has not had the same shattering experience as they.

The worker is like a screen against which are projected the parents' feelings toward all outsiders as critical, uncaring, judgmental, and punitive. He represents all authoritative figures who have failed to protect the parents from an irrational and malignant fate, who will not give answers, and who force them to think for themselves.

"Will no one give us answers to our grief, will no one hear us?" The cry, at first silent, is soon voiced more and more. The language of the group is commonplace. It is concerned with the ordinary aspects of experience, but suddenly, and sometimes without warning, it slips into expressiveness or expressions that give the speakers themselves a shocking glimpse into their deeper feelings.

> "Do you ever get over it, the depression, I mean?"
>
> "I felt that being around friends who were pregnant was like some curse."
>
> "What did I ever do to have had this happen to me?"
>
> "Sometimes, I wish he had died at birth; the doctor should have killed him and not told me."
>
> "When I did bring the baby into the store, the clerks all admired her and cooed. I wondered whether they knew she was retarded and they did that just to please me. Then, when I didn't bring the baby, they asked about her. I felt guilty and wondered whether I had left her home because I was angry. Maybe the fact is, I'm too sensitive."

The conversation is sometimes drab, superficial; the speakers grope to convey information, search restlessly for contact, for understanding, for an illuminating explanation of the myths, theories, and conflicting beliefs about retarded children. In this search they express fear that the worker will see them as damaged, inferior, and ill and will not see their strength. Then, of course, they hesitate as though wondering how much it is safe for them to see and understand.

They become angry and seem to feel that the group process means they are to devote their lives and their dreams exclusively to the retarded child, to the neglect of their other children and themselves.

They seem to wonder: Are they in bondage? Will the worker let them go? If they express the full measure of their thoughts, their anger, will they be able to control their feelings after they leave the group and do not have each other for support?

They seem to wonder, too, about the worker and his relationship to them: Will he, because of the intensity of their concern and anger, become overburdened and ill? Is he preoccupied with his work, too professional, insensitive, and unobservant to know how they really feel? When a meeting is canceled because he has to be away, where does he go and to whom does he give the words of wisdom that he is denying them? How can they make him do their bidding and gain mastery over him so that he can gratify them more?

These and other questions the parents sometimes ask directly, sometimes imply in their questions or statements about their retarded children, their families, and their lives outside the group. But little by little they delve beneath the clichés and superficial questioning to deeper layers of meaning until they can see the hitherto undreamed of nature of their own true feelings.

Time and time again, parents express surprise about their former narrow views of their families, other people, and the institutions of society and what needs to be done about them. They also express hope about finding ways to handle the tasks ahead of them.

The end of these sessions is like the termination of a voyage. The passengers have come together; have talked, laughed, cried, struggled to share feelings and to achieve deeper, wider understanding of themselves and their children. They have formed close friendships. Now it is time to say goodbye.

. . . .

□ □ □

GROUP THERAPY WITH PARENTS OF SEVERELY RETARDED CHILDREN: A PRELIMINARY REPORT

Arthur Blatt

(Group Psychotherapy, 1957)

The Shield of David is a psychiatric clinic and day school essentially geared and devoted to the problems of the severely retarded child who is not acceptable in the Public School system because of low I.Q. Children, ages four to twelve, are admitted to the day school upon the completion of a diagnostic team study and the recommendation of a staff treatment conference. The diagnostic study consists of intake interviews by social service, medical, psychological, and speech examinations, observation of the child in group activities, and a psychiatric consultation when deemed necessary. All medical, psychological and psychiatric data available from past studies are obtained. A staff conference is then held and the treatment plan for the child and for the parents is proposed.

It became apparent, in the course of our work, that most children could not derive maximum benefit from the school program without simultaneous help for the parents to understand their own feelings and attitudes toward the children. Therefore, a counseling and therapy program was initiated to meet the needs of the parents. In this paper we wish to present a preliminary report on some of the experiences and problems encountered in the treatment of parents in group therapy. A group therapy program was initiated in November, 1954 with the psychiatrist and psychologist conducting individual groups. This study is based on experience with twelve such groups over a two-year period.

Method

Group therapy as a therapeutic medium was utilized because of theoretical and practical considerations. It was felt that the commonable experiences with the retarded child would make for an "in-group" situation which would enable the parents to speek freely of their attitudes and feelings about the child. This "in-group" situation would also facilitate verbalization by the more insecure, defensive parents who had socially isolated themselves, as well as orient more realistically the assertive, expansive parents who tended to deny the reality and seriousness of their own and the child's status. The defensive, insecure parents, on hearing expressed feelings and attitudes which they had suppressed because of shame and/or guilt, would be aided in more freely expressing themselves.

We endeavored to have couple groups. It was felt that by having husband and wife in the same group, we could possibly establish personal communication, emotional rapport, consistency in the handling of the child, and a deeper appreciation of each other's feelings. It was also felt that the placement of the parents in the same group would enable them to utilize the group therapist positively and not as a weapon against each other.

Our primary goal in the group was the realization by the parents that their own emotional status, attitudes, and feelings affected the child-parent relationship, thereby affecting the maximal growth of the child.

The number of members in the group and the length of the group sessions was arrived at arbitrarily. The group enrollment initially was not formally fixed and varied from 8-14 members. At the present time it is felt that a maximum enrollment of 10 members constitutes a feasible working group. The group met once a week for not more than twenty weeks. The session lasted an hour and a half.

Whenever possible the groups were made up of couples, but it was found that an all-mothers group was unavoidable and inevitable.

The recommendation for participation in group therapy is made at the staff conference by the psychiatric consultant. In many cases group placement is deferred until the social worker clarifies with the parents the purpose and goals of group therapy and an initial resistance to "telling all those people my problems" is worked through. It is apparent that parent interest is a primary criterion for group placement. Initially intellectual levels were disregarded in group placement, but this was found to be disruptive, unproductive and unprofitable for the group. At the present time groups are homogeneous only in intellectual level and the fact of having a retarded child. Race, color, religious belief, and age are disregarded as well as social or financial background. Ambulatory psychotics, psychopaths, and severely neurotically disturbed parents are excluded from group therapy.

Discussion

The primary difficulty noted in our group therapy program was the problem of adhering to the therapeutic goal, i.e., an understanding of one's attitudes and feelings toward the retarded child. This was frustrating to parents who wanted to go further into an exploration of themselves aside from the child; and frightening to parents who were threatened by the verbalizing of one's feelings and attitudes about the child. The former view was exemplified in statements such as:

"I feel the questions should be more personal and bring out feelings about each other as well as the child."

"If there was some way to get people to really open up, I think we'd all gain a great deal more."

"We skirted basic problems but never really touched them."

The latter view was expressed in statements such as:

"I would like more professional advice, such as lectures by doctors in various fields."

"I feel I would like outlined discussions."

"I would like films of institutional life as well as films of school life for children of lower levels."

This divergence of opinions suggests the need for a more careful screening of parental needs to determine their ability and availability to utilize group therapy meaningfully. These early experiences with group therapy indicate very clearly the need for various group goals based on the ego-strength (capacities), ego defenses and needs of the individual.

Another bar to the therapeutic process was the viewing of the therapist by the parents as an outsider who could not possibly understand their problems. This appeared to be a hostile projection against all professional people because of their past experiences with workers in the field and a defense against the therapeutic process itself. Statements such as "You can't know unless you have a retarded child," "I know the books say . . ." and "You're here because of your training and background" were usually elicited whenever the parent had been disturbed by the therapist's interpretations or explanations. In a group psychotherapy situation this could be treated as a resistance and dealt with accordingly, but in our therapeutic paradigm, the therapist would have to wait for another member of the group to literally "re-say" the interpretation before it was acceptable.

> "Mr. R. had read a great deal on the problem of retardation and was quite active in a local organization dealing with retarded children. At the group sessions he utilized his humor and wit to dispel the seriousness of the various feelings expressed by other group members. The therapist at one session pointed out that he seemed to take the group sessions as a joke. He denied this, noting 'Psychologists are always reading things into what people say.' At a subsequent session a few parents,

> piqued by his humor, pointed out to him that he was acting like a clown. The following session he noted, 'I guess I joke around a great deal because it hurts when I get serious about my child.' "

It has been our experience that those parents who resort to divinity as a protection against their own feelings are difficult candidates for group therapy. As long as the group does not threaten their defense, they will remain in group and maintain an attitude of aloof, disinterested spectators. When other members question them as to "why they feel that it was God's will," they do not show up for further group meetings and rationalize their absence at meetings. They do not say they do not want to be in the group but rather that they just can't seem to find the time, no adequate baby sitters, the weather was poor, etc., until such time as they are dropped from the group. Their resorting to God may not at all be related to their active participation and belief in the religion and as such represents a personality problem. Often they will misrepresent the precepts of the religion as saying they must keep the child at home. It is our impression that these parents require intensive individual therapy and should not be placed in a group therapy situation.

Our observations indicate that many parents have intense, aggressive impulses toward the child. Although these feelings may be effectively suppressed, the individuals are nevertheless left with a feeling of guilt. We have found that quite often the need to release these feelings will come out in a dream which the parent feels impelled to tell the group. This generally releases the group whose perception of the dream is echoed in their own psyche.

> After a few sessions spent on a discussion of the parent's acceptance of the child and in which no mention was made of hostile feelings toward a child, Mrs. L. felt that she had to tell the group a dream she had. "I dreamed I was on the subway platform with L. When the train came in, I waited until the doors were almost closed and jumped in, leaving him on the platform. I waved to him and suddenly felt that I wanted to get out of the train." When one parent noted, "It sounds as if you want to get away from him," this opened up a flood of anger and resentment toward the child. This first expression of anger and resentment enabled other members to express their hostile feelings toward the children.
>
> In another group, Mrs. R. casually mentioned to the group that she had a dream which was annoying her. She noted, "I dreamed that R. fell out of the window and was holding on to the window sash. I watched him and then slammed the window shut on his fingers." The meaning of the dream was clear to her, but what impelled her to tell the dream to the group was the need for catharsis with its concomitant reduction of anxiety. The group response was immediate with other members speaking about their own aggressive impulses toward their children.

It seems to be inevitable that the sessions following such a release are essentially tense, but quiet, with the members seeming to be apprehensive of each other. At this point, the explanation by the therapist that parents who have "normal" children will also feel the way they do at times clears the air for further therapeutic progress. We have also noted that in these parents there is a quality of "superforgivingness," a tendency to idealize themselves with more than the normal allotment of forgiveness as a reaction formation to guilt over hostile feelings toward the child. This becomes an almost circular mechanism, in that the least suggestion of guilt or hostility incurs an increased need to forgive which in turn increases their inner vindictive drives.

One of the major problems that has to be dealt with in group is that of externalization, i.e., the feeling of group members that the environment they are in is hostile toward the child. Most often this is found to be an externalization of the parents' feeling that the people staring at the child are staring at them. This activates their own neurotic structure and inadequacies which they do not have to face since the problem is foistered on to the child.

Mrs. N. noted in group her feelings of hostility toward a strange woman who kept staring at her daughter while at a public swimming pool. As she talked it became apparent to the group that her feeling was that she was the one who was embarrassed and in effect felt that the woman was looking at her. Even more fundamentally it was she herself who was staring with hostility at the child externalizing these feelings onto others.

It has been our observation in group that the guilt over having a retarded child is intimately related to the trauma experienced by the parents to their own self-concept . . . .

In presenting the following case summaries, we will illustrate how the inability of the parents to utilize group therapy positively was a function of their personality structure to show successful utilization of group therapy by parents.

Case #I. Mr. and Mrs. R., ages forty-seven and forty-six respectively, began Group Therapy in February, 1955 in separate groups. A psychiatric consultation noted that "Mr. R. is predominantly of a self-effacing character structure. In a group, Mr. R. may find it possible to be more self-expressive." "Mrs. R. displayed considerable tension characterized by psychomotor activity. She is constantly on the defensive and rationalizes quickly and well. It is conceivable that Mrs. R. in her aggressive, opinionated, and self-righteous attitude would act as a stimulus for the group as well as perhaps acquiring further insights for herself."

Their child, aged eleven, an only child, is severely mentally retarded, non-verbal and physically handicapped. After two years of treatment of the child, the concensus of staff opinion was that the child ought to be placed in a state school. Mr. and Mrs. R. are against placing the child away from home.

The course of group therapy for Mrs. R., who was in a predominantly mothers' group, was stormy. Although she would orally argue with the group, in practice she modified some of her rigid practices with the child, e.g., she stopped giving the child suppositories to regulate his bowel movements, and instead of constantly carrying or wheeling him around, gave him more freedom to walk. In spite of some modifications in practice she still felt that she had to defend her position as a harrassed mother who was obligated to help the child.

Mr. R. attended a primarily couples' group. His attendance at group was marked by a stolid silence or monosyllabic responses to questions directed at him by the group. His response to friendly overtures on the part of group members was to deliberately shut them out. The only break-through occurred once when the group discussed a film on institutions they had seen on TV. At this time Mr. R. insisted that he would not place R. and in the next breath resignedly noted that someday it would have to be.

In both parents it became obvious that their rigid character structures would not be able to tolerate an exposure of their inner hostility toward the child. Hardship and difficulty with the child were idealized into virtues and were experienced as a not uncommon "masochistic" mechanism. It is felt that this reversal is usually an indication of extensive hostility toward the child which is suppressed and reversed into a martyr-like acceptance of the child. Since the group threatens the reality of their views they defend themselves by 1) an active offensive toward the group, which diverts the group from themselves, 2) a passive withdrawal from what is going on in the group and 3) a complete refusal to be in group.

Case #II. Mr. and Mrs. J., ages thirty-four and thirty-three respectively, began Group Therapy together in November, 1955. At the Staff Conference it was noted that "there appeared to be some familial difficulty in that despite the mother's intensive interest, the father is a rather withdrawn and resigned type of individual. This generates further difficulty for the mother and it is felt

> that both parents can derive considerable help from group."
>
> Their child, aged five, is the older of two siblings. She is a moderately retarded mongoloid who has shown progress in the one and one-half years she attended school.

Their course of treatment together in group led to many open arguments and denouncements of not caring for the child. When they first came to group they had still not let their own parents know that the child was retarded. They were able to work out many of their feelings of guilt, shame, and frustration over having a retarded child and ceased to blame each other for the child's condition. As they explored their feelings about the child and each other, they found that they could more freely communicate with each other in a way that they never had before. Mr. J. became more emotionally involved with the child and what was happening at home. They were able to inform their parents of the child's condition and felt "as if a load of bricks was taken off my back." These parents were able to utilize the group for the goals that were set for the group. Through catharsis, emotionally facing each other, identification with the feelings of other group members, support from the group members and from the therapist, they were able to derive maximal benefit from the group.

Summary

For the past two years a group therapy program with parents of children who are severely mentally retarded has been held at the Shield of David. We have found this to be a meaningful therapeutic medium for many parents. It is unique in that it allows for an emotional rapport between parents that enables them to discuss their feelings more extensively in a shorter period of time than it would take in individual treatment.

At the present time, we foresee the need for three types of groups:

1. Educational Group Counselling: to include those parents whose defenses are fragile and brittle. This group would have as its core matter the techniques of child rearing and development.
2. Group Counselling: to include those parents whose ego strength is sufficiently strong to explore their attitudes and feelings as related to the child.
3. Group Psychotherapy: to include those parents who indicate a desire to delve into their own emotions and feelings. This would only incidentally be related to the child.

The need for a more formal psychotherapeutic group became apparent as it was found that ofttimes the problems of the parents transcended the immediate problems with the child, that many parents used the problem with the child as a protection against seeing their own psychic problems and/or as a protection against the possible dissolution of a poor marital situation.

The group structure can be used meaningfully for most parents if the group goals are structured to meet the needs and capacities of the parents.

□ □ □

SMALL, SHORT-TERM GROUP MEETINGS WITH PARENTS OF CHILDREN WITH MONGOLISM

Mary L. Yates, Ruth Lederer

(*American Journal of Mental Deficiency,* 1961)

Various means have been used to help parents cope with the knowledge that they are the mother and father of a retarded child. These may include the group approach or individual counselling, both of which have been successful. An attempt was made to find out whether in a clinic setting short-term, undirected group meetings would help both parents of retarded children. Since parents of children with mongolism (Schipper, 1959[1]) raised similar questions with regard to the developmental prognosis of their child regardless of their degree of acceptance of the diagnosis, it was decided to include such parents in a first attempt to try out these groups. It was felt that four couples should be the maximum number included in any one group because the emphasis in the meetings was to be on the sharing of experiences and that more than this number would perhaps be a deterrent to this goal.

A series of three evening sessions was planned with each of three groups, meeting at monthly intervals, so that both parents could attend. In the course of a year ten meetings were held. A total of sixteen parents participated, all of whom had had their children evaluated in the clinic and had received interpretation. The children represented ranged in age from one year to four years with the exception of one child who was seven. There were five boys and four girls included.

Services for the Retarded Child is a special program of the Bureau of Maternal and Child Health of the Government of the District of Columbia Department of Public Health. (The staff consists of: a pediatrician-director, two social workers, a psychologist, a child development worker, a nursing consultant, and a psychiatric consultant. This clinic also has at its disposal other special services which are available within the Health Department and include speech and hearing, neurology, electroencephalography, physical and occupational therapy, orthopedics, ophthalmology, and cardiology.) The clinic offers diagnostic as well as treatment and following-up services. The diagnostic study is an unhurried process, often involving several contacts with the various staff members because it is felt that these appointments can be of therapeutic value as a step in preparation for interpretation. Interpretation is given by the pediatrician-director and efforts are made by the staff members immediately concerned to help parents carry out the recommendations. In many instances parents need help in accepting and understanding the diagnosis and this is offered through continued casework service. Or, if the child is in need of stimulation in developing self-care skills, help in this direction is provided.

Following interpretation, parents' reactions may vary from seeming acceptance to hostile rejection and inability to use help. The question was raised as to whether it is possible, regardless of the degree of acceptance, understanding, and awareness of the situation a parent may have, to provide something, in addition, to facilitate their ability to restructure their way of living to include this experience.

Although in the last few years the public has become more enlightened about mental retardation, much misconception still persists. Mongolism, for example, is still, even among professionals, equated with idiocy. Historically, the term mongolism embodies characteristics which have been associated with the concept of the fool or idiot. Because of this, the parents of these children have to cope with their own feelings about their child as well as with the ambivalence shown toward him in their contacts outside of the home.

In other situations group meetings have been utilized successfully in helping parents. It was felt that the group process might be of use here to assist parents to find their equilibrium more easily and handle more appropriately their feelings about what has happened to their child.

Purpose, Goals, and Form of the Meetings

The purpose of these meetings was to encourage parents to share their experiences and concerns with each other by permitting them to assume responsibility, not only in conducting the meetings, but also in bringing up subject matter for discussion. It was hoped parents would feel free to bring up common concerns, what they did about them, their feelings about having such a child, and that the very sharing with each other would help them make a more satisfying adjustment. All of the families who participated in these meetings were told individually about them and their structure. It was emphasized that these were their meetings, a time during which they could bring up and discuss any concern they might have about their child and that all parents invited had a child with mongolism. Thus the groups were to be composed of parents who met the following criteria: children with the same diagnosis, both parents able to attend when possible, and who were not so severely disturbed about the diagnosis as to need special individual help.

As members of the group, the staff participants did not function in their usual professional roles of psychologist and social worker, but rather as sponsors of the group taking leadership only to get discussion going and to keep it along lines within limited goals. The social worker assumed the responsibility for the meetings and the psychologist participated as co-sponsor. They acted as sympathetic listeners, redirected questions back to the group, took initiative at the beginning of the sessions and at the end, answered questions, and gave information only if it was obvious that the group had misinformation or lacked knowledge about the subject.

The meetings were held in the conference room of the clinic, and as the parents arrived they were invited to sit around the conference table. In order to stress the informality of these meetings, light refreshments were available and informal conversation was encouraged because it was felt best to wait until the majority had gathered so that all parents could have equal benefit of the exchange of ideas. This went on until such time as the sponsors indicated that the meeting would begin. Although the sponsors had in mind some time limit as to when the meetings would draw to a close, they were not rigid about this. Sessions were permitted to go on until they reached a logical and natural termination point, and it usually turned out that they lasted for approximately one hour and one half. At the close of the meetings there was always a pulling together of what had gone on. This was done either by a parent or the social worker. However, if the social worker took responsibility for doing this, every effort was made to include the parents in the summing up.

Pattern of the Initial Meetings

The initial meetings of all three groups seemed to follow a similar pattern. The sponsors usually had to take more initiative in the initial session of each group than during the remaining meetings of the series. They opened with a review of the purpose for which the group had been called together and with clarification of the role the sponsors would take. It was then suggested that the parents describe their child in order that he might be identified for the group. This was eagerly responded to by the parents. Some took this quite literally and described him in physical appearance, size and weight, while others immediately brought up problem areas.

One of the concerns presented first in all three groups centered on growth and development. The earlier questions in this area usually involved the onset of the basic achievements in motor development skills, that is, at what age a child sat up, walked, talked, and the like. This immediately set up a contact point between the parents. More than just an exchange of information, it was a sort of emotional interchange. Most of them had not known the parents of any other child with mongolism, and this was their first opportunity to really discuss mutual concerns. This led to a very rapid feeling of relatedness among them and enabled them to quickly move into other areas.

Almost immediately following this physical description of the child, the question was raised as to when the others had learned of the diagnosis. Another question that came up early was whether they had told anyone else, and, if so, how they had handled it. These questions were emotionally charged and were brought up by the parents who had experienced difficulty in dealing with them. There was usually a parent in the group who had been able to handle his own anxieties in this area who could help clarify the underlying feelings the parents had about this. Those involved seemed able to listen to what was said.

Having shared this kind of information with each other seemed to release a certain tension that had existed and they began to participate very actively in discussion. In a first meeting, they seemed to cover the whole gamut of concerns: diagnosis and timing of being told of the diagnosis, their feelings about having such a child, not only now but at the time they were given the diagnosis, rate of development, resources, and schools. They also raised questions about what can be expected of their child in the near future as well as in terms of long range plans, reaching into adolescent and adult years. One group broached the possibility of some type of insurance plan.

These subjects were really just skimmed over, and gave the impression that these questions had been on their minds and they had to get them out. It was usually very difficult for the first session to break up because there seemed so much more still to be said.

The Pattern During a Series of Three Meetings

In all three groups, the trend seemed to be that most areas that were discussed in later sessions had already been touched upon in the first meeting. The emotional tone of the first meeting was one of positive feeling for the sponsors and for each other. They seemed glad to have an opportunity to meet with other parents with similar problems. It was more or less a sharing with people who feel very close, but not in an intimate way. The deeper feelings they might have about their particular situation did not usually come up. Although many factors enter into this, one might be that they were grateful for the opportunity to share information with others who can be sympathetic out of experience.

At the second meeting, the same subjects were raised that had been brought up during the first sessions but, in addition, some of the more serious details as well as their more deep concerns came out. They tended to look to the sponsors for answers, and when redirected to the group they displayed hostile feelings toward them. Since the sponsors did not assume responsibility for answering questions or taking over, usually some member of the group assumed leadership, and they were able to work out some of their feelings and answers to the questions. Those persons who took the role of leader seemed to rise to the position and to gloss over some of their deeper feelings about their own situation in order to help some of the others with theirs. The way they handled this was to display extreme acceptance of having a retarded child, pointing out some of the assets and actually to distort some of the situation.

The subject of whether they had found it necessary to conceal the fact that they had a retarded child came up. How they had handled this and what were their feelings about sharing this information with others? They wanted the details of whether you tell other members of the family and members of the community and, if so, how one goes about it and how much one tells. It was the parent leaders who were able to help the other members of the group look at this more realistically and work out how this could be handled. Although this was not resolved to the point where some of the more reluctant parents would agree that they would tell others, there was a feeling of relief from having expressed their feelings about why they had not told others about the child. This was a rather uneasy session, one during which they had to face up to reality. No matter how they attempted to couch many of their problems and feelings, someone of the group always saw through it. The parents seemed to look forward to the third session. They appeared to need each other and they even planned what they would cover.

The last meeting of the series was usually a more intellectual type session, during which there was some attempt to solve their problems and an evaluation of what had come out of the meetings. The solutions they offered were usually beyond their immediate problems, reaching into adolescence and adulthood. There was some criticism of the sessions, what they had expected of them and still needed and, also, some criticism of the role the sponsors took. They seemed to have expected more informative and instructional-type sessions, but were able to see what the sponsors meant by setting up limited goals within which they themselves would attempt to face their situation. Once having "hashed out" what had gone on in these sessions, they seemed to feel that they had gained some benefit from this type of meeting. Often they felt that some of the needs that had not been met in these brief sessions could be found within existing community resources such as the Association for Retarded Children or could be fostered through such facilities.

Evaluation

The impressions gained are based upon a limited number of cases and therefore are tentative.

Small, short-term, undirected group sessions, spread over a three-month period, with both parents attending, appeared to the sponsors to be quite helpful and useful. This approach would seem to work best with persons who have some ability to put their feelings into words. The number of meetings was limited because goals were limited and the sponsors wanted to help these parents during their period of adjustment to the diagnosis and its implications. Three meetings seemed to be ideal because the first meeting served to throw open the problems; the second, to delve more deeply into certain aspects of the problem; and the third, to help them pull together and integrate what had been accomplished during the sessions and begin to think more realistically about the future.

With the first group, a fourth meeting was held in compliance with the demands of the parents. During this session the parents planned for expansion of the group. They were interested in increasing the members, bringing in speakers on various topics, and also in changing the role of the sponsors to include discussion of the more emotionally charged issues. As this did not fall within the purpose and goals of this project, the sponsors discussed with the parents the resources in the community where this could be met. It would appear that this type of group might not be able to maintain its non-directive character beyond three sessions, but would tend to become more therapy-oriented or educational-informative in nature.

The focus in these group meetings was to encourage parents to discuss their feelings about their child and help them come to grips with the situation. The small group sessions were effective because the size made it a face-to-face relationship, yet enough different from a one-to-one relationship as to present a non-threatening situation conducive to sharing and enabling parents to bring up areas of concern one might anticipate they must have.

The meetings did not change the parents' basic attitude but did enable them to see, for example, that although it was "terrible" to have such a child it was all right to feel this way and seemed to relieve some of their shame and guilt. Although their problems and feelings were not resolved, in some it had been so bottled up, they had been unable to express any feelings except hostility, withdrawal, and denial. As the meetings progressed, there seemed to be less need for denial toward other people and a more realistic appraisal of their situation and their feelings about it. As a result, the parents seemed better prepared to consider the next steps in planning. For example, they seemed more aware of their own needs in relation to such planning and in a position to recognize the need for direct help whether it be in relation to their feelings about the diagnosis or help in the area of management. They also seemed able to look at the broader implications of mental retardation and to wonder what they could contribute as parents in areas outside their immediate situation.

In the group setting, with both parents present, the sponsors became more aware of how difficult it is for fathers to accept the diagnosis of mental retardation, since they tend to cover up their real feelings. Their early comments were more general, and they had a tendency to intellectualize their problems. Mothers, on the other hand, responded in a more personal way. Their comments were closely related to specific incidents from their experience with their child. Fathers and mothers looked upon the sponsors differently, too. The mothers used the sponsors in their role more appropriately, and the fathers tended to place the sponsors on a more social level. One factor of significance which emerged from these meetings is that fathers do want to be included in planning for their children. It was pointed out that fathers were not always able to participate as much as they would like, but they felt strongly that they wanted to be the ones to decide to what extent they could be involved rather than have it assumed that they could not participate.

At a first meeting, either the father or the mother seemed to take over and the couple functioned as "one," with the less verbal parent reinforcing the other. In later meetings, the husband and wife spoke up as individuals, free to express their own ideas regardless of whether their comments were in agreement with the spouse. In one case they even sat on opposite sides of the table. The emphasis was on clarifying their own thoughts. This was made possible because they gained support from the other couples. What occurred was different from, for example, mothers supporting mothers and fathers, fathers. At the end of the sessions, they again seemed to be united, voicing more or less similar feelings.

It is important for parents to be able to attend meetings together. Although the couples seemed to speak to the point of the reality factors in the situation, when only one person of a couple was present, the members of the group seemed to jump to supporting that person more quickly. Also, when there are couples present, the core of the issue is forced because they do not have to accentuate their sex-linked role.

These meetings appeared to help parents in their adjustment during the period following interpretation. The spacing of the meetings at monthly intervals seemed to give them time to absorb some of what they had brought up during the meetings. The role the sponsors took was different from their professional one in the clinic. It took time for the parents to accept this, and occasionally their hostility was aroused. But they went along with this, selecting their own leaders who were able to assume the role they wanted the sponsors to take. Because in the third session they were able to evaluate what had gone on quite objectively, being able to discuss both the negative and positive aspects of the meetings, it was felt that steps toward adjustment had been initiated.

At first the parents felt a very strong link with each other because of the factor of mongolism. Discussion was unproductive when they attempted to analyze and understand the physical attributes of mongolism *per se*. Only when they realized the futility of this were they able to examine the basic issue of retardation and discuss their children who had varying degrees of retardation rather than "having to deal with a mongolian idiot."

It should be remembered that the children represented by the parents in these groups were still young. The children themselves had not yet had to face the community. The parents will, perhaps, again have to analyze their feelings in terms of mongolism when they meet situations as their children grow older.

This type of group can be effective as a regular part of such a clinic program and is thought of only as an intermediary step in the process of adjustment.

REFERENCE

1. Schipper, M. T., "The Child with Mongolism in the Home," *Pediatrics,* 1959, 24:32-144.

□ □ □

EVOLUTION IN GROUP WORK WITH PARENTS OF RETARDED CHILDREN AND ADOLESCENTS

Manny Sternlicht

Toni Alston

(Paper read at AAMD Convention, 1964)

A great body of literature is available which describes group discussion, group counseling, and group psychotherapy techniques which have been useful with parents of retardates. However, while this literature is replete with discussions of specific techniques and individual psycho-dynamic understandings and insights, there are precious few studies which focus upon group dynamics *per se*. It is toward this end, to describe the evolution of a group of parents of retardates (institutionalized and noninstitutionalized), that this paper is directed.

The specific parents' group that we will be discussing here was conducted under the aegis of Staten Island Aid for Retarded Children (SIARC). SIARC is a local, nonprofit, nonsectarian, Community Chest-sponsored agency, which operates a day care center and vocational training workshop for retarded children and adolescents. The agency has three basic objectives: 1) to ascertain, through study and research, the problem and means for improving the condition of the retarded child; 2) to develop a better understanding of, and a more wholesome attitude toward, mental retardation and mental health; 3) to assist the parents of the mentally retarded in meeting their problems.

The leader of the group was a qualified psychiatric social worker (junior author), who operated under the supervision of a consulting clinical psychologist (senior author). All of the group sessions were held in a very large executive board room; the furniture consisted of a long table and many comfortable contoured chairs.

Initially, the group was constituted as a "closed" parent counseling one. The goal was to offer the parents a service which would provide them with an opportunity for group discussion and counseling on problems common to all, and to assist them in either more effectively adjusting to their having a retarded child or in planning for institutional placement. In addition, the leader also was available for individual consultations concerning unique, specific problems.

The group was composed of a total of sixteen parents, including five married couples. Each member had a retarded child or adolescent, who either was in attendance in the SIARC program, in a CRMD class in the public schools, or institutionalized at Willowbrook State School. Half of the group of parents (and also half of the retarded children) was male and half was female. Ages ranged from twenty-seven to forty-eight, and the educational level varied from six years of grammar school to one year of college. The socioeconomic strata from which this group derived was either "Upper-Lower" or "Lower-Middle" (Warner's classification). The group sessions were held three times a month, for an hour and a half each, on Friday evenings. Attendance was wholly voluntary, and postcards were sent in advance of each session. The parents in the group were selected from a larger pool of parents who expressed a desire to participate in such a parent counseling discussion program. Each was seen individually before being placed in the group situation.

This closed group counseling phase lasted for one full year (ten months). As one might have anticipated, the content of the sessions focused upon the problems that the parents were having with their retarded sons and daughters. Especially cogent and significant problem areas included the setting of limits and general disciplinary procedures, under- and overestimation of their children's capabilities, overprotection, intrafamilial relationships, and peer adjustments.

In this phase, the group leader promoted a supportive, permissive discussion milieu, one in which the parents felt sufficiently free and comfortable to ventilate some of their problems, and to emotionally abreact. The overall approach to the group counseling sessions was a plastic one, with some focus placed upon didactic-like advice-giving, in terms of offering the parents several behavioral alternatives to the ones that they had been engaging in. Group interaction was excellent, and many of the members became close personal friends.

Approximately eight members were present at any given session, ranging from a low of three members to a high of fourteen. Toward the end of the year, the group elected to have a couple of "open" meetings, which were advertised in the local newspaper. As a consequence of these two open meetings, many of the members were amazed at their own progress (i.e., some of the "new" parents exhibited the same kinds of problems that the older ones had had, and which they had now successfully resolved).

At the start of the second year of the group's existence, several members started talking more about themselves and less about their problems with their retarded children. Reacting to the group's needs, the leader suggested that perhaps the members might prefer to move into a more therapeutic kind of situation, where the focus would no longer be upon the problems of mental retardation but rather upon themselves and their own problems. The parents responded enthusiastically to this proposal, and a more decidedly therapeutic milieu prevailed. The composition of the group also was altered somewhat, in that six of the original members dropped out and two new members substituted in their place, leaving a new group membership of twelve parents.

The group was sufficiently advanced to actively participate in this new therapeutic program. Individual and marital difficulties were brought out and worked on, rather freely and openly. The leader was essentially nondirective, and she encouraged the group to proceed at its own pace. There was never a lack of activity and emotional feeling in the sessions.

That the group had actually actively entered into a therapeutic phase was borne out by the results of a brief sentence-completion questionnaire administered after six months of therapeutic sessions. Thus, in response to the sentence-completion that failure in therapy may be expected when we obtained such completions as: *one doesn't want to help himself,* and *a person does not permit himself to say what he thinks.*

The group decided, toward the close of the second year, to enter into an open discussion setting, effective the following September. This decision was prompted by two major factors: first of all, the attendance was beginning to slacken, and, secondly, the group grew aware of the fact that a great many more parents wished to participate in these sessions. An additional variable, and one which may at least partially have accounted for the gradually poorer attendance showing, was that several of the parents felt that the depth of the therapy was commencing to greatly threaten them and their defenses.

Accordingly, the following year saw a great increase in the group's average attendance as the group entered into its final phase, an open discussion setting where the focus was on preventive mental hygiene in general. This change in emphasis was in line with the current increasing identification of parent education with preventive mental health. Guest speakers were invited to lead some of these sessions, while three or four sessions a year were designated as open sessions, where the parents could be free to discuss anything at all of interest to them. A partial listing of the major themes discussed in this phase is appended.

The group currently is in the midst of its third year of participation in this phase, and interest in the group discussions continues to remain at a peak. Since the group is now an open one, we feel that this final phase will probably continue for several years. And this phase, we believe, represents a final evolutionary one in the history of a parents group such as we have been describing here.

. . . .

A Partial Listing of the Major Themes Discussed in the Open Group Discussion Phase

1. The community, mental health, and mental retardation.
2. How to cope with mental health problems.
3. Religion and the mentally retarded.
4. Psychosomatic medicine.
5. Dream interpretation.
6. Psychodrama.
7. Dramatic presentation—"And You Never Know."
8. Film—"The Wall Between."
9. Record—"The Inquiring Parent."
10. Social work in the public school setting.
11. Hypnotherapy.
12. Problems with teenage children.
13. Religion in mental health.
14. Drug addiction.
15. The need to love and be loved.
16. Hereditary factors in mental illness and retardation.
17. The meaning of maturity.
18. Vocational guidance and counseling.
19. The problem of overprotection.
20. Is suicide a problem in our society?
21. Jealousy and competition between children.
22. Prejudice and its effects.
23. Leisure time activity.
24. Symposium—Mental health.
25. Symposium—Marriage and the family.

□ □ □

from A COUNSELING PROGRAM FOR PARENTS OF SEVERELY RETARDED PRESCHOOL CHILDREN

Robert M. Nadal

(*Social Casework,* 1961)

In a society in which intellectual achievement is highly valued, giving birth to a mentally normal child is often considered a first essential in functioning adequately as a parent. For this reason, the parents of a mentally retarded child find that they are given much less support and acceptance by the community than the community extends to the parents of an emotionally disturbed child, or even a criminal. This point has been well made by Kelman[1] who, in discussing the refusal of many agencies to serve the child whose outlook for improvement is not favorable, poses the question whether this refusal is consonant with the traditional tenets of social work in relation to providing services to those in need.

The literature on mental retardation is replete with statements about the upset and stress created for parents by their having a severely retarded child with an I.Q. below 50. One recent study[2] documents the validity of this often repeated, but infrequently proved, allegation. The presence of a retarded child in the home is often a precipitating factor in individual or family maladjustment or breakdown.

To provide suitable services for all the retarded children in one community who were not in institutions or in public school classes, the New York State legislature passed an act in 1958 to establish a comprehensive community demonstration project. Monroe County, in which the city of Rochester is located, was selected as the project area.

The Day Care Center for Handicapped Children in Rochester is a Community Chest agency, originally organized by parents, which has had over ten years of experience in working in the field of mental retardation. Under the project plan, this agency was authorized to establish two training groups for severely retarded children under seven years of age who seemed unable to fit into other groups in the community. The agency was also authorized to establish individual and group counseling sessions for two groups of parents. A trained social worker was to provide counseling. This paper offers a brief description of the first year of the parent counseling part, begun September 1959.

Composition of the Parent Groups

The goal of the group counseling program was to improve the parents' social functioning and to involve at least one parent, and the child, in the agency's program at an earlier time than had previously been possible. It was hoped that by giving the parent a better understanding of the child's needs and his own expectations in regard to the child, improvement in parental role performance and in interpersonal relationships could be effected.

Two groups, each made up of twelve mothers and twelve children, were established. The composition of these groups, the meeting-place, and the number of sessions to be held during the school year were determined in advance by administrative decision. During the early meetings of the groups, when the objectives of the program and its structure were discussed, the mothers were told that sessions would terminate June 1960.

The primary basis for selection of participants in a group was that the parent's pre-school child met certain criteria for admission into the Center's program. No attempt was made to select parents who needed group counseling, or who were most highly motivated to use it, or had the greatest capacity to profit from it. Our method of selection was based on two assumptions: (1) that as a result of having a retarded child the parent's role performance and his competence as a parent were affected; and (2) that counseling under these circumstances would be an appropriate service irrespective of the parent's motivation to use it. The selection of members for each group was limited by the number of children in the Center and by the availability and interest of parents in participating in this aspect of the Center's program.

Since selection of the group members was made on the basis of the child rather than the parent, some group imbalance resulted which was revealed in the differing rate of development of the groups, particularly in the earlier sessions. The average mother in Group 1 was older and had fewer children than the average mother in Group II. She had completed high school, and had come from a middle-class cultural and socioeconomic background. As borne out by clinical impressions and by the findings of a specially designed rating scale, the Group I mother was more passive both as an individual and in the group situation. She was less verbal and, at times, was overwhelmed by alternating feelings of guilt and inadequacy. She was resistant to involving herself in either group or individual discussions. By contrast, the average mother in Group II was younger, had had more children, had had some college experience, and was familiar with and enjoyed discussion methods; she also came from a higher economic and social stratum. In the group situation, this mother's initial reaction to new members or guests was one of warmth, friendliness, a desire to help, and an apparent desire to receive help and find solutions to her problems.

Parental Attitudes and Discussion Themes

In the early sessions with both groups the need to foster group cohesion and group structure predominated. The leader undertook a certain amount of demonstration for the purpose of relieving the mothers' anxieties and initial awkwardness in a group setting, and increasing their perceptions about what was expected of them. Many of the mothers also required help with immediate and pressing problems with which they apparently had been unable to cope, such as, "How do I get my child to eat?" "How can I toilet train him?"

It should be remembered that the children were also involved in the program. Some mothers were inclined to ask impatiently, "What is this demonstration all about anyway?" Since many of them experienced a high degree of hopelessness, ambivalence, and resignation in relation to the child and his condition, one of the more persistent themes concerned the normal as well as the special growth problems peculiar to a mentally defective child. Feelings of inadequacy in handling these problems were common, despite the fact that frequently the mother had demonstrated a high degree of success and competence in handling similar situations with her normal children.

Another difficult area for the mother related to the matter of discipline and limit setting. Discussion of this topic was highly charged with emotion. Some of the mothers ascribed all the child's behavioral difficulties to the fact of mental retardation itself. Many of these mothers found it extremely difficult to think of the child as an individual because of his severe retardation, his apparent insensitivity to others, or lack of social adaptation. The question of overprotection, as contrasted with realistic handling of the child, was a particularly complicated one for one-third of the mothers because, in addition to being severely retarded, their children were physically disabled.

The experience that allows a mother to observe her child in a group and to participate as a helper is often invaluable as an aid in helping her to learn to understand her child. It also tends to explode fantasies and preconceived ideas held by some mothers. The group itself and the counseling offered did much to cushion the impact of this experience. Several of the mothers who tended to undervalue their child's achievement were encouraged by this experience, which helped them "to understand and to act toward their child as a developing personality in his own right."[3]

Parental Conflicts and Hostilities

The effect a retarded child has on the family and on intrafamilial relationships is far reaching and has many ramifications. This problem consumed a considerable portion of the discussion time for both groups. It also served as an important basis for counseling. For example, Mrs. A reported that both she and her husband could recall vividly the embarrassment and chagrin they felt when, their suspicions confirmed, they learned that their son was mentally retarded. By moving to a more rural and isolated community they had hoped to resolve, almost by magic, the problem of having to face and accept the realities of the child's limitations and their own feelings about him.

Outstanding among the various effects on the family constellation was the parents' inability to share feelings and communicate with each other. Frequent mention was made of the fact that the need for the mother to invest increasingly large amounts of her time and energies in caring for the child precipitated conflicts between the parents. Although several mothers complained about the husband's lack of understanding and help, an almost equal number denied this problem and felt, in a general and nebulous way, that the husband had been understanding and helpful. Despite this apparent difference of opinion, all the mothers reacted favorably to more active participation by the husband in the project's program, which included "stag" meetings and meetings of couples that took place later in the year and are not reported here.

Members of both groups of mothers expressed a tremendous amount of hostility toward professional groups, including social workers and social agencies, and much of it related to their own past experiences. Several of them questioned the value of the group meetings: "It is the children who need help, not us." "Why do I have to attend these meetings? I don't for my other children." In a much later session, one mother described at great length her experiences and problems in relation to her son. When she was confronted with her apparent unreadiness to mention these problems earlier, she said, "Oh, we talk about these things among ourselves when you aren't here!" This response was highly significant and appeared to be representative of what many of the mothers were feeling.

An important factor involved in the high degree of hostility and aggression that now characterized the reactions of these mothers was the way in which professional persons had told them that their child was mentally retarded. Many of the mothers became emotional in describing this extremely stressful experience. In many instances the information had been given abruptly or in an almost flippant and casual manner. In some cases the professional person had recommended placement for the child—a recommendation that was totally unacceptable to the mother. Even when a thorough diagnostic study and evaluation had been followed by parent counseling and interpretation had been well handled, the mother often had been unable to accept the finality of the diagnosis. As a result, the parents would "shop" from one doctor to another in the desperate hope of being given a more promising diagnosis. One mother repeatedly insisted that her son would "get better" once his convulsions were better regulated. Another refused to acknowledge that any fundamental retardation was involved; she blamed her daughter's condition wholly on an auto accident which, she claimed, coincided with the onset of the child's retardation.

The passage of time between confirmation of the diagnosis and the present appeared to have made no difference in the mother's opinions. Obviously, the experience of having a mentally retarded child had not been integrated by the parents as a reality of the family's way of life. Although a few of the mothers had completely repressed incidents surrounding their learning of the child's condition, most were able to recall this experience in minute detail and to retell how it had been handled. In some instances there were obvious exaggerations. Although some reported that in the beginning they had been depressed, they were now more likely to react with extreme and overt expressions of hostility and aggression, which were frequently undirected.

The main source of contention between the group members was their difference of opinion about one of the perennial questions in child-rearing which has particular pertinence to bringing up the child who has special needs. The question is whether parents should emphasize the full development of the child's personality and help him become a happy, contented person, or whether their main efforts should be directed toward stimulating and motivating the child to greater achievement. Some of the recent literature has reflected uncertainty about whether both goals can be achieved simultaneously.[4] Many of these mothers appeared to have settled on a middle course of action.

The Role of the Leader

The principal aim of the leader was to improve the mothers' functioning by relieving their anxieties, offering them alternative suggestions on child-rearing, increasing their repertory of possible solutions to the problems they faced, and modifying their destructive attitudes and behavior. Although the words "counseling" and "therapy" were omitted from descriptions of the program, the parents were aware of the therapeutic effects of these sessions and recognized their purpose.

The group leader's role was essentially that of a non-threatening person. Although content for the group discussion usually came from the parents themselves, the leader felt free to suggest areas of discussion if he felt that the mothers were purposely avoiding certain topics or that certain topics were not being fully developed. Primary emphasis was placed on the mothers' questions about current experiences and problems. In many respects these group sessions were not essentially different from casework interviews.

As was noted earlier, a certain imbalance was created, owing to administrative considerations, which was reflected in the differing rates of growth and development of the two groups. Specifically, in Group I, an inarticulate and incohesive group, considerable attention was devoted to helping the members participate. The leader was very supportive, permitted the free ventilation of feelings, and worked to establish group identification. Group II had all the earmarks of a well formed group. Many of its members, if given an opportunity, were able to make their own interpretations in certain areas. The main problem for the leader was not that of stimulating discussion and participation but of giving scope and direction to what the members presented.

Counseling the Mothers Individually

Since the mothers had not been screened prior to their admission into the program, it was inevitable that there would be some who were unprepared for and unsuited to the group experience because of the high pitch of their anxieties and conflicts. Even within the relatively "safe" confines of the group these mothers received only marginal, if any, benefits. Because of their conflicts, however, and their resistance and lack of motivation for help, these mothers were probably less threatened by group treatment than they would have been by individual counseling. Despite their need for more intensive help, which became evident as the program progressed, they were not excluded from the group.

The decision as to which mothers should also be given individual counseling involved several considerations, not the least of which was the current effect of the child upon the family. Moreover, because the same therapist had to serve in the dual capacity of group leader and counseling therapist, it was difficult to establish a counseling relationship with certain mothers.

Several other factors that influenced the decision about selection of mothers for individual counseling interviews were: 1) the mother's extreme difficulty in absorbing and accepting the severity of the child's retardation, as evaluated by clinical judgment and as graded by the specially designed rating scale referred to earlier; 2) the presence of certain parental attitudes and behavior that were affecting the child's school adjustment; and 3) specific school adjustment problems of the child. Mrs. B's situation included all these factors. The worker employed ego-supportive techniques with this woman in an attempt to help her mobilize her few strengths for the purpose of handling specific problems in relation to her son. An effort was also made to strengthen family ties through working with both parents.

> Mrs. B, forty-six years of age, married her brother-in-law after a brief mourning period that followed her husband's death. At birth their only child, George, was diagnosed as mongoloid. The parents did not accept this diagnosis, although they became very worried when George was three years of age because of his delayed speech and generally slow development. Other behavior which was also upsetting to the family included George's complete rejection of any attempts to toilet train him, his eating difficulties, and his inability to walk despite the absence of any orthopedic difficulties.
>
> Mrs. B could not completely accept the fact that George was mentally retarded, and Mr. B denied it utterly.

The mother, a passive, overpermissive, and dependent person, alternated between anxiety and a depressive type of reaction in her handling of George. She put little effort into understanding or handling the problems he presented. George treated her literally as his servant. In the classroom Mrs. B was constantly fearful of George's hurting himself or being hurt by others, and she found it extremely difficult to allow him to relate to the teacher. George's reaction to demands and limits was symbolically expressed in his attempts to gag and vomit as soon as he came in sight of the school.

Because of the persistence of these problems and the mother's increased anxieties, casework intervention became essential. Supportive efforts generally met with little success and much resistance. Finally, in the best interest of George, the parents, and the other children in the Center, George was temporarily withdrawn from the program. In the interim of his absence both parents were interviewed intensively by the worker and were encouraged to attend the group meetings.

George is now back in the program. He is adjusting on a slightly higher level and has been transferred to a different group. Although it is too early to determine whether he will continue to progress, the parents appear more resolute now that they have taken the first step, by returning George to the group and by working on their own problems. Also they now appear more accepting of him because of his improved performance which lessens some of his other problems. They appear to be more accessible to help for themselves. It is hoped that this attitude will sustain George in the program and will eventually permit some modification of destructive parental attitudes and adaptive patterns.

Children with Severe Disabilities

As stated earlier, the only criteria used in selecting a mother for individual counseling were her lack of acceptance of the child's condition and the child's adjustment difficulties in school. These criteria were met by most of the parents. There were, however, some children who had pathological and autistic tendencies or severe physical and congenital disabilities in addition to their severe retardation. Although these children did poorly in the school setting, they were accepted warmly by the parents who frequently regarded these other difficulties as part and parcel of the child's retardation. The decision to offer individual casework treatment to the mother of this type of child was based solely on the child's school adjustment. Mrs. C, a foster mother who accepted Mary warmly for what she was despite the multiplicity of her problems, can serve as an example. Along with visual handicaps and a history of severe temper tantrums, the child also had severe autistic and aggressive reactions.

Mrs. C demonstrated considerable understanding and flexibility in the discussion group and was of genuine help to many of the more inhibited mothers whom she encouraged to participate. However, she appeared to be unable to relate this special kind of understanding to her own handling of Mary. She was unable to stimulate the child and she had little real awareness of many of the child's special problems. When the teacher confronted her with Mary's substandard adjustment and bizarre behavior in the group, Mrs. C denied the existence of these problems. When she could no longer do so, she attempted to project the child's difficulties onto the group situation, the other children, and finally the teaching methods.

Because of the persistence of Mary's problems and Mrs. C's continued resistance, referral was made for casework assistance. Mrs. C related well, and in some ways she was able to become less defensive in her discussions about Mary's school adjustment. At times she was willing to admit that she, too, found Mary's behavior trying. However, because the child's difficulties have continued, it is possible that she will have to be excluded from the group. In one of the more recent interviews, Mrs. C appeared somewhat discouraged. She was hopeful that Mary would benefit from a downgraded program in the fall, and she was still unable to accept the fact that Mary eventually would require residential care.

In addition to being trapped by her own inner conflicts, and her feelings toward the child, Mrs. C is faced with community pressures, such as the school situation. These pressures have forced her to appraise her child's limitations more realistically. Although this is a very painful experience, it has been made less so by the availability and use of skilled counseling help.

Evaluation and Impressions of Improvement

No standard measuring device was employed in evaluating improvement, or the lack of it, in the mother's role performance or in her interpersonal relations. Several rating scales were utilized, however. On the basis of clinical and raters' judgments, it can be said that genuine improvement was made in such areas as attitudes toward the child, child-rearing practices, ability to handle the child, and in the general level of the mother's communication of her concerns and problems.

Improvements such as these, which must be assumed to be related to the counseling given, can be achieved despite obvious shortcomings related to administrative structuring or to the experience and skill of the counselor. Even though the outlook is often bleak in terms of the child's potential, and even when the parents' resistances are high, positive results may be attained by helping them achieve fuller self-realization, a more realistic appraisal of the child's needs, and a better understanding of the effect on the child of their own attitudes and behavior. . . .

FOOTNOTES

1. Kelman, Howard R., "Social Work and Mental Retardation: Challenge or Failure?" *Social Work*, Vol. III, No. 3 (1958), p. 40. See *also* Arthur Mandelbaum and Mary Ella Wheeler, "The Meaning of a Defective Child to Parents," *Social Casework*, Vol. XLI, No. 7 (1960), pp. 360-362.
2. Schonell, Fred and Watts, B. H., "A First Survey of the Effects of a Subnormal Child on the Family Unit," *American Journal of Mental Deficiency*, Vol. LXI, No. 1 (1956), p. 218.
3. Allen, Winifred Y. and Campbell, Doris, *The Creative Nursery Center*, Family Service Association of America, New York, 1948, p. 41.
4. Brim, Orville G., *Education for Child Rearing*, Russell Sage Foundation, New York, 1959, p. 92.

from THE DEVELOPMENT OF A GROUP COUNSELING PROGRAM IN A CLINIC FOR RETARDED CHILDREN

Lawrence Goodman
Ruth Rothman

(American Journal of Mental Deficiency, 1961)

. . . .

The Retardation Clinic at Flower-Fifth Avenue Hospital has for more than ten years offered a multidisciplinary service to retarded children and their parents with individual casework help built into both the diagnostic and treatment plans. Three years ago, the social service department initiated a self survey to measure effectiveness of its' counseling program. This review showed clearly that parents who had involved themselves in treatment had benefited from the counseling and concrete help made available to them. It also showed, however, that many of the parents, while expressing or demonstrating need for such assistance, met offers of individual casework help with marked resistance. . . .

. . . We became convinced that while many parents will still require individual help focused on their own personality disturbances, a large proportion of our caseload could be helped, and perhaps even more effectively, through group counseling. . . .

We have come to feel that the group counseling method can be constructively utilized at almost any time in the life experience of parents of retarded children. With limited staff time available, we have tried to choose those periods when our clients would appear to be most vulnerable to the impact of their problem, and most accessible to help. We were also anxious to find those important periods when help, if given effectively, would have the longest range value. We were interested to find that educators and researchers in human behavior have given much consideration to the question of factors affecting readiness for change.

Currently we are using group counseling primarily for two categories of mothers—those whose young children have just completed the clinic team evaluation process—and those whose children are entering or are at adolescence.

With confirmation of the child's retardation, parents are faced with the task of reorganizing their concepts of their children and themselves into balance and perspective. Mothers who have participated in group counseling at this period seem to us to have found relief earlier than others from the impact of the diagnosis—which we know can reinforce previously felt concepts of uniqueness and problem-centered parenthood.

At the child's adolescence, mothers again seem to feel in new and even more threatening ways the sharp impact of the dependency and the intellectual and social immaturity of their children. Additionally, many seem overwhelmed by anxiety about what adulthood holds for them and their children. Even mothers who showed good capacity to interrelate with their children on a younger level now express this uncertainty through attempting to repress normal growth drives in the adolescent retardate. These retarded youngsters, like all children, need parental support as they try out more autonomous, independent ways of behaving. Yet this may be the very period when parents, reacting to inner concerns, are least well able to view the retarded child as an individual person.

For the past two years we have conducted parallel counseling-activity groups for adolescent girls and boys whose mothers were in group counseling. . . .

While we have concentrated on establishing groups at these crucial periods, we have also been exploring the application of the group process to other aspects of our clinic program. In order to work more constructively with a previously largely unserviced section of our caseload, a continuous "open-end" group for Spanish-speaking Puerto Rican mothers has been set up. Utilizing an interpreter who also helps the group counselor to understand social and cultural patterns in this not yet assimilated ethnic group, we have been able to maintain rapport with these mothers for whom the concept of individual casework service seems strange and alien. These groups have been characterized by informality, loose structure, and a combination of permissiveness and direction. We have provided supervision in a play situation for both their normal and their handicapped children, whom these mothers often must bring with them when they come to the groups. The greater availability of these mothers to counseling in groups is certainly worthy of further study.

Encouraged by the usefulness of the group method in our undercare caseload, we have been experimenting with intake screening groups as well. When not contra-indicated by the referral and application material, the parents of six or seven children are invited to attend a group meeting at which we provide the parents with a basic orientation to the function and services of the clinic. From the generalized discussion of the children involved, the intake worker is able, usually without additional interviews, to determine the appropriateness of our services for the family and to make alternative referrals where indicated. The most valuable aspect of this procedure seems to lie in the strength and support parents receive from each other in this immediate group situation. They are better prepared to face the waiting period—and later well prepared to participate in a regular, ongoing counseling group. . . .

In a typical group there is some range in the ages, diagnoses and degrees of handicap of the children represented by the mothers. It is not unusual for a client to ask to meet with mothers of children with identical diagnoses. When helped to express this more exactly, a mother may suggest that having seen the variety of problems in our waiting room on a typical clinic day—she knows that there are mothers of "very damaged children, even mongoloids" within our parent population. Careful, noncritical handling here gets across our concept that what we deal with in our group is not each child's diagnosis, but how parents can cope more effectively with their children on whatever level they may be. The fact that each mother can get something from the group and is welcomed for the contribution she can make is certainly implicit here. We place considerable importance on this interview in which we offer the group experience. The prospective group member is always interviewed individually by the worker who will conduct the particular group for which the mother is being considered.

In advance of the beginning of each group series mothers know that the group counselor is prepared to offer the collaborative content of educational, medical, and social services which each group member can use to help her child to develop as fully as possible, and that the group offers an opportunity to deal with those conflicts to which they may react with denial, compensation, or repression. While helping group members to express their differences in thinking and feeling about and reacting to their retarded child, the group counselor continually underlines both choice and guidance. The broad differences that come out as mothers are able to express their points of view and feelings are used by the counselor to let group members know that there is no single way to feel or to live as the parent of a retarded child. Thus a mother who is still clinging to the hope of her child's normalcy is not coerced to give this up. We have never in a group seen such a mother attacked. Instead in various ways group members indicate that they understand what this mother is experiencing and offer out of their own experiences the reassurance that she can come to accept the reality and live with it.

The point of view of the group leader in such a group represents a conscious attitude about family life, child development, and the realities of all parenthood. While he does not deny recognition of the factors in retardation which tend to disturb family equilibrium, he consistently relates the experience those mothers are having to the broader concepts of parent-child relationships and family integration. In one of our sessions, a Mrs. R. discussed her concern over how to make it possible for her normal teen-age daughter to have a party without her younger retarded sister at home. The following session she reported she had separated the children for the evening of the party, not on the basis of her child's retardation but because an elder sister is entitled to entertain friends without the intruding presence of a younger sister. Earlier, she had viewed the plan of sending the retarded sister to visit relatives as further deprivation of an already hurt, deprived child. Thus Mrs. R. was not only enabled to work out a plan which appropriately met family members' needs but saw how her feeling about the retardation, rather than the retardation itself, could distort the reality situation. It is an important part of the learning within the group that parents are better able to look at the problem they are feeling and to examine what may be underlying their conflict. This results in their learning how to work out their individual and family problems with less distortion of the reality problems which retardation creates.

While no one would deny that they can encounter both open and concealed hostility from the community, parents sometimes respond as though society was totally arrayed against them. Some express the feeling that no one wishes to help and if pushed far enough by this, develop attitudes which make it difficult for them to reach out and constructively use the help that the community does provide. Here they have an opportunity to react to other human beings who basically want to and are able to help. A mother, who reports back to the group on her improved ability to deal directly with a sibling's questions about his retarded brother, is not only reflecting her improved self-image but is also letting group members know that they did help—that she sees them as helpful. We are able to identify many situations in which mothers gain an increased feeling that they deserve and can utilize help, then move back into the community to use services from which they have felt cut off.

Not only do these mothers have feelings of separation from the larger community which they see as not accepting them or being ready to relate to their need, but they also experience these same feelings within their immediate relationships. In a session we see a group member responding with hostility as she tells of a friend's suggestion that for her younger child's sake she think about the possibility of institutionalizing her difficult-to-manage mongoloid daughter. One might question why this should be so disturbing since this child may at some point require custodial care and at times Mrs. P. herself has viewed this as a realistic, ultimate plan. With group help Mrs. P. will come to be able to examine whether there must be insult and attack involved in the friend's suggestion—and whether it may not be an attempt to think about workable alternatives. There is much intact health and ego in these mothers and while they have some anxieties in common, they do not all handle identical situations with the same kind of "illogical" reactions. Almost always we would be able to depend upon the strength of another mother to view the suggestion of Mrs. P.'s friend around placement with less associated anxiety. Otherwise the group counselor using other group members may be able to elicit a reality-based concept of the friend's interest. As they see how their own problem feelings interfere with their interpersonal relationships, they are better able to elicit and use the more clearly understood questions and interest of those around them.

An important aspect of the activity of each group is the opportunity provided for mothers to discuss successes and experience pleasure with their children. We all know that parenthood is a two-way path and that children need to be able to feed back through their responses so that parents can be restimulated to try new and different ways of working and living with their children. Most of these mothers feel themselves cut off from the normal channels of exchanging the "plus values" of the mothering experience with other members. With present-day community values on achievement, mothers of retarded children find few ways of interchanging with pride in their children. Here they can "enjoy" their children with each other—can move beyond the "specialness" and "problems" to credit themselves and the children for what they achieve. In one session Mrs. C., who would certainly not have had the attentive understanding and empathy of mothers of normal children in her attempts to help her nine-year-old son to accept being moved from her bed to his own room—reported back that their suggestions had worked. She had repainted John's room—given him adequate emotional and psychological support so that for the first time since his initial seizure three years earlier he was in his own bed. That she would have been unable to achieve this without the group supporting her can be understood in the light of our awareness that various team members had attempted to help Mrs. C. with the problem as she brought it up in clinic contacts over a protracted time period. What it feels good to report is the warmth with which group members responded to this evidence of increased strength in Mrs. C. and her frustration tolerance for her child. It is important to mention that in following sessions, three other mothers brought up similar problems. That the question was handled within the group on a reality basis with understanding and acceptance rather than in terms of its threatening symbiotic features must have encouraged these other mothers to let group members know that they had also been sleeping with their retarded children—and to ask for help in working out other sleeping arrangements.

Mothers, apologetically and hesitantly at first, begin to report on such progress as toilet training, a good restaurant experience with their child, a well-managed visit to a friend's house with the entire family, etc. That one mother has been able to help her child with self-feeding encourages another mother to attempt such help for her child. What worked for her may be different than what worked for the first mother, but still another group member is readier to use her own inituitive feelings about what may help her own child. Thus, the somewhat static concept of "how to do" for the retarded child, which seems to us to have little value, is broken through as the mothers begin to function on a level much more related to the particular needs of their individual children.

As in individual counseling, interpretation is given as group members can use it. If, for example, the group leader attempts to open up the area of the special burden of caring for retarded children and meets with general denial, it is not pushed further. The group counselor is able to let the mothers know that he is available to consider with them the additional complications of bringing up retarded children—and to work with them on the limitations which are the results of the retardation, and the continuous effort involved in obtaining services for them. At some future time the members may be able to express their feelings about this more openly. For the time being they have been left with the group counselor's conviction that they have a right to feel and even to acknowledge that this is a difficult role. As parents become better able to view themselves and their children, the mother's picture of the child is not so beclouded by the projection of her own needs. Through the mother's discussion of her daily living experiences with her child, we come to understand aspects of the child's development which can clarify diagnostic questions, and permit further help by clinical team members. We have also learned more about the specific challenges that mothers meet in living with their retarded children at the various levels of their development. We recognize that we do not have answers to all of the problems —and that the mother, who comes closest to her child, understands his needs, and struggles to devise ways of meeting them, has much to contribute to our knowledge in this field.

Conclusions

We have reported on our experience over the past three years with fifteen counseling groups for mothers in an outpatient treatment center for retarded children. From the beginning we have recognized the importance of planning groups for fathers and mixed couples and hope that in this next year it will be feasible. We think it important to stress that the group counseling method is not a replacement for individual counseling; it is an additional level of service geared to meet the needs of selected families who as Ackerman suggests in "The Psychodynamics of Family Life" are readier to begin to work on their problems "from the outside inward." We feel that group counseling has unique and dynamic possibilities as a treatment method not only for parents of the retarded, but for all parents who are confronted with the necessity of working out solutions for themselves as parents of handicapped children.

□ □ □

HELPING PARENTS UNDERSTAND THEIR MENTALLY HANDICAPPED CHILD

Cleo E. Popp
Vivien Ingram, Paul H. Jordan

(American Journal of Mental Deficiency, 1954)

Most parents desire to have their children lead happy, well adjusted lives and to become adequate social beings. This desire brings into sharp relief the inadequacies of the mentally handicapped child, inadequacies which increase as he develops and is measured over and over against his own brothers and sisters, his neighborhood playmates, and later his school companions. As the mentally handicapped child approaches school age, his parents feel increasingly frustrated and helpless.

The primary needs of the mentally handicapped child are no different from those of any child. The parents alone cannot provide all these needs, nor can the school alone. Since the child is a part of society, many agencies of the community must cooperate with the parents to satisfy these needs. The problem, therefore, lies *first* in helping the parent to understand the needs of the child, his growth and development, his limitations, his frustrations, and his relationships with family and peers.

[The] *second* [part of the problem is to] help the parent to know his community so that every and any agency that can help his child may be used. Within the last few years when parents have come to the school with problems about their mentally handicapped children, the school and the Child Guidance Clinic have tried to work with these parents on an individual basis, but such a method is time-consuming. Since all parents can profit by a knowledge of basic principles which are common to such groups, it was soon apparent that much work could be done more successfully on a group rather than on an individual basis. Further, it was realized that the sharing of these common problems might provide a release for some of the inevitable frustrations which these parents are bound to feel. Therefore, early in 1952, members of the staff of the Lapeer State Home and Training School, the Child Guidance Clinic, and a public school representative compiled a list of parents of retarded children under ten who had been excluded from school. These children may or may not have had a trial in kindergarten or first grade before they were thought to be uneducable. This list also included parents of children who were waiting to be admitted to state institutions for the mentally handicapped.

These parents were invited to meet at the clinic with the psychiatrist and the mental hygiene nurse. The purpose of the meeting was to learn whether these parents were interested in coming together to discuss their common problems and, if so, to suggest what should be the program for future meetings. The response in numbers was good, with twenty-two parents representing seventeen severely retarded children reporting. In the course of the subsequent discussion the parents expressed concern about many things. A few are suggested here: need for special training facilities in Flint; habit training; social experience; problems of insecurity, hostility, undesirable habits, sexual feelings in the child; recreational outlets; understanding convulsive disorders and brain injury; and the child's relationship to family and community.

Following this first meeting with the parents, a planning committee was formed to outline subject matter for the course, using as a guide the expressed interests of the parents. Subsequently, the psychiatrist and the mental hygiene nurse met again with the parents and presented for their consideration the tentative course outline which the parents adopted unanimously without a suggested change. The planning committee met again and worked the course outline into a complete prospectus encompassing subject material, instructors, teaching methods, and teaching aids. The course which evolved was subsequently accepted for inclusion in the Adult Education Program of the Flint Public Schools and the Mott Foundation.

The following is a summary of the subject material presented or discussed and the teaching aids and methods used. Each of these broad areas encompassed one to three class sessions. The psychiatrist and mental hygiene nurse were always present, but other personnel carried the responsibility for instruction under the supervision of the psychiatrist.

Causes and effects of mental retardation was the subject of the first several sessions. With the use of books, charts, and projector this subject was discussed by the psychiatrist. This covered the causes of mental retardation, including a discussion of the neuroanatomical changes; the effect of brain damage or retarded development on the function of the human organism; the effect on neurological and intellectual function and emotional control; the effect on qualitative and quantitative learning; and the limitations, emotional, social, and educational, that are imposed by the fact of retardation. These sessions with the parents gave the background and setting for the rest of the course.

The second general subject discussed was how the child feels and what his emotional needs are. The presentation of the materials in this area of information was made by an educator, and a psychologist. The basic primary needs of all children and the special needs of the retarded child were included in the content of this session and a film, *Preface to a Life,* provided background for discussion.

Relationships of the retarded child in the family and neighborhood provided the area of discussion for several class sessions. In presenting this subject, role playing, with parents participating, was used as the principal technique in making real the feelings of parents, sisters and brothers, the child himself, and the feelings and reactions of playmates in the neighborhood. Instructors for these sessions included a psychologist and a psychiatric social worker.

A Saturday inspection trip to Lapeer State Home and Training School under the guidance of the director of education and the principal of the institution school was the next part of the course. There the parents observed all phases of the school program, much of the training program, and the very stimulating work which is being done with the so-called "custodial" children. At the next meeting of the class the instructors aided the parents in evaluating what they had observed on the field trip.

Following this, three full class periods were spent discussing what parents can do to meet the child's needs. The films, *Children Learning By Experience* and *When Should Grown-ups Help* were used for motivation. Areas of discussion included handling of dependence-independence, habit training, provision of appropriate stimulation, learning experience, and constructive recognition. Time was also spent on how to provide appropriate social experience with help in learning to meet social demands and to operate within limits imposed by society, and on how to train toward development of occupational skills.

The first semester closed with discussions on what the community can do for the retarded child and what its limitations are. Representatives from public schools, the Lapeer State Home and Training School, social work agencies, and recreation agencies provided a panel to cover this subject material. Areas discussed included the special education facilities provided by tax funds, the program in the public school and state training school, as well as a review of facilities through private training schools. The exploration with parents of existing community recreation programs and how to use them, and a description of the clinical agencies and their functions provided material for several class periods. . . .

One naturally asks the question, what are the results of such a project? We do not know yet what the full effects may be, but certain observations appear significant and certain trends seem to be developing. An average of twenty-two parents have attended the sessions. They did not begin to participate actively in the discussion until the third session, and the use of role playing in the fourth session definitely led to more participation with more spontaneity and more interaction on the part of the parents, and, for the first time, a highly intelligent but depressed mother of a severely brain-injured child really began to talk. A week later her husband reported that she had become more relaxed and was beginning to take part in group discussion for the first time in years. Since the field trip to Lapeer, another bright mother of a brain-injured child has been more relaxed, friendly, and less defensive than any of us have known her to be. Also, since the field trip the parents of three severely retarded children have become interested in giving their children the advantages of the facilities at the State Home and Training School where formerly they were resistant. Two of the above-mentioned families are now filing for commitment. A number of parents have expressed a growing awareness that they had expected too much of their children, and have evidenced a better acceptance of the limitations of their children. In the sixth session a mother of a three-year-old mongoloid child asked, "What can we parents do now to provide our children with the social experience and training they need?" Since then this same question has been raised by the parents of two other children.

We see the following trends developing: 1) relief from feelings of guilt, anxiety, and shame on the part of many parents, 2) marked reduction in expression of hostility toward the public schools, 3) practically a disappearance of any fear of the state training school, 4) better acceptance of their retarded children, 5) a growing interest in developing a cooperative nursery school to provide habit training and social experience for their children, 6) formation of a Flint Chapter of the Michigan Association of Parents and Friends of Mentally Retarded Children.[1]

The several agencies that have actively participated in this course have also received some benefits and have gained new perspectives. The Flint Public Schools are contemplating re-evaluating their special education program, especially in respect to meeting more effectively the needs of the uneducable but trainable child.[2]

The responsiveness of the parents has been stimulating to those instructors from the Lapeer State Home and Training School and provided added and well deserved recognition for their work with retarded children. There has been a decrease in pressure on the Child Guidance Clinic from parents of severely retarded children.

The second semester of the course is yet to come. Enrollment will be limited to those parents who attended the first semester. It will consist largely of the clinical discussion of the children whose parents are enrolled in the course. It is expected that two cases will be covered each night. The clinical "team" will consist of a psychiatrist, psychologist, mental hygiene nurse, the director of the education program at Lapeer, and a member of the special education committee of the Flint Public Schools. The discussions will be based on full clinical case studies on the children concerned, and it is hoped that further gains may be made in dealing with this frustrating problem.[3]

Extension of Project to "Slow Learners"

Although the parents served in the course described in this paper were parents of severely mentally handicapped children who had been excluded from school, there probably is just as great a need for such help for parents of children who are in school, but who are beginning to show unusual behavior patterns because they are "slow learners." Since much of the course outlined covers the primary needs of *all* children, there would need to be very little modification of the content to make the course profitable to parents of children who are less severely handicapped and who will probably become socially competent citizens if given the proper chance to develop. With less emphasis on causes and classifications of handicaps and more emphasis on the development and needs of the child, the background information in the course could be the same for the parents of the "slow learner group." The desired outcomes would be very much the same as those that seem to be emerging from the experimental course; namely, relieving parents of feelings of guilt, anxiety, and aloneness and helping them to accept more readily their child's limitations and to be more relaxed in dealing with his problems.

FOOTNOTES

1. Developments between December, 1952 and May, 1953: In the early spring, a chapter of the Parents for Mentally Handicapped was formed, and they have been very active on several projects: a) they have set up a car pool so that five of the children in the group are participating in a day-school program at the Lapeer State Home and Training School twenty miles from Flint; b) they are working with the City Recreation Department on a summer recreation program for their children.
2. Developments between December, 1952 and May, 1953: The Board of Education of the Flint Public Schools has authorized the setting up of two rooms for the severely mentally handicapped child, and has worked out a very flexible working relationship with the State Home and Training School through the probate judge. This makes it possible to try the child in a training situation and then move him if it is found that his needs and best interests may be served by a different agency.
3. Developments between December, 1952 and May, 1953: These clinics proved to be very successful. The attendance of parents held up to the last. The therapeutic value could not be measured, but it was evident that parents relaxed and were willing to bring their problems out before the group. The planning by the panel for each child and the discussion of problems by the whole parent group opened the way for a complete understanding of the child's problems and resulted in a satisfactory plan for the parent and child. Furthermore, parents were able to see their own problems in their proper perspective and were ready as a result to work as a unit for all the children rather than just for their own child.

□ □ □

from GROUP APPROACHES IN WORKING WITH PARENTS OF THE RETARDED: AN OVERVIEW

Gunnar Dybwad

(*Challenges in Mental Retardation,* 1964)

A survey of the available literature and of the services now in existence reveals that group programs are being offered to parents under a rather wide variety of names of which the following are most frequently encountered: group therapy, group counseling, education counseling, parent education, parent seminars, parent group training, parent group information.

While it is true that these services are offered only sporadically so far and by no means in any measure commensurate with the extent of the problem of mental retardation[1] actually a great deal is being done now and a considerable amount of material is available in the professional literature. . . .

Quite a few of the mental retardation clinics that have developed over the past decade or so are offering group programs. The following quotations will provide some indication of what is offered:

> Group counseling sessions provide an opportunity for parents with similar problems to achieve insight and help as they get together and talk over their questions and problems with a qualified psychiatrist.

Or:

> Counseling may be offered during or following the diagnostic study. This may be on an individual basis or a group basis, may involve help with specific problems in dealing with a

child, or may involve assistance in improving the general climate in the home in order that the child may function more effectively.

Group therapy approach is an effort to help the parents achieve better understanding of themselves and their children. Mothers are seen in a group under the direction of the psychologist or social worker under clinic staff.

Another clinic states:

Our goal was not to attempt to bring about any significant changes in personality problems but to help the parents feel more comfortable and to be more realistic and effective in their dealings with the child.

Another clinic which places considerable emphasis on counseling parents of retarded children both individually and in groups states:

In group counseling we are not concerned with intensive group therapy, but with casework counseling in groups. Goals are: personality reintegration and adjustment to reality. Group processes and teaching methods are combined to afford the individual relief from tension, understanding of children's behavior, and techniques for handling specific problems.[2]

A family service agency in a large city provides "leadership of family life education groups," and includes under that heading programs for parents of retarded children.

A metropolitan agency which serves severely mentally handicapped retarded children through a combination of educational and clinical programs offers an educational counseling program consisting of a series of fifteen lectures, followed by group therapy—an interesting combination.[3]

Adult education programs under the auspices of public school systems offer parent-education group meetings, and a handbook published by the Bureau of Adult Education in the State of California has a special section dealing with such programs for parents of mentally retarded children.[4] In some cases, extension divisions of state universities have included parent education programs in their schedules.

The state board of health in an eastern state conducts parent education classes with a rather specific purpose: to give parents a better understanding of their retarded children's speech problems.

In some cases state institutions are conducting group meetings over a period of time, either to assist parents who are facing a long waiting time before their child can be admitted to the institution or else to achieve on the parents' part a better understanding of their children's needs and how the institution, now caring for the child, will meet these needs.

In numerous instances all across the country, parent-sponsored associations for retarded children are offering group programs. They range from group therapy sessions conducted by a psychiatrist[5] and group counseling sessions under the direction of social workers to informal discussion meetings conducted by parents for parents and lecture meetings. In one case, a state Association for Retarded Children organized, on a demonstration basis, parent seminars on a state-wide pattern—two in large urban centers and one in a rural county.[6] Another state association organized in one of the Great Plains states intensive one-day institutes with a structured agenda of lectures and group discussion.

This hasty enumeration will serve to give an indication of the many different programs which are in existence in such a wide variety of agency settings. If one considers further that there is no consensus as to what constitutes appropriate subject matter for discussion, that there is no agreement as to what disciplines should handle such programs, what special preparation, if indeed any, should be required, and what type of grouping is appropriate as far as the participants are concerned, then it stands to reason that one is hard put to discern any clear over-all lines which would allow even a fairly rough delineation of one type of program from another.

In order to arrive at any kind of over-all picture, we shall have to look at the component parts, specifically the areas from which the subject matter was drawn, the selection and grouping of participants, the methodology used, and the patterns of staffing and training of staff.

As one reviews the approach to the content of such groups, either as described in the literature of the past ten years or as available from unpublished materials in the files, it becomes fairly evident that change is taking place. Earlier material centered very heavily on what were considered the overwhelming guilt feelings of parents of retarded children and on what was seen as a deep-seated and fairly acute state of disturbance as a result of the traumatic experience of having a retarded child.

In a chapter, "Guides for Parents," contributed in 1959 to the volume *The Child with a Handicap: A Team Approach to His Care and Guidance*"[7] Dr. Elizabeth Boggs pointed out that

> much has been written about the "guilt feelings" of the parents of the handicapped child. What are sometimes called guilt feelings may in reality be a form of grief. Grief is a normal and appropriate human emotion whose suppression is unhealthy. Parents of a handicapped child must live with their continuing form of grief. As an individual he should be assisted by the knowledge that his emotions are respected.

It is interesting that in two successive issues of the journal *Social Casework,* published in 1962, two authors—one a social worker, the other a social scientist—picked up and developed further this important theme.

> The caseworker should be careful to guard against viewing the initial grief reaction as the parents' inability to accept the handicapped. As with any injury, there comes a narcissistic blow. It takes time for parents to adapt themselves to this painful reality. The best way to help them is to understand and recognize their need for a period of adjustment during which they can absorb the shock.[8]

In an article entitled "Chronic Sorrow: A Response to Having a Mentally Defective Child," Simon Olshansky proposes:

> Most parents who have a mentally retarded child suffer from a pervasive psychological reaction, chronic sorrow, which has not always been recognized by the professional personnel–physicians, psychologists, and social workers –who attempt to help them. . . . The helping professions have somewhat belabored the tendency of the parent to deny the reality of his child's mental deficiency. Few workers have reported what is probably a more frequent occurrence, the parent's tendency to deny his chronic sorrow. This tendency is often reinforced by the professional helpers' habit of viewing chronic sorrow as a neurotic manifestation rather than as a natural and understandable response to a tragic fact. All the parental reactions reported in the literature, such as guilt, shame, and anger, may well be intertwined with chronic sorrow.[9]

A second shift I have discerned in this present view has been a move away from overemphasis on the diagnostic process and in particular on the post-diagnostic period during which continued interpretation and reinterpretation to the parent of the diagnostic findings was considered a very important point to be followed. It would appear that there is now more of a realization as to the limited value of the diagnosis as available today so far as the child's future performance is concerned. While it is of course true that most parents ask with a great sense of urgency "What happened?" it would appear that in our own need to identify causative factors, we tended in the past to accentuate that particular question of the parent as against a more fruitful one: "What can I expect from him and what can I do for him?"

In other words, in mental retardation, the clinical diagnosis in early childhood, essential as it is, often provides very little meaningful guidance for the parent who is anxious to know what level of performance he might expect from the child.

There is a third area that should be mentioned here: what once was considered most unrealistic striving by the parent or even considered a symptom of his neurotic nonacceptance of the inevitable limitations of his retarded child, now comes to the fore in an increasing measure as quite feasible expectations.

What is suggested here is that one can see a shift in the content of the group discussions—not just because shifts in community attitudes and other vital factors have given the parent a better capacity to deal with this problem, but because the group leader, too, has gained a different, more positive, and more hopeful outlook on mental retardation which is reflected in his work with the group.

A recent report on "The Development of a Group Counseling Program in a Clinic for Retarded Children" states: "There is much intact health and ego in these mothers, and while they have some anxieties in common, they do not all handle identical situations with the same kind of 'illogical' reactions."[10]

Aside, of course, from those lecture courses or lecture discussion meetings where a topic selected in advance sets the framework for each meeting, in most cases the specific topics for discussion are now selected by the group as they move on from meeting to meeting.

> The parents were encouraged to bring up and pursue whatever subjects were of paramount interest to them. They understood there would be no fixed curriculum. In the opening session, the leader asked the group members what they wished to discuss, and a tentative agenda was drawn up. The original list of topics was referred to from time to time by the members or the leader, and it was used flexibly, as a reminder of initial interest, rather than as a fixed outline. Topics for discussion were selected by the members from meeting to meeting. Therefore, at each session, the members and the leader faced the task of selecting areas for discussion that were both of immediate and general concern.[11]

The following is a selected list of topics considered by a group of parents of retarded children during the course of a ten-session group counseling project.[12]

1. The meaning of the retarded child to his siblings, his effect on them, their acceptance of him, etc.
2. The services offered by the institution, both positive and negative values.
3. The question of placement, its value to the child and its meanings; the meanings to the parents.
4. Problems of discipline for the retarded child and the other children in the family.
5. The future care of the retarded child and the responsibilities of the institution, the parents, the siblings.
6. Legal and financial questions about the future care of the retarded child.
7. Difficulties of accepting the diagnosis and term "the retarded child."
8. Some of the emotional meanings to parents of having a retarded child.
9. The shortcomings of professional help which is available.
10. Some of the various meanings to parents of joining an association for retarded children.
11. The retarded child and religious meanings.
12. The values and expectations of a group process for parents.

Moving from the area of content to that of selection (groupings) of participants, it is again hard to discern any one dominant pattern. Some leaders seem to feel that as long as the group process does not involve deep therapy the choice of participants requires only a relatively superficial screening (to eliminate the obviously disturbed for whom the group experience would be too traumatic and who in turn might tend to disrupt the developing group process).

Other leaders feel that a careful screening interview is very important because it also serves the purpose of preparing the parent for the experience he may expect as a member of the group.

While some leaders feel that having a "mixed" group representing a variety of handicaps is a distinct advantage in that parents might tend to get a more balanced view of the child's handicap if they see the problems encountered in another family burdened by a different disability, there is good reason to approach mixed groups with some caution:

> Other variations in group movement are found in groups composed of parents of children with different disabilities or children who have a similar disability but a wide range of impairment. The basis for these parents coming together is that they share the common experience of having a handicapped child but differences in the nature or degree of the child's handicap may set each family off in a separate category. Even in groups built around a common label, such as mental retardation or orthopedic handicaps, parents often become preoccupied with the fact that their child is much more (or less) disabled than the children of the other group members. Whether they are deeply envious of the other parents or relieved at their own favorable situation, their awareness of the differences makes it hard for them to see and share their common problems and so to learn from one another. These groups too work at a slower pace and require unusually sensitive leadership.[13]

Bernard L. White called attention to the fact that thought needs to be given when it is planned to have both parents attend the same group.

> We are now encouraging both parents to participate. Those who have reported that they tended to be more consistent in their treatment of the child and gained a greater understanding of their partner's role and feelings. However, if both parents are to be included more stringent selection would seem to be indicated. Basically secure, compatible marital situations seem to be enhanced by an experience of this sort; those of a doubtful nature would be expected to gain less and might possibly be harmed. In any event, the group session should not be a battleground for familial differences, with the leader and other participants cast in the role of referees.[14]

One further point needs to be stressed in discussing methods of selection of participants in parent group efforts. The parents who have participated in the therapy groups, group counseling, and group education projects referred to in this text or described elsewhere in the literature have largely, if not exclusively, been parents of retarded children whose mental defect was related to causative factors in the biological area and usually was accompanied by physical debilities of one kind or another.

If we were to extend this program broadly to families where the mental retardation problem is related to cultural, economic, and social causes, we might likely encounter serious problems in communication between the kind of group leader we are now furnishing and the parents coming from a socially, economically, and culturally deprived situation.[15]

Turning now to methodological considerations, one is confronted with an obvious confusion regarding the term "group therapy." References to it in the literature and in announcements and reports of programs indicate that only rarely is there a clear conceptualization as to how a program announced as "therapy" would differ from an educational approach. This can most likely be related to a lack of clarity in the setting of goals for such programs.[16]

One (unpublished) report of a series of ten sessions conducted by a psychiatrist contains these statements: "Since the exploration of hidden feelings and thoughts and the deepening of one's self-awareness are psychotherapeutic goals, the pilot project was undertaken frankly as therapy, and a psychiatrist experienced in group therapy was utilized as group leader." And then: "Deep-seated emotional conflicts relatively unrelated to the immediate problem of retardation were carefully avoided by the therapist. It was not expected that any major changes in attitude would be accomplished in so short a time." Again: "These people did not gather together into a group for psychotherapy because of any realization of emotional conflict within themselves."

James C. Coleman, in his article "Group Therapy with Parents of Mentally Deficient Children,"[17] states in reporting on a group therapy project: "In a sense the interaction was maintained on a relatively surface level since the group discussion was restricted to parent-child relations and did not take up various personal problems in other life areas." Also, "The term 'group therapy' was not used and no attempt was made to structure the situation as therapy in any form."

A succinct statement as to the difference between parent group education and group therapy is given by Aline Auerbach:

> In parent group education, the goal of the leader is to help group members explore all aspects of the situation in which they find themselves with their children, to gain greater knowledge and understanding of their children's physical and emotional development, of their own role as parents, and of the complexity of parent-child relationships. They do this through exchange of ideas and experiences within the group interplay, looking at both facts and feelings—theirs and their children's. Sharing their reactions with others under skillful leadership seems to free parents to move on to new attitudes and new behavior, or to have greater confidence in what they are already doing.
>
> The goals and techniques of group education are different from those of group therapy. The group education leader does not focus on the pathology of the members, or probe into the unconscious. Although he must take into account the unconscious factors that influence behavior, he deliberately directs group thinking toward aspects of ego functioning to develop ego strengths.[18]

In spite of the lack of clarification in the use of the two terms, there was at least universal recognition that group therapy was somehow going into more depth. The term "counseling," however, seems to be used with almost any connotation—from a specific treatment approach to instructional guidance.

The urgent need for clarification of these various terms and the approaches they do (or should) represent becomes obvious when we approach the problem of training leaders for these various programs. In our present review, we found in both the published material and the unpublished reports universal agreement about the very definite value of group approaches in helping parents of handicapped children. This obviously suggests a broad application and this in turn necessitates preparation of appropriate leadership.

One outstanding example of such training is the Program of Training of Professional Workers for Parent Group Education of Parents of Handicapped Children developed over the past several years by the Child Study Association in America, the oldest organization in the field. Their experience extends to social workers, educators, psychologists, and public health nurses[19] and has included specifically work with groups of parents of retarded children.

This is not to say that only professional workers can make a contribution to the programs here under discussion. In her article "The Impact of the Handicapped Child on the Family," Pauline Cohen stresses the point that parents of retarded children, because of their own experiences, *can* be particularly effective in helping other parents work through their grief, and indeed carefully selected parents have been used for such programs. But certainly this would imply a carefully delineated approach, in clear distinction to the type of programs which can be undertaken by the professional worker.

Altogether, it seems abundantly clear that there is an urgent need for systematic efforts along three lines:

1. conceptualization of the various group approaches to parents of handicapped (and particularly mentally retarded) children;

2. clearer recognition of the types of training appropriate for these different group programs;

3. development of program-oriented research to test the effectiveness of these programs.

FOOTNOTES

1. Gardner, William and Nisonger, Herschel W., "A Manual on Program Development in Mental Retardation," Monograph Supplement to the *American Journal of Mental Deficiency,* January, 1962, p. 26.
2. Beck, Helen L., "Counseling Parents of Retarded Children," *Children,* November-December, 1959, p. 228.
3. The Institute for Retarded Children of the Shield of David, "Program for Pre-School Trainable Retardates and Their Parents," mimeographed NIMH Grant Report, 1958-61.
4. Babitz, Milton, *Parent Education—Curriculums, Methods and Materials.* Sacramento, Calif.: State Department of Education, May, 1961, pp. 69-73.
5. Gadpaille, W. J., M.D., "Parents Group Pilot Project," unpublished mimeographed report, Denver, 1959.
6. Bauer, Warren C., and Switzer, Ann, *Adjustment of the Retarded—A Research and Demonstration Project.* Connecticut Association for Retarded Children, 1962.
7. Martmer, Edgar E., ed., *The Child with a Handicap.* Springfield, Ill.: Charles C. Thomas Company, 1959, p. 355.
8. Cohen, Pauline C., "The Impact of the Handicapped Child on the Family," *Social Casework,* XLIII, No. 3 (March, 1962), p. 138.
9. Olshansky, Simon, "Chronic Sorrow: A Response to Having a Mentally Defective Child," *Social Casework,* XLIII, No. 4 (April, 1962), pp. 190-91.
10. Goodman, L. and Rothman, R., *American Journal of Mental Deficiency,* LXV, No. 6 (May, 1961), p. 793.
11. Ambrosino, Salvatore, "A Project in Group Education with Parents of Retarded Children," *Casework Papers,* 1960. New York: Family Service Association of America, 1960, p. 97.
12. The author is indebted for this information to Arthur Mandelbaum of Topeka, Kansas.
13. Auerbach, A. B., "Group Education for Parents of the Handicapped," *Children,* July-August, 1961, p. 139.
14. White, Bernard L., "Group Counseling with Parents of Retarded Children," unpublished paper presented at the 1958 convention of the American Psychological Association.
15. Gram, A., *Parent Education and the Behavioral Sciences.* Washington, D.C.: U.S. Children's Bureau Publication, 1960, p. 20.
16. Dybwad, Gunnar and Goller, Gertrude, "Goals and Techniques of Parent Education," *Casework Papers,* 1955. New York: Family Service Association of America, 1955, pp. 138-41.
17. In *Counseling and Psychotherapy with the Mentally Retarded,* edited by Charles L. Stacey and Manfred F. DeMartino. Glencoe, Ill.: The Free Press, 1957.
18. Auerbach, Aline B., "Group Education for Parents of the Handicapped," *Children,* July-August, 1961, pp. 135-36.
19. See e.g., A. B. Auerbach, "How Do Nurses Take to 'New Ways' in Leading Parent Groups?" *Nursing Outlook,* Vol. VI (December, 1958).

□ □ □

SECTION B

Home Management Techniques

An office can be a convenient, cozy, and secure place; and many professionals have been reluctant to leave this haven to carry their services to those who do not come to them. Yet, it is evident that some families in need of help cannot utilize the kind of services that can be given in a professional's office. The home management approaches reviewed in this section describe techniques which have been successful in reaching families which otherwise might have been neglected.

Perhaps one reason professionals have preferred office-centered management is because of the demand that other types of services, such as home visiting, can make upon a person's competence. A professional office is frequently filled with symbols which help to delimit and define the rights and responsibilities of its professional occupant. The home visitor, on the other hand, is stripped of many of these objective symbols, which could make it difficult for him to clearly define his role to himself, his peers, and his clients. Without precise clarification, the home visitor may be cast into many and varied roles such as therapist, child development specialist, health expert, social worker, teacher, homemaker, home economist, chauffeur, and perhaps even truant or probation officer.

We must recognize that sitting across the desk from the professional may constitute a strange and artificial situation for a family. Words that are used, evaluations that are expressed, and sanctions that are taken may all be quite different in such an artificial setting than in the home setting. This raises the question whether such artificiality might distort professionals' perceptions obtained in their offices. If it did, it would provide one rationale for home visiting. While this rationale has to do with the professional's perceptions, a second one can be constructed with the parents' responses in mind. It is quite likely that the relative unreality of the office setting and its unfamiliarity to the parent incapacitates or repels him so that he becomes less available to constructive management.

A home visiting project which has drawn considerable attention is described by Cianci. While most programs of this nature have utilized social workers or health-oriented visitors, the home visitors in this project had their formal training in education. In describing the functions of these home visitors, Cianci provides no specific evaluation, but successful management outcome is implied.

Goodman advocates that agencies should reach out more aggressively to families in need of help, particularly those apt to isolate themselves in response to the impact of a handicapped child. In a second article with Arnold, the same author relates experiences with a homemaker program which might function in conjunction with other clinic services, and especially as an emergency or crisis resource. Arnold and Goodman feel that the initial parental reaction to a child's retardation can block the development of a therapeutic relationship. They advocate the introduction of a homemaker or home aide at this point, as a means of simultaneously providing psychological support and direct evidence to the parents of the community's readiness to help. Comparison of two groups of parents, one receiving such aid and one not, indicates that home visiting was successful. The selection by Dittmann demonstrates home counseling oriented toward practical child development and homemaking, in conjunction with group and individual counseling, as an extension of other clinic services. While the outcome of the illustration cases may leave something to be desired, the management approach appears to be meritorious because of its multifaceted nature.

Lipsett describes a program in Canada in which a clinic draws upon about one hundred volunteers to provide home contacts. These volunteers play primarily a liaison and ego-supporting role, also helping the mother to be more realistic toward the child. This report, unfortunately, provides only limited information about the characteristics of the volunteers.

In addition to the programs described in this section, home management is also involved in a number of selections from other parts and sections of the book as in Sections C and D of this part. Home services are among the most under-utilized options in family management. Quite aside from their potential for great or even unique effectiveness with some families, such services can have great financial benefits since home assistance at very modest expense can often forestall costly institutionalization. Despite the high face validity of home management programs, more definitive empirical demonstration of their effects and advantages may be necessary to bring about wider adoption of this management alternative.

HOME TRAINING *Vincentz Cianci*

(American Journal of Mental Deficiency, 1961)

In September 1943, the Department of Institutions and Agencies of New Jersey took the initiative in pioneering a new type of community program called Home Training. A program similar to this had been tried in Massachusetts for several years by the Department of Mental Health and found to be most worthwhile. The difference in the two programs was in the type of personnel. The one in Massachusetts was carried out with social workers, while the one in New Jersey was to be developed by a person trained in education. If the approach was different, the objectives were the same; namely, better community understanding of the problem of mental deficiency and better home and family adjustment.

Because there was very little literature concerning this type of work, the home teacher had to develop her own materials and techniques. There was also an advantage in having such a person on a state level for it made it possible to cross county and district lines, making her services available to anyone within reasonable distance from the North Jersey Training School.

Referrals at first came through the Division of Classification and Education, Department of Institutions and Agencies. Later, as the work became better known, referrals from schools, social agencies, clinics, and nursing services were accepted. The type of retarded child the teacher met and worked with in the homes was that usually labeled institutional.

Many times these children create problems in the home because parents are at a loss as to how to handle them. It has been found that when parents have insight into their problem and recognize and accept the limitations of their retarded child, much more can be accomplished. One cannot minimize the effect of a retarded child in the family, nor should one take this handicap lightly, for all handicaps that a person can have, the one which affects the mind is most crippling from the standpoint of social adjustment. Any progress or improvement can be gained only at the cost of hours of patient training by the parents and sympathetic and intelligent understanding by the other members of the family and the community.

It has been found that the majority of parents of retarded children are more than capable of assuming their responsibility and facing the realities which result from such a problem, provided they are guided into right thinking, and their doubts and fears are replaced by truths. Patience and understanding must be the keynote, not only with the children but also with parents. The home teacher must never lose sight of the fact that these problems cannot be resolved overnight. It takes years for these people, who are emotionally involved with the problem, to appreciate the full significance of this truth.

It was found that all the cases fall in two groups. In the first of these are those children who are grossly retarded. In these cases the home teacher places emphasis on elementary habit training, emotional control, self-help, speech and play activities. Visits are made to each home on the average of once every two months and last approximately one and one-half hours. The training period is spent with both the mother and the child so that the parent can learn and continue the methods used to develop the potentialities of the child. The majority of the children in this group are considered as urgently in need of institutional care, and parents need direction and encouragement to carry on until these children can be received by the institution.

Habit training with special emphasis on body function is the most important phase of this program. In this case, parents are given simple directions on how to go about establishing such favorable habits. Parents must be constantly encouraged to persist in their efforts. They sometimes find it more expedient to do things for the child rather than take the time to teach him. Such parents need to be guided in the right attitude and they must be made to realize that the time spent in training the child is time well spent. Parents are given simple directions of how to go about establishing these correcting habit patterns, and the advantages which will result from this training are pointed out to them.

The mother must be advised that teaching these children will be a long-time process and can be accomplished only by a systematic established routine. The need for repetition and perseverance on the part of the person doing the training cannot be overemphasized. It must be said that a number of mothers are doing a remarkable job of habit training, but only need the confirmation of someone else that they are doing the right thing or they need help in choosing proper play equipment.

Children of this type develop all sorts of bad habits and persist in them much longer than a normal child and for that reason it is important that the child be kept occupied doing some worthwhile play activity. Parents need help in choosing toys which will appeal to the child's senses. They need toys which they can push, pull, throw. They like toys that make noise, toys that roll or float. Toys do not have to be expensive, and many parents have made their own with the help of the suggestions given by the teacher. A few parents have built sliding, climbing, and swimming apparatus in the yard, and this has been a source of enjoyment to both the retarded child and his normal brothers and sisters.

In the second group, are those children, who although severely retarded, can be considered of trainable level of intelligence who, in addition to habit and emotional training can further profit by handcraft and modified primary work. These children are visited on the average of about once a week and the lesson usually lasts one hour. Here again, both mother and child participate in the work, and as necessary, part of the lesson is devoted to discussing with the parent any problem which concerns the child. Efforts are made to point out to the mother how important it is that the work should continue during the interim of the visits. The meaning and purpose of the training must be explained to the parent. For instance it can be shown how certain play activities develop eye and muscle coordination which will aid the child in doing simple craft and kindergarten work. This, in turn, will lead to more efficient and continuous concentration and better emotional control, and ultimately these factors result in more adequate social home adjustment.

Lessons are prepared by the teacher beforehand and brought to the home. Materials are at first provided but later the parents are encouraged wherever possible to buy what is needed. The programs, although varied according to the potentialities of the child, follow the same pattern. Basic habits of eating, dressing, cleanliness, and eliminating are first established. Worthwhile handcraft projects are taught which will help the child utilize his leisure time. Children have learned to weave mats, make belts, do simple sewing projects, and embroidery work. Emphasis is placed on enjoyment and satisfaction the child receives from doing a piece of work. A few of the children have even sold some of the articles they made.

The teacher can't possibly teach the child everything in the one hour. She can only show the parent what the child is capable of accomplishing and give suggestions on how to go about doing it. A well rounded program will include such craft work as weaving, sewing, cutting, coloring and clay work. Wherever possible the child's number concept should be developed. The child should learn to discriminate colors and know the names and purpose of many objects which are in his immediate surrounding. Many of the children find pleasure in doing reading readiness activities and although only a very few learn to read, the majority of the children gain much in doing the activities in the book. Many of the children have phonographs, and parents buy them records which they enjoy listening to.

Another important phase of the program is teaching the child household skills. These children can do such simple tasks as setting tables, washing dishes, keeping clothes in order, making beds, keeping toys in order, folding towels, dusting, sweeping porches, and running errands. These duties keep the child busy in a constructive way and keep him out of mischief. The child also develops a sense of responsibility and belonging.

The lack of understanding that people have concerning the emotional makeup of mentally deficient children is appalling. The percentage of children who are oblivious to their surroundings is very low. Generally speaking, mentally retarded children have the same emotional drives as other children and need and want companionship. Mothers generally find it very difficult to fulfill this need. There have been instances where mothers have encouraged the normal children in the neighborhood to play with their retarded child by organizing parties and buying elaborate equipment which would attract these children. In most cases this has worked, but interest was short-lived and when the novelty wore off, the retarded child was exactly where he was before—alone. To fill this need for companionship, wherever possible, the home teacher brought two or three children of the same mental level together. The mothers were also introduced and in many cases fine friendships have developed, both among the children and the mothers. Meeting each other informally has helped the mothers to develop a bond of understanding and has helped to alleviate that feeling of futility and aloneness.

Society's lack of understanding of the problem of mental deficiency has forced parents to raise a protective wall around their child and family, forcing themselves to limit their interests among a few intimate friends and relatives. The home teacher found a few brave parents who dared participate in the normal activities of the community and neighborhood, but on the whole, the majority kept to themselves, not daring to risk the chance of being hurt. This seclusion has had a bad effect on the mental health of parents, causing tensions which result in antisocial attitudes.

The teacher, through her numerous home contacts, found that the questions and problems faced by parents of retarded children were more or less similar. Part of the time of the home visit was always spent in discussing some phase of the problem which might have been of immediate concern to the parent. This might include a discussion on proper use of discipline or on the development of family attitude concerning curious looks and whispered remarks on the part of the public.

Some mothers may need particular help in explaining the retarded child to the normal siblings, and others need guidance in understanding the intellectual and physical limitations so as to eliminate pressures which might have harmful effects on the child and family.

At one time, the parents' greatest concern was the lack of school facilities. However, today for some people this problem is not as acute. Nevertheless, parents still need a great deal of help in understanding what schooling can accomplish. A home teacher cannot only help the parents of children who will eventually be accepted in classes but can be a source of understanding and encouragement to those whose children will not meet the standards of trainable classes.

The home teacher, recognizing that these children also needed some extra home contacts, organized four play groups with the help of volunteers. The majority of children attending were the type who could not participate in the directed activities of a class but who found some enjoyment from group contacts.

The home teacher, because of her home contacts and intimate knowledge of the many problems associated with mental deficiency, can be of service to social agencies in the community. In cases where parents are forced to apply for help to many places, she can use her skill and knowledge to coordinate the information to the best advantage.

The home training service can be an integral and important part of the total program for retarded people, and the home teacher can be considered a community worker. Her services can be manifold, a resource person to social agencies, consultant and guide to parents, teacher and friends to the retarded child.

Part of the work too will be to help educate and enlighten the public concerning the problems of mental deficiency, for without community support little can be accomplished. Always on the alert in the field of mental deficiency for the new and untried, she can be in a position to make her contribution to society to make this a better world for the mentally retarded.

□ □ □

from CONTINUING TREATMENT OF PARENTS WITH CONGENITALLY DEFECTIVE INFANTS

Lawrence Goodman

(*Social Work,* 1964)

. . . .

A demonstration treatment program sponsored by the New York State Department of Mental Hygiene provided an opportunity to see clinically 140 families in the process of adjusting to the birth of a mongoloid infant. All had sought state institutionalization, although about forty withdrew their applications following casework contact. Families from the regular clinic case load, who never openly considered placement, did not appear to differ greatly in the extent of their disturbance and in their use of counseling. The study population is, therefore, considered to be reasonably representative of families confronting the crisis of a congenitally handicapped child. Selected cases will be presented throughout this paper to illustrate how the offer of help was responded to in terms of each family's adaptation to crisis and their patterns of coping with it.

. . . .

The program of the clinic has utilized individual counseling, group counseling and therapy (for couples), and home counseling. . . .

The home counseling activity has been a practical response to the needs of part of the patient group. It has been an attempt to cut through the self-destructive pattern of withdrawal and isolation by reaching out aggressively for the client. The mongoloid child can be viewed as an outcast. Through the parents' association with him, which reactivates early feelings of separateness and not belonging, they too feel shunned and closed off from the rest of society. In addition, the intensity of the emotional reaction may be so immobilizing that it is not possible for the parents to reach out for desperately needed help. The following shows how home counseling was able to help one family feel the necessity for constructive action.

> Mrs. E is the thirty-four-year-old mother of a ten-month-old mongoloid child. She is an unsophisticated, dependent, somewhat limited woman who has been depressed and partially immobilized since the birth of her son. She is obese and suffers frequent petit mal seizures. Mr. E is vaguely supportive and passive, one of the few fathers in the project to be involved only minimally. It was with great effort that Mrs. E was able to bring the boy to the clinic for evaluation. She has rarely left the house since his birth and lives a considerable distance from the clinic. The needs of her two normal

children were being denied as she became more and more involved with Louis—a low-functioning child with severe somatic involvement, who needed constant supervision. Although placement in this case was clinically indicated, Mrs. E was wavering in her decision.

Weekly interviews in the home were set up with Mrs. E. At home she appeared overburdened and poorly organized, but was warmly affectionate to all the children. With increasing trust in the worker she was able to discuss her ambivalence around placement, but as the time for separation approached she regressed further. With much support and encouragement she was able to relate her severe separation anxiety to her own feelings of abandonment as a child when she was hospitalized for epileptic attacks. She could also express her fears that her child's defect was related to her own handicap and that she had failed her husband. With continuing intensive support and bolstering, and with much reiteration of the necessity for placement in this case, Mrs. E was able to follow through.

Home visits continued as Mrs. E was helped to handle her fears that the child was being neglected, that he might go into "shock" from loneliness, that he might die soon, alone. Later there was guilt over feeling relieved of the constant burden of his care. The working-through of grief continued.

With much nurturing from the caseworker, a functioning level of adjustment and independence was reestablished. Mrs. E was able to use the worker's support to propel herself toward constructive action in all areas of functioning—for ventilation of feelings of guilt, inadequacy, and separation panic, and for the development of sufficient insight to enable her, after a prolonged crisis period, to face her mongoloid child realistically and free of disabling conflict.

. . . .

Families of congenitally defective infants have had a tragic occurrence fatefully thrust upon them, and a crisis situation suddenly exists. Even parents with a high level of intactness go through an initial phase of regression and disorganization. It is vital that counseling begin as soon as possible so that the family can be helped to mobilize its strength for combating threats on many levels. The family's self-concept is shaken, social position and mobility are endangered, individual adjustment patterns may be permanently damaged.

The decision to institutionalize without the opportunity to face anger, guilt, and conflict can be particularly destructive. At this time, the family looks primarily to the physician for guidance and direction. Since he, however, cannot be expected to assume the required casework function, the hospital social worker must intervene. In planning programs of continuing treatment, the value of home counseling, in situations characterized by withdrawal and avoidance, should not be overlooked. . . .

□ □ □

from HOMEMAKER SERVICES TO FAMILIES WITH YOUNG RETARDED CHILDREN

Irene L. Arnold
Lawrence Goodman

(*Children,* 1966)

In an effort to bring together two social trends which have been slow to meet—the growing concern for the retarded in our population and the increasing recognition of homemaker services in helping families cope with situations of stress—two voluntary agencies in New York City recently carried out a three-year project to demonstrate the potential contribution of homemakers and other home helpers toward preserving families of the retarded. Its results may suggest guidelines for the most effective, economical, and efficient utilization of such services in community plans for the retarded.

Established to examine systematically the effectiveness of homemaker and other home-help services to families with retarded children under five years old, the project was cooperatively conducted by the Retarded Infants Services, Inc. (RIS), and the Association for Homemaker Service, Inc. (AHS), with support from the Federal Children's Bureau. Behind its establishment was the conviction that such services, perhaps with various levels of integration with casework services, have an important place in the chain of services required by families of the retarded at the various times in the retarded person's life. . . .

The project focused on thirty-five families. All were drawn from new referrals to RIS. Twenty-four had been referred from general hospital clinics, six from the New York State Department of Mental Hygiene, three from clinics for the retarded, two from private physicians. The intake social worker's determination that the family needed homemaker service was the basis of selecting the family for participation in the project. The only criteria were that the family have a mentally retarded child under five years of age and appear able to benefit from the presence of a helper in the home.

Of these thirty-five families, nine were referred to AHS for a conventional homemaker service in which a caseworker and a homemaker, both on the staff of the agency, work closely together as a team; and twenty remained with RIS for service, which included the help of domestic workers, called home aides, recruited for the family by the agency and some limited casework treatment. A control group of six families received no service but were put on the waiting list for future service.

A clarification of the two terms, "homemaker" and "home aide," seems pertinent. According to the standards suggested by the Child Welfare League of America: "The distinctive elements of homemaker service are a) placement in the home of a trained homemaker employed as an agency staff member, who works together with a caseworker in carrying out a casework plan to help restore and strengthen parental functioning, or otherwise assure that the child has the care he needs; and b) use of casework as an integral part of the service. . . ." Homemaker service, as thus described, is closely interwoven with casework.

Home aides, as used by RIS, also are assigned and supervised by caseworkers, but the emphasis is placed on their ability to do light cleaning and cooking and their experience in caring for children, rather than on working consciously with the caseworker to help restore parental functioning. The family may concurrently receive some casework treatment focused on helping the parents reach the best plan for the child's care.

Experienced homemakers from the staff of AHS who were selected for the project participated with the casework staff in a seven-session orientation program. These sessions focused on the condition of mental retardation; the differences and similarities between retarded children and normal children; and the kinds of parental responses they could expect.

Most of the home aides who took part in the project had previous experience with RIS. Each was carefully prepared by the caseworker to be aware of the general dynamics of each case situation.

In each case the particular homemakers and home aides assigned to the families were selected on the basis of the caseworker's professional judgment.

The two treatment conditions were not set up for the purpose of measuring the efficacy of one service over the other, but rather to seek further understanding of the impact on families of direct assistance in meeting the burdens of the family's daily routines, whether or not this assistance is interwoven with continuing casework treatment. If improvement were possible without the close caseworker-homemaker teamwork, this would seem to suggest that homemaker services for families of the retarded might be offered at different levels of casework involvement, depending on the families' need, capacity, and readiness to use total services.

Instruments created for the study included a "family rating form" for measuring the quality of interaction within the family; and a "decision-making form" for evaluating the character and adequacy of the parent's decision about the retarded child at the close of treatment. At the end of the period of service, all participating families were seen by a social worker in a followup interview. In this the interviewer attempted to view objectively the carry-over effect of the treatment received.

Both the data secured from testing the case material with the measuring instruments and the data from the clinical followup showed improved functioning in the families served by either homemakers or home aides, in contrast to the families which received no service.

The family rating forms indicated that, in contrast to the control group, families served by AHS made important gains in their intrafamily relations as did families served by RIS, though there were some subtle differences between the two groups in the types of changes which occurred. For example, the AHS group showed a greater increase in friendliness among family members than the RIS group, but the RIS group showed greater development in rationality of conduct.

The decision-making forms indicated that families in both serviced groups rated much higher than those in the nontreatment control group in the quality of plans made for the retarded child. Little difference existed between the AHS and RIS groups.

Similarly, the clinical followup of cases indicated a high degree of sustained gain in families which had received service, regardless of which agency had served them. Some parents, who had become involved in relatively intensive casework, were able to face openly some of their basic conflicts about their child. However, even families in which the parents regarded the casework they had received as superfluous, but who had a high regard for the help they had received from the homemaker or home aide, improved in intrafamily interaction. Also, the families who had in the past only occasional encounters with a caseworker, focused on specific problems, showed sustained improvement.

Thus the findings suggest that, in families confronted with the reality of retardation, help from a homemaker or home aide, selected and supported by a casework agency, can in itself be salutory.

The following two cases illustrate how this may be so at different levels of casework involvement.

The A Family

Mr. and Mrs. A were referred to RIS by a diagnostic clinic. At the time of referral, their retarded child Amy was four years of age. Her brother James, age nine, had normal intelligence. Mr. A was unemployed because of a strike. Mrs. A. said she was at the breaking point because Amy was completely unmanageable, could not be left alone at any time, and had proved to be a tremendous burden to James, who was charged with some of her care.

Both parents seemed immature, demanding, and manipulative. A severe marital problem had developed out of conflict around Amy. The mother was particularly anxious, describing herself as confused, forgetful, and fearful of harming Amy. Mr. A and his parents were pressing her to send Amy to an institution; Mrs. A was not yet ready to do so.

RIS referred the case to AHS, which sent a homemaker into the home. She was trained not only to assist the mother in carrying the burden of household management and child care, but also to observe changes in behavior and attitudes. Part of her role was to help find out whether or not Amy was educable.

Under the regular supervision of the AHS caseworker, the homemaker assumed a nurturing, maternal role with both the children and the parents, but she was careful not to encourage lingering dependency. Amy responded well to her special attention and soon began to show remarkable improvement. Mrs. A apparently had been too tense to handle her in a way that could bring out her potentials.

James, too, showed improvement. He had not only been relieved of Amy's care, but was also getting more attention from his parents. Soon he seemed less withdrawn and behaved in a more forthright and appropriately aggressive manner.

Mrs. A seemed more relaxed, since for the first time in years she had some time for her own needs. The tension between the parents also relaxed a little, and both seemed to have less need to reject Amy.

The AHS caseworker kept in regular touch with the staff of the referring diagnostic clinic, who soon reported that the homemaker services had helped clarify the condition of the child and the dynamics of the family situation. It was then agreed that the AHS caseworker would take over the family counseling role from the clinic and would attempt to bring about better relations between the parents by helping them both to a better understanding of the needs of their retarded child, of their normal child, and of each other. As a result, it became possible to enter Amy into a special day class for the retarded instead of into an institution.

This case exemplifies homemaker service in its complete sense. The steadying influence of the homemaker, working in close partnership with the caseworker, expanded the understanding on which a diagnosis could be made, thus making possible more appropriate recommendations for the child's management and care.

As is common with organically damaged children, Amy had responded negatively and with hyperactivity to the anxiety-ridden, erratic handling she had been getting from her parents, and thus her true functioning ability had been obscured. The consistent, well-planned approach of the homemaker helped the child function less destructively and on a higher intellectual level. The resulting decrease of tension in the home increased the parents' ability to make use of casework help. Thus, an institutionalization, likely to be harmful to both the child and the parents, was avoided.

The M Family

The following case illustrates the provision of home help chiefly to relieve harried parents while they are mobilizing themselves to adjust to a severe emotional blow.

Mr. and Mrs. M were first known to RIS in 1962 after they learned that their two-year-old daughter Ruth was severely brain damaged and hopelessly retarded. With the assistance of the agency the child had been placed in an institution. Recently the tragedy was re-enacted. RIS received a call from Mr. M, who was crying hysterically. His wife was in a hospital having an operation and he had just been informed by the family's pediatrician that his seven-month-old son John was also severely retarded. Mr. M seemed to be at the breaking point.

The RIS social caseworker made a home visit the next morning and immediately arranged for a home aide to go into the home to assist Mr. M in the care of both the retarded baby and the family's five-year-old normal child. Within a few days, Mr. M had recovered sufficiently to go back to work.

After Mrs. M returned from the hospital, the home aide, a person of much warmth and sensitivity, remained in the home to help out while Mrs. M recovered from her physical weakness as well as from the emotional shock of the baby's retardation. At the same time, the social worker and the family pediatrician worked closely together to help both parents accept the diagnosis and again prepare for placing a child in an institution. Mrs. M also received help from the social worker in explaining the baby's condition to the five-year-old.

Throughout our analysis of the project cases, the effectiveness of the help given by the homemakers appeared most clearly when, as in this case, it was extended to families in the early stages of their response to a crisis. By providing instant help with the burdens of daily existence, the home helper often made it possible for parents to begin to regain enough psychic balance to be able to use casework counseling and help with planning for their child's future.

Some Conclusions

The nature of parents' early reaction to their child's retardation—often with the need to deny reality and to isolate all feeling—can block parents from entering into a therapeutic relationship with a social caseworker, as well as from being able to encourage their child's progress or create the kind of emotional atmosphere that can stimulate development. While not all parents respond to a crisis in the same way or experience trauma with the same intensity or duration, many do remain fixed in a state of emotional turmoil for long periods of time. Suppressed anger toward the retarded child, and toward fate in general, becomes internalized and thrust upon the self.

When such psychic turmoil is taking place, the introduction of a homemaker or home aide, who offers warmth and support and provides direct evidence of the community's desire to share their misfortune, can cut through some of the sense of hopelessness. Freed sufficiently to deal with the needs of other family members and to resume activity outside the home, the parents may then be able to perceive the retarded child with sufficient objectivity to consider alternatives in planning and to participate in the kind of continuing casework treatment than can build up the strength in the family. Thus the dynamic potentials of homemaker services go far beyond the practical assistance offered.

We found in the project that most families were enabled to maintain the child at home until a reasoned, reality-based decision about his future had been made. But even when parents proceeded with inadequate planning, the home helper's assumption of many of the responsibilities of the retarded child's care tended to mitigate their guilt and anxiety regarding their child.

Because existing homemaker agencies can obviously play a major role in helping retarded children and their families to a better life, community plans for comprehensive care for the retarded should incorporate such agencies into the overall design and goals of their programing. Ideally, these agencies should be able to provide home help flexibly, according to the varying needs of families of the retarded. Some families can benefit by home help which is not so closely interwoven with casework treatment as is required to help other families. Where such flexibility is not possible, home aide services might appropriately be offered by specialized agencies for the retarded.

While the project described here focused on the needs of families with young children, homemaker service should not be regarded solely as an emergency resource. Actually it is badly needed by many families on a long-range basis. The demands of a severely or moderately retarded child can be so consuming that at least part-time home help may be needed as long as the child remains in the home.

The complex needs of retarded children and their families require bold new planning that includes the creative use and adaptation of existing approaches to families in trouble. Agencies which specialize in service to the retarded must provide the direction that will encourage others to open up a variety of previously unobtainable services to families of the retarded.

□ □ □

from HOME TRAINING FOR RETARDED CHILDREN

Laura L. Dittmann

(Children, 1957)

When the District of Columbia Department of Public Health established a clinic for retarded children as a special project in its Bureau of Maternal and Child Health, it determined on two important features: geographic location outside of a hospital and the provision of continuing service to the family after diagnosis. . . .

As part of its continuing service, the clinic provides, on a selective basis, social casework services, short-term psychotherapy, home training, and referral to other community agencies.

The home-training program is worked out by the child-development specialist, who focuses on helping parents with the practical problems of daily living with a mentally handicapped child. The specialist participates with the team in planning the over-all treatment program by giving reports on the child's behavior. Her reports are based on observations usually made in the clinic's playroom when the child is playing by himself, though occasionally they are supplemented by observations of the child's behavior with other children there or in his own home with his parents, his brothers or sisters, or adults other than his parents.

The child-development worker learns something of the ways in which the child relates to people and the anxiety or ease with which he accepts separation from his parents. She also notes how he handles his body and how he uses his sensory equipment, thus getting an idea of the picture he has of himself and of whether or not there might be a defect in his sensory endowment. She learns something of the degree of his social adjustment by observing his play habits, his ability to communicate, how he handles his own clothing, how he deals with aggression, and whether or not he has any understanding of the rights of others. She reports further information about the child stemming either from her own observations or from parent's reports bearing on such matters as feeding, toileting, and patterns of expressing affection.

At its evaluation conference, the team sets up goals for helping the child and his family which may require a continuing relationship of the child-development worker with the family. This may mean planning with the family to help the child achieve specific skills within his area of competence, such as learning to pull off his shoes and socks or to feed himself. The following cases portray the variety of activities included in a home-training program.

A Severely Retarded Boy

The mother of John, aged two, came to the clinic in an effort to avoid having to institutionalize her son. He had already been studied carefully at the Johns Hopkins Hospital and was under private neurologic care for seizures. These, nevertheless, continued from three to twelve times a day in the form of mild loss of contact with his surroundings.

The family was referred by a private social agency, to which the parents had gone originally to discuss placement. As time went on, several factors had changed their purpose: a slight improvement in John who began to control his body movements, pressure from his grandparents who were shocked at the idea of "putting him away," hearing other parents talk before and after committing a child, and finally, a visit to the institution under consideration.

Since the parents were now asking help in training, the clinic accepted the referral.

Medically, John was summarized as a child with convulsive disorder which showed up in a markedly abnormal electroencephalogram. When he was a year old, a psychologist at Johns Hopkins University found him to be functioning at a twelve-week level in most areas, with a stronger ability—about sixteen weeks—in motor areas. The home-training program consistent with such a diagnosis included:

1. Advice on ways of handling this heavy (thirty-five pounds) boy at home.
2. Study of feeding techniques.
3. Assistance to the mother in making a more accurate evaluation of the child's potentialities. The mother had shown an understandable tendency to exaggerate progress, having pitted herself against medical advice to put the child in an institution.

The child-development worker carried out her services through visits to the home. On the first visit the mother was feeding the child liquid food in a low "baby-tenda" from which lifting was difficult. He sucked the food in very fast, throwing his head back to swallow it without stopping to taste it. At the end of the meal the mother tried to demonstrate how her son handled a cup and a spoon, but he had lost interest and accomplished nothing. During this visit the worker stressed the values of the following:

1. A more convenient kind of seating arrangement (higher).
2. A more civilized rate of speed.
3. Self-feeding opportunities at the beginning of the meal.
4. The use of other food textures.

The worker later discussed these recommendations with the pediatrician, particularly those regarding food textures. The pediatrician suggested solid foods such as banana, cooked carrot, hard-boiled eggs, and zwieback, in rather large pieces which John could handle himself.

Revisiting the home a month later the worker noted some change. John brought his head toward the spoon. Also, the mother had slowed down the feeding process—a difficult achievement for her since the child's dispatch in tucking away a large plate of pureed food was one of the few real satisfactions in her day.

On subsequent visits the worker discussed toilet training with the mother, suggesting that complete continence was an unrealistic goal and recommending cutting down on the amount of time the child was left on the toilet seat. She also recommended certain bathing techniques.

At each visit the mother made some comment either for or against institutional placement, as though she were arguing out the problem with herself in the worker's presence. Eventually, she formulated the idea that she would "place" John when he learned to walk, which she thought would occur at about three or four years of age. Since this plan made it desirable to evaluate the child's rate of growth, the worker made an appointment for him with the clinic's psychologist.

The psychologist found John to be a child who "does little in coming to grips with materials." She reported: "He is able, at two years and two months of age, to succeed in some items at the two-month level, and had scattered successes through five months. Motor development is superior to other areas, and on the report of the mother he scored at eight months largely because of this. He did not transfer objects from one hand to the other; he did not turn at the sound of a voice or the ringing of a bell. Left to his own devices on the floor, he made active cooing and laughing sounds, scratched his clothing and sucked his fingers."

These findings were interpreted to the mother by the clinic's medical director in the light of what could be projected for John in the future. By a comparison of this test with the previous one, the parents were given some idea of the rate at which development was occurring. They finally had to face the question of whether or not John would ever be able to walk.

Meanwhile, the mother continued to try to improve feeding techniques and to stimulate John to move about on the floor. At the end of eight months, John had made limited but nevertheless real progress. He showed less messiness in swallowing; he spilt less milk and reached for the cup to bring it to his mouth, although he still needed a guiding hand. He could carry a filled spoon to his mouth for three or four successive trips. He would drop the spoon, however, when it reached his mouth. The mother had become more relaxed with the boy and seemed to feel that since her efforts had produced some results she did not need to pad the picture to make the clinic understand her drive to keep him at home.

At one point the mother purchased a walker in order to get John to move about a bit by himself. However, the walker turned out to be too short for him and possibly too light. The worker suggested that a consultation with other mothers having similar equipment problems might be helpful. John's mother as well as several other mothers of heavy, non-walking, convulsive children, enthusiastically accepted this idea and decided to meet together regularly to discuss their problems.

At these group meetings with the child-development worker, the mothers talked about walkers, where to buy rubber pants big enough for such children, what kind of a bed other than a crib could be safe for a child who might convulse at night, and how to build outdoor play yards stronger and bigger than playpens, which would not require lifting the child over an edge. They talked about potty chairs versus toilets, how to build outdoor swings, where to buy clothes which did not look too old for children who still seemed like babies. The clinic's psychiatric social worker sat in on some of these meetings. From time to time the mothers discussed such problems as how to deal with typical manneristic behavior—studying the hands, rocking, weird noises—and how differently they felt about such behavior when it occurred at home or in public.

Toward the end of the series of discussions, John's mother told the child-development worker that she was pregnant. Thereafter, her feelings toward her son began to change and she could say that sometimes she would look at him and "just be tired of him," though she would hasten to add that this was not all the time. At this point she began to consider institutional placement with an entirely different point of view. Because of this change, the child-development worker referred her to the social worker for help in thinking toward this step. When she eventually committed the child, she was invited to return to the clinic at any time she wished. She did not return, and the one time she phoned she announced that she felt all right about the commitment.

The experience of working under supervision to train her child apparently helped this mother to see his limitations more clearly and helped to free her to go ahead with her own life and family planning.

A Mongoloid Child

Not all of the children seen at the clinic need such elementary instruction in self-care as did John. For example, there was Sammy, a frail, spindly, five-year-old mongoloid boy. The team's study showed him to be a child who had achieved the basic self-help accomplishments but who had badly needed social opportunities.

Sammy was referred to the clinic by a public health nurse, who had known his family through her work at school where she saw his three older brothers. The mother, a tired, tense, thin woman, tended to two extremes in her way of looking at her youngest child. Sometimes she expressed the fear that he would stop growing completely and be just as he was for the rest of his life. At others she would reveal the hope that when he was able to go to school he would catch up with other children completely.

Sammy's mother had done a remarkably good job in exploiting her son's capacities for training to the fullest, and yet she seemed unable to relate his actual progress to her dreams or fears about him. Although she had watched in her three other children the orderly progression of development from one small understanding or skill to the next, she was unable to expect any such developmental pattern in Sammy.

Both of Sammy's parents were foreign born. The father came from England, where he had been a valet and chauffeur, and the mother from Finland. Now the father, unable to find other work, was making a meager income driving a cab.

Sammy's mother indicated that he was toilet trained if she assumed some responsibility for catching him, that he played with toys with interest, that he was a slow eater and would not touch food with his hands, that he tried to dress himself but could not button, and that he could not undress himself. He had been a slow child from the beginning and had not walked until he was three. He still slept in a crib and was prone to rock.

The pediatrician's examination revealed that Sammy had very bad tonsils, which contributed not only to his failure to gain weight but also to poor resistance to infection. An eye examination showed that his retardation was not aggravated by poor vision. The psychologist described Sammy as a "fragile-looking, socially responsive child who enjoys playing with materials." This specialist reported: "At age five he tested at about eighteen months, somewhat penalized by his lack of speech. However, the social quotient as determined by a Vineland scale was higher, around twenty-one months."

Sammy's relatively high social quotient was testimony to the mother's achievements in training. The clinic team, therefore, outlined the home-training program in this case as: 1) providing support for the mother in her training efforts, 2) helping her to see Sammy's potentials for further learning in specific terms, 3) examining the child's eating habits for the possibility of teaching him to pick up things with his hands, 4) encouraging the parents to follow through on the physician's recommendation for a tonsillectomy.

On her first home visit the worker watched Sammy eat, neatly, two bowls of vegetable soup and an eight-ounce jar of baby food consisting of fruit and farina. He refused to pick up crackers in his fingers and the mother complained that he also would not pick up candy, bread, toast, or cake. In discussing this idiosyncrasy with his mother the worker learned that Sammy liked to eat puddings, bread in food, fruit, meat, potatoes, eggs, bacon, two cups of milk a day, fruit juice, broccoli, ice cream. After some explanation of the adequacy of Sammy's present diet and a reference to other mothers' troubles in keeping their children from candy and cake, the worker suggested to the mother that perhaps she should settle back and enjoy the excellent and neat manner with which Sammy could handle utensils.

Sammy's mother showed that she had a fine working understanding not only of the ways to teach Sammy, but also of how to select specific goals. Said she: "I wait for him to give me the things to work on." When he showed an interest in learning how to get upstairs, helping him with this became the most important activity of her day. When he became interested in taking off his shoes, she allowed him all the time he needed to unlace his orthopedic shoes, remove them, and place his socks inside them before he went to nap. Through her patient efforts she revealed that on a day-to-day basis she accepted her child's limitations.

During the worker's visits this mother also revealed an ambivalent attitude toward Sammy's condition by saying in one breath that she could not wait for him to go to kindergarten, and in the next, that she was afraid of having him be with big, normal children who would shove him around and knock him down.

During the next few months Sammy's tonsils were removed, thus freeing the boy from a tremendous drain of colds and infection. At a home visit after the operation the worker saw him eat three bowls of cereal with lots of milk and a bowl of applesauce for breakfast.

At this time, the family was having an unusually difficult time financially. Since the mother was continuing to buy a special vitamin-A milk for Sammy, though she could hardly stretch her food money to cover school lunches for the older children, the worker suggested that she come in for a conference with the Bureau's nutritionist, who could counsel her on how to choose less expensive, though nourishing, foods. She readily accepted this suggestion.

Sammy's lack of association with other children increasingly worried his mother. When he was refused admission to a nursery school for physically handicapped children, the worker suggested that the mother organize a small play group in her own living room to provide him with a not-too-demanding social opportunity and, hopefully, to lead him eventually into other living rooms. The mother commandeered three children almost at once, but after the first meeting complained that Sammy just watched while the others came in and broke his toys. The worker suggested that she cut back the size of the group to include just one other child, the youngest of the three original visitors, a little boy, aged three.

At her next visit the worker helped the mother to see how to divide the morning into periods of free play, a more quiet, organized activity, and solitary-but-adjacent doings. The worker also showed her how to read a story to younger children, taught her some simple circle and finger games, and discussed with her techniques of handling a small group.

Sammy now meets with two other children twice a week. So far the group has not left his living room. However, both Sammy and the young visitors show evidences of social growth and some understanding of the rights of others.

Here, while the skills of team members have contributed to a more comfortable situation in the family, the mother's own devotion and patience have been primary factor's in the retarded child's growth.

A Potentially Normal Child

Another child with whom the child-development specialist has worked might be considered normal potentially. In this case the worker strove more to bring about a change in the parents' attitude than to teach skills. The child, Joe, aged five, was referred to the clinic for psychological testing after he had failed to adjust in his second try at attending kindergarten. Other specialists had noted that the parents were smothering Joe with overprotection and had recommended foster-home placement. At the clinic Joe underwent a complete diagnostic study, with his family's consent.

This boy's outstanding symptom was his difficulty in separating from his parents. At the clinic he could not accept their being in an office adjacent to the playroom with the door open. His parents reported the following:

He fed himself but was picky, disliking vegetables, fruits, and meats. He was afraid of the dark. He was very slow in dressing himself, could button but not tie, and was apt to get things on backwards. He made a lot of noise, talking mostly to himself in gibberish. His behavior was "flighty," and they could sometimes control him only with a strap. He was beginning to stop sucking his thumb, but had many temper tantrums during which he would hit his head and rock.

These parents said that they had felt "life was not worth living" after they had discovered that Joe was retarded. They were not clear about who had told them the child was retarded.

Psychological testing at the clinic scored this five and one-half-year-old boy with a mental age of not quite four, but the test pattern indicated higher potentials. He showed unevenness and variability in functioning. Some of his behavior was negativistic, while his responses showed immaturity in some developmental areas such as fine coordination. The psychologist's recommendation included a "positive experience with an accepting adult and an opportunity to be with other children in a structured situation."

Physical examination showed no medical problems or abnormalities.

The child-development worker's visit to the home revealed that there Joe was in even less control of himself than he was in the clinic. He acted as though he resented his mother's attempt to talk to the visitor and exhibited an extremely short attention span and very little common sense. The worker also noted that many of his play materials were fragile or too complicated for him. His puzzles, for example, would have been hard for an eight-year-old. Most of all he liked to get behind his bed and beat upon a drum.

During this visit the mother seemed somewhat less tense than she had in the clinic.

The staff program for this family included work with both the mother and the child. Coincidentally, the clinic at this time had decided to observe a group of children for a few weeks to see if they were ready for kindergarten. Joe became part of this group. The plan was for the psychiatric social worker to hold both individual and group conferences with the mothers of these children while the child-development worker worked with the children individually and in groups. The sessions were carried on in the clinic.

At the first of these an attempt was made to help Joe let his mother out of his sight for a very short interval. This was given up when it proved too distressing for him. On his second visit Joe arrived at the clinic in tears lest a separation occur. His mother assured him that it would not but in an aside to the child-development worker said that she would leave the playroom surreptitiously. This gave the worker an opportunity to discuss the desirability of a straightforward approach to the child, without cajoling or lying. No separation was attempted at this visit.

A few weeks later Joe seemed ready to play with another child, but when he did so his behavior became so wild that he had to be removed from the room and kept away until he could pull himself together. The child-development worker's discussion with the mother at this time centered on the importance of setting limits for the boy and giving him a clear-cut notion of what was expected of him.

Six group sessions a week followed during which the prekindergarten program included activities organized by the teacher as well as some modified free play. Joe was able to participate in this program with special assistance from the teacher. Eventually he seemed ready for a regular kindergarten.

During the summer the family moved to a new neighborhood. In response to the clinic's interest in knowing how Joe adjusted to kindergarten, the family made an appointment to visit the clinic after school had begun.

At this visit Joe showed signs of having grown considerably in self-control, in his ability to face another person and talk directly to him, and in the quality of his play life and handling of materials. His mother reported that he no longer beat drums constantly. After Joe and his mother made two more trips to the clinic, a conference with both mother and father was held to suspend the clinic's relationship with the family for a while. Both parents remarked that a miracle had occurred. Nevertheless, they were unable to see the cause and effect of their slightly modified ways in handling their child. They were continuing a pattern of overprotection in such ways as accompanying Joe to and from school, although none of the other children in the class had this kind of supervision. It seemed impossible to help these parents understand that Joe would need increasing independence.

The parents left the clinic's service with the understanding that the staff would recheck by telephone during the winter and review Joe's situation the following spring, when next steps might be formulated. Meanwhile, one can only hope that in the absence of more fundamental changes, the introduction into the social world which entering school has meant for Joe can assist him in continuing the healthy growth already observed. . . .

□ □ □

from A VOLUNTEER PROGRAM: HOME CARE FOR THE RETARDED

Renée Lipsett

(Canada's Mental Health, 1964)

Fundamental changes have developed in recent years in the care of the mentally retarded. There is a growing appreciation for the slogan "a family of his own for every child." Studies conducted by specialists . . . point out the adverse effect of early institutionalization and observe that children cared for in their own homes show a decided improvement in intellectual capacity, physical growth and development, as well as in social adjustment. Thus, contrary to previous practice, more and more parents are being encouraged by professionals to keep their child at home so as to play a more positive role in his development.

But this is no simple task. Most parents of retarded children need a good deal of help, counselling, and understanding. To help them with these problems and to provide the kind of support they need in order to keep their child at home, the Quebec Association for Retarded Children (QARC) in Montreal established what is now known as the Home Care Service.

This Service is run by carefully selected volunteers who have had some previous training, and who are supervised by professionals. The volunteers visit parents of retarded children to discuss and help them with practical suggestions for the day-to-day problems of living which tend to beset most parents of handicapped children.

Although originated by QARC in Montreal, the program has developed as a joint service of the Quebec Association and the Mental Assessment and Guidance Clinic of the Montreal Children's Hospital under the direction of Dr. F. W. Lundell. The Service has been in operation since the spring of 1963 and continues to be looked upon as a pilot project. Many difficulties must still be overcome before it can be regarded as a well-established community service.

A complete home care service for the retarded should concern itself with all age groups. However, the parents of preschool children are a group who seem particularly isolated in dealing with their children. After they first learn of their child's handicap they usually need a good deal of supportive help, especially during the period when their child is ineligible to attend a special school. As important as sound diagnosis and assessment of the child may be, at our clinic we believe that following these procedures, it is equally important to provide the family with a counselling service. But few clinics now have sufficient staff to do this.

Our Mental Assessment and Guidance Clinic was established in June 1956 because of the conviction that families with retarded children need specific medical information and guidance that is focused squarely on the family's needs. It was also realized that a specialized clinic would allow a professional team to build up special knowledge and skills in dealing with mental retardation.

By 1960 the clinic was assessing 450 patients a year and was staffed by one full-time psychiatrist, two half-time social workers and one psychiatric resident. In 1962, with some minor expansion of staff, 845 cases were seen. In the first eleven months of 1963, one thousand and six children were assessed by two half-time psychiatrists, three resident psychiatrists, a half-time psychologist and three social workers. However, because of a shortage of staff, follow-up services for these parents were quite inadequate and could no longer be ignored.

Obviously it is not possible to fully staff a home care service with professional personnel. Perhaps it never should be. In any case, we have been able to secure volunteers interested in working in this area. They are screened for maturity, motivation, attitude, etc., by a professional social worker. Usually a group of fifteen to twenty are selected and given an indoctrination course within the hospital. Theoretical knowledge about retardation is provided through lectures by a psychiatrist, psychologist and pediatrician. Attitudes toward retarded children and their parents are handled by a social worker. A graded program for the preschool retardate is demonstrated by an occupational therapist. . . .

The Home Care Service, at least for the present, is concentrating on parents of preschool children. Regular clinic referrals come from the waiting list of the five schools for trainable retarded children in Greater Montreal, as well as from psychiatrists, psychologists and social workers in the community. The clinic social worker, who is also chairman of the Association's Home Care Service, interprets and discusses the service with the parents who, in all but one or two cases, have welcomed it. A volunteer is then selected. She is given the parents' name and telephone number and proceeds to make an appointment to visit. Some volunteers work with two families, some with one, depending on how much time they have to give.

At the time of referral, a master card is prepared on the child which gives all pertinent information. This is kept by the chairman. The volunteer records in her own words what takes place during each visit, thus providing her supervisor with a means of evaluating her work. It should be noted that the volunteer is given no special medical or other information about the children. If parents press for this, she has them make an appointment at the clinic.

The volunteer visits the home for about two hours every other week. She offers sympathetic understanding to the parents. She learns through experience how these parents are helped by this reassurance. She has also been trained to appreciate how other parents are extremely sensitive to any suggestion or implication that the volunteer is "taking over"—and she has been helped to see how such feelings of wanting to do this can easily arise within her! She helps the parents to recognize the slower learning pace of their child, and the need to let him develop at this pace and not be pushed beyond his capacities. The mother is taught how to enjoy simple activities with her child, as outlined in the manual. These are designed to develop the child's motor skills, as well as to lengthen his attention span. Many of the children are not toilet trained, do not know how to dress or undress, and the volunteer is prepared to make suggestions in these areas based on the training she has received from the occupational therapist and others at the clinic.

The children have all been assessed once, but if the volunteer discovers that the child has not been assessed in the last two years, she is authorized to refer him to an assessment clinic. She also encourages the parents to join the Quebec A.R.C. She may, in addition, offer baby-sitting services. When parents are unable to pay for this, the Home Care Service has a small budget to cover it. Finally, the volunteer has, or knows about, a variety of informational material that is of practical guidance to the parents.

There are now approximately one hundred volunteers involving one hundred thirty-seven families. At present, seven supervisors work with the Home Care Chairman: three social workers, a public health nurse, two teachers and a child care worker. The chairman is available to the supervisors at any time, in addition to their scheduled monthly meetings. The supervisors, in turn, maintain a similar supervisory relationship to their volunteers. The service also promotes and organizes seminars on needs of retarded children, not only for parents, volunteers, and other lay people, but for professionals as well. This kind of education and interpretation helps to stimulate broader community support and understanding.

We are only scratching the surface of the need for this type of program, and we have little doubt as to its value. With proper selection, training, support, and supervision, volunteers can and do provide very fine services in this area, just as they supplement or strengthen professional services in other health, welfare and recreation areas. Listen to one recipient of our Home Care Service, a thirty-two-year-old, well-educated mother of a mongoloid, tell what the program has meant to her:

> "It was a terrible blow to be told by the Clinic, even in the kindest possible way, that our Mary would need protection all her life. All the other mothers I've known just didn't have my kind of difficulties. There was no one to talk to—until Mrs. R. (the volunteer) appeared. Her kindness and understanding changed all this. The anger, even hatred, I felt for other people because they didn't care, slowly began to disappear."

□ □ □

SECTION C

Long-Distance Management

Under the continuous and comprehensive service umbrella of the future, families of the retarded will probably receive appropriate, prompt, and diversified management. However, until this utopia arrives, long waiting-lists will attest to the scarcity of services. Even with increased service provisions, their typically uneven geographic distribution will leave many families far removed from sources of help. This section documents two techniques developed to span such temporal or spatial distances.

The article by Adams describes a technique which can serve as a sort of "first aid" management until the "management ambulance" arrives. This "first aid," consisting of light counseling over the telephone, has been found useful with other problem groups, especially with potential suicides. Such telephone counseling can serve two distinct purposes. First, it can help bridge the time span until problem-specific management can be initiated. Time spanning can be accomplished by providing either emotional support, and/or feedback that the family's need for services has been acknowledged and that the wheels of action have been set in motion. Such feedback and reassurance may lower parental uncertainty and anxiety. Further, periodic telephone contact between family and agency assures that a service demand does not get lost during a service agency's caseload processing, and may provide information useful in setting service priorities. The second purpose served by telephone counseling is to actually provide direct and immediate problem-specific assistance. By talking the situation over on the phone, the parent may arrive at a clearer definition of the problem, which, in turn, may lead him to discover solutions himself. The counselor may be able to suggest measures which escaped the parent and which may be effective in either alleviating or even dispelling the crisis.

It is widely recognized that sometimes management crises dissolve with little or no help. "Dial-a-management" can provide an option through which this marginal but important element of help can be rendered, or through which administrative decisions can be facilitated.

Winterbourn describes an apparently unique project developed in New Zealand to assist families residing in remote geographical areas. The major medium of the project was correspondence, augmented by infrequent home visits. Par-

ents were sent information and instruction for conducting a home program of child development and education. Educational materials for the child were mailed as needed, and program requirements were determined by correspondence with, and feedback from, the parents. Although this project was educationally oriented and was operated by teachers, it could easily be broadened beyond educational concerns. Such a program could also be adopted in the United States, where it might add a desirable option in the management of families residing in remote or otherwise unserviced areas.

from FIRST AID TO PARENTS OF RETARDED CHILDREN

Margaret E. Adams

(Social Casework, 1967)

Counseling by telephone as a short-cut means of offering help to people under stress has long been recognized as a bona fide tool of casework and, with the increasing use of the telephone by even relatively unsophisticated persons, it is likely to assume greater importance in day-to-day practice. An article written by David Hallowitz and Albert Cutter[1] and another by Paul Widem[2] describe the use of telephone counseling in clinics for disturbed children. And the fact that it is often the lifeline by which potential suicides seek help is well known.[3]

This article describes the use of telephone counseling in providing limited interim support for families of retarded children at the time of application and during the waiting period preceding admission to a special evaluation clinic. Because there is heavy demand for service for this kind of handicap and a limited number of available facilities, many special clinics have a long waiting period before a child can be seen. In an effort to counteract the distress caused by this delay, social workers in one such clinic devised a scheme for combining limited telephone counseling service with the application intake process that is normally conducted by telephone.

The practice was established because parents reported the existence of many problems beyond the presenting one of mental retardation. In addition, a high proportion of children between three and five years of age were being referred, with a probable waiting period of at least a year before admission. At this age a year represents a long span of development, during which a good deal of maladjustment in behavior can evolve, and the parents' description of management problems and intrafamily tensions suggested that this was happening in many families. Furthermore, brief telephone conversations indicated that many of the families, given some guidance and support, could probably mobilize positive resources to tackle their problems more effectively in the interim period and thereby prevent deterioration in the child's overall development. Since many parents were extremely fearful lest the retarded child should lose ground through lack of professional care, they had to be given the kind of help that would make them feel they were handling their situation optimally during the waiting period and were contributing positively to the child's development and progress.

[The service for which application was being made consisted of a multidisciplinary evaluation of the child, and the provision of whatever subsequent rehabilitation measures were relevant and available. The clinic population of retarded children included 1) preschool children with an already identified syndrome (e.g., Down's syndrome); 2) school-age children up to fourteen years of age who had been classified retarded by educational authority and were in, or awaiting placement in, a special class; and 3) children of the preceding age groups who showed a marked developmental lag. A wide variety of clinical conditions and resulting functional disorders were found within these categories, and the following brief analysis of cases referred over a three-month period illustrates the varied nature of problems that may be encountered in telephone applications. The problems covered a wide range of developmental and behavioral anomalies from severe physical disability, such as cerebral palsy at one end of the spectrum to more psychiatrically determined symptoms of bizarre mannerisms.]

Although many children were described as having more than one disturbing symptom, the most frequent cause of parental concern (reported in thirty cases) was disturbance in speech, characterized either by its complete absence or by a marked lag in communication or by substitution of socially unacceptable noises, such as grunting. The child who is unable to express himself, who resorts to temper tantrums to relieve his frustration, and who is inaccessible to verbal stimuli ("does not want to listen") seems especially threatening to some parents' systems of control, and the fears that are aroused by this serious developmental lag create a strong climate of anxiety in the home. This observation is in accord with Juanita Dalton and Helene Epstein's suggestion that a marked delay in speech represents a crisis stage for parents in their developing awareness of their child's retardation.[4] Twenty-seven children had delayed motor skills, making it second on the list of associated problems. The third most recurrent symptom, present in fourteen children, was hyperactivity and short attention span, which is often related to serious management problems. Parents of twelve children reported a specific clinical entity, such as Riley-Day syndrome, Down's syndrome, or gargoylism. Brain damage in eight children had been diagnosed previously.

All these problems were selectively determined by the informants' levels of education, familiarity with medicopsychiatric terms, and powers of observation, as well as their degree of anxiety. Subsequent contact with the child did not always confirm the existence of the symptoms described. But, from the point of view of this article, which is primarily concerned with the stress caused by a child's handicap, what parents *see* as upsetting in their child's development or behavior is of significance.

The anxiety in the families was caused by both subjective and objective factors in their situations. The subjective sources were a variety of psychological reactions, which have been well documented in the literature,[5] that all parents suffer at some point after they have discovered they have a child with markedly slow or deviant development. In this specific circumstance of applying for clinical help, however, the usual feelings of disappointment and anxiety were frequently sharpened by the fact that a tentative and disquieting diagnosis had already been given by a physician or medical facility. Many parents desperately needed another specialist's opinion to refute or confirm the distress-provoking news, especially when the person making the diagnosis had used the terms *brain damage* or *childhood schizophrenia,* both of which carry fantasy-provoking connotations of rapid deterioration and residual damage or of frightening mental disorder stretching into adulthood.

The objective factors that caused worry were confusion about the extent and meaning of the disability and uncertainty about the effect it would have on the child's development. This baffling uncertainty caused many parents to feel frustrated and defeated in their efforts to cope with the child's poorly comprehended needs. The parents' anxiety about inappropriate management was realistic, since it is well known that developmental delay is intensified when a child is deprived of the training and stimulation that his maturational level requires. If self-help skills are not fostered in a child during the preschool years, he may not be ready for special schooling when he reaches the age for it. Unreliable toilet habits, for example, invariably act as a major stumbling block to acceptance in educational or training programs, and overdependence and infantile behavior interfere with classroom adjustment.

The Telephone Counseling Process

Effective telephone counseling for parents of retarded children is based on recognition of its definite inherent limitations and on the selection of goals that are attainable despite these limitations. In planning for this service, the social workers at the Jewish Hospital of Brooklyn realized that their first task was to provide reliable advice that would relieve the stress of the focal problem, the child's retardation. However, since the only clinical information available was the parents' description or their not-always-accurate version of previous diagnostic formulations, counseling had to be focused on the social rather than the clinical aspects of the stated problems—not why the child was unable to talk, but how well the family coped with this serious lack.

Careful inquiry into the child's current functioning, with heavy emphasis on self-help skills and social responsiveness, usually provided enough information for the social worker to use as the basis for nonspecific guidance, in which general rules of child management, appropriately modified, were applied to handicapped children. For example, a three-year-old child who does not tell his mother that he needs to go to the bathroom but runs there after he is wet or soiled is making some connection between that special place and toilet activities, but the mother's uncertainty about how much he understands may prevent her from appreciating the purposiveness of his behavior. This interpretation and some constructive pointers on how to establish a training schedule to reinforce the child's semi-awareness may succeed in converting it into the desired behavior.

Another major limitation of telephone counseling that was immediately apparent was the brief contact between the applicant and the social worker. Of necessity, the social worker utilized a single interview—from five to forty minutes' duration—for the multiple purpose of eliciting sufficient information to identify the problem and assess its severity and, at the same time, meet the parents' obvious need for clarification of their more pressing anxieties and for support to contain them until more extensive help was forthcoming—at a considerably later date. In order to avoid being overwhelmed by the massive needs of some families, the social worker had to keep the limited nature of the help she could offer clearly in mind and be able to convey this at the beginning of the conversation. Otherwise, her sympathetic involvement in the parents' very real difficulties might have had the unintended effect of encouraging hopes of more immediate assistance. Emphasis had to be placed on the primary purpose of the telephone interview, which was intake for subsequent future treatment, and on the fact that it was not feasible to provide more than limited guidance to reduce stress in the interim period. These modest goals could only be achieved by very careful selection of the kinds of problems and situations that lend themselves to partial solution and by full exploitation of telephone interview techniques.

The Nature of Problems Tackled

It was envisioned that the kinds of problems most likely to respond to help in the brief contact possible by telephone are those stemming from reality factors that create stress responses in parents or families. Included in these are the behavioral anomalies that are symptomatic of the child's condition—disturbed sleeping patterns, hyperactivity, aggressive or destructive behavior, and delayed developmental and social skills. In addition, there is the normal anxiety experienced by parents because of their inability to cope with these pervasive deviances, and there are the feared implications for the future. Difficulties that obviously originate in more complex psychopathology, such as long-term disturbances in personal relationships or unstable patterns of functioning, were not regarded as suitable for telephone counseling. No effort was made, therefore, to meet stresses of this kind beyond the therapeutic gesture of listening to the problem, acknowledging the parents' legitimate distress, and pointing out that making an application constituted a positive move that would eventually result in treatment. Cases with a bona fide medical emergency could be given priority at the clinic director's discretion, but this was done sparingly to avoid inequities.

In cases in which intrafamily disorganization was extreme and unlikely to be helped by the clinic's services, suggestions for more appropriate care were made. For example, a thirteen-year-old educable girl with severe behavior problems was being threatened with exclusion from school. Since she had already had three years at a very good residential treatment center without appreciable improvement, and both child and parents appeared too disturbed for outpatient treatment, the mother was encouraged to follow through on an application to a state school that had been recommended by the residential agency.

Although a strong emotional component was usual in the management problems reported, counseling was directed primarily to practical surface aspects and was rooted firmly in understanding of the less conscious dynamic factors present. An attempt was made to deal with some of these by noninterpretive, indirect techniques. When an overanxious mother of a toddler expressed concern that he had not started to feed himself, the direct focus of counseling was on this developmental lag, but there was implicit awareness that her emotional attitudes might be colluding with his dependency needs and contributing to his infantilism. Helping the mother realize that self-feeding is normally within the child's competence and that his overall development would improve with the acquisition of this basic social skill made it possible for her to channel her fundamentally sound nurturing drives into furthering his independent growth. But to make this kind of advice convincing, the social worker must be acutely aware of the personal and cultural factors in the relationship between the mother and child. A poor pattern of maternal care, illustrated by infantilizing, may be the result of absence of knowledge about how to handle an atypical child, a diffuse sense of inadequacy in the maternal role, or cultural attitudes that sanction prolonged dependency in young children. Direct guidance on practical ways of tackling an overt feeding problem meets these needs on differing levels. It offers the inexperienced parent structured advice and provides an authority figure with whom, at a less conscious level, the inadequate parent can identify constructively. Since many mothers of retarded children feel intensely devalued in their role and have no one who can give them support, limited benign interaction with the social worker, including the support of authoritative guidance, may be a helpful experience.

Interviewing Technique

The main content of the telephone interview is the structured interrogation that is an essential part of the application procedure for determining the child's suitability for future clinic service. Used purposefully, this fact-finding embodies certain therapeutic qualities. In practice, the social worker learned that the interaction of question and answer about the child, which aroused painful emotions, involved the parent in an active relationship with the social worker at least temporarily and represented the initial stage of his participation in eventual long-term treatment. The social worker, through her familiarity with retardation and its problems, provided the first essential ingredient of the helping process—acceptance.

The interview itself can benefit a parent by helping him to make a more realistic appraisal of his difficulties. When a parent is compelled to give a precise account of his child's condition and behavior, he is set at a distance from the child and is enabled to put his problems into better perspective. The interviewer, concentrating at first on immediate problems and the level of functioning and then shifting back to earlier stages, evokes awareness of a developmental continuum that had become obscured by the family's bewilderment and preoccupation with the child's abnormal aspects.

Furthermore, an objective discussion of abnormal features helps reduce anxiety, and the emotions that are evoked by bizarre behavior can be relieved when the behavior is seen as a clinical entity rather than a mysterious manifestation. The empty repetitive gestures, such as the hand-waving of a young brain-injured child, are ominous to the uninformed parent but become more acceptable when they are interpreted as a partially physiological manifestation of an unstable, immature central nervous system. The fact that such symptoms are well known to the social worker implies that even though they are peculiar, they are not unique.

Inquiry into social aspects adds a dimension of normalcy by implying that, in spite of his handicap, the child of retarded development has a social role and function. The social behavior of these children in the preschool years is very important because it is an index of potential readiness for school or training later on. By helping parents to appreciate this and suggesting how they can provide opportunities for social experience for the three- and four-year-old child, the social worker mobilizes their energies and skills for making a substantial contribution to the retarded child's development. Discussion of the way in which the whole family and its social nexus relates to the retarded child—whether he is shunned by his siblings and their friends or is the cherished pet of the family—alerts parents to the significance of family patterns of interacting.

Counseling

Two main ideas dictated the direction of counseling. First, the functional relationship between the parents and their handicapped child is a constant source of anxiety to the former, and they need to be reassured that they both desire and are able to meet the child's needs. Second, the deviances of retardation are invariably threatening. Because of these two important factors, parents must be afforded an opportunity to ventilate their doubts and fears and to gain clarification of the child's condition so that they may be able to meet the special demands of their situation.

To meet these needs a particular technique was employed that is found to be generally useful in casework with parents of retarded children. The social worker concentrated on the positive factors—those related to the child's innate capacity, the parents' management of him, or the total family interaction—and made suggestions for amplifying of reinforcing these manifestations of health and progress. Unless a child is very young or his defect is slight, most parents are only too familiar with his pathological features, and harping on them is not very profitable, especially when clinical help is unavailable. But when the assets of the child and the positive evidences of good care are identified, the parents' feelings of defeat and inadequacy are lessened. The social worker can point out to the mother who has toilet-trained a difficult-to-manage child that this is a considerable training achievement on her part and an important social milestone for the child. Favorable comment may be made about a child with gross neurological impairment who recognizes and responds to the other children in the family, with the suggestion that this is a "growing point" to which all the family can contribute.

Whether the child's development will be significantly influenced is uncertain, but the family is made to feel that they are doing something to alleviate the child's disability.

Setting limits to the retarded child's activities was another area that perplexed many parents and is tied up with their ambiguous perception of his capacities and their expectations of him. Frequently, the parents' inability to control a troublesome child resulted in a chain reaction of maladaptive relationships and reactive psychological problems. When the social worker clarified the child's capacities and explained that his bad behavior was a reaction to the anxiety that arose because of his incomplete grasp of his environment, exasperation was often diminished. Parents were then able to accept advice on how to structure the pattern of life in the home to minimize these frustrations. For example, a child who has a serious language deficit may respond much more quickly to nonverbal control, and parents can be advised to use other than verbal means of communication, such as gesturing or taking the child bodily away from a prohibited activity.

Some hints on mild disciplinary action can also be helpful because they imply sanction. Some parents disapprove of restraining or chastising a retarded child on the ground that he does not understand and is therefore not responsible, but they are nevertheless faced with the difficulty of controlling the erratic behavior of a retarded or brain-injured child. This attitude can be counteracted by interpreting discipline as helpful intervention and emphasizing the value of imposing social controls on handicapped children, who cannot impose their own. In discussing management tactics, it is also important to be aware of the emotional distortions that often affect parents' handling of the situation. Some parents indicate a reparative tendency not to impose limits because the child "has enough to bear." Sometimes an unconscious denial of the long-range social implications of retardation underlies the parents' tendency to prolong the child's infantile behavior. Most parents, however, are anxious to rear their retarded child well but are confused about how firm they should be. They tend to repress as inappropriate their natural feelings of anger toward the child's bad behavior. The social worker's implicit permission to react toward unacceptable behavior in whatever way seems appropriate builds up confidence that they can carry out their parental role satisfactorily.

In view of the serious emotional and practical pressures that affect almost all families who have a retarded child and the lack of professional facilities to help them at points of crisis, the telephone interview serves a useful purpose. Because it can address itself to the family's need for help at the time it is recognized and aims at clarifying the immediate pressures, telephone counseling acts as a first-aid holding operation to keep families viable until more comprehensive assistance is at hand.

References

1. Hallowitz, David, and Cutter, Albert, "The Pre-intake Phase: The Beginning of the Intake Process," *Mental Hygiene*, Vol. XLIII, January 1959, pp. 53-63.
2. Widem, Paul, "The Telephone Intake Interview in a Child Guidance Clinic," *Social Casework*, Vol. XXXVIII, November 1957, pp. 485-89.
3. Farberow, Norman L., and others. "Suicide Prevention Around the Clock," *American Journal of Orthopsychiatry*, Vol. XXXVI, April 1966, pp. 551-58; Chad Varah, "How 'The Samaritans' Combat Suicide," *Mental Health*, Vol. XXI, October 1962, pp. 132-34.
4. Dalton, Juanita, and Epstein, Helene, "Counseling Parents of Mildly Retarded Children," *Social Casework*, Vol. XLIV, November 1963, pp. 523-30.
5. Cohen, Pauline C., "The Impact of the Handicapped Child on the Family," *Social Casework*, Vol. XLIII, March 1962, pp. 137-42; Simon Olshansky, "Chronic Sorrow: A Response to Having a Mentally Defective Child," *Social Casework*, Vol. XLIII, April 1962, pp. 190-93; Sylvia Schild, "Counseling with Parents of Retarded Children Living at Home," *Social Work*, Vol. IX, January 1964, pp. 86-91; Albert J. Solnit and Mary H. Stark, "Mourning and the Birth of a Defective Child," in *The Psychoanalytic Study of the Child*,- Ruth S. Eissler (ed.), Vol. XVI, International Universities Press, New York, 1961, pp. 523-37.

□ □ □

from HOME TRAINING THROUGH CORRESPONDENCE: A NEW ZEALAND PROGRAMME

R. Winterbourn

(*International Child Welfare Review,* 1965)

Can much be done by correspondence to further the development of trainable intellectually handicapped children and give much needed support to their parents? In the light of experience gained over the past fourteen years by the Correspondence School of the New Zealand Department of Education, the answer is undoubtedly, "Yes."

Throughout this period, the Home Training Section of the school, which until 1963 consisted of only one dedicated teacher with some clerical assistance, has unobtrusively progressed through an experimental stage and firmly established itself as a small but important part of our education system. Even now there are only two teachers, both women, who successfully provide this service for almost a hundred children who because of distance from large centers of population or for other reasons are unable to attend occupation centers (as we call our classes for trainable children).

The Section was established in order to provide for the needs of trainable intellectually handicapped children and their parents. These remain the predominant group. However, developments such as the extension of our school psychological service have resulted in the enrollment of other kinds of children as well. They include some who are emotionally disturbed, autistic, cerebral palsied, severely crippled, hyperactive, or immature who require a pre-primary type of programme. The age range is from five to sixteen years.

An important feature of the work is parent guidance and support. The teachers aim at establishing good relations with parents so that mutual confidence develops. An easy two-way communication is the essence of this. It is believed that it is better to provide parents with simple material and advice *at the time that it is needed,* rather than expecting them to assimilate the information in some comprehensive book. This aim is achieved through special leaflets and personal letters.

The teachers carry out as much field work as possible. Pupils within easy range of the correspondence school are visited regularly. In the words of the teachers, "To some extent, this varied and changing group has been used as a touchstone or 'control' to help us in our understanding of other children who are seen only rarely." Three one-week visits are made annually to suitable districts, but it is not possible to visit more than half the pupils in any one year. During these district visits, face-to-face contacts are made with psychologists, social workers, teachers, and others who are valuable allies of the Section's teachers.

The use of radio has not yet proceeded very far, but the two annual broadcasts are very well received by those concerned.

In order that the teachers may know initially at what level to pitch a given child's "lessons" and with what problems the parents are grappling, a brief confidential personal questionnaire is sent out in advance. It covers family pattern, eating, dressing, speech, physical handicaps, manageability, and normal daily pursuits, plus anything else which a parent cares to add.

Over the years a large pool of simple printed material for parents has accumulated. As indicated earlier, this material has been developed in the course of meeting the practical needs of parents faced with their particular problems. From year to year, similar problems recur, so that the teachers may now draw upon suitable material from the pool. Personal letters are not superseded by such material—each supplement the other.

Material is normally posted to parents in a large, tough envelope. With each envelope of work and advice goes a page headed "Parents' Comments" on which the teachers have listed all the lessons and suggestions for the month. A parent is requested to record on this page how her child got on with each item, and then return it to the teacher who can plan the next month's programme accordingly.

Any material which parents have found unsuitable is returned monthly along with that in which the child has now lost interest. Some material which continues to be of use may be retained as long as is desired.

What is this material to which I keep referring? Some is for the children, and some for the parents. The latter includes leaflets conveying information aimed at orienting the parents to the overall situation and to specific problems and also what one might call "teaching aids" which accompany the play and learning material sent for the children.

Material for the children, with accompanying explanatory notes for parents covers the following fields: language, development through construction, toys and games, simple handcraft skills, skills required for painting, drawing and printing, music and movement, and other unclassified activities. An appropriate monthly newsletter is also sent to all the parents. This draws upon contributions made by parents themselves. Through this the teachers can deal with matters of importance at any given time and supplement the individual supportive procedures.

Emphasis is placed upon the importance of scheduling a set time each day for "lessons" and of having a set of shelves set apart for "school" equipment. In addition much is accomplished throughout the day by means of appropriate participation in the daily activities of cooking, gardening, housekeeping, dressing and eating, etc. . . . Sound advice is offered on this. . . .

□ □ □

SECTION D

Training the Parent in Operant Behavior-Shaping Techniques

Most management approaches described in this volume, while not necessarily widely employed, are well-known. A number of them have been commonly employed in other problem areas before being transferred to the area of mental retardation. There is, however, a novel approach which is still in its early phases of exploration: training of parents to apply operant behavior-shaping techniques to child rearing.

Operant conditioning or shaping techniques evolved from the learning theories of Thorndike, Watson, and Hull, have been particularly developed by Skinner, and are being refined by Skinner's followers and successors. While there has been considerable evidence that operant behavior-shaping techniques are powerful tools in extinguishing undesirable, and developing desirable, behavior in animals, spectacular results are increasingly being reported in the operant behavior shaping of normal and disturbed children and adults.

The article by Hawkins, Peterson, Schweid and Bijou is typical of a number of similar studies that have appeared recently. In this instance, specific undesirable behaviors in a retarded child were defined and their frequency ascertained; the mother was taught what to do (or not to do) when these behaviors occurred; and a dramatic decline in the frequency of the undesirable manifestations was demonstrated. The substitution of techniques which, in effect, condition both child and parent is only one unusual element of this study. A second unorthodoxy is the expressed view that undesirable behavior can be treated most effectively where it is most likely to occur—in this instance, in the home.

Workers in the operant learning area are becoming increasingly skeptical and critical of clinic-type treatment, and more enthusiastic about teaching parents and teachers to shape behavior in the two main sectors of a child's life: the home and the school. The human management manpower situation is such that it is unrealistic to hope that all children in need will ever receive all the services they could utilize. However, there is approximately one teacher for every twenty-five children, and one parent for nearly every child. It thus appears much more promising to mass-teach operant principles to parents and educators than to attempt to treat every needy child individually. As the authors of our selection point out, by teaching a parent, one teaches long-range management rather than merely crisis management; one could also add that all children in a family may profit from the improvement in child rearing.

Methods used in teaching machines and automated programmed instruction—which some people predict will revolutionize education—are derived largely from operant conditioning work. It is very likely that child development techniques generally will be profoundly affected by such operant principles, and that training in the use of operant principles will become part of the education of every layman. Much like driver or sex education, education in operant child-rearing techniques may become an important, or even mandatory, subject in high school.

from BEHAVIOR THERAPY IN THE HOME: AMELIORATION OF PROBLEM PARENT-CHILD RELATIONS WITH THE PARENT IN A THERAPEUTIC ROLE

Robert P. Hawkins
Robert F. Peterson
Edda Schweid, Sidney W. Bijou

(*Journal of Experimental Child Psychology*, 1966)

. . . .

In recognition of the important part parents play in the behavioral (or personality) development of the child, various agencies dealing with child behavior problems have often utilized techniques whose goal is to modify parent-child relationships. For example, the parent of a child who exhibits deviant behavior may, himself, be given psychotherapy in order to change his behavior toward the child. Alternatively, the parent may merely be given advice as to how he should react differently toward the child, or both parent and child may be given psychotherapy and/or counseling. The technique employed is likely to depend on the type of therapist consulted and the therapist's theoretical orientation. A general discussion of therapeutic techniques with children has been presented elsewhere by Bijou and Sloane.

Traditional types of therapy have a number of deficiencies. First, the child's behavior is seldom observed by the therapist, leaving definition of the problem and description of the child's behavior totally up to the parent. Second, the behavior of the parent toward the child is seldom observed. Thus considerable reliance is placed on the verbal report of the parent and child and on the imagination of the therapist. Third, when "practical suggestions" are made by the therapist, they may be so general or technical that it is difficult for the parent to translate them into specific behavior. Fourth, since no objective record· is kept of behavior changes over short intervals (e.g., minutes, hours, days), it is difficult to judge the effectiveness of the treatment.

Wahler, Winkel, Peterson, and Morrison (1965) have developed a technique for effectively altering mother-child relationships in a laboratory setting, with objective records being kept of the behavior of both mother and child. The present study was an investigation of the feasibility of treatment in the natural setting where the child's behavior problem appeared—the home. As in the Wahler *et al.* studies, the mother served as the therapeutic agent. She received explicit instructions on when and how to interact with the child. The behaviors of both the mother and the child were directly observed and recorded.

Method—Subject

The child in this study was a four-year-old boy, Peter S. He is the third of four children in a middle-class family. Peter had been brought to a university clinic because he was extremely difficult to manage and control. His mother stated she was helpless in dealing with his frequent tantrums and disobedience. Peter often kicked objects or people, removed or tore his clothing, called people rude names, annoyed his younger sister, made a variety of threats, hit himself, and became very angry at the slightest frustration. He demanded attention almost constantly, and seldom cooperated with Mrs. S. In addition, Peter was not toilet trained and did not always speak clearly. Neither of these latter problems was dealt with in the study.

Peter had been evaluated at a clinic for retarded children when he was three years old and again when he was four and a half. His scores on the Stanford Binet, form L-M were 72 and 80, respectively. He was described as having borderline intelligence, as being hyperactive, and possibly brain-damaged.

Procedure

The experimenters (*E*s), observing the mother and child in the home, noted that many of Peter's undesirable behaviors appeared to be maintained by attention from his mother. When Peter behaved objectionably, she would often try to explain why he should not act thus; or she would try to interest him in some new activity by offering toys or food. (This "distraction" method is often put forth by teachers as a preferred technique for dealing with undesirable behavior. Behavior theory suggests, however, that while distraction may be temporarily effective in dealing with such behaviors, repeated employment of such a procedure may increase the frequency of the unwanted set of responses.) Peter was occasionally punished by the withdrawal of a misused toy or other object, but he was often able to persuade his mother to return the item almost immediately. He was also punished by being placed on a high-chair and forced to remain there for short periods. Considerable tantrum behavior usually followed such disciplinary measures and was quite effective in maintaining mother's attention, largely in the form of verbal persuasion or argument.

Prior to the study, the child's difficulties were discussed thoroughly with his mother. She was told that therapy might take several months, was of an experimental nature, and would require her participation. She readily agreed to cooperate.

Treatment consisted of two or three sessions per week, each approximately one hour in length. Peter's mother was instructed to go about her usual activities during these sessions. His younger sister was allowed to be present and to interact with him in her usual way. Peter was allowed to move freely through the main part of the house—the recreation room, laundry room, dinette, kitchen, and living room—because the wide openings between these areas made it possible to observe his activity with a minimum of movement on the *E*s' part. The *E*s never responded to Peter or his sister. When the children asked questions about them or spoke to them, they were told by the mother to "leave them alone; they are doing their work."

Initial observations showed that the following responses made up a large part of Peter's repertory of undesirable behavior: 1) biting his shirt or arm, 2) sticking out his tongue, 3) kicking or hitting himself, others, or objects, 4) calling someone or something a derogatory name, 5) removing or threatening to remove his clothing, 6) saying "No!" loudly and vigorously, 7) threatening to damage objects or persons, 8) throwing objects, and 9) pushing his sister. These nine responses were collectively termed "Objectionable behavior" (O behavior), and their frequency of occurrence was measured by recording, for each successive ten-second interval, whether or not an O behavior occurred. This same method was used to obtain a record of the frequency of all verbalizations Peter directed to his mother and of the frequency of her verbalizations to him.

In order to assess interobserver reliability, two *E*s were employed as observers on eight occasions and three *E*s on one occasion. . . . Agreement on O behaviors ranged from .70 to 1.00, with a mean of .88. Agreement on mother's verbalizations to Peter ranged from .82 to .98, with a mean of .94. Agreement on Peter's verbalizations to his mother ranged from .90 to .99, with a mean of .96.

Treatment was divided into five stages: the first baseline period, the first experimental period, the second baseline period, the second experimental period, and a follow-up period.

First baseline period. During this period Peter and his mother interacted in their usual way. Their behaviors were recorded by the *E*s and after some 16 sessions, when an adequate estimate of the pretreatment rate of O behavior had been obtained, the next stage was begun.

First experimental period. Prior to the beginning of this period, the mother was informed of the nine objectionable behaviors which would be treated. She was shown three gestural signals which indicated how she was to behave toward Peter. Signal "A" meant she was to tell Peter to stop whatever O behavior he was emitting. Signal "B" indicated she was immediately to place Peter in his room and lock the door. When signal "C" was presented, she was to give him attention, praise, and affectionate physical contact. Thus, every time Peter emitted an O behavior, Mrs. S. was either signaled to tell him to stop or to put him in his room. On the first occurrence of a particular O behavior during the experimental session, Mrs. S. was merely signaled to tell Peter to stop; but if he repeated the same response at any subsequent time during that session, she was signaled to place him in his room. (This isolation period may be viewed as a period of "time out" from stimuli associated with positive reinforcement. See Ferster and Appel, 1961.) Occasionally, when *E* noticed that Peter was playing in a particularly desirable way, Signal "C" was given and his mother responded to him with attention and approval. Mrs. S. was asked to restrict the application of these new behavioral contingencies to the experimental hour. She was told to behave in her usual way at all other times.

The period of Peter's isolation was not counted as part of the experimental hour, so each session consisted of one hour of observation in the main living area of the house. When placed in his room, Peter was required to remain there a minimum of five minutes. In addition, he had to be quiet for a short period before he was allowed to come out (a technique employed by Wolf, Risley, and Mees, 1964). Since all objects likely to serve as playthings had been previously removed from the room, he had little opportunity to amuse himself. Neither Mrs. S. nor Peter's sister interacted with him during "time out." On two occasions, however, it was necessary to deviate from this procedure. These deviations occurred when Peter broke windows in his room and called out that he had cut himself. The first time Mrs. S. entered his room, swept up the glass, reprimanded him for breaking the window, noted the (minor) nature of his injury and left. The second time she bandaged a small cut and left immediately. Peter broke a window on one other occasion but since no injury was apparent, the act was ignored.

Second baseline period. When, after six experimental sessions, the frequency of O behaviors appeared stable, contingencies were returned to those of the earlier baseline period. Mrs. S. was told to interact with Peter just as she had during previous (nonexperimental) observation sessions. This second period consisted of fourteen sessions.

Second experimental period. After the second baseline period, the experimental procedure was reintroduced and continued for six sessions. Contingencies were identical to those of the first experimental period except that special attention for desirable play was excluded, save one accidental instance.

Follow-up. For twenty-four days after the second experimental period, there was no contact between the *E*s and the S. family. Mrs. S. was given complete freedom to use any techniques with Peter that she felt were warranted, including "time out," but she was given no specific instructions. After this twenty-four-day interval (whose length was limited by the impending departure of one *E*), a three-session, post-treatment check was made to determine whether the improvements effected during treatment were still evident. These one-hour follow-up sessions were comparable to earlier baseline periods in that Mrs. S. was instructed to behave in her usual manner toward Peter.

Results and Discussion

The frequency of Peter's O behaviors in each treatment condition is shown in Figure 1. Asterisks mark sessions in which observer reliability was assessed. These nine reliability sessions are plotted in terms of the mean of the frequencies obtained by different observers. During the first baseline period, the rate of O behavior varied between 18 and 113 per session. A sharp decrease occurred in the first experimental period; the rate ranged from one to eight per session. In the course of this period, Peter was isolated a total of four times, twice in session 17, once in session 18, and again in session 22. He received special attention twice in session 17, six times in session 18, and once in sessions 20 and 21.

During the second baseline period, the rate of O behaviors varied between 2 and 24 per session. Although this was an increase over the previous experimental period, the frequency of response did not match that of the first baseline period. This failure to return to earlier levels may have occurred for several reasons. For example, midway through the second baseline, Mrs. S. reported considerable difficulty in responding to Peter as she had during the first baseline period. She stated she felt more "sure of herself" and could not remember how she had previously behaved toward her son. It was apparent that Mrs. S. now gave Peter firm commands when she wanted him to do something and did not "give in" after denying him a request. The *E*s also noted that Peter was receiving more affection from his mother. This increased affection, however, seemed to be due to a change in Peter's behavior rather than his mother's, since Peter had recently begun to approach her with affectionate overtures.

The rate of O behaviors in the second experimental period was comparable to that of the first experimental period. . . . Special attention was (accidentally) given once in session 38.

Data obtained during the Follow-up period show that Peter's O behaviors

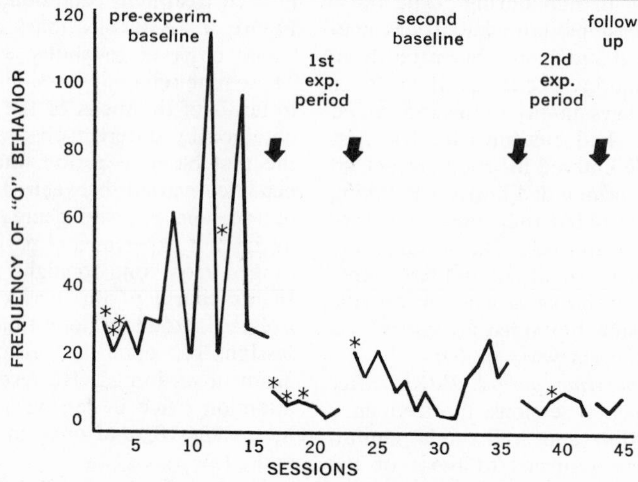

Fig. 1. Number of 10-second intervals, per 1-hour session, in which O behavior occurred. Asterisks indicate sessions in which reliability was tested.

remained low in rate after the passage of a twenty-four-day interval. Mrs. S. reported that Peter was well behaved and much less demanding than he had previously been. She stated that she had been using the time out procedure approximately once a week. (It was the *E*'s impression that not only the quantity but also the quality, i.e., topography, of O behaviors had changed. As early as the second baseline period it had been observed that O behaviors frequently lacked components which had been present earlier, such as facial expressions, voice qualities, and vigor of movement that typically constitute "angry" behavior.) Thus, it would appear that not only were the treatment effects maintained in the absence of the *E*s and the experimental procedures, but they had generalized from the treatment hour to the remaining hours of the day. These developments were being maintained by the use of occasional isolation (contingent, of course, on the occurrence of an Objectionable behavior) and other alterations in the mother's behavior.

Evidence that Mrs. S.'s behavior toward her child did change during the course of treatment is presented in Figure 2 which shows the verbal interaction between Peter and his mother. It can be seen by comparing Figures 1 and 2 that the frequency of O behavior and the frequency of the mother's verbalizations to Peter sometimes covaried. A positive correlation is particularly evident during the second baseline period; and a negative correlation during the followup. The correlation between O behavior and mother verbalization was determined for each of the five stages of the experiment. During the first and second baseline periods the correlations were .17 and .47, respectively, while for the experimental and followup periods they were –.41, –.20, and –.71 in that order. None of these correlations differ significantly from zero. Combining these figures into nontreatment (baseline periods) and treatment (experimental and followup periods) yields correlations of .39 for the former and –.41 for the latter. These coefficients were found to be significantly different from one another ($z = 2.48$, $p = .007$). This finding may indicate that Mrs. S., when left to her usual way of interbehaving with Peter, attended to (and thus maintained through social reinforcement) his undesirable behaviors while ignoring (extinguishing) desirable (non-O) responses. A number of studies (Allen, Hart, Buell, Harris, and Wolf, 1964; Harris, Johnston, and Kelley, 1964; Hart, Allen, Buell, Harris, and Wolf, 1964; Wahler *et al.*, 1965) have demonstrated that social reinforcement in the form of adult attention can influence the behavior of the young child. It is interesting to note that Mrs. S.'s proclivity to respond to Peter's O behaviors was reversed during the two experimental periods and thereafter.

. . . figures 1 and 2 also show that the time-out procedure operated in a selective manner. Even though the isolation technique reduced the rate of undesirable responses, other classes of behavior such as verbalizations were not affected. This is evidenced by the fact that Peter's verbalization rate during the combined treatment periods did not differ significantly from his rate during nontreatment periods ($F = 2.24$; $df = 1, 43$; $.25 > p > .10$).

The results of this study show that it is possible to treat behavioral problems in the home, with the parent as a therapeutic agent. Home treatment may, in some cases, be more effective than treatment in the clinic, particularly when the undesirable responses have a low probability of occurrence in settings other than the home. Since it is widely held that many of a child's problems originate in the home environment, direct modification of this environment (including the behavior of other family members) may arrest the difficulty at its source. One limitation of this type of study, however, is the requirement of a cooperative parent. If this requirement can be met, the use of the parent as therapist can not only free the professional for other duties, but the parent, in learning to use techniques of behavioral control, may become generally more skillful in dealing with the responses of the developing child and more capable in handling any future difficulties that may occur.

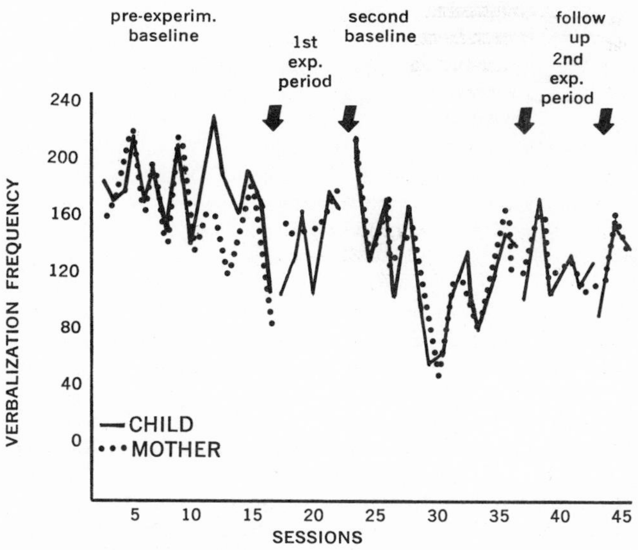

Fig. 2. Number of ten-second intervals, per one-hour session, in which Peter spoke to his mother or the mother spoke to Peter.

References

1. Allen, K. Eileen, Hart, Betty M., Buell, Joan S., Harris, Florence R., and Wolf, M. M., "Effects of social reinforcement on isolate behavior of a nursery school child," *Child Development,* 1964, *35:* 511-518.
2. Bijou, S. W., Sloane, H. N., "Therapeutic techniques with Children," in L. A. Pennington and I. A. Berg (eds.) *An Introduction to Clinical Psychology* (3rd ed.). New York: Ronald.
3. Ferster, C. B., and Appel, J. B., "Punishment of S^{Δ} responding in matching to sample by time-out from positive reinforcement," *Journal of Experimental Analysis of Behavior,* 1961, *4:* 45-56.
4. Harris, Florence R., Johnston, Margaret K., Kelley, C. Susan, and Wolf, M. M., "Effects of positive social reinforcement on regressed crawling of a nursery school child," *Journal of Educational Psychology,* 1964, *55:* 35-41.
5. Hart, Betty M., Allen, K. Eileen, Buell, Joan S., Harris, Florence R., and Wolf, M. M., "Effects of social reinforcement on operant crying," *Journal of Experimental Child Psychology,* 1964, *1:* 145-153.
6. Wahler, R. G., Winkel, G. H., Peterson, R. F., and Morrison, D. C., "Mothers as behavior therapists for their own children," *Behavior Research and Therapy,* 1965, *3:* 113-124.
7. Wolf. M., Risley, T., and Mees, H., "Application of operant conditioning procedures to the behavior problems of an autistic child," *Behavior Research and Therapy,* 1964, *1:* 305-312.

□ □ □

Part VI Special Types of Guidance

There are a number of conceivable special types of guidance. Two of these are covered in this part: genetic counseling and religious-pastoral management. These forms of management are distinguished from others in that they may be only selectively applicable or even desirable, and deal with only a part of the family problem. In some cases, management without these types of guidance would be incomplete, but management relying exclusively upon them would usually be insufficient. While some management problems and methods, such as parental dynamics and group techniques, have received extensive theoretical treatment in the literature, relatively little has been written on the two management types covered in this part of the book, both of which now appear to be on the threshold of significant expansion.

One of the functions of a skilled manager involved in comprehensive management of a case might well be the determination of the special types of guidance needed. It is quite conceivable, for example, that a family would need no genetic guidance but would be in dire need of management in the area of nutrition. In any event, it is clear that special types of guidance can be instrumental to fulfillment of the goals of a total management approach.

SECTION A

Genetic Counseling

Unfortunately, much that has been written about genetic counseling is more pertinent to the problem of genetic risk assignment than to the handling of parental feelings. Individuals competent to give parents genetic facts are often not competent in the handling of parental dynamics, and may not be sensitive to the fears, irrationalities, etc., associated with beliefs about heredity; or to attitudes and conflicts regarding sex and reproduction. On the other hand, those trained in counseling usually lack knowledge about genetics or the techniques necessary for genetic diagnosis. As a consequence, genetic counseling has consisted mostly of recitation of genetic facts to parents, and has tended to be isolated from the larger management context.

Ideally, the case manager should probably be present during the informational session so as to be aware of the content of genetic counseling and to observe the parental reaction. He is then more likely to be able to carry on the total management process effectively. Of course, the geneticist might possess some of the qualities of a skilled counselor, but the entire management program established for the family must be comprehensive and must go beyond the genetic features of the case. The readings in this section were selected not so much because they solve, or perhaps even discuss, this continuity problem, but because they do make some positive contribution toward an exposition of the role of genetic counseling in the management spectrum.

Selections by Hauge; by Tips, Meyer and Perkins; and by Reed discuss procedures in genetic diagnosis, risk assignment, and counseling in general terms. Hauge describes genetic counseling in terms of provision of information and explanation of the genetic aspects of a given situation, suggesting "advice and recommendation" as a natural consequence. He does not, however, suggest another professional to serve as an advisor. Tips, Meyer, and Perkins present a rather similar statement, emphasizing the importance of good genetic diagnosis. Reed indicates that while the geneticist may attempt to be objective in the presentation of genetic facts, emotional issues may be raised which might lead him into expression of his own personal attitudes.

In the fourth selection, Baroff goes beyond risk assignment and information presentation, discussing certain realities and parental dynamics which, though relevant to genetic counseling, are sometimes minimized by managers lacking training in counseling. He emphasizes that the counseling approach in general includes parental responsibility for decision-making, and while the geneticist can provide relevant information, the parents must make their own decisions. They, not the counselor, must live with the consequences.

The last three selections discuss the effects of a retarded child upon subsequent reproductive patterns and attitudes of the affected families. Tizard and Grad present results of a study which elicited parents' intentions about having further children after an impaired child had been born into the family. Holt conducted a similar type of study in which parents of the retarded were asked to express their attitudes toward more pregnancies, and in which the number of pregnancies theoretically expected was compared to the number of pregnancies that actually occurred. Tips' study demonstrates strikingly how knowledge of the presence of perceived genetic risk not only affects the reproduction patterns of the parents immediately concerned, but also that of the parents' more extended family.

from GENETIC COUNSELING

Mogens Hauge

(International Copenhagen Congress on the Scientific Study of Mental Retardation, 1964)

. . . .

Genetic counseling in general forms one of the tools of preventive medicine. The growing relative importance of genetic factors in the development of disorders in human beings and the increased understanding of the mechanisms of hereditary transmission make the need for genetic counseling more and more pronounced. Although the strict meaning of the word counsel implies only advice or recommendation, the initial step of genetic counseling is always to produce information on and explanation of the genetic aspects in a given situation; next, advice and recommendation are most often wanted and given as a natural consequence. It should, however, be kept in mind that many more considerations than the purely genetic may be of decisive importance when the question about which measures to be taken is raised. It ought to be stressed immediately that genetic counseling does not include any element of compulsion.

The prevention of inherited abnormalities and disorders may be considered as the primary goal of genetic counseling, but other significant purposes may also be served, such as an early establishment of a diagnosis and thus the early treatment, sometimes lifesaving, in cases of hereditary anomalies.

Genetic counseling may be carried out on different levels which may grossly be defined as the population level and the family level. Only the last-mentioned will be discussed here, as some of the problems related to populations are highly specific and of quite other dimensions. On the family level the questions which meet the counselor are usually concerned with the risk of recurrence of a specific anomaly in a family where such an event has already taken place. This information is, for obvious reasons, usually not required until some anomaly or disease has been observed in a family, and sometimes not until the same unfortunate event has occurred two or even more times in the same family. The latter situation raises the question of whether genetic counseling should be regarded as a duty by all those who are engaged in examinations or treatment of individuals with more serious anomalies which may be genetically determined. If the families concerned are given adequate information about the prospects of recurrence of such abnormalities, this might prevent unexpected experiences of this kind.

The main principles of genetic counseling will appear quite clearly from a consideration of an example of the type very often encountered in practice. Two parents, seemingly quite healthy, have had a child with mental retardation. Unexpected as this was, they want to know why this has happened to them and if the same thing could happen again. The genetic counselor can, however, give no immediate answer to their questions, and he is quite often unable to solve the problems alone. He is member of a team, small or large, which is primarily charged with the task of collecting the most complete medical and genetic information about the child and its family, including first of all the full life history of the child right from the earliest stages of prenatal development and a complete account of the circumstances of the birth as well as of any signs of later disorders. A number of supplementary examinations of the child may be indicated; it is not unusual that more detailed knowledge is needed before counseling can be performed than before treatment can be instituted. The aim of this work is to create the most complete picture of the individual and to uncover any existing disturbances of a biochemical, cytological or any other nature, even if they seem to be quite trivial. A complete examination and elucidation of each individual case is indispensable if the most precise genetic information is wanted. But this does not end the preparatory stage. Many data related to the parents and their families are equally important. Here again, supplementary examinations of the parents or perhaps other relatives may be desirable, and in most cases this need is understood and accepted by the individuals concerned. Contacts with hospitals, general practitioners and practicing specialists are often established in order to verify diagnosis of disorders observed among the family members. These data are usually obtainable by the physicians of the team who carefully observe professional secrecy. Thus, the preparations for the basis of genetic counseling may call for very active collaboration and conferences between specialists not only from the various medical disciplines, but also from many related fields.

The medical geneticist now puts all the pieces of information together and tries to imagine what the genetic situation is like in the present family. It is the responsibility of the genetic counselor to have an intimate knowledge of all studies relevant to the present case and to be able to tell if any supplementary examinations should be carried out in order to increase the precision of the estimate of the genetic risk. Two individuals may show what seem to be identical types of mental retardation, but even very minute anomalies in one of the individuals, or a special pattern in the family distribution of the same type of abnormality, may disclose that quite different genetic mechanisms are at work, leading to quite different genetic prognosis in the two cases. A few spots in the cornea, a displacement of a tiny bit of only one chromosome, much less than one thousandth of a millimeter in length, a minimal decrease in the amount of just one of the hundreds of proteins in the cells of some organ may be the decisive guide to an exact answer to the questions asked by the family. It is the task of the counselor to make sure whether an exact genetic prognosis, based on genetic theories, could be given in the case under consideration, or whether one has to resort to the so-called empirical risk figures. The genetic prognosis indicates the risk of recurrence of the same or a related type of abnormality in a relative of an individual with a given hereditary anomaly. The exact or theoretical figure is applicable if the mechanism behind the abnormality in question is genetic and of a simple nature, and if there is no reason for suspecting that the laws deduced from previous studies of this type of anomaly do not apply in this particular instance. If it happens to be a case determined by a fully elucidated, abnormal gene the counselor may sometimes be able to give the family some facts of interest in addition to the mere estimate of risks; it may be known from previous research that cases of this special type usually show very little if any variation as to severity within the same family; this means that there is no reason to expect a more serious degree of the abnormality in any new cases which may appear; in this way the future possibilities are depicted even more clearly.

It is, of course, the hope that the use of exact risk figures will be made possible in all counseling situations, but this stage has not yet been reached within any group of disorders. When the etiological background, in spite of all efforts, has not been made clear, and the possible influence of genetic factors is not excluded, genetic counseling has to rely on empirical risk figures. They are also based on research which may be even more extensive than in cases of anomalies with a simple mode of inheritance, but the research workers have been unable to formulate any hypothesis which could explain the observations made in these studies and, consequently, exact risk figures cannot be deduced from any theories. If, however, the studies conform to a number of specifiable requirements, fully reliable risk figures may be calculated on the basis of these materials; as these risk figures do not rest on any theory regarding etiology, but directly on the findings, they are labeled empirical figures. Here, modern statistics have contributed greatly to the increase of the amount of information which can be extracted from family and population studies. Although the empirical risk figures can be applied safely in a high number of situations, their natural limitations should always be kept in mind; some of these are mainly the headaches of the counselor, such as the possible influence of the original selection of individuals for studies; it may happen that only severe degrees of a given anomaly which needed hospital treatment have been included, or, on the other hand, only milder cases having survived until the reproductive age may have been taken into account. Other limitations are of more general significance: the empirical risk figures are based upon collections of cases which undoubtedly very often have various—genetic as well as non-genetic—causes, and although the risk figures are fully valid on the average, they may be too high or too low in a given situation. The specific case encountered may in reality have been caused by purely non-genetic factors which implies that the empirical risk figure is too high as the true risk of recurrence is negligible; on the other hand, the case under consideration may happen to be one of the extremely few caused by a rare gene, and the true risk figure may here be higher than the average which includes all cases, genetic as well as non-genetic, as long as we are not clever enough to separate them into homogeneous groups before a study is undertaken.

Many counselors prefer to explain these complications to the families seeking advice; this will also make it easier for the family to understand why the estimate of the genetic risk may be greatly changed when, for instance, a new case of the same or some analogous anomaly appears somewhere in the family. This last fact forms one of the reasons for asking the families to come for renewed consultations if the etiology is not quite clear and an exact risk figure cannot be given for some reason or other, provided that the family takes interest in getting an advice based upon the most up-to-date facts and findings. The same applies to cases where the counselor must admit that it is at present impossible to give any reasonably valid estimate of the risk in the situation which is presented to him; here it is admittable to suggest that a repeated consultation some years later may be rewarding, considering the speed at which new facts about human abnormalities and disorders are brought to light. The principles and procedures described above are also used when other relatives [besides] parents of some individual with an abnormality come for genetic counseling. Extensive and thorough investigations will always precede any advice. If, for instance, a brother of a patient with mental retardation due to phenylketonuria has decided to marry a cousin, biochemistry comes into the picture as specific biochemical examinations of the blood of the prospective parents may lead to an exact reflection of the genetic constellation. When it is a case of a younger couple with a child displaying symptoms of Down's syndrome, you know that the cytogeneticist may be able to give decisive help and information to the relatives of these parents by an examination of the chromosomes of some cells from the blood. In some instances of mental retardation accompanied by eye symptoms, the hematologist may, by examination of a clinically healthy relative of a patient, be able to tell whether he or she carries the genetic factor responsible for this abnormality and thus give the basis for an exact estimate of the genetic risk. From what has been said above, it may be evident that general statements about genetic risks are of very limited value and a simple tabulation of risk figures could be very misleading.

At present genetic counseling in the field of mental retardation has in no way reached a satisfactory stage. As has been amply demonstrated by many of the papers and discussions in the present congress, the causes of mental retardation are numerous and to a deplorably large extent unknown so far. We should, however, not forget that the situation has changed quite rapidly during the last decade; more etiological factors of importance have been revealed, more possibilities for prevention and treatment have thereby been opened, and the basis for valid genetic counseling has improved considerably.

The practical performance of genetic counseling may vary. In Denmark, where this activity was taken up by the late Professor Kemp more than twenty-five years ago, thousands of cases have been referred to the University Institute of Human Genetics in Copenhagen. The information has been given, in some cases, directly to the family in personal interviews or in other cases through the physician with whom they have for one reason or another established the closest contact. In all cases the family doctor gets a full report about the results of our investigations, our estimate of the genetic risk and what we have said or would have said to the family.

What is to be expected from genetic counseling? The immediate results are easier to see than the more remote effects. The family gets an understanding of the genetic risks when the situation as we see it has been carefully explained to them. They are quite often asked to see us again after an interval of some weeks. This allows them to absorb and digest the new information received and to bring forward any problems which may have turned up in the meantime. Furthermore, the second interview enables us to find out whether our explanations have been grasped by the family; this is a field where misunderstandings may have very serious consequences. It is a personal impression that even if only a rather vague assessment of the risk has been possible, the family is less often disappointed by the lack of precision of the estimate than the counselor. A feeling of relief is pronounced more often than one might have expected when the situation has been carefully explained. It is not uncommon that people have quite unrealistic and usually exaggerated ideas about the risks involved. Quite a few parents find it easier to face a risk of known order of magnitude than to live with complete uncertainty on the chances of mishaps. Feelings of guilt may lie heavily on some parents because they fear that they have done or omitted something which has influenced the development of their child, who may be found to present an inherited abnormality. In some cases it is of value that the parents come to realize that they have both contributed to the genetic constitution of their children. We never try to make any decision on behalf of those who come for genetic counseling. We just try to assist them in finding their own solution to the problems. As is known, Danish legislation admits various preventive measures in cases of high genetic risks; these possibilities are mentioned and may also profitably be discussed if this is wanted by the family. If a couple, after the full explanation of the situation, decides to take the risk, the genetic counselor may contribute to the early diagnosis and adequate treatment, if the inherited abnormality should turn up, by informing the family doctor and perhaps suggesting what could be done in the present situation.

The genetic counseling service ought to be extended, even in our country. This presupposes more widespread genetic knowledge so that more problems with genetic implications will be referred to the centers for genetic counseling. It is, for instance, still happening that parents restrain from having more children after the loss of a child due to some disorder supposed to be hereditary and with a high risk of recurrence in any subsequent child, even if it has not been tried to verify this assumption; in such a case the parents may even apply for adoption of a child instead of having more of their own, thus enhancing the demand for the very limited number of children available for adoption.

An increase of knowledge will also make genetic counseling on the population level indispensable. In many problems related to public health, the need for genetic advice is obvious, and genetic counseling in a wider sense is certainly indicated. This brings up the question about the relation between genetic counseling and eugenics, which ought to be made clear. It is not to be expected that genetic counseling of families will appreciably improve the qualities of the population as a whole, and this is one of the first aims of eugenics. Genetic counseling is related to what is called negative qualitative eugenics, but eugenics must include many other measures and is based on a number of other sciences in addition to human genetics. What is of special significance is that complicated value judgments are involved in eugenic programs. Furthermore, it may be found difficult to reconcile personal liberty on which genetic counseling rests with effective eugenic measures. As stated above, genetic counseling should be considered as one of the tools of preventive medicine; it intends to transform medico-genetic research and theory into information and measures of practical value as a particular branch of medical practice.

Genetic counseling is thus intimately connected with medical and genetic research. A real improvement of this valuable service is only to be expected at the rate of extension of our present knowledge. In the field of mental retardation as well as in other fields of human disorders it is, however, not only a question of genetic research, but many other types of study may add highly useful information; whenever feasible genetic aspects should, however, be taken into account; therefore, close collaboration between all those who do research work within this field is highly desirable. The present conference has been a valuable step forward in this direction.

□ □ □

from THE DYNAMICS OF GENETIC COUNSELING

Robert L. Tips
Donald L. Meyer
Audree L. Perkins

(*Eugenics Quarterly*, 1962)

Genetic counseling is an integral part of the overall management of families with members affected with genetic diseases. This presentation formalizes the procedures required for effective results as they relate to the correlation of basic genetic principles and modern clinical practice. It describes three family situations which illustrate certain fundamental aspects of the underlying dynamics of counseling. The methods stem from our experience in the application of current research data in selected family units.

Effective counseling is a specialized consultative procedure which requires the full cooperation of the referring physician in order to yield the optimal benefits to the patient and his family. Such benefits have been evaluated in terms of the facilitation of medical management of the affected family member, the emotional readjustment in the family milieu, and the analysis of reproductive performances of kindred members with respect to the number of conceptions per 1000 potentially fertilizable ovulatory cycles which occur prior to the birth of the propositi and before and after counseling (Tips *et al.*, 1962).

Counseling Procedure

The counseling procedures require adherence to protocol. Cases are selected primarily on the basis of the referring physician's interest and the willingness of the family to make application. Receipt of past medical records and pertinent laboratory data help immeasurably in predetermining the needs of the referred family.

To begin the initial consultation visit, a conference is held with the family in order to outline the purposes and procedures. During the conference, which includes the patient and his parents and siblings, observations accumulate relative to the group psychodynamics, emphasizing modes of interrelationships and individual identification.

Next, the mother and patient are interviewed to review in detail the clinical manifestations of the disease. Physical examinations of both mother and patient emphasize the immediacy of the condition in question so that a pattern of clinical inquiry is developed for later use. The patient is then dismissed and the mother's pregnancy record is sensitively explored in chronological sequence and with reference to paternity. At this point the mother's interview is interrupted for clinical evaluation of the patient's siblings.

The father's interview is initiated by his physical examination. Confidential and careful interrogation with respect to previous marriages and extramarital children is explored first. Then, an outline of the family pedigree is constructed, utilizing his knowledge of surnames and maiden names, marriages and paternities, birth dates and places, and health and death data of the kindred.

The family pedigree is privately reviewed next with the mother, during which the details of pregnancy and offspring records of all kindred members are emphasized. Through recall of the patterned medical inquiry, developed during her initial interview, the mother releases information spontaneously as each kindred member is discussed and thus provides clues to unsuspected, misdiagnosed, and subclinical cases. Other hereditary diseases are noted also.

Followup visits with the patient and his mother are planned as indicated. The medical management is reviewed first. Then further discussion with the mother is reoriented to consider reproductive records of kindred members, especially in terms of menstrual and sexual histories. Sometimes these histories reveal additional pregnancies, extramarital paternities, and marital problems. Such discussion stimulates the mother's interest and inspires intelligent inquiry into genetic considerations, once guilt and doubt are relieved and attention is focused on tangible problems.

As the mother approaches a plateau of mature comprehension of the genetic implications, she is instructed in simple principles of gene combinations in fertilization as they are applicable to her family situation. The proficiently instructed mother, recognizing her own genetic potential, begins to envision the genetic status of other kindred members. Through her own experience, she aids immeasurably not only in providing information to the family, but also in solving the subtle problems that arise as psychological ramifications of the genetic situation.

Case Examples

. . . .

Family 2. A low phenylalanine diet was prescribed for a six-month-old male with phenylketonuria. The anxious young mother tried conscientiously to continue the diet, as she was repeatedly assured of its efficacy. However, despite concentrated efforts and rehospitalizations, the nutritional status of the child progressively deteriorated.

During the next four months, severe marital problems ensued and culminated in the husband's desertion, leaving the wife with another pregnancy. The three older normal children became unmanageable and caused disturbances in the neighborhood.

In the counseling session, the mother related her previous experiences and expressed overt condemnation first toward the paternal family and then toward her own family. She believed that the phenylketonuria resulted from "bad blood" in the family.

Through counseling, the mother gained insight into the pathogenesis of the disease and into the true significance of the hereditary influence. Her anxiety concerning the affected child lessened to such a degree that medical management and a dietary control were readily instituted. Improvement in the patient's condition inspired the mother to effect realistic adjustments in the attendant family problems. The existing pregnancy gave issue to another phenylketonuric child, who was readily managed on the appropriate diet. . . .

Comment

Genetic counseling consists of clinical procedures whereby the patient with genetic disease is evaluated in terms of his relationships and management in the scope of his family environment (Kallman, 1952, 1956; Tips, *et al.*, 1962). The opportunity for such family units to participate in a therapeutic program, which creates an atmosphere conducive to the exploration of overall family problems, distinguishes this from the traditional, stereotyped, mathematical probability approach (Herndon, 1955; Reed, 1955, 1957; Hammons, 1959).

Empathetic communication with the family is established through interviews and physical examinations of pertinent kindred. Oriented initially to pathological manifestations of the disease, the procedure is directed next toward investigations of reproductive records of family members. In the cases described herein, the concern about chronic illness is reflected in apprehension and overprotectiveness of the patient, neglect of the normal siblings, marital problems of the parents, and overt hostility with the kindred. In the structured counseling atmosphere, elucidation of these problems forms the subject for communications.

The exploration of the family pedigree in detail with the father and its review with the mother, coupled with the clinical assessment of each member through the patterned medical inquiries and with an evaluation of the reproductive performances, promoted an oral catharsis from each parent which eased the barrier of defense mechanisms such as projection, rationalization, repression, and feelings of misdirected guilt and hostility. . . .

Since the counseling procedure is directed toward unveiling the overall family situation as well as the extreme anxieties which envelop and encounter parents, the genetic counselor must maintain a realistic perspective of family dynamics. Impetus is given to family readjustments which redirect energies into constructive channels so that the patient's medical management, as prescribed by the referring physician, is enhanced. . . .

References

1. Hammons, H. G., 1959, *Heredity Counseling.* Paul B. Hoeber Inc., New York.
2. Herndon, C. N., 1955, "Heredity Counseling," *Eugenics Quarterly, 2:* 83-89.
3. Kallman, F. J., 1952, "Human genetics as a science, as a profession, and as a social minded trend of orientation," *American Journal of Human Genetics, 4:* 237-245.
4. Kallman, F. J., 1956, "Psychiatric aspects of genetic counseling," *American Journal of Human Genetics, 8:* 97-101.
5. Reed, S. C., 1955, *Counseling in Medical Genetics.* W. B. Saunders Co., Philadelphia.
6. Reed, S. C., 1957, "Counseling in Medical Genetics," *Acta Genetics, 7:* 473-480.
7. Tips, R. L., Meyer, D. L., Perkins, A. L., and Shininger, F. S., 1962, "Heredity counseling in pediatrics." A review of 300 families. Presented *American Society of Human Genetics,* A.I.B.S. meeting, August 30, Corvallis, Oregon.
8. Tips, R. L., Meyer, D. L., and Perkins, A. L., 1962. *Clinical counseling in human genetics.* Presented at the State Medical Association, September 26, Portland, Oregon.
9. Tips, R. L., and Lynch, H. T., 1962, *The impact of genetic counseling upon the family milieu.*

□ □ □

from GENETIC COUNSELING

Sheldon C. Reed

(Counseling Parents of Children with Mental Handicaps, 1958)

. . . .

What is it that the parents of the retarded child wish to learn from the geneticist?

In the first place, they want to know whether the child's retardation has a predominantly genetic or [an] environmental basis. Regardless of the cause, the parents are also acutely interested in the chances of a repetition of the anomaly in each subsequent pregnancy. Some parents have decided that they do not wish to have any more children, regardless of the causation, and inquire about acceptable methods of prevention. Parents are also interested in the chances that their normal children might have retarded offspring. These four questions are appropriate ones which the geneticists can answer with varying degrees of accuracy and satisfaction. These are questions in genetics, and presumably the geneticist is best qualified to answer them.

A good counselor in human genetics speaks from his heart, but he is also a scientist and must speak the truth as it is accepted at that time. No counselor is clairvoyant, and none can predict the scientific discoveries of the future. The counselor cannot make decisions for the parents, but he can give them facts they need in order to make decisions themselves. These decisions may not be perfect ones; they may even be sinful to some people. However, the social worker learned long ago that the hasty judgment of others is often false righteousness. This lesson of "not throwing the first stone" was clearly explained by Jesus and by many others with insight long before Him. Fortunately, quite a few people in every generation learn and practice the withholding of hasty judgment.

Please do not think that genetic counseling includes sermons. I am merely trying to explain to you that it is a helping process and is thus a type of social work.

The parents of the handicapped child are helped by teaching them the biological facts and the expectations associated with the particular kind of mental retardation which has appeared in their family. . . .

If the retardation is not due to genetic causes, the counseling is a great pleasure. If retardation resulted from an infection of the mother, one can predict that present day antibiotics will help protect the mother from any subsequent infections.

Our final, largest, and most puzzling group of mental retardates are those where there is no evident physical disability. At birth the child seems to be perfect. The mother has had a happy healthy pregnancy but the child never learns to talk well and is incapable of school work. Since there has been no warning of retardation, the child becomes established in the home and, later, the idea of institutionalization is usually unacceptable to the parents. The following case represents the dilemma faced by some of the parents of the undifferentiated mentally retarded.

> This particular couple has a nine-year-old retarded girl and a five-year-old retarded boy at home. Both are handsome children but with little mental capacity. No one has been able to state the cause of the retardation though the children have been seen by a large number of specialists. The father and mother decided to have no more children because they have no desire to produce another defective child; nor could they see any merit in producing a normal child, who would have to adjust to the two older mentally deficient siblings. Recently the mother discovered that their contraceptive technique had failed in some way and she had her pregnancy confirmed. Her physician referred the couple to me with the hope that I could dissuade them from their insistence upon a therapeutic abortion.

I not only failed to dissuade the couple but was converted to their point of view. As this couple absolutely refused to subject a normal child to the hazards of the home environment which they could foresee through the years ahead, one could not expect that quoting a favorable genetic ratio would convince them that they should have more children—and it didn't. A correct decision for this family is by no means the correct one for other families. It must be made on an individual basis always. . . .

□ □ □

from MENTAL RETARDATION: A FAMILY PROBLEM

George S. Baroff

(Conference on Psychological Problems in the Habilitation of the Mentally Retarded, 1962)

. . . .

Some of the needs of the families of retarded children became evident to me during my affiliation with the Department of Medical Genetics at the New York Psychiatric Institute. Many families feared that their child's condition was hereditary, with probable recurrence in future offspring. Others were convinced of the hereditary nature of the disorder because it *had* recurred, ofttimes in spite of the well-meaning but vain reassurance that "lightning never strikes twice" and "accidents like this are one in a million."

Assistance to parents whose experience has created fear about future pregnancies involves more than a determination of whether the condition is hereditary—though such a finding is obviously of great consequences. Their decision about enlarging their family, whether consciously or unconsciously arrived at, will ultimately be based on more than a simple statistical risk—assuming one is available. It will be made according to the relative strengths of their hopes and fears. It may appear to be a constructive course of action based on reasonably realistic appraisal of their capacities to handle future stress, or it may be an essentially neurotic choice associated with parental conflict and with the needs of one overriding those of the other.

The focus of the professional is not restricted to an estimate of statistical risk—which generally bodes well for future offspring—but also on the probable effect that a second handicapped child would have on the integrity of that family's organization.

What has been the effect of one retarded child on this family?

Are the parents functioning effectively in terms of each other and their normal children or has what was always a precarious level of adjustment been so shaken that the family is threatened with dissolution?

Is the mother continuing to guide and love her normal children or has the handicapped child become the center of her emotional universe?

Does she proudly proclaim that all of her energies will be devoted to the care and development of her retarded youngster? When one gently inquires about the rest of the family, she is startled and then replies that they are healthy and able to care for themselves. Is her attitude of self-sacrifice a defensive reaction against negative feelings toward her child or does she really believe that exclusive dedication to her sick child will be helpful to him and to her family?

What of father? How has he responded to disaster? As parents we invest our aspirations in our children. How do we cope with the experience of being the parent of a child who *must* fall far short of our most modest expectations.

Do we turn away from this symbol of frustration, disappointment, and perhaps, masculine failure or, contrariwise, do we deny that there is a handicap? The child is just lazy—he'll catch up—it's emotional or there is a mental block—he needs another teacher—or another school—another doctor—or, does he say as one of our father's recently stated, "You can achieve anything if you have the will to do it"?

Do father and mother see the problems similarly? Are their attitudes complementary or are they in conflict? I recall a young couple—the wife much shaken by this unhappy experience of motherhood. She was a tense and frightened woman who dreaded another pregnancy but her husband had not been responsive to her fears. He was determined that they should have another child "to make up for this one."

Siblings will eventually participate in the family reactions to abnormality. For the very young sibling, his brother's handicap may have little meaning, but assuredly this non-recognition will be replaced by awareness and the development of some form of acceptance or rejection. Indeed the relationship between retardate and sibling may be a crucial determinant in the decision regarding residential placement. Older adolescent and adult siblings are likely to wonder whether their own future parenthood is threatened. It is usually possible to reassure them, as well as their parents, but the kind of reassurance I refer to is quite different from the "lightning never strikes twice" variety.

In fact, only a small proportion of retardates born to normal parents represent known genetic entities; here at The Training School, approximately two per cent of the population are siblings. Of the hereditary forms of mental deficiency, phenylpyruvic oligophrenia or phenylketonuria is perhaps the best known because of the recent discovery of dietary procedures which, if begun early in life, can purportedly nullify the metabolic abnormality and thereby permit normal mental growth. Parenthetically, please note that dietary control of a gene-determined defect illustrates the fact that we are not merely helpless recipients of a fortuitous assortment of good and bad genes, but rather that we can modify our biological as well as experiential destiny.

Assuming that the retarded child whose family seeks assistance does not present a known hereditary syndrome, a fact which often is ascertained only after extensive medical and laboratory study, it is then reasonable to conclude that the defect is due 1) to a developmental anomaly of prenatal origin—the effects of maternal rubella in the first trimester would be a case in point, 2) to hazards of birth, a diagnosis which I fear has often been a wastebasket classification for conditions whose etiology is obscure, or 3) to some neo- or postnatal condition usually of infectious origin. Unfortunately, in many cases the etiology remains unclear, but insofar as future risk is concerned, it is obviously of greatest import to tentatively eliminate genetic factors as causative. I say tentative exclusion of heredity because unfortunately often the first indication that we get that a condition is probably hereditary is when it occurs in a second child.

But even the ruling out of heredity does not free the parents of all concern for future offspring. These parents still share, at the very least, the same risk that all parents share for abnormality of some kind in any given pregnancy. Recalling our statistical training, each pregnancy like the throwing of dice is an independent event subject to more or less the same probabilities as each preceeding or subsequent pregnancy. The consequence is that a previous disorder is neither protection against recurrence nor a sure sign of future abnormality.

Based on a frequency of mental retardation in the population of three per cent, it is estimated that the risk for normal parents at any given pregnancy is at least one-third or one per cent. This estimate is derived from reports of the composition of the retardate population according to parental status and degree of defect. Approximately three-fourths are classified as borderline, or mildly retarded, with the remaining one-quarter representing the severer degrees of handicap. Parents of normal intelligence—and these are the individuals who are more likely to be concerned with the possibility of a second handicapped child—are relatively heavy contributors to the severer degrees of defect in contrast to parents of the higher level retardate who are, themselves, more likely to be of subnormal intelligence. Normal parents, to a lesser degree, contribute to the higher grade defective population, and their total contribution is approximated at one-third or one per cent, which is a recurrence risk of 1 in 100. While to many this may seem to be a small risk—to others not so small—it is, nevertheless, probably much greater than the likelihood of lightning striking twice and is certainly far greater than the proverbial "one in a million"—ten thousand times greater to be exact. If our patient is an older mother, then the risk is increased, because women over age thirty-five produce a disproportionately high frequency of mongoloid children. The risk of a mongoloid child for women in the age range of forty to forty-four is from one to two per cent.

But supposing the condition is hereditary in origin. If the child represents one of the so-called inborn errors of metabolism—Tay-Sach's disease, for example, a condition which is inherited as a simple recessive, the risk of recurrence in any future pregnancy is as high as one in four. In tuberous sclerosis, a dominantly inherited disorder, the risk is increased to one in two. Both conditions offer formidable risks which parents should not unknowingly take. In this regard, I was struck by a recent item in *Children's Limited,* the NARC publication in which a substantial proportion of parents of children with phenylketonuria were never informed that the condition could be expected to recur with a one in four probability in future children. It is my view that people have the right to information which can vitally affect their lives. How they utilize this information, and the steps that they eventually take, are a matter of individual family decision. A major aspect of counseling parents who fear recurrence is helping them to understand the information that is available and exploring relevant attitudes and feelings so that they can most adaptively use this information in terms of their own particular family needs. . . .

The counseling approach includes parental responsibility for decision-making as an integral part. That parents decide what is best for themselves is not only desirable from the point of view of personal responsibility, but it is also consistent with the reality that only the parents, and not the professional, must live with the consequences of that decision. The professional, who has blandly reassured the parents that the bolt of lightning will not again touch them, is no friend when the "impossible" occurs. He does not have to bear the emotional, let alone financial and often physical, burden of caring for two abnormal children. . . .

□ □ □

from THE MENTALLY HANDICAPPED AND THEIR FAMILIES: A SOCIAL SURVEY

Jack Tizard, Jacqueline Grad

(Oxford University Press, 1961)

. . . .

Parents' Attitude to Having Further Children

It seemed reasonable to suppose that the parents' attitudes towards having further children were affected by the knowledge that one child was mentally handicapped. Many mothers told us that the fear of giving birth to a second defective had had a serious effect upon their marital relationships. Often they had been unwilling, or had not known how, to prevent further pregnancies; and they were diffident about discussing this with the doctor.

Many women do not have clearly thought-out views which they are able to formulate succinctly on matters such as these; and among the families we visited a rational approach to family planning was uncommon. Hence, it was not considered feasible, in our already long interviews with the mothers, to inquire into their sex practices and how these had been influenced by the birth of a mentally subnormal child. Our data are, therefore, seriously inadequate and are presented here because the subject is one about which little has been written.

We asked the mothers *a*) how the knowledge that their child was mentally handicapped had affected their attitude to having other children, and *b*) whether they had sought advice about having other children. In eleven cases no information was obtainable, and in a further twenty-eight cases the baby had been born to a woman who was menopausal, or the parents were separated. There were, therefore, 211 women at risk, about whom information was obtained. Since, as has been mentioned, 21 per cent of the defectives had been born to a woman aged forty or over, it is probable that our sample included other women who were no longer fecund. We have, however, ignored age differences in our analysis.

Of the 211 women, one hundred (47 per cent) said that having the defective had not interfered with their wish to have other children. Many had not discovered the condition until they were already pregnant again or had had later-born, normal children. With others the defective had been the last planned child, or an unwanted pregnancy, and considerations other than his condition had caused them to limit the size of their family. Still others had not allowed the child's handicap, which they knew about, to influence them.

The remaining 111 parents said that their attitude to having further children had been influenced by the fact that one child was mentally subnormal; and the way in which they had been affected is summarized in Table 8.4. Nine parents said they had tried to increase the size of their family when they had not previously planned to do so, in order to 'make up for' the defective, or to give him a companion, or sibling to take care of him in later life. Of the remaining 102, twenty-nine (14 per cent of the 211) postponed having another child but finally decided to take the risk. A further seventeen (8 per cent of the 211) had become pregnant, though not wishing to do so because of the defective, while the remaining fifty-six had had no more children because of the defective. Had the defective been normal, these women might have wished to have other children. The data suggested therefore that at least one-third of the women had wished to limit their families because of the defective, and it was apparent that the majority of the mothers in the sample had been deeply concerned about the chances of bearing another defective.

In these circumstances, it was surprising to find that only sixty-nine parents (33 per cent of the 211 families at risk) had sought medical advice as to whether to have further children. Of these, seven had been advised not to have further children, ten were told it was unlikely but possible that they might have another defective and fifty-two were advised that the risk of having a second defective was negligible. In some instances, such advice was not in accordance with the known facts, and parents had been told that they might confidently expect a subsequent child to be normal when the risk of having another mental defective was by no means negligible.

Table 8.4

Attitude to having further children after a defective was born

Parents' attitude	Home group		Institution group		Total	
Birth of a defective made no difference	66	(53%)	34	(40%)	100	(47%)
Wanted others because of the defective	7	(6%)	2	(2%)	9	(4%)
Very worried but had others	13	(10%)	16	(19%)	29	(14%)
Tried to avoid but had others	9	(7%)	8	(9%)	17	(8%)
Succeeding in avoiding others so far	30	(24%)	26	(30%)	56	(27%)
N.A. (menopausal or separated)	20		8		28	
Not known	5		6		11	
Total	150		100		250	

Thus, the parents of one child with phenylketonuria said that they had been told that the chances of their having another, similarly affected, were 'a thousand to one against.' (The true figure is three to one.) They had had another child who was an idiot. A mother whose child had tuberose sclerosis and who herself had a *forme fruste* of the disease, said that she had been advised to have a second child, though she had not yet done so. (The chances are even that such a child would be affected.) Several other mothers had not had the nature of the Rhesus factor clearly explained; two or three had previously had lightly damaged children and might not have had the defective had they known the dangers involved. Another mother had had three children with amaurotic family idiocy.

Only seven mothers had been advised not to have further children after the birth of the defective. Many others clearly desired further information.

One mother of an idiot with cerebral diplegia had consulted a specialist who had referred her to a genetic advisory clinic. There she had been told that the child's condition was due to a birth injury and that there was no reason to think that a second child would be similarly affected. She had therefore decided to have a second child, who was normal. It seemed unfortunate that this service was not readily available to all parents, and that more general practitioners had not sought expert guidance before giving advice in doubtful instances.

Conclusions

The data we obtained confirm the findings of other investigations in showing that mental defectives are born to women who are on the average older than other women at the time their child is born. This is particularly true of the mothers of mongol children, but it is also true of the mothers of other imbeciles and idiots. The fact that the women are older may in itself lead to problems of management associated with ill health in the parents, but we did not investigate the extent to which this was so.

About half of the parents had been worried about the possibility of having another mentally subnormal child. Three-quarters of these had not wanted further children, though some of the mothers had in fact become pregnant again.

Despite the great and widespread anxiety about further pregnancies, only one-third of the women had had medical advice about the risks of further children being mentally subnormal. (The chances of such an event will of course depend upon the type of mental defect from which the child suffers, and sometimes upon the past history of the mother.) Many mothers were too embarrassed to ask the doctors about these matters, and many doctors, it seems, do not raise them themselves.

□ □ □

from THE INFLUENCE OF A RETARDED CHILD UPON FAMILY LIMITATION *K. S. Holt*

(Journal of Mental Deficiency Research, 1958)

It is a clinical impression that following the birth of a retarded child many parents are unwilling to have further children. Some pertinent information about the extent of this desire to limit the family was obtained during a recent survey of the problems of families with mentally retarded children in Sheffield.

With the permission of the Medical Officer of Health, the names were obtained of all children born after 1st July, 1939, who had been ascertained to be mentally defective before 1st July, 1955, by the Local Mental Deficiency Authority in Sheffield. During this period some families had moved away, and some re-

Table 3

The Ages of the Retarded Children in July 1955

Age	Number
3—5½ years	7
5½—10½ years	86
10½—15 years	108
Total	201

tarded children had died, but 226 families were available for study. It was possible to obtain information from 201 families by detailed personal interviews in the homes. Twenty-five families could not be seen. . . .

Most severely retarded children, after the earlier years of life, became known to the Local Authority, and . . . the 201 families studied were reasonably representative of the general public (Census 1951) with regard to occupational class. . . .

The ages of the retarded children in July 1955 are shown in Table 3. [Tables 1 and 2, on the reasons why the twenty-five families could not be visited and on occupational classes I-V in comparison to the rest of the Sheffield population, have been deleted.] There are only seven in the younger age group.

The Parents' Attitude to More Pregnancies

More pregnancies after the birth of the retarded child were not possible in forty-one families either because of the menopause or the death or separation of the parents. Pregnancies were theoretically possible in the other 160 families (Table 4). In twenty of these, the parents were quite indifferent to the question. They were subnormal families living from day to day with little thought for the future. Their homes were squalid; not one of them was adequately furnished, and in only two families were the homes reasonably clean.

The parents had very definite wishes for the future in the other families. Thirty-nine wanted more children, and 101 did not. The reasons given by the 101 families not wanting more children could be divided into three groups. In eleven families more children would not have been wanted anyway; the presence of the defective child did not apparently affect the parents' decisions in these cases. In thirty-three families the parents feared that another child might be similarly affected, and in fifty-seven families more children were not wanted either because the defective child required so much work, or because the mother wished to give the defective child all her attention.

The reasons given by the parents wanting more children could not be placed into groups easily. Several were rather indefinite in their views but they did genuinely look forward to more children. Seven mothers had wanted more children once they were satisfied that there was little chance of their having another retarded baby. Three of these seven had been reassured on this point by doctors, and in the other four cases the mental retardation was attributable to a post-natal illness. The parents in four families said that they wanted more (normal) children to help their retarded child to develop.

Table 4

The Possibility and Desirability of More Pregnancies in 201 Families with Retarded Children

Parents indifferent to question of more pregnancies	20	families
More pregnancies wanted	39	"
More pregnancies not wanted	101	"
More pregnancies not possible (menopause, death or separation of parents)	41	"
Total	201	

Table 5

Analysis of Factors that Might Influence the Mother's Desire for More Children

Factor influencing parents' desire	Number of mothers: Wanting more children	Number of mothers: Not wanting more children	χ^2
Age of mother			
30 years or less	26	48	4.1*
Over 30 years	13	53	
Position of mentally deficient (m.d.) child in family			
First born	23	34	7.5†
Not first born	16	67	
Age of mother in families with m.d. first born			
30 years or less	19	27	0.1‡
Over 30 years	4	7	
Position of m.d. child in families of younger mothers			
First born	19	27	2.0‡
Not first born	7	21	
Severity of retardation			
Feebleminded	19	40	0.9‡
Imbecile or idiot	20	61	

*Significant at 5 per cent level
†Significant at 1 per cent level
‡Not significant

Factors Affecting the Parents' Desires for More Pregnancies

An attempt was made to analyse the part played by several factors that might be expected to influence the parents' decisions about future pregnancies. The younger mothers might be more anxious to have more children than the older ones. The mothers were grouped into those aged thirty years or less and those aged over thirty years when the affected child was born. Twenty-six of the seventy-four younger mothers wanted more children (35%), as compared with thirteen of the sixty-six older mothers (20%) (Tables 5 and 6). This difference is statistically significant by the chi square test at the five per cent level.

Another factor considered was the position of the retarded child in the family. Twenty-three out of the fifty-seven mothers whose retarded children were the first born in the family wanted more children (40%) as compared with sixteen out of the eighty-three mothers whose retarded children were not the first born in the family (19%). This difference is statistically significant at the one per cent level.

These two factors are, of course, inter-related, and when analysed separately the differences are not statistically significant.

Thus, the age of the mother at the birth of her retarded child, and the position of that child in the family, when considered separately, have little influence upon the mother's desire for more children, but together they may affect her decisions. In the families studied the group of mothers showing the highest proportion willing to face another pregnancy were the younger ones whose retarded children were the first born. Similar observation might well apply to the general population, but figures are not available as control groups were not studied. However, even in this most favorable group of mothers as regards subsequent pregnancies, in the families studied there were approximately 60 per cent who did not wish to have more children. It is suggested that this is probably a considerably greater proportion than might be anticipated in the population generally. Crew (1959), for instance, reported that 90 per cent of mothers thought that the best family size was two or more children.

The desire for more children might be influenced by the severity of the retardation of the affected child. The families were divided into those with a feebleminded child, and those with a child classed as either an imbecile or an idiot (Table 5). Nineteen of the fifty-nine families with a feebleminded child wanted additional children (32%) as compared with twenty of the eighty-one families with a more severely retarded child (25%). The proportion of families wanting more children is lower in the group with more severely handicapped children than in the group with feebleminded children, but the difference is small and is not statistically significant. It is unlikely that the severity of the handicap has an influence upon this question.

It was not possible to detect any appreciable influence of occupational class upon the desire for more pregnancies apart from the subnormal group mentioned earlier who were quite indifferent to the question of future pregnancies. Similarly it was not possible to make any observations upon the influence of religious denomination.

The Extent of the Family Limitation

The period of observation of the families was between four and fifteen years after the birth of the retarded children.

It was possible to estimate roughly the number of pregnancies that might have been expected in these families had not the presence of the retarded child affected the parents' desires (Table 7). Twenty-nine of the thirty-nine mothers wanting more children had at least one more successful pregnancy. It was assumed that in the families where the retarded children affected the parents' desires that they would otherwise have had a similar number of pregnancies to the first group. Actually, thirty of these ninety families had further pregnancies, thirty-four fewer than calculated. Thus if it were not for the presence of the retarded children an additional thirty-four of the 160 mothers of child-bearing age would have at least one more pregnancy, an increase of 21 per cent.

Table 6

Influence of the mother's age and the position of the retarded child in the family upon the desire for further pregnancies. (Fractions give number of mothers desiring more children out of the total mothers in each category.)

	Birth rank of affected child		
	First	Not first	Totals
Mothers 30 years or less	19/46 (41%)	7/28 (25%)	26/74
Mothers over 30 years	4/11 (36%)	9/55 (16%)	13/66
Totals	23/57	16/83	39/140

The Methods of Family Limitation

The parents who did not want more children were asked how they prevented further pregnancies. Sixty-two families used contraceptive methods and sixteen families tried to abstain from intercourse. In both these groups there was a "failure rate" of approximately 25 per cent. The remaining twenty-three families, whilst definitely not wanting more children, did not take active measures and trusted to "luck." Their "failure rate" was 74 per cent.

Discussion

This study supports the clinical impression that family limitation often occurs when there is a retarded child in the family. But for the presence of the afflicted children more pregnancies might have been expected in an additional fifth of the mothers of child-bearing age.

Most authorities now recognize that the home care of retarded children is the best form of care whenever possible, but this usually imposes some strain upon the family. This study illustrates one aspect of the problem and others have been described elsewhere (Holt 1957). Recently stress has been laid upon the need to ensure that all help is given to make home care possible and satisfactory (World Health Organization 1954, O'Connor & Tizard 1956). Families need help if the attention demanded by the retarded child prevents the parents [from] having further children. All those parents who do have more children deserve help to enable their additional commitments to be successful. In the theoretical calculations above it was assumed that the families' burdens in caring for the retarded children had been relieved, that the mothers' desires to devote themselves to their handicapped children had been resolved, and that it was reasonable for more pregnancies to occur. The need to attend to these aspects cannot be stressed too strongly.

Some of the mothers wanted to devote themselves entirely to their retarded child. This usually meant that they would not consider further pregnancies, but it is interesting to note that this attitude went so far in four families as to make the parents want additional normal children to help the retarded one. This attitude is thought to derive from feelings of guilt and inadequacy (Repond 1955, Holt 1957), and might be resolved by careful counseling. Advice and guidance for most of the parents in this study had been extremely rudimentary, and in some

Table 7

The Extent of Family Limitation

Age of Mother	*Mothers wanting more pregnancies*		*Mothers not wanting more pregnancies*			
	Number at risk	Number having more pregnancies	Number at risk	Number having more pregnancies	Number of pregnancies expected*	'Loss' of pregnancies
30 years or less	26	21 (81%)	44	19 (43%)	36	17
Over 30 years	13	8 (61%)	46	11 (24%)	28	17
Total	39	29 (74%)	90	30 (33%)	64	34

*The number of pregnancies expected is calculated by assuming that the proportion of mothers having more pregnancies in the second group would be the same as that for the first group but for the presence of the retarded child.

cases had been completely absent.

The fear of another affected child is common and leads to limitation of the family. Sometimes the parents' fears are justified and the risk is a considerable one. In others the chances are small, and in some cases we have to admit that we do not know enough yet to be able to advise the parents with certainty. Much more needs to be learned about the causes of retardation. In the entire group the number of parents who received advice about future pregnancies did not reach double figures. Quite often the parents had been told that their child was "M.D. and nothing can be done." A thorough examination was never performed. Many practitioners seem to have a meagre knowledge of genetic principles and are uncertain in their advice.

A large proportion of the parents who did not want more pregnancies used methods of prevention that left much to be desired. As many as sixteen out of 101 abstained from intercourse, a procedure that in itself can lead to much marital unrest; and a further twenty-three, while taking no active measures against conception, nevertheless dreaded another pregnancy. The doctor can play a large part in helping these families.

References

1. Crew, F. A. E., "Biological Factors Affecting Family Size," *Journal of Preventive and Socialized Medicine,* 3, 1949, 1.
2. Holt, K. S., "The Impact of Severely Mentally Retarded Children Upon Their Families," M.D. Thesis, University of Manchester, England, 1957.
3. O'Connor, N., & Tizard, J., *The Social Problems of Mental Deficiency.* London: Pergamon Press, 1956.
4. Registrar General, *The 1951 Census of England and Wales.* London: H.M.S.O., 1951.
5. Repond, A., *Family Mental Health and the State; Proceedings of the Eighth Annual Meeting of the World Federation for Mental Health,* Istanbul, 1955, p. 58.
6. World Health Organization, *"The Mentally Subnormal Child,"* World Health Organization Technical Report Series. Geneva: World Health Organization, 1954.

□ □ □

CLINICAL GENETIC COUNSELING

Robert L. Tips

(Texas Medicine, 1965)

Modern genetic counseling involves investigation into family psychological problems that stem from the genetic nature of disease.[1] Such problems arise from misunderstandings about heredity and reproduction. Expressed as psychosexual disturbances between parents, they rapidly lead to alteration in family adjustments and stability. Such imbalances, in turn, permeate the entire kindred as multifaceted emotional conflicts between members.[2] These problems become so severe that reproduction essentially ceases in the kindreds.[3]

The hereditary nature of genetic diseases usually becomes known to affected families through their physicians and the lay literature. However, the hereditary nature of certain sporadic conditions that are genetically determined sometimes remains unknown to families.[4] Certain cytogenetic disorders are not inherited; yet family members, not understanding the mechanisms involved, consider the conditions heritable and avoid more pregnancies.[5] Thus, it seems that a major factor in the development of psychosocial problems is the attitude the family members have regarding the origin or cause of the disease.

The purpose of this study was to compare the reproduction patterns of three groups of families before and after birth and diagnosis of a genetically diseased child. These patterns were used as a measure of the impact of hereditary concepts on the families.

Clinical Materials

The family pedigrees of fifty-seven patients with mental retardation were selected from the files of the genetic counseling clinic extending over a two and one-half year period. These pedigrees included twelve cases of non-hereditary Trisomy 21 Down's disorder, where the mother was less than thirty-five years old at the time of the birth of the propositus; fifteen cases of autosomal recessive disease, such as phenylketonuria and galactosemia; and thirty cases of idiopathic developmental retardation, where the genetic nature was unknown.

The marital and pregnancy records of all their parents and their brothers and sisters were analyzed. The records were categorized into the three appropriate groups of kindreds. The conception rate (pregnancies, miscarriages, and stillbirths) of the parents and the married relatives was calculated for the years prior to and after the diagnosis of the index case. These data were limited to the five-year period prior to and following the birth of the affected child.

In the Trisomy 21 Down's disorder group, the conception rate was calculated by dividing the total number of pregnancies by the accumulated years of marriage of the parents and relatives. In the autosomal recessive disease group and the idiopathic developmental retardation group, the conception rate was calculated from published data.[6, 2]

Results

Table 1 contains the pertinent data for the parents and married aunts and uncles of the propositi for the three groups. The means in ages of mothers at the time of diagnosis of the index cases are statistically similar for the three groups. Thus, pregnancy records for the groups are directly comparable.

In the Trisomy 21 Down's disorder group, seventy pregnancy records represented 241 accumulated years of marriage prior to the birth of the proband and 197 years after the birth of the child. There were ninety-six pregnancies before and thirty-one after the birth of the child. Thus, the pregnancy rate per year dropped from 39 per cent before the propositus to 16 per cent after his birth and diagnosis.

In the autosomal recessive disease group, there were 129 pregnancy records accounting for 312 accumulated mar-

Table 1

Analyses of Pregnancy Records in Families of Patients with Trisomy 21 Down's Disorder, Autosomal Recessive Diseases, and Idiopathic Developmental Retardation

			DATA PRIOR TO BIRTH OF PROBAND			DATA AFTER BIRTH OF PROBAND		
NUMBER OF PROBANDS	Average Age of Mother at Birth of Proband	Number of Family Pregnancy Records	Years of Marriage	Number of Pregnancies	Percentage of Pregnancies per Marriage Year	Years of Marriage	Number of Pregnancies	Percentage of Pregnancies per Marriage Year
Trisomy 21								
12	25	70	241	96	39	197	31	16
Autosomal Recessive Disease								
15	23.5	129	312	198	63	610	132	22
Idiopathic Developmental Retardation								
30	26	124	604	304	50	586	281	48

riage years before, and 610 marriage years after the birth of the propositus. The pregnancy rate dropped from 63 per cent conceptions per year to 22 per cent after the diagnosis of the child.

In the idiopathic developmental retardation group, utilizing 124 records, the pregnancy rate only dropped from 50 per cent per year prior to the birth and diagnosis to 48 per cent after the birth of the child.

Thus, it is obvious from the results that there was a great decrease in reproduction in kindreds of children with Trisomy 21 Down's disorder and of children with autosomal recessive disease after the birth and diagnosis of the index case. However, in the idiopathic developmental retardation group, there is very little change in the reproduction pattern of kindreds after the birth and diagnosis of the child.

Discussion

The three groups of patients selected represented genetic and cytogenetic abnormalities causing severe mental retardation. The data demonstrate that knowledge or concepts of heredity, whether correct or not, produce emotional problems in families that lead to a marked decrease in reproduction.

With respect to the first group, Trisomy 21 Down's disorder has been popularly and traditionally considered a genetic defect. Actually the condition results from "nondisjunction" of chromosomes and is not a truly inherited defect. Thus the disorder represents a nonhereditary anomaly where misconceptions about genetics give rise to problems in kindreds, as indicated by the marked drop in reproduction after the birth of the affected child.

In the autosomal recessive disease group, the condition is a true genetic defect that becomes well known to the parents. The conception rate among these kindreds demonstrates a severe decrease of reproduction similar to that in Down's disorder.

In the idiopathic developmental retardation group, the condition is genetically determined, yet this fact remains obscure. Families apparently appreciate the severely abnormal condition without being burdened with the problems stemming from the hereditary nature of the disorder. Their reproduction rate does not appreciably change.

Through research in genetic counseling, it has been learned that the severe emotional problems develop from misconceptions and misinterpretations of genetic phenomena and lead to feelings of guilt and hostilities in the families.[3] Prevention of these adverse emotional stresses can probably be accomplished through accurate genetic diagnosis of relatives (especially the heterozygotes and normal homozygotes), reassurances concerning emotional reactions by relatives, and careful consideration of the emotional and intellectual needs of parents geared to their sphere of comprehension. *Whereas accurate genetic risks must be explained in detail to some parents, this may be completely unnecessary or very deleterious to others.*

Treatment of severe, long-standing emotional reactions to knowledge of genetic phenomena, as evidenced in two of the present groups of kindreds, requires a highly specialized counseling approach by the clinical geneticist. Essentially this procedure consists in establishing a deep lasting rapport with the family, in elucidating psychosexual problems, and relating them to genetic concepts and reproduction, in elaborating the psychodynamics of family reactions to the recognitions of genetic phenomena, and in aiding parents to gain realistic insights and reasonable acceptance of their genetic situation. Adjustments in emotional conflicts usually follow counseling such that reproduction among normal and heterozygote (carrier) kindred rapidly resumes a more normal pattern.[2]

Summary

A study of reproduction patterns among kindreds of fifty-seven patients with severe mental retardation has demonstrated certain basic concepts in genetic counseling. One group of patients (Trisomy 21 Down's disorder) represents a nonhereditary entity where parents and relatives mistakenly believe there are hereditary factors. Kindred reproduction essentially ceases after the birth and diagnosis of the affected child. The second group of patients show well-known genetic diseases. Reproduction essentially stops among relatives after the knowledge of the occurrence of the disease permeates the family. This is the result of emotional conflicts stemming from the disease's genetic nature. The third group of patients show obscure genetic diseases; however the hereditary concepts do not penetrate the family, and reproduction remains unchanged. Clinical genetic counseling aims toward defining and alleviating these psychosocial problems that stem from knowledge of heredity or misconceptions of the genetic nature of disease.

References

1. Tips, R. L., *et al.*, "Dynamics of Genetic Counseling," *Eugenics Quarterly*, December, 1962, 9:237.
2. Tips, R. L., *et al.*, "'Whole Family' Concept in Clinical Genetics," *American Journal of Diseases of Children*, January, 1964, 107:67.
3. Tips, R. L., and Lynch, H. T., "Impact of Genetic Counseling Upon the Family Milieu," *Journal of the American Medical Association*, April 20, 1963, 184:183.
4. Tips, R. L., "Family Studies in Patients with Congenital Spastic Paraplegia," *Journal of Mental Deficiency Research*, December, 1962, 6:94.
5. Tips, R. L., *et al.*, "Genetic Counseling Problems Associated with Trisomy 21 Down's Disorder," *American Journal of Mental Deficiency*, November, 1963, 68:334.
6. Tips, R. L., *et al.*, "Reproductive Failure in Families of Patients with Idiopathic Developmental Retardation," *Pediatrics*, January, 1964, 33:100.

□ □ □

SECTION B

Religious and Pastoral Counseling

Man often turns to religion in times of crisis or radical change, either for comfort or to seek sanction as mediated by traditional procedures and symbols (e.g. passage rites). Yet studies have shown that in the past, even religious parents of the retarded have found little guidance and comfort from their spiritual leaders. Perhaps this is a consequence of the frequent definition of mental retardation as a medical problem, which sends parents to an array of medical and health facilities. Having spent their energy going from one health practitioner to another, the parents possibly never considered their clergyman as a resource. This is all the more surprising when we learn that some writers in the field have viewed religious counseling as being of unique and/or optimal benefit to some parents. Fortunately, within the churches there has been a considerable awakening of interest in pastoral guidance and counseling generally, and in families of the retarded specifically. We can confidently expect that pastoral counseling will become a frequently employed option in the management continuum.

In the first selection, Stubblefield, an institution chaplain, gives us a capsule overview of the significance of religion and religious guidance for parents of the retarded. Next, Pruyser focuses on the importance of congregational and even ecumenical support that church members can offer to the retarded and their parents. This type of support is one more means by which families can be saved from the maladaptive isolation they have so often been observed to develop. Pruyser also presents a long list of questions and problems that bear upon religion and mental retardation. These questions may arise not only in pastoral counseling, but also during secular management of religious parents.

A person in our society is likely to be a member of social systems and subcultures which contribute to his socialization generally and to his value and attitude formation specifically. Examples of such significant affiliations are social class, neighborhood, ethnic ties, and religion. Religion, like other affiliations, can crucially affect a parent's frame of reference in regard to mental retardation. In the final selection Hoffman, a social scientist, reminds us that sensitivity toward and understanding of religion-mediated values may be essential to successful management. He illustratively contrasts the management problems that may arise when families hold values associated with Christian Scientism, Catholicism, or fundamental Protestantism.

from RELIGION, PARENTS, AND MENTAL RETARDATION

Harold W. Stubblefield

(Mental Retardation, 1965)

The role of religion in the parental acceptance of a retarded child is frequently acknowledged in the literature on parent counseling. One study (Michaels & Schucman, 1962) observed that while the religious faith of parents may serve as a constructive, supportive force, religion, in too many instances, is used in a negative fashion, impeding a realistic handling of the problem.

Such specific religious factors as religious affiliation and religious interpretations of illness influence the parents' response. These are noted by Eaton and Weil (1955), Farber (1959), and Zuk, Miller, Bartram and Kling (1961). Other studies (Murray, 1959; Stubblefield, 1964, 1965) demonstrate that the birth of a retarded child may precipitate a theological crisis for the parents. Furthermore, particular emotional reactions have distinct religious meanings. Zuk (1959) suggestively explored the problem of guilt in relation to Catholic theology, while Lynd (1958) related the feeling of shame to parental attitudes toward defective children.

Unfortunately these insights have resulted in neither controlled depth studies into the religious aspects of the parents' experience nor systematic organization of these data. This article is an attempt to organize these data into a meaningful pattern, to interpret the role of religion in the parents' response to a retarded child, and to suggest specific areas for future research. Such a perspective should prove helpful to counselors in dealing with parents' religious concerns and should also demonstrate that this is a fruitful area for scientific investigation.

Retardation as a Theological Crisis

When research findings are analyzed, two definite patterns of relationship between religion and parental acceptance are apparent. The first pattern is that the birth of a retarded child precipitates a theological crisis for many parents.

The emotional impact upon some parents is severe enough to shatter their religious faith. One mother (Murray, 1959) of a retarded child contends that having a child who will remain a mental cripple for his entire life places parents, at least in their feelings, outside the province of God's mercy and justice, if they can still believe that there is a God. This mother further charges that these theological problems are almost always ignored by professional workers.

Moreover, a survey (Stubblefield, 1964) of 220 Protestant and Catholic clergymen disclosed that fifteen per cent of these ministers believed that having a retarded child had caused doubt about the goodness of God in the parents known to them, and thirteen per cent had observed reactions of guilt. Failure to resolve this conflict, they noted, often resulted in attitudes of chronic bitterness, resentment, or apathy.

Another dimension of the theological crisis is the belief that the retarded condition is the punishment of God. Involved here, of course, is the problem of sin, guilt, and forgiveness. In some instances, such a belief represents man's persistent need to affix responsibility and to believe that God visits the sins of the fathers upon the sons (Oates, 1957). It may simply reflect the religious training which the parents received as children.

Attributing mental retardation to God's judgment is not always the result of faulty religious instruction. Guilt also operates at a deeper, more unconscious level where direct confrontation and re-education are not sufficient. For some parents this belief is a way to preserve self-esteem in the face of an irrevocable tragedy. Feeling punished for sins may be more tolerable than to believe that this event has no meaning and is unrelated to one's personal identity. It reflects "a universal human tendency to avoid the anxiety of feeling helpless in the hands of what seems to be an impersonal, irrational fate" (Thornton, 1964).

Feelings of punishment also result from the sense of social isolation which parents of retarded children experience in our culture. Guilt caused by alienation from social relationships is thus interpreted as alienation from God.

A distinction, however, must be drawn between a sense of guilt and genuine guilt. Belief that one is being punished is often realistically related to concrete deeds for which forgiveness is needed.

> For instance, in conversation with a minister, the mother of a retarded son stated that she could not understand why God was punishing her. When the minister explored why she felt this way, the mother reported having attempted an abortion during the pregnancy because she did not want any more children. Now the mother was literally attempting to make "atonement" by overprotecting the child, even to the extent of refusing to let other family members care for him.

A further distinction should be noted between shame and guilt. In guilt feelings, the person feels that he has committed sin or transgression, that he is no good, and that atonement must be made. In feelings of shame, the person feels that he has failed to live up to his highest aspirations, that he is inadequate or inferior. One aspect of the experience of shame with particular religious interest is what Lynd (1958) calls the "threat to trust." This experience so contradicts what one has been led to expect that he questions his own adequacy or the values of the world of reality. Lynd further contends that feelings of shame for one's children become codified as a parental defect. Thus what is frequently interpreted as guilt may be closer to a sense of shame.

While the theological crisis is most often interpreted negatively, in terms of guilt and punishment, some positive effects may result. Nothing here is to be construed to mean that mental retardation is a "positive blessing in disguise" as some theologians and even parents have indicated. Nevertheless, as the Judaeo-Christian tradition has rightly emphasized, suffering is redemptive as well as destructive. Through suffering, religious faith can be deepened, strengthened, and one's ultimate beliefs and values clarified.

In the survey of clergymen, forty-one per cent had observed that a retarded child stimulated greater faith in the parents known to them, while twenty-eight per cent had observed families who were brought closer to the church as a result of this experience. Parents themselves have testified that as a result of their experience they were turned "from the superficialities of life to those things that really matter;" that they learned the deeper meanings of patience, humility and gratitude; and that they developed a "strange kind of courage" because in one sense they had borne "the ultimate that life has to offer in sorrow and pain" (Murray, 1959). These positive effects, when they exist, need to be accepted by the counselor and assimilated by the parents as a legitimate response to a retarded child.

To set this crisis in its proper context involves a longitudinal perspective as well as a cross-sectional one. The process of discovering, accepting, and planning for a retarded child is similar to a grief process. What is appropriate and healthy at one stage is inappropriate at another. The health or pathology of the theological crisis is partly determined by the time factor. For parents, initially, to feel anger and bitterness toward God and to project blame on God is quite natural and can be dealt with sympathetically and reflectively. For these same feelings to be strongly expressed six years later, as in the mother who wondered why God was punishing her, may indicate severe emotional disturbance, requiring more intensive treatment.

Religious Factors in Parents' Response

Thus mental retardation as a theological crisis is best understood in relation to the religious history of the parents. Not only does the birth of a retarded child affect religious faith, but religious faith also affects the parents' response to this event. This is the second pattern of relationship between religion and parental acceptance. At least three religious factors have been recognized as formative influences.

One is the religious affiliation of the parents. Two recent studies disclosed that Catholic parents tend to be more accepting of a retarded child than either Protestant or Jewish parents. Farber (1959) found that removing a retarded boy from a Catholic home had little effect on the marital integration, but that non-Catholics seemed to be benefited when the retarded boy was institutionalized. In Zuk's questionnaire study (1961) of seventy-two mothers, the Catholic mothers, on three items more frequently reflected greater acceptance of the child and indicated greater intensity in religious practices of prayer and church attendance.

In accounting for these differences, Farber suggested "that participation in the Catholic church and/or Catholic definitions of home and family life were supportive." Similarly, Zuk believed that the Catholic mothers' greater acceptance resulted from the Catholic doctrine that parents should not feel guilty for bearing a retarded child. Instead, they should accept the child as the gift of God. Neither Protestant or Jewish teachings are this explicit. The rationale underlying these conclusions seems to be that the greater acceptance of the Catholic parents results from different attitudes toward homemaking and children in general. Some studies (Lenski, 1963; Masland, Sarason, and Gladwin, 1958) support this conclusion. Religious affiliation, however, "is but one aspect of broader subcultural differences which are at work." It should not be used as an independent variable without qualification.

A second factor is the religious interpretation of the cause of illness. Contrast the results of these two interpretations. In a study of the Hutterite community, a close knit, communal, religious group, Eaton and Weil (1955) found considerable social acceptance of the retarded. This acceptance apparently stemmed from two sources. First, genetic reasons were usually advanced to explain the prevalence of fifty-one cases of mental retardation. No moral or social stigma was attached. Second, the care of handicapped persons was considered to be a religious obligation. In this atmosphere, retardation is accepted matter-of-factly. When retardation is recognized, the person is taken to the doctor to determine if there is any medical remedy. The community provides the family with additional care if needed. Other children are punished if they ridicule or take advantage of the afflicted child. Retardates who reach adulthood are encouraged to work.

In contrast, belief that retardation is the punishment of God creates extreme guilt and prevents parents from realistically planning for a retarded child.

> Mr. Tucker, the father of a six-year-old retarded son, remarked to a minister at an evaluation clinic that if he and his wife had been "the kind of persons that God wants us to be, it wouldn't have happened." Moreover, he believed that if they now became the kind of persons God wants them to be, their son would be cured. So strongly did he believe this that he sent his son's name to Oral Roberts for prayer. Mr. Tucker refused to accept the limitations of his son. Instead, the child became the center of the family, and the needs of the other son and the mother were sacrificed in the care of the retarded child.

A third factor is the religious teachings regarding the expression of feeling. Every religion and culture structures acceptable patterns for the expression of emotions and reaction to such crucial events as illness and death. Moral values are even attached to the kinds or intensity of emotions permitted to be expressed.

When a religious group interprets mental retardation as a sign of God's disfavor, and this interpretation is accepted, as in Mr. Tucker's case, guilt tends to be the dominant emotion expressed. When parents, however, cannot accept the interpretation of the religious community, they either suppress their deeper feelings or reject the community's interpretation. Mr. Tucker's wife, for instance, openly disagreed with his viewpoint. Instead of feeling guilt for producing a retarded child, she felt hostility toward God for allowing this to happen. She could not understand why they of all people had a retarded child. As she said, they were as good as most people, and many other persons could have endured this crisis better than she.

With other parents, negative and socially unacceptable feelings are suppressed, as Winburn Davis (1962) noted. These unexpressable feelings included guilt, disappointment, fear of the future, failure, shame, repulsion of the child, and hopelessness. Many of the parents that Davis, a social worker, interviewed reported that they stopped crying after the birth of their retarded child. Their feelings were "frozen." Only after freedom to honestly acknowledge their emotions in the presence of an accepting person were they able to cry again.

Areas of Research and Collaboration

Emerging from this discussion are several areas in which explanatory research is needed. These are: 1) the effect that the birth of a retarded child has on the religious faith of parents; 2) the teachings of religious groups regarding attitudes toward children, their beliefs about acceptable responses to crucial life events, and how parents use religious beliefs to structure their response to a retarded child; 3) the distinction between a healthy or pathological use of religion; 4) the process through which parents move, over a long period of time, in interpreting retardation in light of their religious faith; and 5) a comparison of the degree of acceptance of retardation by "religious" persons and "nonreligious" persons.

At the present stage of knowledge, observation and exploration on a descriptive level need to be done before research limited to a formal design is undertaken. There is still need to ask questions and explore "hunches" for which no research instruments may be available. However, testable hypotheses should emerge that can be explored in formal studies.

Two procedures are indicated. The first is the collection of clinical data. This includes surveying existing clinical records of parent interviews and encouraging parent counselors to record interviews in which religious concerns are expressed. Questionnaire studies are needed to furnish comparative data as Zuk (1959) and Farber (1959) found in relation to religious affiliation and parental acceptance. Future studies, however, should inquire directly into religious matters and elicit the parents' interpretation rather than the interpretation being superimposed by the investigator. Personal interviews with parents would also yield valuable data. These would be depth interviews with a minimum of structure, in which parents are encouraged to discuss freely the religious concerns associated with their retarded child.

A second procedure involves historical and theological studies. Some topics are suggested in the following questions: What are the teachings of the Catholic, Jewish, and Protestant faiths on sin and guilt, providence and predestination? To what degree do these teachings make parents feel responsible for a condition such as mental retardation? What are the teachings of these groups on marriage, the family, and children which structure the parental response to a retarded child?

What is being suggested here is that clinical data cannot be rightly interpreted apart from the perspective of the disciplines of theology, sociology of religion, and psychology of religion. The role of religion in parental acceptance cannot be adequately appreciated apart from an understanding of the functions of religion in the "life-economy" of persons and the theological teachings of the religious community to which they belong. Attention must be given to the belief systems which give meaning, order, and purpose to life and to the uses to which these beliefs are put in meeting actual life situations.

To this end, collaboration with clinically trained clergymen, hospital chaplains, and professors of pastoral counseling is imperative. A maximum level of collaboration would be to use such a person as a theological consultant. In a clinical setting, a theological consultant could render such services as counseling with parents when the minister's role is appropriate, interpreting the religious concerns of parents and the beliefs of specific religious communities to staff members, and participating in research. Two of the illustrations in this paper were taken from parent interviews of such a theological consultant, functioning as a member of the diagnostic team in the evaluation clinic of a children's hospital. To some degree such collaboration is occurring in a few state hospitals. . . .

"A man's religion," says Gordon Allport (1950, p. 142), "is the audacious bid he makes to bind himself to creation and to the Creator. It is his ultimate attempt to enlarge and to complete his own personality by finding the supreme context in which he rightly belongs." Thus the parents' search to find meaning and peace through religion is one of the unexplored frontiers of mental retardation. It presents a unique opportunity for creative interdisciplinary collaboration and research.

References

Allport, G., *The Individual and His Religion.* New York: Macmillan, 1950.

Davis, W., *Emotional Acceptance of Mental Retardation.* Paper read at Southern Baptist Conference on Guidance and Counseling. Nashville, Tennessee, September 25, 1962.

Eaton, J. W., and Weil, R. J., *Culture and Mental Disorders: A Comparative Study of the Hutterites and Other Populations.* Glencoe, Illinois: The Free Press, 1955.

Farber, B., "Effects of a Severely Mentally Retarded Child on Family Integration," monograph, *Society for Research in Child Development.* Antioch Press, 1959.

Lenski, G., *The Religious Factor.* Anchor Books edition, Garden City, New York: Doubleday and Co., Inc., 1963.

Lynd, H. M., *On Shame and the Search for Identity.* New York: Harcourt, Brace and Co., 1958.

Masland, R., Sarason, S. B., and Gladwin, T., *Mental Subnormality: Biological, Psychological, and Cultural Factors.* New York: Basic Books, Inc., 1958.

Michaels, J., and Schucman, H., "Observations on the Psychodynamics of Parents of Retarded Children." *American Journal of Mental ficiency,* 1962, *66,* 568-573.

Murray, Mrs. M. A., "Needs of Parents of Mentally Retarded Children," *American Journal of Mental Deficiency,* 1959, *63,* 1078-1088.

Oates, W. E., *The Religious Dimensions of Personality.* New York: Association Press, 1957.

Stubblefield, H. W., "The Ministry and Mental Retardation," *Journal of Religion and Health,* 1964, *3,* 136-147.

Stubblefield, H. W., *The Church's Ministry in Mental Retardation.* Nashville, Tenn.: Broadman Press, 1965.

Thornton, E. E., *Theology and Pastoral Counseling.* Englewood Cliffs, N.J.: Prentice-Hall, Inc., 1964.

Zuk, G. H., "The Religious Factor and the Role of Guilt in Parental Acceptance of the Retarded Child," *American Journal of Mental Deficiency,* 1959, *64,* 139-147.

Zuk, G. H., Miller, R. L., Bartram, J. B., and Kling, F., "Maternal Acceptance of Retarded Children: A Questionnaire Study of Attitudes and Religious Background," *Child Development,* 1961, *32,* 525-540.

□ □ □

from THE CHALLENGE OF MENTAL RETARDATION FOR THE CHURCH

Paul W. Pruyser

(McCormick Quarterly Supplement, 1966)

Receiving a mentally retarded child into the family arouses anger, not only diffusely at the schemes of nature, at fate, or at God, but also specifically at the marital partner, the parents or grandparents of either spouse, and the child himself. Dealing with these dynamics of anger, by recognizing them without judgment, then by channeling them through directed thought and activity, is one of the major pastoral tasks. But all suffering also tends to isolate the sufferer, and some attention should be paid to the feeling of having been set apart, as family, as parents, or as child from the common groups to which one belonged. Keeping these families within their customary group settings is another major pastoral task. With the feeling of isolation, families may become prone to engage in magic, superstition, fears of infection, "bad seed" fantasies, or even demonology. These attitudes too should be understood as responses to inner pressures, albeit that they need to be corrected by more realistic thinking. . . .

For want of a better term, the next issue to be considered is *congregational support* for the retarded church member and his family. While any congregation would seem to have a clear enough mandate to care for all its members, relations between families with retarded children and their churches can easily become strained. Since rejection can take many forms, and often occurs unconsciously, or against loftier intentions, even rational and well meaning church people may avoid contact with retarded persons. To be presented with suffering or deformation nearly always arouses guilt feelings, fear, or shame, and tends to expose whatever ineptness or awkwardness each of us has in dealing with other people. Conversely, to be the parent of a retarded child tends to make one watchful for any sign of avoidance, rejection, or mockery even among one's best friends. This can lead to suspiciousness, hypersensitivity, and expectancy in which signs may be misread or overinterpreted. Some families may withdraw from their customary relations and groups, like the burnt child who dreads the fire. Conversely again, members of the congregation, half-aware of their own apprehensions or biases, may handle these feelings by overdoing a good thing and becoming meddlesome, patronizing or intrusive.

I am really pleading here for a trite thing: that congregational support be given by a basic, steady, and fearless acceptance of both the retarded child and his parents. In a culture which tends to deny all evidences of suffering and evil, this is not easy to accomplish. An "out of sight, out of mind" philosophy permeates our lives. It is conspicuous in the political relations among nations, in the segregated housing patterns of races and ethnic groups, in the increased use of embalming in the modern mortuary rituals, and in the avoidance of confrontation with the poor, the deformed, and the handicapped. All of us need to be given a full and realistic view of life in all its vicissitudes, especially in the church. I am thus pleading for a complete and unabashed visibility of the retarded in the congregations, not only for the sake of those who are hungry for acceptance, but for the sake of the congregation as a whole. Christianity knows no untouchables; it is meant to be an embracing demonstration of reconciliation. . . .

My last point goes well beyond the life of any local congregation or denomination. It consists of *ecumenicity*. First affirmed as a logistic necessity, it may come to be pursued out of noble desire as well, which has been the case with many ecumenical endeavors. The incidence of mental retardation is small enough that congregations of average size cannot marshal the special technical resources which would be desirable for teaching church classes and organizing special worship services. The use of scarce manpower, the cost of teaching materials, and the scarcity of classroom space will force many communities to pool their resources on an inter-church, interdenominational and perhaps even an inter-faith basis. If a community has only one person skilled in special education, his advice and leadership must be put to maximum use, which can only be done when churches are willing to work together. The point I wish to make is that this should not be done halfheartedly as an inevitable compromise, but wholeheartedly in a spirit of avowed ecumenicity. The larger vision of the Church should take precedence, particularly when the issues at stake are not points of polity or theological finesse, but the most profound problem that has always faced mankind: the problem of pain and suffering.

The following questions and statements, literally taken from actual encounters between parents of retarded children and ministers of various denominations, illustrate the many perplexities and feelings which parents bring to the church. In one case, the questioner was himself a minister and father of a retarded child.

Why is it so difficult for many people to discipline a retarded child?

How should you counsel with a parent who feels that the retarded is "an angel in the room?"

Why is it so difficult for ministers to become involved with problems of the retarded child?

Where is there a place for the trainable retarded child in church? They soon outgrow the younger classes, and where then?

I prayed as sincerely as I know how, just that this baby be healthy—didn't I pray hard enough?

My baby is so terribly damaged—to me it seems that God's will was for it to die, but that man is intervening just to keep him breathing. He would have died months ago, had God's will been done as I feel He intended. Now he exists, but that is all. What does the church say?

We can get everyone in our community interested in our local association efforts but our ministerial alliance. The Junior League, the PTAs, the Civitans, Kiwanis, Lions, all types of civic and service groups have shown a very definite interest in the programs we are trying to promote in behalf of the mentally retarded, but somehow the clergymen just don't seem to care.

We know our ministers are busy—are they too busy trying to settle the problems of the masses to know or to care what happens to their individual families and the child who is "different?"

I am confident there is a place for my retarded children in heaven; I am not sure there is a place for them in my church. **Is there?**

I agree that "sorrow can make you better, or make you bitter," and those of us who are parents hope we are becoming better, not bitter. But our lesson in learning seems at too great an expense when we know it is at the cost of full opportunity for our **child.** This is the basis of our real struggle in understanding and acceptance. How does the minister reply?

We feel that the fact that our child is severely retarded was simply an accident of nature, not that we were "willed by God" to have this retarded child. Instead we find comfort in knowing that God cares just as much as we do, and feel honest sorrow, not "guilt" as such. When our minister expresses himself from the pulpit that such tragedies are "the will of God," should we try to talk with him about how we feel, or are we simply being "defensive" about our beliefs, and is it better for all of us to quietly maintain our own spiritual beliefs?

Why do people say when the retarded child dies: "Isn't it a blessing!"?

Why don't special needs of the retarded child and family come up at church board or committee meetings? Are not church officials interested in their needs?

What can parents do to help the congregation accept their retarded child?

What can a clergyman do in helping the parents and congregation and community in understanding and accepting the problem?

How do the parents of the retarded feel about others doing things for their children, such as taking them to local churches for worship, Sunday School, and other functions?

How does the family of a retarded child decide whether the child should be placed in an institution or remain at home? How can the pastor help in this decision?

Should the retarded marry? What about sterilization from the point of view of the parents, the law, and the Church?

Parents say: "Why did this happen to me? What did I do to deserve this?"

Why does this happen to the innocent retarded child?

Parents feel anger and frustration but often feel they can't be angry with God. Why not? Can we? Does the Church, including the pastor, allow anger?

How can the parents and pastor accept themselves more realistically as to their limitations and expectations as well as their sense of worth and capacity to help?

Parents wonder if they are not more rejecting of their retarded child than society.

How rejecting is society of the retarded child? How can we help society to be more accepting of retarded children?

How far should parents go to push the retarded child out into society? How much should the pastor stress church attendance and participation for the retarded child and family?

Why do we feel that we and our child are unacceptable to the congregation?

Can the sorrow of a parent with a retarded child be compared to the sorrow experienced at the death of a loved one?

What is the doctor's attitude toward the birth of a retarded child in helping the family? How can the doctor help?

How does the birth and care of a retarded child affect the family and marriage interaction?

To what extent should we talk with other children in the family about the limitations of the retarded sibling?

How protective should parents be toward the retarded child?

Are there certain periods of greater growth in skills and maturity than at other times in the life of the retarded child?

At what age or stage of development should religious training begin in the home and at church? How much does a severely retarded child really perceive spiritually?

What is God's purpose in allowing the birth of a retarded child?

Does the pastor feel the child is less in God's sight than a normal child?

Why doesn't the pastor go to the parents of the retarded child? Is the pastor afraid to talk to the parents about this problem?

Does the pastor know what facilities this community has for the retarded?

□ □ □

from MENTAL RETARDATION, RELIGIOUS VALUES, AND PSYCHIATRIC UNIVERSALS

John L. Hoffman

(American Journal of Psychiatry, 1965)

It is often tacitly assumed that a mentally deficient child is, or ought to be, the same child to all persons. The child may be received with acceptance, ambivalence, or rejection, but for levels less than acceptance, it is held that the persons involved should be educated into assuming better attitudes. By implication, these varied receptions are made in reference to a common background of values.

Such a common background is by no means an actuality. Culturally dictated values differ independently along a rather extensive range of categories that define the retardate and his position....

The whole subject of values as they relate to mental retardation is one that is largely unexplored. A profitable region for immediate study here is that of the major religions or denominations, which act as vehicles for comprehensive, unified, and delimited value groupings. Secular values tend to come in smaller, more discrete or more diffuse units, parts of much more free-floating congeries, from which individuals make idiosyncratic and eclectic assemblages. Although equally important, they are usually harder to filter or net from the value pool.

Religions or denominations emphasize then, implicitly or explicitly, particular types and colorings of reactions to retardation, seen as a unique type of distressful situation. They have defined the more general premises for these reactions, and these premises are integrated into the whole fabric of the religion. Needless to say, adherents of these religions will follow the theological patterning in their own thoughts and reactions.

Three brief examples of religious or denominational positions, along with a non-religious but supernatural one, are given below. These are intended not to establish at this time any analytical framework of limited universal choices within the sub-areas, but to suggest the relevance of the sub-areas in working toward such an end, and to provide illustration of the possible cultural diversity in regard to the sub-areas. A brief discussion follows these illustrations.

Christian Science supplies the first illustration, revealing the ideological approach toward an afflicted but not retarded child. Transposition to the retardation situation is not too difficult an exercise here. From the basis of a non-Christian Science viewpoint, the major emphasis is on not accepting the diagnosis or reality, on minimizing resentment, and on seeking magical solutions. The selection is taken from "Testimonies of Christian Science Healing," *Christian Science Sentinel,* Dec. 28, 1963, pp. 2282-84. Christian Science has many more insights and resources than suggested in a superficial glance at this testimonial seen against a possible backdrop of mechano-medical value orientation. The degree to which the reader is surprised may be an index of the degree to which he is value-bound. Telling how her child had been bitten by a dog, the testimonial writer continues:

> . . . I ran from the house and took the child from the neighbor and carried her into the house . . . and immediately called a Christian Science practitioner, whose first words to me were: "Forgive the dog that did it."
>
> . . . I suddenly realized the importance of complete forgiveness. I reasoned that if I did not forgive the dog, I would be giving power to a lie: that one idea of God can harm another idea.
>
> . . . The next morning there seemed to be quite a lot of swelling and discoloration around the eyes and mouth, but we denied the lie every time we saw the child and affirmed her actual spiritual status as the image and likeness of God, perfect, free, and without spot or blemish.

Medical treatment consisted only of having the injury cleansed by a physician. Despite alarm expressed by the physician and others over possible danger to an eye and over lack of further medical treatment, the family adhered to its principles and its denial of the lie of mortal mind. The child's recovery after some ten days is gratefully ascribed to Christian Science.

Guilt feelings may be fostered by certain religions and denominations. Elements of Fundamentalist Protestantism seem at times to promote this position. Here, any unfortunate symptoms on the part of the infant or child can be ascribed to the parents because "the sins of the fathers are visited on the children." One parent may ascribe the guilt to the other, or the guilt may be externally ascribed to the parents. Two examples known to the investigator of somewhat different expressions of this ascription follow:

> An educator in Massachusetts, who had worked in the field of retardation for

some twenty years, and was a member of the Governor's Council on Retardation in that state, described to the investigator the facts of the history of a Protestant minister known personally to her. The minister and his wife had a blind, retarded child. To his parishioners this was proof positive that their minister had in some way been sinful, and the minister was forced out of his church and had to leave the town.

A university administrator in the Boston area had a child who had been afflicted with poliomyelitis. The etiological position taken, within a Baptist framework, was a more modified one. He said that while both he and his wife believed that this affliction was due to sinfulness on the part of parents or perhaps grandparents, they did not feel that they could or should try to identify the particular person or wrong actions. Sinfulness was seen as a kind of overwash of imperfection to which no one was immune.

The "sins of the fathers" is a fairly rampant Fundamentalist theme, and it should be looked for in various educational levels of parents in influenced denominations.

Within Catholicism, there occurs an interesting mode of dealing with the problems of guilt, resentment, and projection. God is seen here omniscient, omnipotent, and entirely good. God's intention has determined the child's condition and his presence within a particular family. Although not all of God's actions can be immediately understood, all of His actions are for good purposes. Immediate human experience of these divine actions can often be painful, but suffering is a normal and expected part of human life.

Accordingly, the retarded child in many Catholic families is accepted, and well and warmly treated, without rancor directed at the child or physicians, or mirrored back at the parents. The Catholic definition of the retarded child, of adults, and of other central aspects of human and supernatural affairs and their interrelationships also help to define the retarded child as "human" and acceptable. The trans-oceanic generation of ethnically Irish parents, however, seems far more preoccupied with guilt than the American born generations of Catholics.

Coexisting with formal religions, extrareligious supernatural beliefs and practices continued at least through the 19th Century in certain parts of Europe and the British Isles. Although these do not concern the American physician of today, they do afford an interesting example of the cultural variety that can exist and of the interplay of the basic sub-areas of reaction to the presence of a severely retarded child or infant. Emphasized here are non-acceptance of the reality, blame placed on an outside source, seeking of magical solutions, and the wish to be rid of the burden.

In this body of folk belief, a quasi-human group (elves, trolls, fairies or the like) is thought to have removed the human infant from the cradle and to have replaced him by one of their own, usually an ugly creature that will neither speak nor laugh. This creature is the changeling of folk belief. The purloined human infant remains in the hands of the quasi-human group, usually in some underground kingdom or dwelling place. If the human parents ever hope to get their rightful child back, they must take the best of care of the ugly changeling.

Usually after a period of time, some kind of definitive action is taken. In one of these actions, the mute changeling is variously induced to talk and to laugh, at which point he vanishes and is replaced by the rightful child. (Are speech and laughter here seen as certain of the essences of being "human"?)

In another kind of action, the changeling is put into a dangerous and potentially fatal situation. He may, for example, be placed naked in a magic ring of stones outdoors on a bitterly cold night. The cries of the changeling are supposed to be heard by the quasi-human group, who in turn are supposed to rush upon the scene to rescue their distressed member, replacing him with the rightful child.

Symbolically, this is a most interesting situation, as it permits the parents to test out the ultimate in rejection. In the lore, of course, the magical remedy always works. Doubting the supernatural mechanism, we can see several actual parental reactions here.

In one, with full sanction of the folk belief, the "changeling" is actually left to die, it being the failure and fault of the quasi-human group to rescue him. This may be likened to the failure of any legitimate and prescribed process; consider, for example, our own sentiments when a patient deteriorates under psychiatric treatment, or expires under surgery.

Another reaction is possible. Moved by his cries, the human parents may rescue the child themselves before death can occur; perhaps he continues on the same provisional basis, or perhaps in discovering that their wish for him to live is greater than their wish for him to die, the parents also discover that the retardate is "human" after all.

. . . .

From these short and rather fragmented illustrations, which do, however, reveal wide variability and difference, it is perhaps evident that a knowledge of such values and their expression is a very real necessity to physicians or other professionals who deal with retarded children and their parents. Lack of such knowledge decreases and may negate altogether the physician's ability to deal with the situation. Physician and parents may have altogether different value backgrounds, and the assumption that these are the same may be disastrous.

With a full understanding of parental values in any given case, what then should be the role of the physician or other professional? Certain religious or other cultural positions taken toward retardation may from a psychiatric point of view seem unsound and even unwholesome. But to attempt to move parents too forcibly from a particular reaction syndrome is perhaps to pry them apart from a whole religion that is a real necessity to their continuing stability. When persons adhere with deep conviction to any large system of beliefs, separation from this system may have dire results.

With reference to the above illustrations, to detach the Christian Scientist from his beliefs is perhaps to plunge him into a world of harsh realities that he is unequipped to bear, and as a consequence drive him altogether from the real world. (In some contexts Christian Science might be seen as providing a sort of working relationship with a too oppressive and painful reality. By identifying painful experiences as "unreal" and pleasanter ones as "real," it permits over-sensitive or sensitized persons to continue to function in the world. In other or related contexts, the psychosomatic aspects of treatment might be stressed.)

To persuade the Fundamentalist that unfortunate events are not the direct result of religiously prohibited actions is to remove him from a patriarchically governed, yet rigidly secure world of moral cause and moral effect, and to drop him into a gray and clouded universe with neither sky above nor earth below.

To detach the Catholic from his belief may produce a variety of effects, depending upon the areas of detachment. (Is God indifferent rather than concerned? Is God punitive rather than benign? Is there no causality at all?) Here again, dislocations in this rather complex working relationship may turn powerful forces inward against the self or the immediate group, or against the retardate.

If individuals are better left attached to their belief syndromes, what alternative course should be pursued?

It is suggested here that the anthropological approach of cultural relativism provides an answer. That is, the physician should attempt to work within the logical framework of the particular religion. He may suggest more beneficial alternatives within the framework, since religious or denominational frameworks do seem to offer alternative routes and possibilities. Or he may suggest alternatives that although not directly given by the religion, are nevertheless logically supported by its basic premises, or at least not in contradiction to these premises. Or he may discover that for the particular religion, parents have reached the best working arrangement possible, and that a laissez-faire policy is best.

In any case, the family's awareness that the physician is conversant with their own personal or religious values will greatly increase the mutual rapport, and will implement the physician's advisory and therapeutic role.

□ □ □

Part VII Management Considerations for Various Disciplines

Representatives of a number of disciplines have laid claim to a leadership or primary role in the management of families of the mentally retarded. Yet when one takes a global view of management and observes the typical mode of operation of various disciplines, one sees much generality and little specificity of role performance. While virtually every helping discipline can contribute a unique element to management, the better part of management consists of the application of knowledge and principles accessible to all disciplines.

Many selections throughout this book were originally addressed to members of a specific professional discipline. However, most of the content of these selections was applicable to anyone in a manager role; and appellations to social workers, psychologists, physicians, nurses, nutritionists, home economists, etc. could have been replaced by reference to case managers or counselors in general. This part of the book is devoted to material which is truly of exclusive or primary interest to specific segments of the manager pool, each of which shares a more narrow commonality of competence, function, or problems.

As the reader examines each of the more discipline-specific selections, he will note many similarities in general orientation and repetition of certain key themes regarding proper parent management. Authors tend to imply or set forth a basic philosophy, and then to place unique disciplinary contributions or problems into perspective. We have included selections from the areas of education, nursing, medicine, and psychology because these disciplines have unique problems, make specific contributions, and play major roles in the management of the family of the mentally retarded. Other disciplines might also have been included to illustrate unique problems and contributions. However, the social work area was deliberately omitted because its role can be perceived as being so general as to largely underlie all family management.

SECTION A

Educators

Educators work primarily with the child, but on occasion they will make a significant contact with parents. We have already encountered educators in the somewhat unusual role of home visitors. Most commonly, however, the educator will meet parents on occasions either designed to inform them of the child's progress, or to obtain the parent's support of an educational program. In either case, we must be aware that for many parents the school teacher is a significant value and problem definer. The educator's observations and recommendations could be extremely important in shaping parental perception of the child, not only in regard to his school behavior, but as a person in general. Furthermore, in many cases the special education teacher may be the only professional with whom the parent is having any or prolonged contact. Under these conditions the educator might, in the eyes of the parents, become a representative of helping professions in general and, without being aware of it, could come to be viewed by the parent as representing agencies other than the school, or even society at large.

In the first selection, Zudick describes a conference program with parents of the mentally handicapped. This technique was designed to inform parents of the child's school progress and to obtain parental support of the educational program. As workers in many other management areas have noted, it was felt that special services to the child often fall far short of the goals unless the parents understand the program, support it, and perhaps even make relevant adaptations in their own child-rearing practices.

In the second selection, the problem of feedback to the parents is of major concern. Since such feedback can have significant effect on parental management of the child, some authorities would eliminate any kind of report card for special class pupils (or even for all children), perhaps substituting conference methods instead. While this is still a controversial topic, those who favor some kind of written report will find themselves in further conflict about what it should contain. For instance, should progress be reported in terms of general growth norms, such as achievement tests? Should it be couched in terms of norms for other handicapped children? Or should a child be compared against a baseline of his own performance at an earlier date? Evelyn Disner Hanschaka presents us with her solution.

As mentioned earlier, some selections have intimate relevance to more than one topic; and the decisions as to where such selections should be placed must be somewhat arbitrary. The reader's attention is drawn to the article by Winterbourne which was included in an earlier part on long distance management. It is appropriate to recall here that Winterbourne described a program successfully used in Australia in which educators guided parents by means of a regular correspondence exchange in conducting educational and child development activities at home.

from A CONFERENCE PROGRAM WITH PARENTS OF THE MENTALLY HANDICAPPED *Leonard Zudick*

(*Exceptional Children,* 1955)

Parent-teacher conferences have come into their own as an important aspect of the educational program for mentally handicapped boys at the Marxhausen School in Detroit. . . .

The parent-teacher conference program was initiated several years ago. There was a feeling on the part of the school staff that many parents were uninformed and, therefore, lacking in understanding of the purposes and scope of a special education program for the mentally handicapped. Several members of the faculty felt that much orientation could be carried out with parents if they were given the opportunity to confer with teachers and make first-hand observation of the school at periodic intervals. It was proposed that these conferences would supplant report cards for the classes involved.

Instructors and the school administration designed the program with great care. The support of the director of special education and the supervising principal of the school district was enlisted. They expressed interest in this pilot attempt to secure closer parental contact with the school and granted the necessary permission to proceed with the project. The responsibility for the detailed planning of the conferences was relegated to the school.

It was decided that such a departure from procedures of the past would hold most promise for success if it were introduced slowly and on a limited scale. From among the interested instructors, one was selected to hold the initial conferences. A letter of explanation was dispatched to the parents of this teacher's students. In the letter, parents were polled as to whether they were interested in participating. The responses encouraged the launching of a program of conferences. Over the course of the next several years various instructors, either singly or in combination, conducted school conferences with parents.

There was a consensus among participating instructors that many benefits were being derived from the parent conference program. Not only did these instructors feel that they understood their students better as a result of the conferences, but also they placed much emphasis upon having clarified the thinking of parents in regard to what the needs of these particular children were, and in what ways school was attempting to satisfy them. As a result of these favorable experimental experiences, the staff decided upon a total-school approach to parent-teacher conferences for the school year 1953-54.

During the pre-planning phase of the conferences, the staff agreed that the following were major purposes:

1. to establish a cooperative relationship with parents in understanding and helping these children academically, socially, emotionally, and physically;
2. to furnish periodic reports of progress to parents in regard to educational and social adjustment;
3. to interpret for parents the purposes, scope, and procedures of a program designed specifically for mentally handicapped children;
4. to provide opportunities for first-hand observation of the facilities available for a program for the mentally handicapped.

Four parent-teacher conferences were held during the course of the school year at approximately eight-week intervals. Attendance varied from 130, or 65 per cent of all (200) parents at the first conference to 150, or 75 per cent of all parents, at the fourth. Such factors as both parents working, parental illness, and indifference to conference values prevented a higher rate of turnout.

Procedures for the Conferences

Before the first conference, certain details of procedure were formulated:

1. A form letter explaining the purposes and scope of the conference was sent to each parent. Parents were asked to indicate whether they could attend the conference.
2. Parents who could attend were then sent a form on which they indicated the day and time of day which would be most convenient for them. This information was to be for advisory purposes only in planning conference times for the various classes. Therefore, the actual scheduled day and time did not necessarily coincide with parental choices.
3. A schedule of conferences was drawn up, wherein, insofar as possible, teachers who worked with the same classes held their conferences on the same day. A half-day was allocated for the conferences.
4. Parents were then sent an appointment time in order to stagger appointments.
5. Boys whose parents could not attend were required to report to school as usual and were assigned to a definite class for the day.
6. Parents who came for the conference brought their boys with them. These boys attended the conference and then remained in school for the rest of the day.
7. Teachers who did not have conferences on a particular day were asked to use their coordinating periods for handling classes of teachers who were conducting conferences.

It became evident during the first conference that certain modifications in arrangements and procedures were required. Teachers were asked to evaluate the conference and pointed out the following problems:

1. A half-day was insufficient for adequate conferences. Parents were unable to see teachers other than their boys' conference teachers.
2. Some parents were confused as to when they were to come. Teachers felt that too many notices had been sent home.
3. Parents had to wait too long for their conferences.
4. There were inadequate turn-outs in some sections. Teachers felt some students had not delivered the notices about the conferences to their parents.
5. No provision was made for reporting to parents who were unable to attend the conferences.

In the light of the above-mentioned and other related problems, the staff worked out a number of suggestions for improvement of subsequent conferences. These suggestions included:

1. All conferences should be for a full day and on the same day.
2. Students whose parents could not come should report to school as usual. The music teacher (who did not have a home-room group) should handle this group.
3. Boys should accompany their parents to the conference and return home with them.
4. At least fifteen minutes should be allowed for each conference.
5. The date for a conference should be set at least two weeks in advance, in order to allow sufficient time to complete arrangements.
6. Parents should sign all notes sent home and return them to school.
7. Homeroom and special subject teachers of the same classes should be located in the same room or close to one another.
8. A report on school work should be sent home for boys whose parents could not come.

These suggestions were incorporated into the planning for the three remaining conferences and did much to lend to their success. Students also aided the program by serving as guides in the halls and shops. Boys in the cooking classes prepared and served coffee and cookies in the lunchroom during one of the conferences. Mother hostesses were in charge of refreshments at another conference. The work of the students and instructional materials were displayed in both the academic and vocational rooms. It was found that the involvement of students and parents in the program planning did much to foster the conferences.

In order to approximate the material covered in interviews, a five-point check-list scale was constructed and sent home with boys whose parents were unable to attend. This scale included evaluations in the academic, vocational, social adjustment, and attendance areas, and carried the designations "superior," "good," "average," "fair," and "poor." In addition, a section was provided on the report for comments in regard to any particular problems the boy was experiencing in relation to his total-school adjustment.

Values to the Parents and the School

As with other aspects of education, it is necessary to carry on a continuous evaluation of the parent-teacher conferences. This assessment of the strengths and weaknesses of the program has as its basic purposes the continuation of desirable features and modification of those procedures and practices which seem to be of questionable value. It was felt that a comprehensive evaluation required a three-level approach in which parents, teachers, and administrators were afforded the opportunity to react to the program.

Seventy-seven parents, representing over 50 per cent of those in attendance at the final conference of the year, responded to a questionnaire which was sent home following that conference. Among those parents who responded, sixty-eight (over 90 per cent) expressed satisfaction with the conference program and wished to see it continued. They cited such benefits as these:

1. understand my boy's problems better than before;
2. know how I can help my boy after talking to his teachers;
3. know what kind of work my boy can do after visiting the classrooms;
4. understand better why my boy is in a special school.

Thus, it was evident to the staff that, for the majority of parents who responded to the questionnaire, the objectives of the conference program, as outlined during the pre-planning meetings, were being achieved. There were a few parents who indicated a preference for report cards, but in the main the reaction to this new type of reporting was enthusiastic.

Members of the staff were asked to make a written evaluation following each of the four conferences. In addition to the many valuable suggestions for change which added much to the program, teachers were in unanimous agreement as to the value of meeting with parents.

Some of the specific values mentioned by the teachers were as follows:

1. There was an opportunity to discuss, in a concrete way, the educational and social adjustment problems of each student.
2. Much was learned from parents about the students' adjustment outside of school.
3. Counseling and guidance could be carried on with parents in regard to specific problems, such as attendance and health.
4. Parents were able to learn about the school program by observation and by asking questions during the conferences.
5. There was an increase in parent cooperation following the conferences.

From an administrative standpoint, one of the major purposes of the parent-teacher conferences was to promote greater community involvement in the school program. Through such involvement parents could begin to appreciate more fully the reasons for special class placement and special class educational procedures. The fact that mothers served as hostesses at one of the conferences, as well as the increase in spontaneous visits and telephone calls by parents following the conferences, was felt to indicate an increasingly closer relationship between school and community.

Additional Provisions

Unfortunately, it was found that parental non-attendance at the conferences was weighted heavily among the parents of students who were making a poor adjustment at school. Although the cause-and-effect relationship here would require further study, it was felt by members of the staff that this apparent parental disinterest could be contributory to the school difficulties of these particular students. It also helped to point up the fact that conferences could not be expected to reach all parents. It was recognized that conferences were but one means of reaching parents, and that the conferences would have to be supplemented by home visits, telephone calls, letters, and mimeographed releases.

Administrative responsibility for the successful implementation of the conferences was also recognized. This included preparation and dispatch of notices to parents, provision of adequate space and physical facilities through the cooperative efforts of professional and custodial personnel, arrangements for the teaching of students in attendance on conference days so that staff members involved in conferences would be completely released from teaching responsibilities, and the myriad other details that always seem to arise during any special school activity.

A further administrative responsibility concerns the training of teachers in reporting to parents. Teachers possess varying degrees of understanding and experience in working with parents. Teachers' meetings devoted to a consideration of the content to be included and the procedures to be followed during parent conferences are prerequisite to a successful parent-teacher conference.

As a result of the numerous contacts with parents during the conferences, the teaching staff has come to recognize more fully the importance of cooperation between home and school. Parents and instructors alike have suggested the possibility of forming a parent-teacher group to supplement the interviews. It is certainly feasible that such a group would afford parents and teachers the opportunity to pool their interests and energies. In a group setting, questions could be raised and discussed. Well-trained personnel could be called upon as speakers and consultants to enrich the understanding that is necessary for helping the mentally handicapped.

In summary, a total-school approach to parent-teacher conferences has resulted in benefits to both parents and teachers. Because of increased understandings on the part of parents and teachers, it is felt that these benefits extend, ultimately, to the students themselves. The extent of participation by parents, as well as the favorable responses to questionnaires by parents and teachers alike suggest that a continuation of the conference program is in order.

□ □ □

REPORTING TO PARENTS

Evelyn Disner Hanschaka

(American Journal of Mental Deficiency, 1956)

A system of reporting to the parents of the ten children in the recently established special class for the trainable was needed in Roselle, New Jersey. There are four methods in current use in Roselle for reporting to parents—the report card, individual parent teacher conferences, letters, and home visits. Developing a report card to comply with the existing philosophy was my most immediate problem.

The Philosophy of Report Cards

The present philosophy of reporting to parents is summarized on the back of the report card and reads in part as follows: "The school invites you to recognize the fact of difference among children. In the light of this fact, all children do not do things equally well. Most certainly, neither school nor home should deal harshly and unkindly with children of below-average academic talent. After all, each child is to be challenged and helped to do the best work he is capable of doing."

The message goes on to encourage the parents to make appointments with the teachers for conferences regarding the difficulties encountered by their children. Visits to the classroom and to special activities, such as assembly programs, are welcomed. The note closes by urging the parents to be keenly interested in the report card, to avoid comparing the report with that of siblings or neighborhood children, and last, to avoid using the card as a basis for rewards or punishment.

The underlying thought that the reports are pupil centered rather than subject centered should be developed to suit our particular class. The idea that learning takes place within the whole child and not just with his "mind" should certainly be emphasized.

Why Should We Send Report Cards Home for the Nonacademic?

The children are with normal children in the public school and many have normal siblings. Giving them a report card helps them to feel that they belong and are part of the school society. Since so many forms of encouragement are needed by the retarded, the report card should not be overlooked. It can give a great feeling of achievement, accomplishment, and prove to be an incentive for further learning.

Report cards are the oldest form of communication between school and home, and though they are gradually being supplemented in Roselle by conferences, letters, and home visits, the report card still plays an important role in informing parents of student progress.

For parents who can find so little within their child to compensate for his limitations, a report card can be important. With a report card they have concrete evidence of the things their child can do, rather than the already overemphasized things they can't do.

The report card will influence the parents' attitude in some way toward his child and the school. A report that conveys the message that the teacher is friendly, interested in the child, and uses good judgment will prove advantageous, especially in the homes where there remains a hostile feeling toward the school for placing the child (even though it was with the parents' approval) in the special class.

By appraising the child at regular intervals in a sympathetic and objective way, it will be possible to develop an insight into his developmental pattern.

It is often difficult to recognize minute growth made by normal children in the space of a few months, and even more difficult with the severely retarded. When [children's] growth has to be analyzed four times a year, it is necessary to file samples of their work frequently, and to keep a diary on [their] daily behavior. After a period of time, trends can be seen in a pupil's development intellectually, physically, socially, and emotionally.

Part of the process of education is an intelligent analysis and interpretation of the pupil's progress. The program can best be developed so that the learning or classroom situation will produce good work habits, social skills, and self-reliance when based upon findings of reports made for pupils and the class.

What Kind of Report Card Will Best Suit My Class?

The card should be a report on what the school program is emphasizing. With the trainable class, it will be social living and personality development first, and academic growth last. The emphasis placed on different areas of learning will help the parents realize what our class goals are and the relative importance of different kinds of school achievement.

In planning a report card, it would be ideal to develop it with the parents and school administration together. Such a report could be very effective, for the interest among the parents will be greater when they have taken an active part in planning it. A practical method of proceeding to develop a report card with the parents' cooperation is outlined by Strang in *Reporting to Parents,* pages 50-59 (New York: Bureau of Publications, Teachers College, Columbia University, 1948). With a good leader, the parents could be guided into an understanding of the purpose and use of a report card. After the parents see the need of a report card and know what a card should do, they can proceed to plan one intelligently. The report card that would emerge would be interpreted by parents and teachers in the same way. The parents of the children in my class are in closer contact with the school on the whole than those of the regular class, and to include them in the planning of the card would seem inadvisable.

For children who experience so much failure, and for parents who are continually frustrated by their children's shortcomings, it is vital that the card be written constructively and truthfully, but emphasizing the positive side. There must be a tone of hope along with a plan of action, or the card will not be valuable to those already discouraged.

A gradual change is being made in the Roselle School report cards on the elementary level. It has been found that the card [formerly] used was in such detail that time needed to prepare it was completely out of proportion with time spent on other educational processes. Many items listed under *Growth in Attitudes* and *Behavior* were found to be overlapping. The items were:

*Works and plays well with others
Works independently
Accepts help cheerfully
Completes work within a reasonable time
Follows directions
Follows safety rules
*Seems to enjoy classroom activities
*Shows self control
Works neatly and carefully
Makes good use of leisure time
Assumes responsibility
Is courteous
Handles school materials carefully
*Respects rights and property of others
Keeps hands to self

The items were rated with numbers from one to four. One [meant] excellent, two good, three fair, and four weak. Not only were the parents misinterpreting the marks given, but from a discussion among the teachers there was found to be a wide gap in what was included under each item as well as what the words excellent, good, fair and weak meant. Planning the report card with parents and teachers, writing the card in a language the parents can easily understand, and including a guide to interpreting the report on the card could eliminate such a dilemma.

In November a card was sent home that rated the trainable children on ten items. *The four items chosen from the above list are starred.* Added to this were the following:

Cooperates in group activities
Assumes responsibility in helping himself
Expresses ideas well orally
Shows improvement in motor coordination
Shows ability to care for own possessions
Listens to and follows directions

Instead of using numbers, each item was listed under one of three headings:

A. John does well in the following.
B. John has shown improvement in the following. Further growth is possible.
C. John needs to work harder in the following. Growth is possible.

This informal report was well received by most of the parents. It was discussed further at an individual parent-teacher conference that followed shortly after the cards went home. After a re-evaluation, it was decided to keep the same format for one part of the card but to omit some of the items and list them under another section of the card. The traits we want to include are ex-

Trait	Explanation	Wording on Card
Sociability	How well is the child liked? Does he listen when others talk, and take turns?	Works and plays well with others.
Participation in Class Activities	To what extent does he take part in the class?	Shows interest and enjoyment in classroom activities.
Consideration for Others	How much regard does he have for others? Does he tease or hurt the others, or take their belongings?	Respects rights and property of others.
Tenacity of Purpose	Is the pupil able to stick with a job until it is finished, or does he give up?	Shows ability to complete a task.
Trustworthiness	Can you rely on his work, trust him as a messenger? Is he likely to take or destroy property if not watched?	Assumes responsibility.
Reaction to Authority	Does he obey willingly and pleasantly, or does he protest or react violently?	Listens to and follows directions.
Self Control	Does he use a soft voice in school? Does he keep his hands and feet to himself? Does he rest at resting time?	Shows self control.

plained above with the wording that will be used on the report card. (The first six traits were suggested by Arthur S. Hill, *The Forward Look,* U.S. Department of Health, Education and Welfare, Bulletin No. 11, 1953, p. 51.)

These are the social skills we are emphasizing but there are other skills [in which] the child could make progress that would be worthwhile to report. Though they tend to be more subject-centered than the personality area, if there is achievement, it should be noted. Rather than grading the items, they will just be listed with a constructive comment made about each . . .

1. Music–
   Enjoys songs
   Keeps time to music
   Carries a tune
2. Speech–
   Talks about things that happen
   Speaks so others can understand
3. Motor Coordination–
   Can cut out a square, circle, etc.
   Works well with crayons, paint
   Can jump on one foot, bounce a ball
4. Habits in Self Help–
   Eating
   Toilet development
   Puts on and removes wraps
   Ties shoes
5. Other Skills–
   Counts 10 objects
   Prints name
   Recognizes own name, names of others

A report card similar to the one that will be used is illustrated below:

Roselle Public Schools
Pupil Growth Report

Student: John Kaplin
Grace Wilday School
Teacher—Evelyn (Disner) Hanschaka
January, 1956

A Note to Parents

The school invites you to recognize the fact of difference among children. In the light of this fact, all children do not do things equally well. Each child is to be challenged and helped to do the best work he is capable of doing.

In reading this report ask yourself two questions. What knowledge does the report give of my child's growth? What can we do to help our child on the basis of this knowledge? These are some of the questions that will be dealt with during your conference about your child's progress. Rather than stressing the academic subjects, we believe that to answer these questions is the true purpose of a report card.

Please take a keen interest in your child's report, for it can be a good incentive to further learning. We urge you to 1) recognize any real progress the child has made, and give approval for it, 2) avoid using this report as a basis for rewards and punishments, and 3) compare the report only with previous reports of your child, and not with the report cards of a brother, sister, or a neighbor's child.

ATTITUDES AND BEHAVIOR

John does well in the following:

Shows interest and enjoyment in classroom activities.

Shows ability to complete a task.

John has shown improvement in the following. Further growth is possible.

Works and plays well with others.

Listens to and follows directions.

Shows self control.

Assumes responsibility.

John needs to work harder in the following. Growth is possible.

Respects rights and property of others.

SKILLS

Music—John enjoys singing. He carries a tune well and learns the words to songs quickly.

Speech—John often has something to show to the class, and with the help of questions from the teacher he can tell us about the object.

Motor Coordination—John has learned to hold his knees stiff and walk like a wooden soldier.

Habits in Self Help—John has shown an interest in learning to tie his own shoes. He always washes his hands before lunch without being reminded, but he still has difficulty in sitting at the table while eating his lunch. He likes to wander around while he is eating.

Other Skills—Printing the letter "J" has been a big achievement for John. He recognizes his own name and the names of four classmates.

ATTENDANCE

Month	Days Present	Days Absent
November	17	0
December	15	3

HEIGHT—

WEIGHT—

We would like you to come to school for a parent-teacher conference on *Tuesday, Feb. 7,* at *2:30 P.M.*

If this is inconvenient please suggest an alternate date and time.

Date.............................. Time.................

Parent Signature......................................

□ □ □

SECTION B

Nurses

Much written on mental retardation by and for nurses has application beyond retardation, or is of greater relevance to management of the child than of the family. Where the nurse has contributed skills specific to her profession, it has been mostly in her role as a public health worker. Still, the nurse's contribution can be of a different nature. Under the usual hospital conditions the nurse is expected to exhibit some degree of compassion for her patients. This demand can be considerable when a mother in the obstetrical ward has just given birth to a child which seems to be impaired. In such a situation of emotional stress for the parents, the nurse has the potential of becoming a key figure in providing emotional support for the mother, or in exemplifying to the mother the reactions she may expect from others. In this very early contact phase of management, the nurse's handling of the case can have long-term consequences for the adjustment of parent and child.

Ruth Woodfall emphasizes the contribution of the nurse as a home visitor. However, the nurse as part of a total team is also emphasized: "Only by clarifying the dynamics of the situation with an objective professional adviser was the nurse able to identify ways of making her service more effective." On the basis of her experiences with parents of the retarded, Woodfall sets forth principles and guidelines to help a nurse work effectively with parents of the retarded who deny the presence of retardation.

The selection by Mrs. Logan, a mother of a retarded child, could have been placed in any of a number of sections of this book. We have chosen to place it here because she strongly underlines the potential role of the public health nurse. She recounts eloquently how she could have profited from public health nursing services again and again—had such services only been available.

from THE NURSE, THE MENTALLY RETARDED CHILD, AND HIS FAMILY

Ruth Woodfall

(*Nursing Approaches to Denial of Illness,* 1962)

. . . .

The nurse caring for a hospitalized child requiring specific treatment usually works directly with the child to achieve nursing goals. However, the nurse providing health guidance in the home must work with and through parents in order to help a child. She brings knowledge, understanding, and skill, but it is the parents who decide which recommendations they will accept and who must put plans into action.

How, then, does parental denial of mental retardation affect the nurse's ability to function in her professional capacity? What skills does she employ to effect the necessary changes that will permit a retarded child to attain his full potential within his limitations? How does she attain the satisfaction necessary to her optimum professional performance? How do her personal feelings about retardation and denial affect her ability to help parents with their very real and difficult problems?

Roberta G: Complete Parental Denial of Mental Retardation

Roberta is an eighteen-year-old profoundly retarded girl with complete spastic quadriplegia, the result of encephalitis at the age of five months. She is an only child whose parents give her excellent physical care and the kind of stimulation appropriate for a young infant. Despite her complete dependence, as well as lack of speech and social development, she is perceived by her parents as a responsive human being deterred only by her physical disability.

Early attempts by physicians to confront the parents with Roberta's mental retardation resulted in their hostility toward health personnel. When the child was nine years old, lacking speech and muscular coordination, the father sought help. Evaluations were made, and Roberta had a trial period of therapy, which was deemed unsuccessful. The parents were unable to use available casework services.

The parents were referred to the local public health nurse for help in giving Roberta an enema. When the nurse explored with the mother other ways in which she could help, Mrs. G expressed the desire for assistance in teaching the child to feed herself, in toilet training, and in play activities—all unrealistic goals. The nurse made frequent visits, but the mother kept the discussion on a social basis, successfully impeding the nurse's efforts to change the situation. The only help she accepted was periodic shampooing of Roberta's hair, which she herself was well able to do. The nurse allowed herself to be manipulated by the mother even to the point of sharing in the denial. For example, when the mother said of this completely unresponsive child, "See, she's saying 'hello'; she wants you to kiss her"; the nurse carried out the request.

Attempts to help the mother solve some of her problems of twenty-four-hour duty, increasing weight gain, and arthritic discomfort were unavailing. The nurse became involved to the point of offering her services for baby-sitting. She developed many feelings of frustration and anxiety as well as hostility toward the manipulative mother. At a case conference, the nurse was advised to discontinue service because her visits lacked nursing content and because the only kind of support she was allowed to give was detrimental; she had become an accomplice in denying the reality of the situation. She was helped to see that such manipulation, invasion of her privacy, and attack on her integrity should not be accepted.

In regard to Roberta's situation, it must be remembered that she was born before parents of retarded children started to tell their story. It is only in the last decade that they have pooled their efforts to promote community understanding of the problems attending mental retardation and to fight for services and facilities to meet their needs.

Mr. and Mrs. G had to adjust to the physical disability produced by illness of their apparently normal infant—no mean task. They responded with excellent physical care, including hours of passive exercises and use of braces, in hopes that the child would walk.

Denial is one way of parents' saying, "This is too much." Is it any wonder that Roberta's parents could not accept her mental retardation in addition to such a devastating physical handicap? One wonders how they felt about their inability to protect Roberta from the original illness.

The nurse was confronted with the parents' long-standing denial of mental retardation and their lack of healthy, reality-oriented attitudes. She needed help with her own feelings about this situation.

Jerry B: Minimal Denial of Mental Retardation

Jerry, aged three, is the youngest of five children of young, competent, well-educated parents. His moderate to severe mental retardation is due to unknown prenatal factors. His parents cooperated in all the procedures of a long evaluation process at a clinic for retarded children and established friendly relationships with the professional workers. At the conference to interpret findings to the parents, they presented thoughtful questions, many of which were quite technical. They appeared to understand the explanations and accepted the public health nurse's offer of assistance in working out methods of training Jerry in self-help skills.

After several home visits the nurse gave the mother a manual on care of the mentally retarded child, which illustrates methods that may help control drooling. The mother, on reading the title page, said, "This says 'mentally retarded'. I know Jerry is retarded but I didn't think he was mentally retarded." In exploring this reaction, the nurse learned that Mrs. B thought mental retardation meant "there is nothing there." After reviewing the evaluation findings, the nurse said, "The word 'mentally' still seems to distress you. Perhaps you'd rather not have this booklet around." Mrs. B said, with a laugh, "Oh, no, I'd like it. If the word bothers me too much, I'll block it out with a piece of paper. I see it costs thirty-five cents. I'd like to pay for it." At the next visit, Mrs. B said she had read the material on drooling and considered all the suggestions too advanced for Jerry's stage of development. However, she had introduced some new, constructive play activities and was eager to demonstrate his prowess.

The nurse commended the mother for her ingenuity, especially in view of her busy household schedule, and accepted her decision not to work on Jerry's drooling for the present.

In this instance there was some denial of the mental defect, but it has not prevented the mother from helping the child. She has continued to ask for and accept some suggestions from the nurse, rejecting others which she cannot yet accept. She has joined the Association for Retarded Children and talks about Jerry's future need for special classes.

The nurse feels that this situation offers a challenge; she can help the mother accept the situation as it changes, and explore with her different methods for meeting Jerry's needs.

Angela C: Denial of Certain Aspects of Mental Retardation

A more detailed report, on Angela C, shows the effect of denial on a parent-nurse relationship. Angela, a six-year-old twin, is moderately to severely retarded due to brain damage in the prenatal period. Her parents are middle-class, second-generation Italians about forty years old. Mrs. C was described as overweight, warm, friendly, voluble, and maternal; Mr. C as rather small, quiet, and supportive of his wife. Members of a large, extended family live in the same town. Angela's nine-year-old brother, Paul, is a good-looking, slightly overweight, rather serious boy who is doing well in school. Andrea, her twin sister, is attractive, intelligent, and precocious; she appears somewhat undernourished. She has adjusted well to kindergarten. Angela has a pretty face, curly hair, and is fairly well-developed. She has an alternating internal stabismus for which glasses have been prescribed. Her hyperactivity, impulsivity, lack of speech, and crossed eyes make it obvious that she is not completely normal. However, she walks, climbs, and throws a ball. She is curious and investigative.

The Problem

Angela and her parents were referred to an evaluation and counseling program by their pediatrician, who has maintained a fairly close contact with the family. At the intake interview in June 1960, when Angela was four years old, the parents expressed a need for help in planning for Angela, who had always been "behind" her twin in development. They indicated increasing concern because Angela, approaching school age, did not talk and was not toilet-trained. When she was one year old, the pediatrician had told them she was "slow." Angela was examined at a child development center at the age of three. Her retardation was interpreted to the parents. Mrs. C said that since she had heard the word "retarded" only in connection with an older child with mongolism who looked very abnormal, she could not accept it as applying to Angela. Both parents said they wished to know more about how Angela's "slowness" would affect her ultimate level of development. Mrs. C, who asked for more information about the cause of Angela's condition, became increasingly excited as she discussed the possibility that she was "to blame." She had had a minor illness during pregnancy, and the baby was a breech presentation. She indicated that she knew these factors were outside her control but thought it important to know if there was causal relationship between them and what had happened to "my baby." Mrs. C was able to raise questions about her own involvement and possible overprotectiveness. On the other hand, she could not gauge her own performance in regard to Angela's behavior, since she did not know what such a child should be able to do. She explained the lack of understanding by saying, "Andrea is unusually bright, and Paul is a boy, so I have no experience." She also revealed some degree of helplessness in handling specific problems such as feeding.

The public health nurse became involved in the evaluation. She planned a home visit to learn more about the child's usual behavior, the specific problems presented, and the situation in which any plans would have to be carried out. When the nurse learned that Paul was ill, she offered to postpone the visit, but Mrs. C urged her to come as "she wanted to get started." She explained that she had arranged for her sister to be there with the children so she would be free to talk with the nurse.

Mrs. C exuded warmth and friendliness to the point that the nurse felt enveloped. After introductions to the children and a few minutes of conversation, three of the mother's sisters arrived. They proceeded to describe Angela's behavior, illustrating their comments by issuing instructions, counter-instructions, and threats until the child was completely confused and upset. When the nurse made an opportunity to speak with Mrs. C alone, she suggested coming at another time, explaining that it was difficult to understand all she was hearing. Mrs. C then made arrangements for a relatively quiet interview and the relatives left, taking Andrea with them.

Mrs. C resumed the interview and controlled it almost completely. When the nurse attempted to find out such things as the routine of a typical day for Angela and her mother, or Angela's capacity for self-help, the initial reply was relevant. But then the mother continued to filibuster by talking about the extended family relationships. She said many times, "We're a close family—a very close family, Miss —," each time using the wrong name. At intervals, she asked questions such as, "Will Angela ever have to go to a training school?" . . . "Will she get worse?" . . . "Am I holding her back?" but did not wait for an answer. When she inquired about the kind of classes available for Angela, the nurse explained that when the study was completed, it would probably provide information about the most helpful kind of class. Angela, in the meantime, was using many attention-getting devices to which the mother responded either by reprimanding—"Don't do bad, do nice" —or by calling attention to the behavior, as evidence of Angela's understanding of her environment.

The nurse was frustrated by her inability to elicit all the necessary information, and exhausted by the barrage of unsolicited material. However, after sifting and sorting what had happened, she had gathered some facts and impressions to contribute to the evaluation. Mrs. C cared for Angela as for a baby, i.e., bathing and dressing her on the table, and anticipating her every wish. Angela was spoon-fed because Mr. C couldn't stand the messiness caused by the child's hand-feeding when she tired of using a spoon. She could drink from a glass but was given milk in a bottle. No toilet-training was attempted, although Angela indicated discomfort when wet by trying to remove her own diapers. She did not play with ordinary toys. She seldom wore her glasses. Discipline was a matter of retaliation in kind—slap for slap, bite for bite. The mother interpreted Angela's sounds as: "Mama," "bye-bye," "ball," and "bot" for bottle, but they all sounded like "Mama," or "aba" to the nurse.

The mother said she had not told anyone about Angela's "slowness," particularly wishing to keep it from the paternal grandmother, "who thinks all her children and her children's children must be perfect." When the nurse asked if Mrs. C had been questioned about Angela, she said, "Yes, but we say it's due to her eyes." She mentioned that Andrea no longer finds Angela a satisfactory playmate, complaining that "She doesn't even talk," and Paul asks why the mother uses baby talk to Angela and not to Andrea.

The nurse had the impression that Angela could participate to some degree in activities of daily living; that she was being kept more dependent than necessary; that she must be quite confused about what was expected of her. She believed that Mrs. C was feeling very anxious and ambivalent about the evaluation; that she was quite unrealistic about some aspects of the situation; that she would be very sensitive to anything she viewed as criticism. The nurse thought that she would need at least one more interview, perhaps at the office, to complete her part in the evaluation. It is interesting to note that she did not find time to follow through on her plan.

At the completion of initial evaluation procedures, Mr. and Mrs. C met with the clinic staff to discuss the study results in relation to their questions. They were told that Angela will undoubtedly always show some degree of retardation, although the future is not definitely predictable; that the defect was present before Angela's birth and they could not have prevented it; and that her physical condition showed she had had excellent care. The staff acknowledged that the parents were confronted with a difficult situation, and that a handicapped child usually is somewhat more restricted and protected than a normal child. Mrs. C's need for some time away from her household was pointed out. The staff brought out evidence of Angela's readiness for such things as learning to feed herself and trying out simple play materials, and discussed the value of a structured routine in controlling hyperactivity. A plan was made for periodic re-evaluation.

The clinic staff believed that the parents, particularly the mother, would benefit from some casework before the nurse attempted to help the mother with Angela's care at home. However, Mr. C felt that efforts should be concentrated on Angela's developmental problems. He seemed reluctant to discuss, or have his wife discuss, the parents' feelings and problems.

Mrs. C participated in one casework interview, during which implications of the evaluation were discussed in more detail, including ways in which the mother could use the findings. It was suggested that many parents gain support through participating in an organized group of parents of retarded children. Mrs. C was encouraged to consider ways of getting away from the situation from time to time.

The nurse planned her first visit to further identify the problems with which Mrs. C really wanted help. The mother, who seemed pleased about the visit, volunteered that she had learned about activities of a group of parents of "slow" children and thought she would attend a meeting, but would wait for the leader to call on her. She planned to have Angela's glasses adjusted; she had been thinking about getting a baby-sitter for occasional relief but didn't yet know where to find someone reliable. The nurse suggested that Mrs. C arrange for any prospective baby-sitter to become acquainted with Angela and her needs before being left alone with the child. The nurse said she could see that Mrs. C had been thinking about ways to improve the situation and indicated her approval. She then returned to the purpose of her visit. Mrs. C brought up problems related to sleeping, eating, toileting, and speech, as well as Angela's tendency to interfere with play activities of her siblings. Mrs. C thought the eating problem should have priority because mealtimes had become unpleasant for the entire family. The nurse knew from the evaluation that Angela could learn to feed herself. She believed the child would have some degree of success in a relatively short time and hoped this achievement would encourage the mother to work with her on other problems. A plan was made for the nurse to visit during the twins' late breakfast, after Paul and Mr. C had left the house, when Mrs. C felt that more could be accomplished. Throughout this discussion Mrs. C injected rhetorical questions and statements: "Am I doing wrong?" . . . "Don't be afraid to tell me" . . . "I need help" . . . "I'm asking you what to do."

As the nurse was leaving, Mrs. C said something that had occurred the previous day had worried her "ever since." Paul, in talking with a teacher, had mentioned his sister. The teacher asked, "Which sister, the retarded one or the other one?" He came home quite upset. "That lady is crazy," he said. "Angela isn't retarded; her face looks all right." He then hugged and kissed Angela. The mother said, "We all know Angela is a little slower than Andrea," but she could not explain further. She told the nurse she had "ranted and raved" to her husband and had phoned the school "to blow off steam." She was angry that anyone knew about Angela's retardation and felt that the teacher was prying into the family's business. The nurse said she could understand that it was difficult to have this information come from outside, and assured Mrs. C that it was natural to want to give her own explanation in her own time.

During three visits over a four-week period, the nurse demonstrated how Angela could learn to use a spoon, and helped the mother to take over. The child showed pleasure when she succeeded and was given approval. The nurse suggested routines for mealtimes and equipment which the child might manage more easily. Mrs. C did little about these suggestions except to relay them to her husband and to an aunt, both of whom made some effort to try them. During these visits the mother was always very disorganized, distracted, and preoccupied with her anger toward Paul's teacher. She often talked loudly and sometimes cried in front of the children, who showed awareness of their mother's reactions. Angela seemed more disorganized and distracted than usual. The fact that the children were exposed to a great deal of emotional stress bothered the nurse.

Mrs. C reported that she had discussed Angela's condition with one neighbor who was understanding, but she had skirted the subject in talking with Paul. She was upset to learn that her husband's co-workers knew about Angela and said, "I guess I'm still rejecting the idea, while my husband is working on the problem." The nurse said she believed Mrs. C, too, was trying to work on it, and cited instances.

During several visits over the next three months, the nurse learned a great deal about the problems with Angela, and the various family members' reactions to them, and especially about Mrs. C's methods of managing Angela. Generally, the interviews were confused and diffuse; the twins often interrupted, vying with each other for the grown-ups' attention. Angela's behavior in this respect was much less socially acceptable than Andrea's. Mrs. C usually responded to their antics with loud, angry threats which she did not carry out. She sometimes slapped one of them across the mouth, or screamed at Angela, "You dirty pig!" She made no effort to find constructive activities for Angela, or to avoid the disturbing behavior by rearranging the environment. She nearly always brought up her snowballing anger at Paul's teacher.

The mother of a retarded child phoned Mrs. C during this period and invited her to a meeting of a parents' group. Mrs. C said they talked for almost an hour. She seemed to derive considerable support from comparing problems but did not attend the meeting. Mrs. C's frequent expressions of bitterness and sorrow over Angela's condition, led the nurse to express her feeling that it must be very difficult to accept, and that it is expected that parents will feel this way.

When the nurse attempted to help with any of Angela's problems, even in response to a request, Mrs. C usually changed the subject or told her why the suggestions were impossible. On one occasion the nurse took sample play materials and showed Mrs. C how she could improvise with materials on hand. She reviewed methods of establishing a toileting routine which other mothers have found helpful. She thought that she had demonstrated her acceptance of Angela, as well as methods of controlling her aggressive behavior. The nurse had great sympathy for the mother; she, herself, felt completely swamped by the problems, at a loss for ways of proceeding. She was also somewhat annoyed by the mother's inability to start somewhere. There were few, if any, areas in which she could honestly and sincerely offer praise.

However, Mrs. C did try out her new-found ability to talk about Angela's retardation. She proudly announced that she had told a relative and the principal of the school in which Andrea will be enrolled, "My daughter, Angela, is retarded." The father tried to put some limits on Angela's behavior at the table and at bedtime, and he took over the children's care for a few hours on Sundays—such slight progress while Angela's behavior indicated that she was experiencing more and more difficulty! The nurse told Mrs. C she was concerned about the value of the visits and asked whether she could suggest ways of making them more helpful. Mrs. C immediately replied that they were helpful and asked questions about toilet-training.

On the nurse's next visit, Mrs. C expressed her angry feelings toward other agencies, neighbors, and God. While the nurse attempted for a short time to engage Angela in a simple play activity, Mrs. C seemed suddenly to become even more anxious. "Angela is not interested," she said. "I was just thinking how her twin would love this and could have done it long ago." The nurse, reflected the idea, asking, "You see quite a difference between the two children?" Mrs. C said she was "getting discouraged." She asked questions that had been raised by relatives and friends concerning brain damage and its significance, and the meaning of terms like I.Q. and mental age.

The nurse believed Mrs. C might be going through a crisis—stark realization of the degree of Angela's retardation—and was again wondering "Why?" She asked if Mrs. C would like to have further interpretation by the clinic doctor and psychologist, but Mrs. C saw no way to manage this. The alternate suggestion that she talk over matters with her pediatrician at the already-scheduled appointment for vaccination of the twins was met with a change of subject. The nurse pointed out that Mrs. C did not seem to like any suggested method of obtaining answers for her questions. She replied that she wasn't sure she really wanted to know; she thought she was afraid to hear the answers.

At this point, the nurse discussed the situation with a psychiatric consultant, because of the direction interviews had taken and lack of progress in helping Angela. She asked whether her visits might be preventing more adequate help for the mother; and, if the visits were to continue, how she could be more effective. The psychiatrist's summary was as follows:

> Progress had been made; the mother was feeling better about herself, even though Angela was experiencing greater difficulty. Mrs. C had needed the intense relationship with the nurse but had been allowed to become too manipulative. Continuation in this way would prevent achievement of the desired goals; the mother would realize the effect of her behavior and develop

> guilt feelings. He advised the nurse to try to gain control of the situation, by structuring the interviews and having the mother go to her office, and by telling the mother just what she is prepared to do. He suggested that future work with the mother be focused on Angela. He felt that the nurse could provide the needed service but wondered if she might want some dilution of the contacts.

The nurse questioned the effectiveness of working on Angela's problems away from the home, since she wanted to use part of each visit to observe the child and try to teach her to play. She found the psychiatrist's other suggestions very helpful. She told Mrs. C that since the children undoubtedly absorbed a lot of their conversation, and might be adversely affected by it, they should plan to be alone for part of each visit.

This seems to have been the turning point. Subsequent interviews have been shorter and more closely related to Angela's care. Mrs. C has continued to discuss her feelings about retardation and has revealed many attitudes that have prevented her from carrying out recommendations. She can now discuss some of her problems more realistically, even though she cannot yet act on many of them. For example, on the question of a nursery school for retarded children, Mrs. C said Angela wouldn't be accepted because she was not toilet-trained. After she was told that toilet-training was not required, she said her husband didn't want Angela to go until this goal had been reached. Methods of toilet-training —which Mrs. C was ready to try—were then discussed, but she brought up other arguments against the nursery school. Angela might pick up unacceptable habits from "the mongoloids," and she had heard that some of the children were badly deformed. The nurse recommended that Mrs. C visit the nursery school to see the children and ask what the teachers thought about Angela's enrollment. The nurse believed that the mother could not consider the nursery school because she would have to admit openly the actuality of retardation. She still makes various excuses for avoiding the group for parents of retarded children: she has not been specifically invited, does not know the time of the meeting, or whom to call. The nurse reminds her that she [has] been given this information, and the next move is up to her.

But despite these aspects, Mrs. C appears to have mobilized her strength for positive action. She told Paul about Angela's retardation in her own terms, and later asked the nurse, in Paul's presence, to verify and amplify her explanation. She managed Andrea's admission to kindergarten and explained Angela's exclusion to school personnel and to Andrea. After careful study of Angela's elimination schedule in relation to her eating habits, she has established a toileting routine, although it is frequently upset because of her fear of "accidents" and constipation. Mrs. C has also tried out some suggestions aimed toward Angela's greater independence. She has recently phoned the nurse several times to report changes and ask questions. On one occasion she seemed annoyed because the nurse had not visited within the usual period. She has expressed delight at certain "new" suggestions, although they had been offered several times in the past, implying criticism of the nurse for not making them earlier: "I could have been working on this all summer." She sometimes berates herself, saying, "How stupid can a mother be?"

Although Mr. C has never been at home during the nurse's visit, his influence has been felt. He discusses Angela's care, and Mrs. C derives considerable support from his interest. He often suggests practical ideas for meeting Angela's needs. Mrs. C says, "He is wise in these things."

The nurse sensed a reduction of tension in the general atmosphere of the home on her most recent visit. She noted that Mrs. C had raised her voice only a few times and that Angela seemed less hyperactive.

Mrs. C's increasing ability to recognize and cope with her problems has given the nurse satisfaction. She respects and admires Mrs. C's accomplishments in the face of her overwhelming feelings of grief, guilt, and bitterness. She can readily offer sincere praise. Although many problems lie ahead, both Mrs. C and the nurse should be in a better position to deal with them.

In terms of denial of illness, Angela's situation brings up some interesting points. The parents accepted referral to an agency which provides services to retarded children. They expressed awareness of the child's retardation in stating their problem, but denied the term "retardation" and its significance. Although the normal twin would seem to offer a yardstick for the parents to measure Angela's appearance and performance, we all know of instances where day-to-day contact diminishes the awareness of peculiarities in a close friend, and where parents seem blind to unacceptable behavior of their so-called normal children. As long as Mrs. C could believe that Andrea was exceptionally bright, she could avoid examining her feelings about Angela's retardation. The tendency of parents to exaggerate their child's abilities is not uncommon. Does it indicate denial of reality or their tenaciously held belief in the achievement they desire for him?

A parent may avoid painful recognition of his child's limitations by adjusting his demands to fit the child's abilities. Angela was encouraged to dance in imitation of "Bandstand," to "shake your pony tail," and "do nice," rather than to learn self-help skills. By keeping Angela dependent, Mrs. C may have hoped to convince outsiders that she was younger than Andrea, thus discouraging comparisons. But this must have been extremely difficult with the constant reminder of a normal twin. The father's reluctance to have his wife discuss her feelings with the social worker may reflect either unawareness of the influence of family interrelationships on a problem, or denial of the reality situation. Children in a family usually reflect the attitudes of their parents. We have seen Paul reflecting his parents' denial, which left him unprotected in a predictable situation.

Evidences of Mrs. C's denial include her resistance to the idea that anything could be done to improve the situation, her inability to discuss the reality even with the "close" relatives or with her other children, and her failure to follow through on anything which identified the family with retarded children. However, her defense against recognition of the implications of retardation was assaulted by the recognition of others, to some extent by her own children, and to a greater degree, by outsiders—particularly the teacher and the nurse.

Mrs. C's reactions to the nurse's early visits may have reflected her effort to deny the reality situation. A "curtain of words" is usually a means of withdrawing from a threatening situation. The nurse posed a threat when she attempted to learn more about Angela's routines, habits, and capabilities. By interpreting the mother's questions literally and trying to introduce training procedures before the mother was ready, the nurse caused the mother to bring recognition nearer to reality and thereby increased anxiety and pain. Whereas a certain amount of anxiety is necessary for motivation, an overdose may prevent action.

The nurse responded to the parents' denial with feelings of impatience and annoyance toward the mother and frustration at her own inadequacy. Her purpose related to identification with the child rather than with the mother through whom any progress must be achieved. The nurse was asking too much and thus threatened the mother's sense of adequacy as a parent.

Only by clarifying the dynamics of the situation with an objective professional adviser was the nurse able to identify ways of making her service more effective. The insight gained decreased the nurse's anxiety and permitted her to give the situation a new look. Had Mrs. C been testing the nurse? Had she been trying to overwhelm the nurse as she felt overwhelmed? Had she been saying in effect: "Will you help me in spite of my bad feelings? Are you strong enough? Can I trust you?"

Conclusion

We have considered three examples of parental denial of mental retardation: one a classic picture of complete denial, one of minimal denial, and one of denial of certain aspects of retardation, illustrating conflicting pulls toward and away from reality. We have seen that the parents of a retarded child are people whose egos are threatened. They can, therefore, be expected to build up strong defenses against the pain that comes with recognition of the child's defectiveness. A defense is necessary to make life bearable at times. If parents can experience support from an understanding, sympathetic, nonjudgmental, helping person, their defenses may begin to crumble. In the meantime, it is essential to build on the strength in the situation, and avoid direct attack on the defense. . . .

□ □ □

from MY CHILD IS MENTALLY RETARDED *Harriet Logan*

(*Nursing Outlook,* 1962)

What I have to say as the parent of a retarded child is, of necessity, subjective; I am not trained either in medicine or nursing. My ideas on handling the problem of mental retardation have been colored by my own background —my family life, experiences, education, religious training, and a strong marriage which has been strengthened by this experience. Your families and all the families with whom you have worked are different from mine, but if dredging my reservoir of emotional conflicts can give you a better picture of some of the problems faced by the parent of a handicapped child, it will have been worthwhile. . . .

It is pertinent for you to know that when I was five years old and my sister was fourteen months, she was stricken with infantile paralysis. Serum was a new medical advance and in short supply; airplanes were slow. By the time antitoxin was flown into our city, my sister's temperature was at the critical mark; there was brain damage, with accompanying paralysis. She passed the crisis, but it was too late to hope for alleviation from the dire after-effects.

In the years that followed, my parents were preoccupied with clinics, massage, studies, special diets, and all the things that people do for a loved one. My yet younger brother and I were not deprived of parental love and affection (far from it), but we were raised under a double standard of behavior. Fortunately for us our parents believed in fairly firm disciplinarian methods, but my sister was seldom punished or expected to follow rules. She was overprotected and spoiled. Although this is a completely normal response of parents, it made an indelible impression on both my brother and me, and we both held, and still hold, extremely strong views on *never* keeping an abnormal child in our homes, and on how such a child should be handled.

You might dwell a moment on this background, and then imagine, if you can, my feelings when our second child, a little girl, was born.

How to telescope sixteen years of effort, defeat, small victories, guilt, and normal parental anxiety into 2,000 to 3,000 words is quite a problem, but I believe I should start with the prenatal and birth period. Our child had been planned for and was eagerly anticipated. I had a normal, full-term pregnancy. But a precipitous birth and evidently brain damage in the pituitary area were the beginning—the events which initiated many years of problems. Delivery was so rapid that I was quite aware of what was happening except during the brief period I was under ether for the actual birth, which occurred about noon.

When evening arrived and my roommate's child was brought to her, I was accepting of the decision that my daughter was not ready yet to visit me. When my husband came to the hospital later that evening, he could not see her because, he was told, she was receiving special care. After a restless night, I anxiously began to ask questions of the nurses. But, "according to policy," they could tell me nothing to relieve my fast-growing fears. As you know, there is nothing worse than fear of the unknown, and with some idea of my strong attitudes toward a handicapped child, you can guess how my imagination began to run wild.

Finally, about mid-morning, the obstetrician came in to see me. He admitted to being a little concerned about my baby, and asked my permission to call in a consultant. I readily agreed. A few hours later a strange physician came into my room and gave me a report something like this: "Your little girl has developed some problems. She is under oxygen. There appears to be some rigidity in her legs, and her heart is enlarged. We will be keeping a close watch on her." And with that he left the room!

Of course, no one who didn't know something of my childhood and attitudes could begin to understand my emotional upheaval. I prayed she would die, recalling the heartaches and the useless efforts of my parents for my sister. Then I prayed everyone was wrong and that God would work a miracle, for He knew what my needs were. But nothing happened, and no one who came by stayed long enough to give me courage or spiritual help.

Things grew worse by the second day. The strange doctor, now very grave, told me that a brain clot or hemorrhage might be the cause of the baby's trouble. By now, one arm was rigid, there was no coordination of her eyes, and we were told that if the rigidity continued to the other arm and reached the heart, we would have to resign ourselves to losing our little girl. On the third day, we signed the permission for an autopsy, and expected hourly to be notified of her death. Sympathy was everywhere, which only made the torrents of tears run faster.

Then, suddenly, everything changed. The rigidity left her arms and legs; her eyes began to move in coordination; her heart began to function normally; and she was taken out of oxygen. With a ribbon in her hair, she was brought to visit me—a beautiful dark-skinned, black-haired doll, perfect, apparently, except that she had no sucking reflex.

I believe that this was the first point at which we could have used some counseling. You can sidestep the issue anyway you wish, but I contend that there is definitely a lack of communication between the patient and the professional staff. The obstetrician gave us so little explanation that, to this day, we do not know what really happened. It is possible that he, himself, did not know what had happened, or whether there was any hope. Certainly, there must have been some type of medical report which eventually was filed away in the hospital records, but which was not made available to us as lay people. If the physician did not wish to be involved further with us, why shouldn't the public health nurse have been permitted to read that report before her first visit to our home so that she could have given us an interpretation of the findings and some idea of what we might expect?

Both my husband and I believe that in cases of brain damage or unusual delivery, it would be a tremendous thing if the physician automatically referred these babies to a public health nursing service for occasional follow-up visits. Although the nurse probably could not have answered our questions directly, she could have suggested questions for us to ask our physician. As it was, we continued in a state of not knowing and we took the path of least resistance, preferring to believe that despite everything that had happened to our little girl, she would grow normally.

Since she had no sucking reflex, she was detained at the hospital for six weeks. During this time I visited the hospital nursery daily and was trained to tube-feed her. On the day we took her home, we were given all the necessary instructions but none of the equipment needed for this type of feeding. It was wartime, rubber goods were a scarce supply, and so we had to improvise. We cut off enough of the tip of a regular nipple to permit the formula to flow into her mouth. Fortunately, her swallowing reflex was fine.

Here again was a time when a public health nurse could have helped, if only the hospital had referred us to a public health nursing agency. No one seemed concerned; there was no follow-up by the doctor, by the hospital, or by anyone. Interestingly, but somewhat ironically, a public health nurse visited me several times before and after our first child was born. But with this second child, for whom we so greatly needed help, no public health nurse ever came to visit.

We took our daughter to the pediatrician who had been caring for her older brother and here, again, there was no communication. Like so many pediatricians, he was extremely busy. Usually, he was very rushed and preoccupied, occasionally flippant, but always objective. I recognize that pediatricians are human and that it isn't easy for them to tell a mother that her child may not be normal, but every time I left the pediatrician's office, I was on the defensive, determined to prove his insinuations wrong. For instance, he regularly measured her head with a tape measure, but never said anything. Parents are not oblivious to the obvious, but they do not accept the signposts, and someone who is objective could be most helpful in pointing them out.

About this time our pediatrician moved his practice to another city, so we found a new one. He, too, was serious and most businesslike. In our many trips to his office he never suggested that possibly we would be wise to think in terms of our daughter's future. By now she was three years old, and we had completely blocked to the possibility that there could be anything wrong with her. She had had several convulsions accompanied by high fever, but we had been advised not to worry. We had no problems with toilet training or teaching her to feed herself, although she was very slow to walk and quite slow to talk. It might have been most helpful if someone had frankly asked us whether we thought the convulsions were indicative of brain damage, or the inability to walk an indication of some other damage. But no one did, so while the child was between the ages of three and five, we continued to delude ourselves that all was well.

Soon after her fifth birthday I took my little girl to the pediatrician for a pre-kindergarten checkup. He abruptly asked me if I planned to enter her in the public schools. When I said that this was my plan, he told me bluntly that she would probably never develop beyond the mental age of a seven-year-old. With only the seeds of suspicion, which we constantly sought to repress, this diagnosis came as a distinct shock to my husband and me. We were unable to accept the prognosis. Probably because of our resistance, the pediatrician referred us to the local children's hospital, thus washing his hands of the whole situation. It is possible that had there been coordinated visits by a public health nurse or some other type of home counselor, we might have been prepared to face the possibility of brain damage, or retardation, and would have been oriented to the idea of sending her to a state school.

So we went to the children's hospital. Because there was no special clinic for retarded children, she was put through the same procedures as for any normal child. When I tried to ask questions, I stated them poorly. As a result, I either received answers that did not satisfy me or was brusquely put off with some noncommittal answer. Everyone was busy; there was a new set of doctors every visit; the completely unpersonalized routine was a nightmare.

Eventually an encephalogram was done, and ultimately brain surgery was recommended on the basis of a vague shadow in the x-ray picture of the skull. This was a trying time, but the encouraging attitude of the brain surgeon gave us renewed hope. It is unfortunate, however, that we were not advised of the possibility that the operation might not be a success. Instead, we were told after the operation that surgery had been successful to the extent that a large amount of fluid had been discovered and had been drained, and that this might reduce the pressure on the brain and allow for a little more development. Also explained to us was the theory that the brain is a remarkable organ, and that it was possible for some other area to take over for the damaged area.

At our final conference with the surgeon, he advised us to expose our child to as many experiences for learning as possible. He said that she would gain a little from each experience and that, if surgery had been successful, she could gain at a rate of two years every year. He said that it was too soon to tell whether the surgery had been successful, and we should observe her for a few years. Two years later, the follow-up encephalogram showed that there was still constant agitation over the brain area from the pituitary section.

It is sometimes at this point that parents succumb to great self-pity. The many defenses they have built up through the years have crumbled. They feel great anger toward the many doctors who have not told them the truth or pointed out related possibilities. We were put on the inactive, outpatient list, with no plan for follow-up. Here, again, the surgeon or someone at the hospital might well have referred us to a public health nursing service for supportive home visits.

I mention this sequence of events in our experience to point up the fact that people who have this type of problem have many questions, strong feelings, great anxieties, and yet no one who understands their needs. Our circle of friends grew small, for there were very few among them who understood or wished to be with people who had a child who was different. The general attitude of the public was: "It's your problem, you figure it out."

I still could not accept the hopeless verdict, although I recognized that my child would not fit into a public school situation. So I threw myself into organizing a community preschool, playschool situation. With the help of the personnel in the Family Life Education program, we soon had a cooperative play group going. Not only my handicapped child but also my younger son had the privilege of being in a supervised play situation. Although I believed strongly that my child should have a normal environment, I still had the feeling that possibly I was not doing all that should be done or had missed something of importance, so I became most active in a parents' organization.

There are a great many positives in a parents' group, but once a person has gained the strength to identify with this group, I believe he must guard against segregating himself entirely, to the exclusion of the more normal social contacts. We never reached this danger point, partly because we did not like deliberate segregation, possibly because we had outgrown the group, but mostly because we had reached the saturation point of being always with handicapped children and parents who had problems with handicapped children. This is a point that the public health nurse might make with families to help them maintain their sense of perspective.

During this time, partly because we were still not satisfied with our child's progress and partially on the suggestions of various parents, we made the rounds of doctors, seeing one after another. At that time there were no mental retardation study centers. Today, the public health nurse would very likely suggest to the parents that they take their child to a study center for a complete work-up, following which they would know for sure what the prognosis was.

By now our daughter was seven years old, and was enrolled in special education classes of the public schools. Also, by now, her difference was noticed by other children, neighbors, and friends. We were going through the problems of community non-acceptance. As you well know, to many people the unknown is fearful, and they react by ignoring it, laughing, or being very unkind. My husband and I, as many other parents, went through this period of rudeness and unkind remarks, which have left a lasting scar.

Unless you have experienced it, you cannot know how much pressure close family and good friends can exert. Apparently it was not enough to have such a problem; we also had to put up with the advice of those who thought they knew how to handle it. There were subtle insinuations, the brutally frank questions, the persistent pressures on us to somehow get this child out of the picture. Because of my experience with my sister, there was this nagging thought in the back of my mind that my sons were experiencing the same things that I had. And still, the mounting frustration of not knowing what to do.

There is a difference between do-gooders and highly skilled consultants, and it is possible that if a nurse had been visiting us regularly, she might have been able to point out the very things we were suspecting but were too fearful to put into words. There were times when both my husband and I had a great desire to ask people if they thought we should drown our child. More and more we felt that no one really understood our problem, and it was at this point that we began to withdraw from many activities rather than face the questions, the probing, and the accusations.

In retrospect, I can see that had there been someone with whom we could have talked plainly about these questions, our doubts, and our frustrations, we might have come through this period in our lives in much better shape.

The announcement that a special clinic for retarded children was to open in our city provided a new opportunity. When we applied, we did so with strong determination to take whatever steps the staff recommended. For the first time in nearly fourteen years we found people at the new center who recognized our problem, accepted us as persons, and were understanding. The recommendation was to apply for admission to the State School for Mentally Retarded. The study showed that our daughter's head was still extremely small, that bone growth had been completed, and that she had probably reached her maximum mental growth. Any further development would probably be only social, and for the sake of our little girl, our other children, and ourselves, we were urged to follow through on this recommendation.

There are deep-rooted connotations to such a situation. The more sensitive the family, the more they have tried and hoped to do for their child, the greater their sense of responsibility, and the closer their attachment to the child, the less easy it is to send a child away from home—and these children remain children as long as they live. The parents need much reinforcement, but their problem is a matter that cannot be discussed with just anyone. The ambivalence, the dreadful feelings, the nights fraught with tears, and the interminable waiting period! If we had been convincingly advised many years earlier to put in an application at the state school, by this time our child's name might have been near the top of the waiting list. But at the time, the only way to enter a child in the school was by court commitment, a too painful step for many parents to take. With the change in the state law, families now can apply directly for admission to the school. The new philosophy is to provide a secure environment for the child which insures that in the event anything happens to the parents, their child will be taken care of.

When our daughter reached adolescence, other problems developed—for her and for us. This period was exceedingly difficult as we watched our friends' daughters of the same age blossoming into beautiful young girlhood. As parents we began to show signs, physical signs, as a result of the years of pressure —ulcers, headaches, all manner of physical problems. Also, we were beginning to recognize the damage that was being done to our other two children, possibly too late because of our preoccupation with our handicapped child. Some people never notice these things, but we did, and it intensified our pain.

During the two and one-half years that we were on the waiting list, the one thing that helped tremendously was a group meeting for the parents of children who were waiting. Possibly misery loves company, but identifying with this group was most gratifying, and knowing that others were having similar problems and learning how they were meeting them was most helpful. It was also helpful to think in terms of not being the *only* parents who were thinking of sending their child to a state school.

The fateful letter from the school finally arrived, and although all the steps along the way had been difficult, this final one was the most difficult. Actually, the preparation of her wardrobe and the examinations were not particularly trying, but the anticipation of the actual day, how we should handle it, what we should say, and what we would do weighed heavily on our minds and our hearts. It would have been most helpful if someone could have talked with us about what we might expect and how to handle the actual parting at the school.

Following that miserable, rainy day when we left our child and her worldly possessions in the hands of unknown people, we suffered tremendous feelings of guilt, loss, and emptiness. We were in great need of therapeutic counseling. Over and over again we asked ourselves: Did we do right? Was she happy? Would they take good care of her? At this point, the mental health of the entire family was at stake, and a public health nurse, or a caseworker, would have been very welcome. Some parents, possibly, would resent or even resist such counseling, but the majority would find it helpful and most comforting.

Now, again, friends came with advice, and they honestly believed they were right in saying such things as "You mustn't see her." "You must start a new life." "Don't bring her home." "Get into a completely new round of activities." The point they missed was that the realization of our great burden of sixteen years had finally been crystallized. Somehow we had to get through this period of adjustment in our own home before we would be ready to face new experiences. Also, they didn't realize that her visits home were therapy for all of us. Only by coming home to visit could she know that she still had the security of her family and that she had not been cast out. Her trips home gave us an opportunity to observe her progress. We saw that she was gaining poise, learning how to make friends, and having training and experiences which we had never been able to give her in our living situation.

Remember, these are the observations of just one parent. But I am quite positive that if you would study the running record of many parents in similar situations, you would find many of the same emotional problems.

Throughout this discussion I have suggested that the public health nurse is the natural resource person. She sees more situations in the home at the grass roots of our society than anyone else. She is accepted as a trained medical person who is not on such a remote professional level that you cannot talk to her. To me she appears to be the natural liaison, trusted both by the lay person and the physician. If she is a sincere, mature, and understanding person, she will listen, suggest, support, and objectively help the family over their mental hurdles as they go through this business of facing, accepting, acting, and resolving the attendant problems of having a handicapped child.

□ □ □

SECTION C

Physicians

In the past, the physician has borne one of the largest shares of the management burden. He has also become the object of most of the criticism, and somewhat of a scapegoat for the general failure of society to provide services for the retarded. The literature is replete with "horror stories" of physicians' mismanagement of families of the retarded. While there can be little doubt that all professions were, at times, guilty of mismanagement, it is particularly important for the physician to be competent in this area, especially if he is to play the leadership role to which he lays such strong claim. Perhaps the physician has been successful in defining his role to his own satisfaction, but his definition may not have been understood or accepted by others. Under any conditions, it is clear that the physician's function is a critical one which, if not carried out successfully, can jeopardize the entire parent management program.

In the first selection, Wishik presents a twenty-five-point creed that sets a standard of responsibility for the physician who manages families of handicapped children. Adherence to this creed would go a long way in placing the physician above the torrent of criticism directed at him in the past.

Selections by Bryant and Hirschberg, and by Solomons, are concerned with the parent-physician relationship and suggest principles and guidelines for management. Bryant and Hirschberg discuss the role of the physician in family management, examining instances of parental dissatisfaction for clues about how the physician can increase his usefulness. Solomons, in presenting some personal experiences and reflections, indicates that "in the field of mental retardation, when dealing with a handicapped child, we physicians . . . have little to offer but counsel in a substantial number of cases, and parents desperately need someone to listen to them." Solomons then discusses such medical contributions as diagnosis, prognosis, and interpretation within this context.

The final two selections included in this section are noteworthy as authoritative statements by bodies representing organized medicine. The statement by the Group for the Advancement of Psychiatry contains a discussion of the emotional reaction of the physician himself, and what effect this reaction might have on handling of parents. The guidelines set forth in the American Medical Association's Handbook on Mental Retardation *(in the chapter dealing with the counseling of parents) are summarized in the last paragraph where the parent-counseling role of the physician is broadly defined as one of helping the parents to integrate the child as a nonstressful part of family life, thus enabling the family to plan objectively and to feel satisfied that they have done everything possible to develop the potentialities of their child.*

THE ROLE OF THE PHYSICIAN

Samuel M. Wishik

(The Child with a Handicap, 1959)

Physicians heal the wounds of sick children to make them well, and they supervise the health of well children to keep them well. Most handicapped children, however, are neither sick nor well. Their continuing and complex needs are ever changing during the growth years. All the physician's ingenuity and understanding are called upon to diagnose and treat, to advise and plan, to support and help toward self-reliance. The twenty-five-point credo that follows tries to outline the standard of responsibility the physician sets for himself in counseling families of handicapped children.

1. I realize that externally invisible conditions, such as heart disease or deafness, can be just as crippling as a paralyzed limb.

As a matter of fact, when it is not obvious to other people that the child is handicapped, he receives less consideration than sympathy. A hearing aid, for example, not only improves the child's hearing but lets other people know that the child may be missing some of the conversation. When the child with a heart condition stops playing with the others at school, the teacher may interpret this lack of participation as a lack of social maturity if she does not know that such a child fatigues quickly.

2. When a child is found to have a handicapping condition, I look carefully for other defects—because multiple handicaps in the same child occur more often than single handicaps.

A study made in Georgia, reports that a group of handicapped children had an average of two and two-tenths different major handicaps in various combinations, such as an orthopedic condition, plus mental retardation, cleft palate plus hearing impairment, or strabismus (crossed eyes) plus a personality disturbance. This knowledge again emphasizes the necessity of treating the child rather than a single diagnosis or handicap.

3. I do not turn a diagnosis into a label for a child. I do not turn adjectives into nouns. He is not "an epileptic"; she is not "a diabetic."

Within any diagnostic group, a broad range of severity and types of involvement, from the extremely mild to the very severe, can be identified. No specific child can be described merely by a diagnosis, such as "cerebral palsied" or "mentally retarded." Almost any child, no matter how handicapped, has remaining capacities that outnumber his deficiencies. The child and his family must be helped by focusing on those capacities rather than on his limitations. Furthermore, the child deserves to be given the benefit of [the] doubt. Only by a trial period of prolonged observation can the physician be sure that the child's seeming limitations are real.

4. When central nervous system involvement exists, I know that the manifestations can be neuromuscular, sensory, intellectual, convulsive and emotional, and at times even more subtle and elusive.

Mild behavior changes especially elude recognition. Such imperceptive disturbances that at times interfere with a child's education also elude recognition. For want of a better term, these children have been called "brain-injured," especially when the brain damage does not demonstrate itself grossly in the usual forms of paralysis, convulsions, or intellectual impairment.

5. I know that various medical specialists can help and that there are elements in care of the handicapped child that are outside the field of medicine.

The physician relies on the orthopedist, cardiologist, opthalmologist or other specialist when he recognizes need for consultation. The physician is less likely, however, to think of the educator, the social worker, or the vocational counselor.

6. I am not an amateur psychometrist. I do not make flip judgments about a handicapped child's intelligence.

The flip prognosis comes back to plague the physician, whether he has erred on the side of optimism or pessimism. Like the lay person, the physician is not immune to being influenced by a peculiar facial expression, a strange voice or other unusual mannerisms that suggest mental retardation. Furthermore, it must be clear that the actual intellectual functioning of a child is affected by sensory disturbances, such as blindness or deafness, by emotional deviations, and by limitations in educational and social opportunities.

7. I try to find out what is known about the genetics of a condition, without injecting my own desires for unwarranted optimism or pessimism.

Telling the parents of a child with congenitally dislocated hips that chances are against the condition appearing in another child is not strictly correct if the approximate odds of another girl baby having the condition are about one in twenty as compared with about one in five hundred in other families.

8. I do not make decisions for the family. I lay all the facts clearly before them so that they can arrive at their own solution.

When the parents have been told the approximate chances, to the extent that information is available, they alone can make the decision on whether or not to have more children.

9. I advise parents on immunization safety and other means of preventing their children from becoming handicapped.

In counseling parents about their well children, emphasis must be given to the important and frequent preventable conditions that are occurring among children in the community. As long as accidents are the leading cause of death and disability of children in all age groups after the first birthday, guiding parents in the rearing of healthy children is incomplete without the routine inclusions of advice about safety and accident prevention. In our day, such words of caution may be more important than instructions on feeding.

10. In the health supervision of well children, I am on the lookout for signs of incipient conditions that may lead to handicaps.

In the routine periodic examination of very young infants, careful measurements of the head circumference may be more valuable than frequent use of the stethoscope.

11. When a child has had an unfavorable health experience that has potential for producing a particular handicap later, I classify that child on my records as "susceptible" or "vulnerable" and make a special point of following him and seeing him periodically.

The occurrence of convulsions in the first weeks of life or evidence of neurological symptoms with an attack of measles is a warning signal for the possible subsequent development of cerebral palsy in the same way, if not to as great an extent, as an attack of rheumatic fever is a warning that makes the physician watch carefully for later heart damage.

12. I know that "case finding" is more than finding a new case: after that, looking for gaps in the child's total rehabilitation—physical, mental, emotional, social, educational, and vocational—is also "finding the case" in need of care.

To the physician, the term "finding a new case" usually means that medical treatment is needed. When a physician who has been following a child with epilepsy discovers, despite effective drug control of convulsions, that the child is not admitted to school because of the prejudices of the school authorities, the physician has "found" a case of a handicapped child—this time, handicapped educationally because of his neurological condition.

13. I am willing and able to work as a member of a professional team, respecting the contributions and opinions of the other disciplines and subordinating my role to the decisions of the group.

For example, the physician may advise the family to postpone elective surgery for psychological or educational reasons.

14. I can flexibly assume varying degrees of responsibility for different children to fit each situation best—sometimes limiting my role to general health supervision and care of intercurrent illness, sometimes sharing with the consultants in the special care of the handicap.

This is a matter of give and take between the physician and the consultants.

15. Although I do not have technical supervision over physical therapy and certain other special treatments, I include them in my overall assessment of the child's needs and progress.

If the orthopedist recommends two years of frequent physical therapy to improve the usefulness of a limb by about 10 per cent, the family physician may raise the question of the balance between the probable improvement and the dislocation in the child's life that would have to occur to obtain it. When the physical therapist reports improvement in a child's walking after a year's treatment, the physician may interject his estimate of the contribution of time and growth to the child's progress.

16. I realize how easily the presence of a chronic handicapping condition in a child can throw the family into medical indigency.

The economic effects on the family are both subtle and extensive. In addition to the mere cost of care, reduced earning capacity of the family, decreased earning potential of the child, as well as other incidental and hidden expenses often adversely affect the economic stability of the family.

17. I am acquainted with the programs of community agencies, and I cooperate with them in the care of my handicapped patients.

When, for example, the school health service refers a normal child to the private physician for supposed vision or hearing defect, the physician recognizes that an effective screening program in the school must produce a certain reasonable amount of over-referral in order to detect those who do need care. In another instance, when a handicapped child reaches his teens, the physician will consider possible referral to the Division of Vocational Rehabilitation of the State Department of Education.

18. I recognize the importance of continuity of care over a span of years. If I lose contact with the family I call for help to get the child back under medical supervision.

Although the private physician is not in a strategic position to keep after a family, the public health nurse can help to send the family back to him for continued observation.

19. I encourage the child to participate in normal social groups, and I work for increasing his acceptance by these groups and by the community in general.

Only by living with handicapped children and playing side by side with them can children grow up to be understanding adults, among whom some day will be those who are in a position to employ handicapped persons.

20. I participate in decisions, plans, and arrangements for the education of the child.

Here the physician has a very important set of responsibilities. The dual goals in the education of a handicapped child are on the one hand to keep him in as normal a setting as possible and on the other hand to give him whatever special education he needs. The balance between these two goals is a delicate one that depends to a large extent on the physician's diagnosis, recommendations, and periodic reappraisals. For example, restricted types of education, such as instruction by a teacher for the homebound or in a residential school are abnormal situations that are not the best solution for most handicapped children. The physician helps interpret this information to over-protective parents.

21. To non-medical professional persons I interpret medical information they should have about a handicapped child.

The physician should interpret certain information to the teacher about the medical condition of a child in her class, such as: the nature of the condition, its cause, treatment, general prognosis, relation to physical activity, infections, diet, nutrition, personality, and the expected attitudes of others.

22. I participate in advising about plans and arrangements for the child's future vocation.

Planning for a child's future vocation should start early. The plan should not be too rigid and should be neither too delimiting nor too unduly encouraging to family and child. School counseling resources as well as vocational rehabilitation services should be called upon.

23. I advise and support the family in the difficult decisions they may have to make on institutional placement for their child.

Even when a child's handicap is very severe, the values in the parents' eyes of keeping the child at home are the final factors in their decision concerning whether or not to place the child permanently in an institution. Many values may be derived from home and family care, both for the child and for the others in the family. If parents decide to keep a child, the physician can furnish them with concrete roles and responsibilities that will help them to give the child more effective care and to make their situation more bearable and meaningful.

24. I help to advise parents' groups and other organizations of citizens about how they can improve services to handicapped children.

In recent years, an increased number of groups of parents organizing for the improvement of community services for children with one or another handicap have appeared on the American scene. These groups are enthusiastic and sincere individuals who at times let their enthusiasm run away with them. Because they lean strongly on the physician for guidance, the physician too may show a tendency to run away with the group, interjecting his personal opinions into his advice without first discovering what patterns of organization of services have been tried and have been successful elsewhere.

25. I strive for the improvement of my community's resources for the care of handicapped children.

This avowal ties in with the previous comment about guidance of citizen's groups. Two common and unfortunate tendencies in the development of new services are first, to establish a completely new service apart from any existing ones, and second, to set up a specialized service for one or another diagnostic group or condition. By and large, a program is much more likely to be on a sound basis if it fits in with existing services. Individuals and organizations should focus on the needs of children as a total group rather than on one or another specific condition handicapping some children.

This credo is the code of feeling and action of an understanding individual, a competent physician, and a conscientious citizen.

□ □ □

from HELPING THE PARENTS OF A RETARDED CHILD: THE ROLE OF THE PHYSICIAN

Keith N. Bryant
J. Cotter Hirschberg

(*American Journal of Diseases of Children,* 1961)

The physician who will take the time to listen, to understand, to support, and to counsel parents of the retarded child will do them a great service, but many parents of retarded children who have taken their child to their family doctor are not satisfied with the help they receive. For this reason we decided to examine the parents' dissatisfactions for clues about how the physician might increase his usefulness to such families.

Part of the parents' dissatisfaction about the help they had received represented their own difficulties and distortions, springing from their intense feelings about their child's problems. Nonetheless, the complaints in part often seemed to be justified. In a surprising number of instances, the physician had treated the parents in ways which seemed to reflect his own uncertainty about his role. These parents described with hurt and anger the doctor's seeming misunderstanding of them and their retarded child, and his inability to help them with the difficult problems that such a child posed.

The anxiety of the parents, their tenacious questioning, their sometimes aggressive approach may lead the physician to avoid "getting involved." However, if he can think of their behavior as not related to him personally, but stemming from their unhappiness and anxiety, and if he can free the time to examine and listen and understand, then he will be richly rewarded for his efforts to help them. To work with these parents and their retarded children with tact, with sympathy, and respect, the physician must remember that the retarded child is still a child with feelings, needs, wishes, and desires to which the parents respond. The physician needs to ally himself with the parents in their struggle with the dilemmas which having a retarded child create. If he cannot deal objectively with the problems, or is not interested in this demanding work which involves more listening than "doing," or if he is already overburdened and cannot free the time, then when possible he should tactfully refer them elsewhere. It is not an example of poor practice to refer such cases—it is rather practicing good medicine to appraise accurately what one can do, and parents will respect such integrity and be grateful for it.

It is our hope that this paper will give some guidance to the physician in deciding whether he can help cases of retarded children, and if he elects to do so, to make his task a little more understandable and rewarding.

The Diagnosis

Parents of the retarded child want from the doctor a *total* understanding of the problem, both with reference to the child and to themselves. While we cannot entirely do this nor grant the wish of the parents that the child be cured, we can, nevertheles, try to help them achieve the best solution for their problem. . . .

The goal then is represented by the ideal combination of services. Yet, even where these are available, it is still usually the physician to whom the parents first turn with their problem, and he must make the initial diagnosis of mental retardation. Then frequently he must direct the family to and help them to use other community resources. Many parents, at the time of diagnosis, are not ready for a referral of their child for a psychiatric evaluation, and they may only come to this gradually; neither may it be the wisest time to refer the child. When the referral is made, the physician may have to coordinate the referral services—he may have to gather and interpret for the parents the various findings and recommendations from a number of different specialists and resources. Ideally each community should have a center with a totally coordinated program from diagnosis through continued training and treatment as needed over the years, but in most communities this is not yet available. Even after the referral is made, the physician frequently must continue to guide the family, since some parents cannot immediately act upon the recommendations; or the child is referred, at various points in his growth, back to the physician for further medical evaluation. It is important to realize that the initial diagnostic study is only the beginning of the helping process.

Parents who are angry because "the doctor looked at our child and said he was retarded and needed to be put away" have been approached in a way that is not helpful to them. New knowledge about mental retardation, and the parents' reactions to it, have made it imperative for the physician to deal carefully with even the most severely retarded child and his parents. The kind of help they need may require from the doctor a series of visits, often repeated over years, as the parents *continue* to help their retarded child. The physician must show the parents he is not going to be hurried or blunt with them, but that he is willing to *share* in their task over a span of time. Even in those cases where it is clear from the very beginning that the child must be referred for psychiatric study, the physician will still need to spend a great deal of time on the case, and it may help to clarify this with the parents at the outset, so that they will expect to be charged for the necessary time spent with them as well as for the time spent with the child.

As the physician obtains a history and diagnoses the condition of the child, he will also seek answers to such questions as:

1. What brought the family to seek help at this particular time?
2. What is the effect of the child on his family and community?
3. What is the effect of the family and community upon the child?
4. What adjustment have the parents made to the problems that having such a child is posing for them?
5. What resources has the community to offer them?
6. How will the parents react to the findings?

The physician must gauge the parents' readiness to understand and their willingness to act on that understanding—and these do not necessarily occur at the same time. Omissions or distortions in the parents' accounts are significant, but a rigid outline for the history-taking is not recommended because much significant material is best brought out spontaneously by the parents. A formal outline should be used only as a framework for thoughts and then in a flexible fashion, allowing the parents to shift topics at will.

A comprehensive diagnosis can scarcely be done in only one brief examination or interview. Each case is unique and requires individual appraisal and planning. Variations in cases may range from a *relatively* simple one, such as the uniformly and severely retarded child within a relatively normal family, living in a community with good facilities, to a more complex one, where there are different levels of retardation in various areas, to those where there is also a marked psychological disturbance in the parents, who are further plagued by intolerant neighborhood attitudes or poor community facilities.

Even when the parents and child must be referred for specialized studies and help, if the physician accepts the case at all, he should go as far as he can in his own understanding of it so as to make the best referral. He is still the medical doctor to whom the parents have come; they will ask many questions, and the more thorough his study has been, the better he can help them.

The Recommendations

One recommendation the physician may elect to make, at some point in helping the family, is to refer them to a psychiatric clinic for a more comprehensive diagnosis, or for further treatment and training for the child and further guidance for the parents. The physician may elect to make a referral when he feels he does not understand adequately the problems and needs at a particular point in the child's development. For example, a baby may be recognized as retarded at birth or shortly after, but it may not be helpful or necessary then to recommend a psychiatric evaluation, whereas by the time the child would normally be starting school, it may be important to get a comprehensive picture of the child's resources. Referral might also be indicated because the physician is unable to deal with the parents' disturbances, or because he does not have the necessary time to be of genuine help to the family. Availability of local resources and the readiness of the parents and child to use these resources may govern the physician's decision about referral.

Even in this present age of relative enlightenment, parents may still feel some hesitation about a psychiatric consultation. They may also be disappointed and feel that the physician is not interested in their difficulties, or that he believes they themselves are emotionally disturbed and require special treatment. When these feelings arise they need to be dealt with carefully. The physician should describe to the parents and the child what will happen to them at the referral center. The evaluation, and the referral for it, always need to be made a therapeutic experience for the parents and the child, and if it seems like some kind of vague, mysterious process, this will increase their anxiety about it. The procedure involved will vary, of course, from clinic to clinic. . . .

A misconception occasionally conveyed to parents is that if the child is emotionally disturbed, it is their fault, whereas if the child is brain-damaged, then the parents are not to blame. This is a false concept and of no practical use. There are many children with schizophrenic reactions where it is extremely difficult to see a degree of disturbance in the parents which would cause such a devastating reaction in the child. Likewise, there are mildly mentally retarded children who are emotionally disturbed because, it would appear, of improper understanding and management. Of course, neither diagnosis—brain damage nor emotional disturbance—is ever of any comfort or reassurance to parents. Each condition is so disconcerting that saying a child has one or the other does not provide any relief. Also, many parents "feel to blame" for producing a congenitally defective child anyway, even though logically they know they had nothing directly to do with it.

Another false concept is that if the child is brain-damaged, nothing can be done to help him (which is certainly not necessarily true), and that if the child is schizophrenic, then something can be done to help him (which is also not necessarily true). What is true is that the kind of treatment program needed may be considerably different in each case, although many children with brain damage also need and respond well to psychotherapy, in addition to the special educational and training techniques they may require. . . .

Sharing the Findings

The physician's most difficult task with the parents is to explain the findings from the examinations in words they can understand, and to gain their acceptance of the findings. The implications of the findings may indicate to the physician the best way to tell the parents. Ideally the parents wish to achieve a full understanding of the total problem, but in some instances this is not even the parents' conscious intent. Their aim toward the ideal goal is always accompanied by enormous worry and fear and mixed feelings of doubt about wanting to find out. These conscious, mixed motives and deeper unconscious ones, complicate the task.

What measures can the physician adopt to gain the cooperation and trust of the parents? His attitude is of paramount importance in imparting the findings; if he is sympathetic and understanding, the parents will be less defensive and can absorb more accurately the findings. . . .

When the physician is in doubt about the diagnosis, he should say so, then as new evidence comes along, it can be given to the parents. Never conceal the retardation by telling the parents the child may "grow out of it." When the child does not "grow out of it," the parents naturally distrust and are hostile toward the physician. When in doubt, an honest "I don't know" should be given. A delay in giving all the findings may be necessary with some parents, who themselves usually give the clue for such a delay. Occasionally parents can move ahead constructively only when they are given clear-cut directions, which they will then solicit. Severe personality disturbance in the parents sometimes requires direct and authoritative action by the physician—for example, when they are too depressed or too emotionally exhausted to act, or when the parents are psychotic or extremely emotionally immature. Here the physician must maintain an objective attitude to be of maximum benefit to all concerned—a feeling of having to rescue the parents from the child, or the child from the parents will *not* be conducive to maximum help to both.

Many parents are overwhelmed and numb after hearing the doctor's report. They say, "I heard his words but they went over my head." Details may have to be repeated a number of times, and the parents may have not absorbed what has previously been discussed with them. They did not hear because they could not face the painful facts. It is important to realize the chagrin, the discouragement, the depression, the shame, and the anxiety such findings arouse. Technical jargon naturally should be avoided, and the terms "moron," "idiot," and "imbecile" should never be used to describe the child because of the emotional meanings these words have in our society. One does much better by speaking of degrees of retardation or levels of intellectual functioning. Even this is not very helpful to the parents who really want information about what the child can and cannot do. Giving them an Intelligence Quotient is of little practical use. . . .

To clarify some of the foregoing comments, these brief case illustrations are given [where]: 1) the physician could have been of help if his orientation and understanding had been different; 2) the physician was of great benefit to the family; 3) referral for specialized study was needed; and 4) neither the referring physician nor the psychiatric center could make much progress in working with the parents.

Case 1. Mr. and Mrs. X brought their second child, Tommy, age three years, for diagnostic study because their physician had told them their child was retarded and "should be put away." They were concerned about the child at a relatively early age, but had been told the child would "grow out of it." The hurt and bewildered parents now insisted the doctor was wrong, desperately related examples of how well the child could perform, and almost pleaded with us to find the child adequate.

Had the physician's approach been different, and had he given the parents an opportunity for frank and understanding discussions, he would have learned about their anxieties, their fears for the future, and their current difficulties with the child. It became clear that the parents knew the child was not developing normally, and with support and guidance, they were able to think about his limitations and make constructive plans for his future. Fortunately, the child's difficulties did not preclude his being kept at home, at least for a few more years. With the beginning of school, the situation might become different, as again it might in adolescence or later life.

Case 2. This case illustrates a child and family with about the same kinds of problems as Case 1, but they were handled differently by their physician. From an early age, the physician and parents had concern about the child's development. The doctor told the parents he was not able to say with certainty that the child was retarded, then as the evidence of slow development increased, he discussed this with the parents, helped them with planning, and at an appropriate time referred them to the psychiatric clinic for an examination to check on his own suggestions and recommendations. The physician has continued to serve them in a guiding role and when necessary has the child and parents return to check on what has been accomplished, what still can be done, and what cannot be done. The physician recognized the family's strength, that they had much love for the child and were able to provide in the home much which could not at her age be provided in an institution. The physician has helped the parents recognize that at some point, as the child gets older, special training away from home may be the most helpful course and that only time will tell what degree of independence the child will be able to achieve and maintain.

In this case, in contrast to Case 1, the parents had an entirely different attitude toward their physician—and to the clinic he referred them to. They looked upon him as a wise, supporting person whom they trusted, whereas the family in the first case lost confidence in their doctor and had difficulty at first in making constructive use of the clinic's resources. In this second case, the parents could make a smooth transition back and forth from their family doctor to the guidance center because they trusted their doctor.

Case 3. This case illustrates another reason for referral. The family physician had made a diagnosis of retardation when the child was age two years, and then began to doubt his diagnosis, suspecting an emotional basis for the disorder. He referred the family to the psychiatric clinic for further diagnostic study when the child was five. Although it was found that the parents too were emotionally disturbed, the child's disturbance was basically a reaction to his primary organic deficit, and he was not a schizophrenic child as the physician had suspected. When such a question arises, it is wise for the doctor to refer the child to the best psychiatric center available to obtain as accurate a picture as possible on which to base future treatment and plans.

Case 4. This case illustrates a situation where the family physician made a referral because of the complications of the case. Our psychiatric center also was unsuccessful in really helping the parents much because of these same complications.

Harold was the only son of a prominent and weathy family in a large city. Throughout the boy's thirteen years, the family physician had repeatedly and skillfully attempted to help the parents seek special training and guidance for their child, who was obviously moderately retarded, but who had some abilities a little more advanced in certain areas than in others. However, neither parent would accept the fact of their son's retardation. The father could not because of the loss of self-esteem this would mean to him—he was a self-made and self-centered man, this was his only child, and he was determined that his son should take over his position in his numerous business enterprises. The father himself was a disturbed person and in fighting off a depression would go on severe alcoholic and gambling binges; it had proved impossible over the years to get him to seek psychiatric aid for himself. The passive mother turned to her son for the dependency and the support which her husband did not provide—the son was her only source of security and solace and thus it was impossible also for her to see the child's real limitations or to consider his leaving the home for the special training he needed. Harold found himself exposed to increasingly difficult problems both at home and in the community. His retardation became more obvious as he advanced in school, and he had more and more difficulty in making and keeping friends. The father blamed the mother for all the difficulties and the mother felt helpless.

In desperation, the parents finally heeded the advice of their family physician and came to the psychiatric clinic for help. Unfortunately, because of the complex and deep-seated nature of their problems, it was not possible to resolve their difficulties. Although they did agree to enroll the boy in a special school—one of the best available for their child's problems—they continued to be dissatisfied and constantly complained, blaming the school for their son's lack of progress. In such situations one has to settle for limited goals with the family, sometimes very limited ones. The most useful thing one can do for the parents in this case is to remain a friendly ally to whom they can hopefully return as their needs increase. Eventually they may recognize their own need to become involved more actively and consistently in treatment for themselves.

Conclusion

If the physician can free himself of biased judgmental attitudes and can take sufficient time to listen, to understand, to support, and to counsel the parents, he will do them a great service.

If he believes in the inherent strength of the parents to reach with his help or with additional outside help the best possible solutions for themselves and the child, then he will have the patience and the objectivity it takes to assist them with dignity in reaching these solutions, and he will be able to serve as coordinator and guide to the family which works toward maximal growth both of the retarded child and the family itself.

□ □ □

from WHAT DO YOU TELL THE PARENTS OF A RETARDED CHILD? SOME PERSONAL EXPERIENCES AND REFLECTIONS *Gerald Solomons*

(Clinical Pediatrics, 1965)

George Bernard Shaw once said that people don't want a doctor; they want an audience. Dale Carnegie in his book *How to Win Friends and Influence People,*[1] concludes a whole chapter on how to be a good conversationalist with the terse admonition to be a good listener. The art of being a good listener appears to be lost in medicine, and it is my belief that the public's nostalgia for the old family doctor is not due to his prowess as a healer, nor even to his supposed immediate response to emergencies, but rather to his ability to lend a sympathetic ear for as long as was necessary. The practitioner of not so long ago had little else to offer for most serious illnesses.

In the field of mental retardation, when dealing with a handicapped child, we physicians are to a certain extent in a similar position to the family doctor of tradition. We have little to offer but counsel in a substantial number of cases, and parents desperately need someone to listen to them.

Much has been written on the needs of and counseling for parents of the retarded; but little has been published on what the physician should tell the parent—and how he should say it. When studying retarded children, we are constantly frustrated by the answer, "no one ever told us anything," to the question of why a child was previously hospitalized, or what the former physician's diagnosis was. The inability of parents to remember their doctor's explanations has been ascribed in the main to denial and guilt feelings, but perhaps this is overstated and unduly emphasized. As a profession we are prone to use professional jargon to a great extent and to assume that our patients or their parents are familiar with the medical terms when they are not; yet this, too, appears to be an oversimplification of the problem.

It should be recognized that when a physician has no empathy for or experience in the field of mental retardation, his discussion and recommendations reflect his uncertainty and often produce antagonism and denial on the part of the parents. Many physicians are aware of this and refer their patients appropriately. Others continue to counsel, unaware of the effects that their own emotional reaction to the condition have on the family.

The physician is expected to "have all the answers" and to do something about the problem immediately. This often leads to peremptory advice and opinions based on a desire to be rid of the whole problem, rather than to initiation of a long-term program for child and family. Too often a physician identifies himself with the parents and concludes without justification that to retain a child in his home will be an intolerable burden for the family. Although identification to some extent with the family is important, unrealistic attitudes of the physician must not influence the therapeutic management. Furthermore, in contrast to this attitude towards the severely retarded, he may tend to overestimate the intelligence of children functioning subnormally.[2]

The situation with parents who have a retarded child is succinctly outlined by the Group for the Advancement of Psychiatry:[3] "The physician is still dealing with parents who have a multi-faceted problem:

1. They may not have fully accepted the diagnosis of mental retardation.
2. They have varying degrees of guilt feelings about their possible role in the causation of the child's condition.
3. They resent the fact that this has happened to them and tend to try to find some outside influence on which they can blame the problem.
4. They hope for a magical solution.
5. They have a wish, usually unconscious, to be rid of this burden.
6. They have come seeking advice.

"Each of these factors deserves separate consideration by the physician, who must realize that he himself will have certain reactions to the child's condition, and to the parents and their emotional problems."

The literature dealing with exceptional children is replete with advice to avoid terms such as brain damage, low IQ, anoxia, and deficiency, and substitute more acceptable synonyms such as cerebral dysfunction, intellectual ability, intellectual level, lack of oxygen, and retardation. This may show great self-control on the part of the physician and prevent unpleasant connotations on the part of the parents, but nowhere do I find an explanation of these latter terms in a form *understandable* as well as acceptable to the average parents. I have often spent an hour or more explaining to an intelligent, educated couple my considered opinion concerning the etiologic factors, diagnosis, prognosis, and treatment of their child's disability and have concluded the interview knowing full well that the message never got across. More frustrating was the belief that the fault was mine and not theirs. They were trying, and desperately wished to understand, but the information I was imparting was not concrete enough to produce the impact desired.

Although I still have those days of "not getting through," I feel I have accomplished much by the adoption of some of the procedures outlined below. This, of course, is an impression, and our clinic is now working on some technics to assess these subjective feelings in a more objective, quantifiable manner.

1. Being a Good Listener

A question like "what are the main problems of your child?" "what would you like to know?" "how can we help you?" before explaining anything, gives the parents a chance to talk to somebody. They have already been listening too long. In many instances the therapeutic release resulting from this mental catharsis is sufficient to produce the stage of "acceptance" of their child's disability, without which a concerted, realistic treatment program cannot be formulated. Some of the impressions obtained by the physician which color the emphasis and interpretation of his findings are dependent upon the sophistication of the parents, their realistic or unrealistic appraisal of the disability, possible marital conflict, hostility to doctors or schools, etc.

2. Review of History

One should go over the salient points in the history in detail. If no past mismanagement is uncovered on the part of the parents, the medical attendants, the school authorities or the various community agencies, this should be explained thoroughly. The bitter hostility which many parents may display towards a particular person or group is a common emotional defense reaction and should be negated whenever possible. In some cases the criticism is, on the face of it, justifiable, but no useful purpose is served by permitting such a belief to be perpetuated. Acceptance of a handicap by parents is all the harder when knowing that someone may be to blame for it. I make no apologies in "bending the record" in order to gloss over a possible etiological factor caused by negligence. By the same token, I may incriminate certain questionable events in a history as probably significant if I believe the parents would benefit from a diagnosis that suggests an organic basis.

In at least 75 per cent of cases of mental retardation, the cause or causes cannot be clearly demonstrated. This, when coupled with a negative physical examination as often occurs, can produce a nightmarish, will-o'-the-wisp sort of existence for parents for whom diagnoses are made, programs outlined, futures planned, and evidences of social ostracism felt, without anyone knowing what is wrong with the patient except that he is "slow." Reducing this fear of the unknown overcomes a major obstacle.

3. *Interpretation of the Findings*

The usual procedure is to enumerate the positive items found on examination and apply them as a basis for the diagnosis. Preferably, a step further should be to paraphrase the song, to "accentuate the negative." A list of the negative findings that are important can be a welcome relief from the stress of all those that are positive. It is our practice in the Child Development Clinic to start with the physical examination, pointing out the obvious strabismus, peculiar gait or stance, incoordination, hyperactivity, etc., but tempering these items with statements that "height and weight are average," "lungs and heart are normal," "there is no evidence of trouble with the thyroid," "he has good muscle strength," "there is nothing we can find wrong with his nervous system, speech or hearing," etc.

I believe in carrying out as complete a work-up as can possibly be done with every patient, even if the diagnosis is fairly obvious and there have been many previous examinations by many doctors. The mere fact that a child has already been seen by several other physicians is a testament to the parents' dissatisfaction. A thorough evaluation will drive home test by test and point by point the previous findings to skeptical parents, as well as ruling out the possibility of a previous error in diagnosis. It may end the phrase of "shopping around" which is the usual precursor of acceptance of the child's problem. It has been argued that such a repeat work-up places an unnecessary financial burden on a family which is destined to have heavy, long-term medical expenses, but I have never found an objection when the procedures were discussed beforehand, and the results reviewed in detail afterwards. There is a paradoxical twist to the concept that laboratory procedures should only be undertaken when they have an almost certain chance to be positive. Parents have a right to be antagonistic if after an expensive series of neurologic procedures the sum total is dismissed with: "our tests showed nothing." Such a statement gives the impression of a fishing expedition with no catch. This interpretation becomes accentuated when the physical examination has likewise "shown nothing," and when opinions are next given which are based on completely negative evidence. No wonder the experts are disbelieved.

The report of the full evaluation, presented with the findings of normality in many areas, can be music to the ears of parents who have wallowed in the dirge of funereal pronouncements. Finally, on this point, keep in mind the axiom that the most important test is the one that has not been done, particularly when dealing with a child whose handicap is chronic. There is no substitute for a complete, thorough, and immediate examination, and usually no excuse for doing it piecemeal.

Laboratory and x-ray reports should also be discussed at length with the parents, listing each test done and the negative and positive results. Much parental guilt feeling is assuaged by the fact that "everything possible has been done," and a detailed report of an extensive work-up is of great therapeutic value. Whenever possible and practical, any x-ray films which show calcification in the skull or other abnormality should be demonstrated, spike waves of an EEG tracing should be indicated, and all other positive findings shown, in order to impress visually on the parents the extent of the involvement of the various systems. . . .

4. Diagnosis

There is no need to dwell here on those conditions where the etiology and diagnosis are clear-cut (*e.g.*, mongolism), although the parents of these children are often resentful of a presentation of the facts. In the main the explanation is relatively easy to impart.

A more difficult concept to explain is that of "minimal brain damage." Although there has been much discussion of abandoning this term and replacing it with that of "minimal cerebral dysfunction," the controversy is really academic and directed to the vocabulary of the professional in the field. Regardless of semantics, the term used has to be defined in simple language that can be understood by parents. One way is to start by stating that no evidence of structural damage to the brain was found on physical or laboratory examination of the child. However, certain facts in the history (*e.g.*, prematurity, anoxia, convulsive disorder, etc.) and in performance and behavior (*e.g.*, incoordination, poor writing, trouble with geometric figures, reversals, hyperactivity, short attention span, etc.) suggest that there is some mild disability of the nervous system. Just as a television set with a blurred picture or a radio with static interference, he performs fairly adequately but the picture or message is not quite clear—almost as if some of the wires were crossed or not attached properly. This may cause him to have difficulty with numbers, poor writing, reversal of figures, etc., and could account for his hyperactivity and unpredictable behavior. . . .

It is convenient to describe the EEG as a "tracing of the brain wave" similar to the "tracing of the heart" of the electrocardiogram. Abnormal foci or patterns can then be called "irregular discharges or bursts of electricity" culminating in seizures or atypical behavior.

When a behavior problem proves to be wholly emotional, the explanation should always be preceded by a review of the criteria which have ruled out an organic basis for the condition. Parents may then realize that the physician has given serious consideration to their observations and beliefs, before discussing intrafamilial relationships.

5. Prognosis

To look into a crystal ball and forecast the future of a retarded child is not acceptable in modern-day medicine. Nevertheless, every day the physician may be called upon to do this. Strictly speaking, he should say he cannot foretell the future and murmur some platitude about "time will tell." Few of us can be that blunt or indecisive. Hope is the commodity which should be dispensed within the bounds of realism, and the amount should depend on the age of the child, the degree of involvement and the outlook of the physician.

Our instruments of measurement of growth and development are not precise for the child under the age of two years, and the clinical picture may change to such an extent that an infant diagnosed in the first or second year of life as having cerebral palsy with associated mental retardation may be adjudged as being within normal limits by three years of age.[4] Consequently, it is wise to be overcautious in the interpretation of psychomotor retardation, particularly in the first year or two of life. The "late bloomer" is a definite clinical entity. Hence, in the absence of definite neurologic impairments no specific diagnosis should be made. This does not mean that one may say, "he'll grow out of it," but rather that "he is not performing up to age level at this time and there is nothing I can find to account for this." A brief explanation may then be given on the unreliability of testing at an early age and the need for a repeat evaluation in twelve months or so before a definite opinion can be stated.

If the degree of retardation is not more than 50 per cent at about one year of age, I tend to leave the parents with a feeling of optimism. When retardation is more pronounced I tend to be noncommittal. I try to give the impression that the outlook is undecided and the next evaluation will likely tell us the degree of retardation we might expect, now that we have a baseline for comparison. When the child is severely retarded, performing at less than 25 per cent of his expected chronological development, the present developmental age in months is pointed out, but even here, the unreliability of testing and the possibility of some improvement before the next examination are mentioned. The degree of my optimism depends to a great extent on the parents and the home environment. If the parents are sensible, realistic, compatible people, with the opportunity and desire of spending considerable time with the child in a warm, accepting home setting, the outlook is good. Rejecting parents with marital and other problems are most unlikely to do a good job, even when the handicap is mild, and then I tend to paint a blacker picture of the condition than I otherwise might, in order to motivate the parents to get together and attempt to produce the optimum environment for their child.

The attitude of physicians towards institutionalization of the retarded is most peculiar. A recent study[5] revealed that most pediatricians are not in favor of early institutionalization, and that only a few look upon the decision to institutionalize as belonging to the parents! I personally feel that this decision is purely a family one, and have never made such a recommendation to parents. In reviewing the management and possible disposition of a patient, institutionalization, as an alternative to be considered, should be mentioned but never advocated, but the family decision should be endorsed once it is made.

The physician's role in giving advice regarding special education has been dealt with at length elsewhere.[6] It is exceedingly easy for a physician to sabotage a program of special education. Simply implying to the parents that "nothing wrong" can be found with the child and that he is "not stupid," often starts a feud with school authorities that is never resolved. The parents may "win" a social promotion and the child lose his chance to catch up. The physician's physical examination of a child with a learning difficulty contributes only part of the picture. He should refrain from passing judgment on the impressions of other disciplines, particularly if his experience in those areas is somewhat limited. Many children with average and superior intellectual ability are problems in school and may require placement in special education. Negative physical and neurologic evaluations do not necessarily rule out the need for a special school program. The physician's resistance to educational recommendations only underscores the social stigma already attached to the "slow learner" by society.

6. Treatment

Treatment of the retarded, like all treatments, should be understood by parents. The discussion can be simplified to a great extent by writing out the instructions. Drug therapy is usually long-term, with much adjustment of dosage. It is advantageous, therefore, to tell the parents the name of the drug and the strength of each unit dose, and have the containers labeled accordingly. This prevents panic when medication runs out away from home. The need for periodic blood examinations and good oral hygiene with certain anticonvulsants should be explained and emphasized. The parents must be made aware that they are part of the "team," and as such have the major responsibility in carrying out the program of treatment.

Finally, although the family must be

given support and direction over the years, the frequency of return appointments should be watched carefully. There is the tendency for all problems, however small, to be settled by the physician, and common sense and parental action evaporate as the physician takes over. Mental retardation is a family matter, and should remain a family matter, with guidance and counsel from professionals. The family should arrive at major decisions through talking things over, and they themselves should decide the future of their child. Few families start out with the wisdom and fortitude to do this. Only when this ideal state is reached can the goal of optimal opportunity for optimal potential of the child be maintained.

FOOTNOTES

1. Carnegie, D., *How to Win Friends and Influence People.* New York: Simon and Schuster, 1936.
2. Korsch, B., Cobb, J., and Ashe, B., "Pediatricians' appraisals of patients' intelligence," *Pediatrics* 27: 990, 1961.
3. Group for the Advancement of Psychiatry, *Mental Retardation: A Family Crisis—The Therapeutic Role of the Physician.* Report No. 56, December, 1963.
4. Solomons, G., Holden, R. H., and Denhoff, E., "The changing picture of cerebral dysfunction in early childhood," *Journal of Pediatrics,* 63: 113, 1963.
5. Olshansky, S., and Sternfeld, L., "Attitudes of some pediatricians toward the institutionalization of mentally retarded children," in: *Institutionalizing Mentally Retarded Children . . . Attitudes of Some Physicians.* U. S. Dept. of Health, Education and Welfare, Welfare Administration, Children's Bureau, 1963, p. 5.
6. Solomons, G., *Pediatric aspects of special education,* The Council for Exceptional Children—Selected Convention Papers, November, 1964.

□ □ □

from MENTAL RETARDATION: FAMILY CRISIS—THE THERAPEUTIC ROLE OF THE PHYSICIAN *Group for the Advancement of Psychiatry*

(Report No. 56, 1963)

. . . .

The Physician's Own Reaction

We have thus far dealt primarily with the reaction of the parents to their problems with their retarded child. Another important factor, however, is the emotional reaction of the physician himself. Anxious patients or parents expect the physician not only to have the answers to their difficulties but also to do something immediately. These pressures may mobilize the physician's need to appear omniscient and to prescribe immediately what he hopes will be a specific cure. This reaction, not unlike that of the parents he is trying to help, may come from a desire to be rid of the whole problem. He may then deal with the parents in a peremptory fashion instead of initiating positive action for the long-term medical management of the child and family.

Particularly if he senses the parents' denial and hostility, he may utilize this as an excuse for dismissing them. In its extreme, this may take the form of "This is your problem, not mine." Another variation is "This is not a medical problem, but really a family problem, or a social, or governmental, or religious problem." All of these are efforts by the physician to avoid facing his own limitations. They also stem in part from his understandable lack of experience with the associated professions and agencies involved in retardation and from the inadequacy of his own training in the subject. He may feel that it would have been better had the child succumbed to an infantile illness. The physician, like the parents, should recognize that these are not unusual reactions and need not be denied. He too must explore his feelings toward the family as well as the child. He should avoid being drawn into the parents' reaction formation because of his own similarly denied feelings. The physician needs to look at his own emotional attitudes toward the retarded child and the family so that he may then be in a position to deal with the problems more realistically.

A physician may tend to identify with the parents and ask himself what he would do if this happened to him. He may conclude prematurely that it is an intolerable burden for the family. While it is important for the physician to identify to some extent with the family and its problems, it is equally important that he not allow unrealistic attitudes of his own to influence the therapeutic management.

> A young couple with an eight-year-old daughter have a five-year-old son who is moderately retarded. He is lagging in development, unable to start kindergarten, and obviously slow. The other child is resentful and upset because she feels her parents neglect her and are overly attentive toward the boy. They, in turn, are irritated by their daughter's attitude. The physician decides that the simple solution is to quickly remove this problem-producing child to an institution. This, however, would be to abandon his responsibility to the family as a whole. Placement of the child might eventually prove to be preferable, but only after the entire situation has been thoroughly explored. Furthermore, precipitous placement of a child to "cure" family tension may boomerang and intensify the difficulties it was designed to alleviate.

It is obviously not possible within the limitations of this report to delineate the specific steps the physician can take in dealing with these families. It is very important that a positive approach be taken, because even very severely retarded children can make some progress. Parents need to feel that they have helped achieve this growth. The more the physician knows about retardation and available resources, the better he can help plan a life-long program.

□ □ □

from MENTAL RETARDATION: A HANDBOOK FOR THE PRIMARY PHYSICIAN

American Medical Association

(Journal of the American Medical Association, 1965)

Counseling Parents

The physician encounters a classic dilemma as he prepares to tell a couple that their child is retarded. How much should he say? When should he say it? And how?

His decision varies with the age of the child, the certainty of the diagnosis, and his estimate of the emotional maturity of the parents. After the birth of a child with Down's syndrome, he may act promptly to inform the parents. He will be more deliberate with the parents of an older child who seems suspiciously slow in development. The most difficult task will confront him in dealing with parents who seem unaware of their child's condition or who react with fear and hostility to any attempt to aid them in facing reality.

The process of conveying the diagnosis and then helping the family work through their emotional reactions to the goal of long-range planning can be one of the physician's greatest challenges. To meet it, he must summon all his sensitivity, subtlety, and skill to practice in its fullest sense "the art of medicine." These qualities can enable him to help parents bear the shattering first impact, and contribute toward their realistic adaptation in the long adjustment that must follow.

Conveying the Diagnosis

After the physician has decided the parents should be informed, he prepares for the interview by reviewing his knowledge of the entire family situation. Each family is unique and deserves a total diagnosis with its individual needs in mind.

He will assemble all relevant data, ask both parents to be present to avoid burdening one with the task of telling the other, and set aside a time for the interview when he will be unhurried and his office quiet. He will set forth the facts briefly in simple language, emphasizing the positive remediable aspects of the situation and giving the parents ample opportunity to indicate their immediate anxieties and to raise the most pressing questions.

This first meeting may well be brief. Parents ordinarily can assimilate only a few of the implications at a time; they may seem stunned, apathetic, or unbelieving. Several subsequent appointments may be necessary before they can express their feelings and formulate their questions effectively. The complete interpretation of the illness may require an extended period of time. By taking his cues from the quality of their questions and the degree of objectivity they have achieved, the physician may time his interpretations in accordance with a gradually increasing parental capacity to meet additional realities.

Parental Reactions

The most apparent defense mechanism is usually denial. Parents may ignore the opinion of the physician and treat the condition as if it did not exist. They may cling to the hope that the physician is wrong, or express their denial through "misunderstanding" what the physician has told them or "forgetting" his instructions. Or they may migrate from one physician to another, hoping that some doctor will have a miraculous new cure or that another will tell them the child is normal and will "grow out of it" after all. These parents are easy prey to quacks and charlatans.

The physician may understandably be disturbed by this behavior, but if he views it as an expression of denial he may be able to accept it and help the parents to a more mature adjustment in time.

When he observes early symptoms of reluctance to face facts, he may be helpful even before arriving at a diagnosis. "Compare your child with the three-year-old next door, and tell me about it the next time you come," he may say. Thus the parents can be led along gradually, participating through their own observations in the decision-making process, and arriving with the physician at the eventual diagnosis.

In the case of parents who have rejected an initial diagnosis and begun to shop for a magic cure, the physician may point out that news of any significant advances is disseminated to the medical profession generally. With his assistance, these parents may come to realize that their good judgment has been distorted by their desperate wish for a way out. Some parents shop around because they have not received adequate emotional support. If they can be led to feel that their physician is sincerely interested in them and that he certainly will have access to any significant new medical discoveries, they may be more willing to listen.

The physician may also recognize the value of denial in sustaining parents until passage of time allows them to deal with reality. In this sense denial is akin to hope, and both are necessary in meeting adversity. The physician may use the time required for gradual reduction of parental denial as a sort of grace period to determine the long-range implications of the child's illness and to prepare to meet it more effectively.

Parents may employ a second defense: projection, blaming someone else. They may blame the retardation on some minor event in pregnancy or on the physician who delivered the baby, or even on the habits of the husband or wife. Later, parents may project blame on neighbors for lack of sympathy, on other children for cruelty, or on society at large for neglecting the retarded.

The physician may find it hard to become the object of this projected blame. Remembering that the animus is not personal but a symptom of the parents' inability to tolerate their own feelings, however, he counters not with hostility in turn, but with understanding. Thus he may very gradually help parents recognize what they are doing, and help them to see that their resentment stems from an inability to accept reality, as well as from an attempt to project their guilt feelings on someone else.

Parental guilt feelings in such a situation seem almost universal. Having conceived the child, parents feel responsible for every aspect of his being. If his conception was unwanted, their guilt feelings may be greater yet.

If parents are not able to work through these feelings, they may react adversely against the child, either by rejecting or overprotecting him. Rejection can be expressed either in outright neglect, or in harsh demands for a level of performance he is unable to achieve. Overprotection may keep the child from normally stimulating experiences and further impair his progress toward independence. These reactions may stem either from guilt or from denial of the complete degree of the child's deficit.

The physician can take an active role in mitigating these reactions. As the parents begin to accept the diagnosis and their earlier denial and projection diminish, they may more easily verbalize about their guilt feelings. The physician may encourage them to talk. He can often relieve them considerably by reassuring them about certain supposedly causative events in pregnancy and delivery, giving them as much information as possible about the etiology of the disease.

Even if personal guilt seems assuaged and denial diminished, the search may continue for a fathomable reason for the tragedy. "Why did it have to happen to us?" is the classic cry of the afflicted parent. The physician will find no easy answer; his response will depend on his own philosophy and his impressions of the character and convictions of the parents. Many parents find solace in religion; he may encourage them to seek counsel from spiritual advisers as well.

The Physician's Response

As he works with the family, the physician may find that his reactions are reflecting the parents' emotions as well as his own feelings, conscious and unconscious, toward the difficult subject of retardation. He may find value in assessing the origins of his own attitudes.

He may be deeply pessimistic, for example, because of his previous experiences with retardation. He may be uncomfortable because he feels his knowledge is limited. Because he can produce no prompt answers to difficult questions, he may feel his medical competence threatened. Lack of an immediate "cure" deprives him of the satisfaction he can often find in the treatment of an acute illness.

The physician may hold, unknowingly, feelings of hostility toward parents because of management practices he disapproves. He may have difficulty in refraining from overly severe value judgments. He may resent the parents for their unanswerable questions, their time-consuming demands, their desire for dependency, and their maladaptive behavior.

In his desire to resolve the problem of retardation quickly, he may take refuge in premature diagnosis, too-prompt referral, or other hasty solutions. He may resort to dogmatic pronouncements: "All mongoloids should be immediately institutionalized." Or he may remain passive, indicating to the parents that the situation is not his problem, and quietly hoping they will just go away.

The physician, like the parents, should recognize that his are not unusual reactions and that they should not be denied. On assessing them frankly, he may find he can meet them more forthrightly and with enhanced effectiveness.

Maintaining a continuous awareness of his own separateness from the family can be a useful procedure. Overidentification with the family can mobilize the physician's own anxieties and complicate the parents' problems with his own. Though he may not be able to remain completely detached, he may strive for a degree of perspective that will enable him to act with some objectivity. He may find it useful to distinguish between "sympathy" or feeling *with* the family, and "empathy" or feeling *for* them and acting *for* them without becoming inextricably entangled in their affairs.

The physician may find it valuable to inaugurate a self-education program to increase his own competence and confidence. Knowledge of potential developments in therapy and rehabilitation can provide a valid basis for greater optimism.

Finally, the physician accepts the fact that the rewards and satisfactions of treating retardation will differ from those of caring for the acutely ill. He finds that though he cannot cure, he can take satisfaction in aiding the adaptation of the family. In the absence of well-defined solutions, he increasingly relies on his own resourcefulness and experience, using himself as an effective instrument of therapy.

The Role of the Physician in Long-Term Counseling

When both physician and parents have come to terms with their own feelings, effective long-range planning becomes possible. In this planning, the physician must recognize the disrupting effect of retardation on family life. The parents' struggle with their own emotions and the reactions of the other children may disrupt the emotional climate of the home, damaging both retardate and siblings and sometimes endangering the entire marital relationship.

Retardation may also inflict heavy financial expense, and it may pose difficult problems in planning for future pregnancies. The family may feel stigmatized and isolated from the social community. The middle-class family with intellectual aspirations may find it harder to accept a child of defective intelligence than does a less-aspiring disadvantaged family, already so beset with major problems that a retarded member becomes only a mild additional concern.

In helping to meet these problems, the physician's most important role is a symbolic one: he is the agent through which hope is communicated to the family. The family knows that he is alert to new developments that may possibly benefit their child. But the very fact that the physician continues his concern for the child in the normal course of events and that he provides the same careful medical care he gives normal children endows the child with significance and worth. Parents often fear that their child will be written off as valueless to society. As a significant member of the community, the physician in his steadfast interest certifies the child's continuing value and diminishes parental feelings of isolation and failure. The physician helps keep hope alive.

The physician also plays an active role in suggesting specific management techniques to the parents. He may help the mother of a hyperkinetic child, for example, to understand that her own anxieties and tensions further stimulate the child. By enforcing firm limits and remaining calm and consistent in discipline, she may interrupt the cycle of this disturbing behavior. Or he may indicate ways in which the parent can help develop the child's skills in eating, buttoning, or tying shoelaces. Parents enjoy playing teacher; they may take pride in the child's achievements as reflecting their own ingenuity. The added companionship comes as an . . . unexpected dividend.

Though he does suggest such specific procedures, more frequently he indicates general problem-solving techniques. He always encourages parents to resolve problems in ways that best meet their needs. Because of his knowledge of the family, he can often point out to parents the strengths they are displaying in coping with their problem. This approval from a respected figure encourages them to further effort. He may forestall some parental discouragement by emphasizing in advance the experimental nature of most solutions to retardation, and encouraging them to discover new approaches when initial efforts fail.

During the child's lifetime, the physician continues to provide an important opportunity for parents to discuss their feelings as renewed crises arise. The intensity of parental anxiety frequently is reduced in the process of sharing it with a professional person. The physician may be that person.

Finally the physician encourages parents to look for further help in the community. He may refer them to the local parent organization such as a chapter of the National Association for Retarded Children. By talking with other parents, families find their problems are not unique. They dilute their anxiety by sharing it; in working for the good of all retarded children they meet their own need for action in a situation which may provide little further opportunity in behalf of their own child.

Such organizations may initiate or maintain a wide variety of services for the retarded. They support scientifically proved methods for dealing with retardation; thus they curb parental shopping and facilitate more constructive action.

The physician's final goal in parent counseling is to help parents integrate the child and his disorder as a nonstressful part of family life, to enable the family to plan objectively without undue emotional inhibition, and feel satisfied in the knowledge that they have contributed in every way possible to the development of the potentialities of their child.

□ □ □

SECTION D

Psychologists

Generally, the psychologist's role in the management of the family of the retarded is not specific. Much of what he might do might also be done, for instance, by the social worker. There is, however, one function in which the psychologist can make a unique contribution—the utilization and interpretation of the psychological evaluation of the child.

In the first selection, Font discusses the role a psychological examination can play in the clarification of the parental attitude toward the child. Upon observing her child's performance during the psychological examination, the mother may express attitudes, doubts, and fears. This sets the stage for later interviews with the mother during which these reactions are used as seeds for discussion and for assimilation of new ideas and points of view.

Roos provides a statement on the use of the psychological evaluation in interviewing the parents. He emphasizes the necessity for clearly informing the parents of the purpose and nature of the evaluation, for clarity in presentation of results, for expediting the findings, for presentation of results in meaningful terms, and for acquainting parents with the limitations of the evaluative findings.

PARENTAL REACTIONS TO PSYCHOLOGIC MEASUREMENT

Marion M. Font

(*American Journal of Mental Deficiency*, 1951)

The diagnostic and therapeutic value of the individual psychologic examination in clinical practice is well established. Not as widely recognized is the part the psychologic examination of an exceptional child may play in clarification of parental attitude toward him and his problem.

Consultation service to the pediatrician provides a special setting in which to observe parental reactions to mental measurement. Complaints voiced by parents as reasons for bringing a child to a pediatrician frequently include speech defect, poor co-ordination, temper tantrums, and difficulty in getting along with other children. Infrequently, parents mention difficulty with school work, inattention, and difficulty in comprehending instructions. Many children referred by pediatricians for psychologic evaluation during a two-year period were found to be so fearful and immature that separation from the mother during psychologic examination represented threat to emotional security sufficient to invalidate results of the test. In such cases the mother was present during the testing session, engendering by her familiar presence feelings of security that are paramount to successful psychologic examination of a child.

Witnessing the psychologic examination of her child is a trying experience for the mother. Anxiety and overprotectiveness prompt her to assist him, but this is anticipated by the psychologist, who conducts the examination in such a manner as to forestall a mother's actual participation. On the other hand, as the mother observes what her child can and cannot do, she is encouraged to verbalize attitudes, doubts, and fears. A defensive attitude toward the examination and the psychologist conducting it is understandable. Defense reactions have protected the mother from facing the reality of her child's condition. She may harbor resentment dating from a previous psychologic examination elsewhere, when she was either given no formulation or was treated tactlessly without regard for her carefully built defense. She clings to the fact that the child cannot talk plainly and therefore cannot be understood by outsiders who do not realize how much he knows. She hopes for some drug that will correct his speech. She may consider the examination unfair because her child has never heard certain words of a vocabulary test, or has had no experience with stringing beads or building puzzles. Sometimes a mother may become angry because she believes her child is placed at a disadvantage and is unduly penalized on a test. Sometimes she may recognize the overall poor showing made by her child during testing and may talk at length about his fine memory for certain songs, places, or events. Yet few mothers display hostility. If their defenses are not too rudely shattered, they welcome the opportunity offered them after examination of the child to talk with the psychologist. The examiner represents to the mothers a sympathetic accepting listener who wants to know what *they* think and what *they* have observed. The psychologist's complete acceptance of the child dispel's a mother's hostility and enables her to feel that she, too, is accepted.

Mothers of exceptional children often feel a need to be accepted by others, seeming to stem from their need for their children to be accepted, or from fear or criticism regarding their methods of training and discipline. They may have trained and disciplined wisely; yet they lack confidence in their own judgment and feel insecure because of criticism from members of their own family. Verbalization of these fears is possible during the interview, for they realize they are accepted without reservation and despite their defenses. One mother, after much hesitation, mentioned her thought of placing her child in a special school and her fear of suggesting such a step to her husband and her mother. Her eager, "What do you think?" was answered by "What do *you* think about your little boy? How do *you* think he compares with his brothers and sisters when they were his age, and with other children of his own age now? Tell me about him." During discussion of the child's past history, his health, special problems and relationship to other members of the family, it was apparent that his mother felt guilty because she harbored a fear that her idea of special school placement might be construed as rejection. Reassurance, praise of the child's good behavior and friendliness, and discussion of the curricula and advantages of special schools relieved guilt feelings sufficiently to enable the mother to focus attention on plans for special schooling, which she would later discuss in more detail with the referring pediatrician.

Another mother seemed unaware of any problem except speech difficulty, and had many rationalizations for her child's inability to succeed in school and certain items of the psychologic examination. During the interview she suddenly confided that she had suspected mental retardation but lacked courage to voice her fears to her husband and grown children, who acknowledged no difficulty other than defective speech. She feared she was being disloyal to her child in considering him mentally retarded. Discussion of his daily activities, his affectionate disposition, and his love of music gradually lessened her tension and enabled her to discuss children's development as an individual and unique problem of each individual child. When her fear of disloyalty was faced frankly, she was able to verbalize her belief that this child was different from his brothers and sisters and should have a different school program and different activities, which would include speech instructions but which would be geared to his own individual pace. She felt able to discuss further with the pediatrician how best to convince her family of the child's special needs and how best to begin a program of special instruction.

One mother spoke at great length of the mutual affection between her child and his stepfather. After she felt secure and accepted by the psychologist she said that her husband called the boy "stupid," and this hurt and worried her. She feared that it might have a harmful effect on the boy, whose speech was almost unintelligible and who was not accepted by the neighborhood children. His classmates accepted him, for he was in a small private school. She had been asked to withdraw him from public school because he seemed unable to learn, although his younger brother did well in the public school. As she expressed concern over her husband's rejection of her eldest child, she was also able to put into words her feeling that the boy should not be unfavorably compared with his younger brother nor held to the same standards, for he could not do the things the younger child could do. She agreed that she was fortunate in finding a special school within her means. Verbalization and a sympathetic listener enabled her to face the fact that the child's speech difficulty was one manifestation of his need for special education and reassured her that she was doing the best possible thing for her child.

Attitudes and fears expressed by mothers during psychologic interviews, as well as manifest rationalizations and defenses, have been present for many years. Unless these fears and attitudes can be crystallized through verbalization, the rationalizations and defenses may render a mother resistant to realistic formulation of her child's problem. Psychologic measurement aids the process of crystallization because it forces the mother to face reality.

An example of uncrystallized fears that had been silenced for many years by rationalization was presented by the mother of a seventeen-year-old girl. She had a severely mutilated, incomprehensible, infantile speech which had existed since she first began to talk. According to the mother "Everyone loves Doris." The teachers told her mother she was "slow," but they made such great allowance for the defective speech that Doris had been permitted to reach the ninth grade. According to the results of psychologic measurement she should have been in the second grade. The mother had never before considered examination necessary but she was beginning to wonder if Doris could keep up with her classmates in high school. Teachers told her that they believed that Doris would respond to individual training, because she was determined and anxious to learn. The mother had never faced the possibility that Doris' speech defect might be one aspect of her inability to learn as the average child learns. By attributing all school difficulties to the speech defect, the mother was rationalizing, and the teachers' willingness to pass Doris from grade to grade helped maintain the mother's defenses. During the psychologic interview she said that she did not believe Doris could do high school work. She knew Doris did not have the same adolescent interests of other girls her age. She wondered if there were some special school where Doris could be with others who had difficulty in learning, as well as difficulty with speech. Discussion of plans for the future was possible when attitudes were clarified and emotions faced objectively.

Observation of a child's performance on psychologic examination is a realistic situation. The performance can be related to a child's performance in everyday life situations. This relationship is clarified during psychologic interview of the mother—not as criticism of the child or of her, but as a basis for planning an individual training program.

The child is referred by the pediatrician for special examination by many specialists. Upon completion of these examinations he and his parents will return to the pediatrician for formulation and recommendation.

There is no pressure for time during the psychologist's interview with the mother. It has been planned purposely to allow for discussion of fears and doubts and for assimilation of new ideas and points of view. It is a preparation period for the formulation-interview with the pediatrician. It is an opportunity for the mother to ventilate emotions that would disrupt clear thinking, perhaps to the extent that she could not accept realistic recommendations. The psychologic interview represents an integration, in the mother's thinking, of all that she has observed during the psychologic examination of her child and all that has preceded it—examinations in other departments and what she has felt and believed concerning them. She talks and the psychologist listens, clarifies and questions. She is encouraged to discuss or elaborate certain points during the final interview with the pediatrician. She will know what he means by a special class or special school and will not interpret this recommendation as rejection of her child. She will be able to accept suggestions to correct her overprotectiveness, and not construe them as criticisms. She will be able to accept a recommendation to return in a year's time for further check and repeat psychologic examination, for she will have clarified her feeling that her child must be taught at his own rate of progress—a rate that is individual and for him alone.

□ □ □

from PSYCHOLOGICAL COUNSELING WITH PARENTS OF RETARDED CHILDREN *Philip Roos*

(Mental Retardation, 1963)

. . . .

Use of Evaluative Findings

Since psychologists are frequently requested to determine the presence of mental retardation, psychological evaluation often becomes the subject of the interview with the parents. If the parents and the psychologist agree that formal evaluation of the child may be desirable, the parents should be informed of the nature and purpose of the evaluation. It is important to acquaint parents with the answers they may expect from the evaluation. If the results may prove to be relatively meaningless, the parents should be so advised. Parents' resentment at being told of uninterpretable results of complex and often expensive procedures is not entirely inappropriate, particularly if they were not forewarned of this possible outcome.

The psychologist should endeavor to expedite evaluative procedures. Allowing parents to linger in the agony of doubt is cruel and destructive. The period of evaluation is usually experienced as highly stressful and distressing by parents, and it should be kept as short as possible. As soon as the evaluation has been completed, the parents should be informed of the results.

Evaluative findings should be presented in terms that will be meaningful to the parents. Operational formulations and concrete examples are to be preferred to abstract and theoretical constructs. Presenting the child's level of functioning in mental age equivalents is usually considerably more meaningful than references to the intelligence quotients or social quotients. As a matter of fact, parents are often surprisingly accurate in estimating the child's level of functioning in terms of developmental level.

Description of probable accomplishments in terms of illustrative behavior is usually extremely helpful. Emphasis on those activities which the child may be able to perform is more helpful than dwelling on areas of limitations and expected failure. A statement such as, "Your child will probably be able to master fifth or sixth grade work," is much less likely to cause pain than saying, "Of course, your child will never complete junior high school," and it is equally factual.

Parents should be acquainted with the limitations of the evaluative findings. Parents usually have questions regarding etiology, diagnosis, and prognosis, and the counselor will, in many cases, of course, have to indicate that in one or more of these areas he is making an "educated guess." Although the majority of parents are blissfully ignorant of such concepts as validity and reliability, it is meaningful to indicate the relative probability that the present findings are accurate and, particularly, the likelihood that predictions will prove to be correct.

Although it is neither realistic nor appropriate to present exact probability figures, the counselor can indicate that his predictions regarding a severely retarded, ten-year-old microcephalic are made with considerable confidence, whereas his predictions regarding a two-year-old, mildly retarded child with no apparent neuropathology are made with less assurance. Comments regarding the possible value of future evaluations can be helpful, and they may include acquainting parents with suitable referral sources. . . .

□ □ □

Part VIII Management of Special-Problem Groups

There is almost universal agreement that families of the retarded differ widely in their dynamics and need for services. Nevertheless, some principles of management are universal, and some management techniques are of benefit to almost any family. There are also situations and problems which are characteristic only to a segment of families with retarded children, and for these special-problem groupings some management techniques tend to be more appropriate than others. This part of the book contains selections which describe management approaches that have been developed to deal with five special-problem configurations.

The limited family and the family with a mildly retarded child deserve special consideration both because of their sheer numbers and because the evidence suggests that these children are very modifiable. Since most retardates come from limited families and are believed to be capable of higher functioning if exposed to early intensive stimulation, it is essential that a major proportion of future management efforts be directed toward such families. Here, much retardation can apparently be prevented or reversed, and the vicious cycle of deprivation, retardation, and poverty can be broken. Certainly, the evidence presented in this section, especially in the selection from the Pine School Project, suggests a rationale for optimism.

Families with mongoloid and with phenylketonuric children are treated here as special-problem groups because they share many problems, and because appropriate literature specific to these problems and their management exists. Furthermore, a book of this nature would have appeared incomplete without a section on the management of siblings of the retarded. Such siblings truly constitute a special-problem group, and thus have a fitting place in this part.

As we indicated in Part V, Section A, a high degree of commonality of problems and needs makes it likely that a group-management technique will be more efficient than individual management, and that the social and efficiency effects interact to produce a powerful management technique. For this reason, it should not surprise us that many selections in this part describe group techniques as their major management medium.

SECTION A

The Limited Family

A disproportionate amount of the literature on the management of the family of the retarded has been concerned with the middle- or upper-class family, and/or families with severely impaired children. Yet the epidemiological evidence has shown that the great majority of the retarded are only mildly retarded and usually come from the lower end of the social class continuum. In this section, we will deal with the management of lower-class limited families who are a source of a large number of retarded children, most of whom are mildly retarded. Compared to middle- and upper-class families with lower functioning children, limited families not only pose problems due to the difference in the children, but, more importantly perhaps, due to differences in capabilities and way of life which call for very special management. Such management may have to differ considerably from that which is offered to middle-class families and which is rooted in middle-class values.

As on several previous occasions, we use selections by Begab to define the problem. In the first of two selections, Begab discusses the limited parent with low intelligence, and points out that limited families tend to be multiple-problem families in which the parent frequently comes to the attention of the agency rather than, or before, the child. Begab calls for management which takes account of parents' limitations and which recognizes their particular way of life. In the second selection, Begab emphasizes that the manager must realize that these families are products of a subculture in which self-confidence and self-help skills are frequently not emphasized.

The third selection consists of a combination of parts from four publications by Roll, Triplett, and Parsons, all describing various aspects of the so-called Pine School project. This project constitutes one of the most significant, imaginative, sensitive, and apparently effective management endeavors directed toward limited families with retarded children. It utilizes a wide range of techniques, including nursery education for the child, group activities and counseling for the siblings, and group counseling and home management assistance for the mothers. The home management program drew upon the skills of public health nurses, social workers, and a rarely-utilized professional: the home economist.

The final selection, by Fackler, describes a project aimed at developing community action by and for families with a retarded child who lived in a lower-class public housing project. Parental interest was aroused, a parent group was formed, and new services by volunteers, professionals and agencies to both parents and children were either developed, or existing services were oriented toward them. Again, the project was marked by an approach more attuned to limited families than most existing services in retardation.

from COUNSELLING PARENTS OF RETARDED CHILDREN

Michael J. Begab

(*Canada's Mental Health,* 1964)

. . . .

The Inadequate Parent

Social, ethnic, and cultural factors have an important bearing on parental reactions and adjustment to a retarded child, but a more significant consideration is the disparity between the intelligence of the parents and child. Counseling with parents of low mentality, severe psychological aberrations, or other personality defects presents very contrasting dynamics to those discussed above [with more adequate parents]. Almost invariably, these parents have limited income and education, are of low occupational status, and live under generally disadvantaged circumstances. For them, achievement is apparently not a fundamental value, and they do not seem to suffer from guilt feelings or threat to their self-esteem. They seem neither disappointed nor anxiety-ridden about the future. Only as the child fails in school, gets into trouble with the law, or runs afoul of neighborhood children are they confronted with the child's retardation. More often, it is the parents themselves who come to agency attention, for from this segment of society, we find, come many of our chronically underemployed relief recipients, one-parent homes, and neglectful parents. The child's handicap is only one—and sometimes the least important—of the multiple problems disrupting family life.

These families, and others among the culturally deprived from whom the large majority of the retarded come, frequently regard agency intervention with suspicion and distrust. They have been confronted by society on many occasions with evidence of their shortcomings as wage earners, parents, and citizens. As a consequence, many become "social isolates," divorcing themselves from community activities and gradually caring less and less about what their neighbors think of them. Lacking motivation to improve their living conditions, and lacking knowledge or appreciation of sound child-rearing practices, these parents have little to offer their children. To forestall repeated generations of retarded persons, these children must be protected from harmful environments. One important way, short of separation and placement, is to help the inadequate parent to develop parenting skills.

By itself, limited intelligence need not disqualify a parent to care for his children properly, but it could have this effect. Through guidance, these parents can be taught the art of homemaking and child rearing, how to budget their meager incomes and manage their households. As they master the tools for social survival and achieve success in areas of former failure, they may gain in self-confidence and pride, take greater interest in their surroundings, and assume a more active role in community life. Benefited by concrete services of this type, these individuals may become less hostile toward offers of agency help. In this more favourable atmosphere, the counselor can better ply his trade in promoting self-awareness and a capacity for change.

Mental retardation, as a family problem, is as diverse as its many causes and many variables which influence family adaptation. To be dealt with, these problems require a wide range of services and facilities. However, none are more vital than parent counseling and guidance. Provided by skilled professionals, this service can prevent family disorganization and provide a healthier climate in which the retarded child may grow. This can do much to reduce future social liabilities and add to social assets.

□ □ □

from CASEWORK FOR THE MENTALLY RETARDED—CASEWORK WITH PARENTS

Michael J. Begab

(The Mentally Retarded Child: A Guide to Services of Social Agencies, 1963)

The Limited Parent

The problems posed in working with parents who are themselves inadequate or mentally retarded usually center around factors other than the child's retardation, unless the child is severely handicapped. Frequently these parents come to agency attention because of the community's concern with the child's antisocial behavior, his school maladjustment, or substandard conditions in the home. Many of these families are particularly difficult to reach because of their social isolation. They seldom participate in the usual civic group activities, have few friends, and are therefore somewhat outside the influence of their neighbors. For these reasons, they have little concern regarding the community's attitudes toward them, their desire for social approval is low, and little initiative is exerted to improve their child-rearing practices or poor living conditions.

The objective of the casework relationship in services to these parents is to strengthen their capacities by guiding them in the more effective discharge of their responsibilities and by motivating them toward self-improvement. This task is one of the most complex confronting social workers, and it is further complicated by the authoritarian role in which the worker is usually placed—a role to which such families often react with resentment and hostility. While there is much to be learned in this area, there is little question that some of our difficulties in working with these parents stem from our own need to be authoritative rather than the use of our authority judiciously in response to the parents' need. Also, we sometimes judge the behavior of these individuals by our own middle class standards and values. We disqualify them (in our own minds) as parents because of their mental aberrations or limitations. Too often, we do not give them sufficient opportunity to demonstrate what they may be able to do with skilled professional guidance.

It is true that *some* of these parents lack the capacity to regulate their own behavior or that of their children. The worker *in these instances* may need to apply his authority in the form of judgments as to right or wrong to protect these parents from choices that are inimical to their best interests. With proper advice and guidance some of these parents can be helped to function more adequately in the immediate situation and gain sufficient insight and confidence from successful experiences to apply these skills in future situations.

These parents usually come to social agency attention with a background of failure, or at best marginal success as wage earners, marriage partners, or citizens. These life experiences are frequently associated with disability for parenthood as well. To confront the parent with further evidence of his inadequacy or to advise him of his child's deficiency—a totally incomprehensible observation for some—is ego-damaging. Some will react with hostility and denial and regard the worker as another source of community persecution. Others may be so psychologically "beaten," that they respond with apathy or docility and have neither motivation nor drive to improve their situation.

If the limited parent is to be helped to discharge his responsibilities more effectively, he must be safeguarded as far as possible from further attack on an already weak ego structure. Though the worker cannot ignore the presenting problem or the complaint that may have initiated the referral, he can convey by attitude and manner that the parent is interested in his child's welfare and is probably in the best position to do something about it. Only as the worker truly respects the integrity of these parents—however substandard they may be in measuring up to social norms—and stresses their abilities rather than disabilities, can progress be anticipated. The worker who is accepting and sincere presents a quite different picture to these parents than they probably expected. Freed of suspicion and distrust, the limited parent can make better use of his resources.

In working with retarded parents accused of neglect, it is wise to keep in mind that such neglect may not be willful in nature but the result of ignorance or of burdens that exceed their limited capacities. The tasks of household management, of providing nutritious meals, adequate shelter and clothing and proper child care and supervision, are a challenge to any family. When these tasks are further complicated by low income and a large family, they can overwhelm the parent who is unresourceful, immature, and lacking in judgment. Sometimes a retarded mother who is devoted to her child appears to be neglectful, because her total energies are consumed with the practical problems of home management and her husband shares in few of the responsibilities.

Many of these mothers want to be better parents but become apathetic about it in the face of repeated frustrations and community threats; their true need is for community support. Casework in these instances often needs to be focused on providing concrete services. It is not enough and probably undesirable to tell these mothers what they are doing wrong or what they have failed to do (at least early in the relationship). They need practical advice and guidance in the arts of homemaking and child care, budgeting, and the judicious use of their time. They—and their husbands too—need encouragement to broaden their sphere of activities and relationships. Above all, they need recognition for their achievements and a sense of self esteem. To the extent [that] these objectives are achieved, these parents begin to care what their neighbors think and strive for self-improvement. Furthermore, they have been provided the practical tools to ward off hostile community pressures and to bring themselves more in line with society's values and standards. Not infrequently, the mother's heightened homemaking skills reduce conflicts with her husband and contribute to a more wholesome family atmosphere.

The social worker-client relationship is particularly well suited to promoting feelings of self-confidence and developing self-help skills. Some workers, however, may not have sufficient technical knowledge of the practical arts to offer guidance in these areas and will need to call upon the homemaker, home economist or other specialist for the complete fulfillment of casework goals. . . .

□ □ □

from THE PINE SCHOOL PROJECT

This selection is a composite of the following publications. Footnotes used refer to these:

1. Roll, Marlin H. "A Study of Retarded Young Children." In National Conference on Social Welfare, *Social Work Practice*, 1962.
2. Parsons, Mabel H. "A Home Economist in Service to Families with Mental Retardation." *Children*, 1960.

3. Triplett, June L. "Environmental Manipulation as an Approach to Mental Retardation." In *Nursing and Community Mental Health and Retardation Programs*. National League for Nursing, 1965.
4. Triplett, June L. "A Women's Club for Deprived Mothers." *Nursing Outlook*, 1965.

The Pine School Project has been concerned with a longitudinal study of young mentally retarded children from inadequate homes and the effects of a broad, interdisciplinary effort at environmental manipulation which would not involve disruption of the family unit. The purposes of the study are: 1) to record in detail the growth and development of a group of endogenous, mentally retarded children for a period of at least five years; 2) to utilize various facilities and techniques in an effort to alter the unfavorable course of development of the children involved. Although the study is still in progress, a preliminary report of procedures employed and results obtained seems warranted.

Procedure

Children selected for the study are necessarily residents of Iowa City and its environs, since part of our interest lies in working with children in their normal home surroundings and also because we are interested in working with the parents and siblings as well. The criteria for selection of children are:

1. Chronological age between three and six.
2. I.Q., as measured on the Stanford-Binet scale, between 50 and 80.
3. Absence of evidence of physical and neurological involvement that would suggest organic etiology of the retardation.
4. Evidence of mental retardation in at least one other member of the family.
5. Parents in the lower socioeconomic status group as determined by a modified Warner Index of Status Characteristics.

. . . .

The children are picked up at their homes between 8:30 and 9:00 A.M. and returned between 3:00 and 3:30 P.M. Because of their dietary deficiencies, the children are offered milk three times a day, and a high-protein, low-carbohydrate lunch is supplied. The primary function of Pine School is to make available the best possible educational program for these children in light of their needs, as determined by comprehensive, individual study. Since the research project as a whole is concerned with the effects of a total effort to improve environmental conditions, attendance at Pine School is only one aspect of environmental manipulation. The program provides stimulation and experiences designed to increase the children's fund of general information, familiarity with the elementary tools of learning and the language and atmosphere of a school, and an opportunity to develop the ability to form more adequate interpersonal relationships.

Experiences offered the children are, frankly, those which are routine for middle-class children. If this group is to succeed in competition with middle-class children in a school taught by middle-class teachers, some commonality of experience with their competition seems imperative. . . .

Two social workers, assigned on a part-time basis to this project, have followed accepted principles and techniques of social work in: a) observing and interpreting the kind and quality of interrelationships within the family; b) assisting the families to utilize appropriate social agencies and programs; and c) offering more intensive casework when necessary to supplement available agency services. . . .[1]

Gradually it became obvious to the staff that, in the follow-up services, large areas of family life were being neglected, such as interpersonal relationships, methods and attitudes of child care, family feeding, money management, homemaking, and health and cleanliness practices. Therefore, a home economist and a public health nurse were added to the staff.

The home economist was charged with finding ways of helping the families to improve their home life and of studying the effects of the methods she devised. The assumption was that these families could be motivated to improve their conditions, that they could be encouraged to learn methods and techniques for doing so, and that the mentally retarded children would benefit from the efforts of their parents to achieve an improved home environment, especially if these efforts were successful. The home economist's services were envisaged as primarily supportive and educational, with the goal of teaching mothers to recognize and to solve their homemaking problems.

The home economist's first step in working with these families was an effort to establish rapport. To accomplish this, she visited each family with the social worker and told the mothers about the kinds of services she had to offer. She followed each initial visit with three more "get acquainted" calls, a week apart, during which she tried to learn something of the mothers' interests and abilities as possible levers for motivating them to improved functioning.

Two facts became apparent from these early meetings: 1) that these mothers were lonesome people, cut off from society, and 2) that they wanted to learn how to make their homes more livable.

Some of the mothers showed immediate enthusiasm when the home economist offered to teach them to sew, clean, plan meals, and prepare food. Others expressed mild interest, and one was almost totally unreceptive. . . .

As soon as the home economist achieved rapport with the mothers, she found her services in demand. Two other members of the staff—the public health nurse and the social worker—were also receiving heavy demands for follow-up services from the families. Therefore, these three staff members decided to divide the responsibility for maintaining regular contact with the families. Under the plan each family would receive at least one home visit a week from one of these workers. If an emergency arose requiring the skill of a worker not assigned to the family, that worker would be called in.

Several times during the ensuing year all three workers found themselves concentrating on a particular problem of one family. At other times, two of the workers were doing so. When the special problem was solved, the responsible worker continued calling on the family every week.

This plan to coordinate the efforts of nurse, social worker, and home economist created no professional jurisdictional problems. The home economist often found herself listening to a woeful story involving a health or social problem, but she made no attempt to deal with it on the spot, except to say that she would send the social worker or the public health nurse out to call. After a staff conference, the appropriate staff member would go into the home and try to help solve the problem. Each discipline represented remained distinct; each worker had more than enough to do. . . .

The loneliness of these families was unmistakable. They did not participate in groups such as parent-teacher associations, women's clubs, or church groups, either because they felt inadequate or because they had tried in the past and had a painful experience which they did not wish to repeat. Most of them had no close friends; their relationships were principally within their immediate families. . . .[2]

Lack of knowledge was not solely responsible for (the women's) ineffective functioning. . . . Most of them were afraid of authority, avoided new situations, lacked confidence in their own abilities, and had poor self-concepts. And why shouldn't they? Society had removed children from some of the homes, which were considered "unfit;" school personnel had complained about lack of cleanliness, truancy, and failure to achieve—all of which reflected back to their failure as parents. They had been recipients of Christmas baskets,

Thanksgiving baskets, Easter baskets—frequently given in such a way as again to imply, "You do not care for your children." They showed little concern for their own appearance, either in clothing selection or grooming. They were hungry for opportunities to receive praise and recognition, and a few wove elaborate stories of their abilities as homemakers in order to secure recognition. . . .[3]

In brief, the parents come to the project with strong evidence of hostility, frustration, feelings of rejection, and an awareness of their social inadequacy and resultant dependency. They might be described as socially alienated from their environment. Their responses to their children reflected these attitudes, and served to transmit to, or engender in, the children similar feelings and attitudes. The most striking characteristic, in the form of observable behavior, was the inconsistency with which the parents managed their children. They rarely promoted acceptance of any general principles of behavior or of ethical conduct. It is obvious that children are permitted to behave very differently, for example, when they are home alone with the mother and when there are visitors. At times the presence of the father demands a different pattern of behavior. The mother often expresses her awareness of other social values by direct means, telling the children that their teachers will expect certain behavior, or that the "cops" will not permit certain acts. The children are more apt to be punished for "getting caught" or annoying an authority figure than for committing an act which is wrong or generally disapproved. If there is a consistent approach, it would seem to be inculcation of the theory that adult displeasure should be avoided in any given situation. It would appear that children are rarely rewarded for a correct response *per se*. The attitude of the adult present becomes an important variable in every situation. This seems to promote, in the children, attitudes of servility toward authority figures, a reluctance to respond spontaneously, and a general feeling of uncertainty about expectations. This uncertainty leads to frequent frustration. . . .[1]

The staff believed that a group organization might fill the mothers' need for companionship and also serve as a teaching medium for the home economist. Therefore, the home economist took a two-pronged approach—individual and group—in providing services.

Work with Individuals

Three families were assigned to the home economist. Each had asked for help on many homemaking problems. The home economist visited each family once a week at unscheduled times—unscheduled to stimulate the mother to keep her house in order at all times. She began by attempting to find out what problem in homemaking was causing the mother the most concern and to help her make plans for a solution that would not require a large outlay of money and that seemed to be achievable. She gave the mother suggestions but left her with the responsibility for carrying them out, calling back at appropriate intervals to discuss progress, and to lend her support and encouragement.

Once—but only once—the home economist made the mistake of taking up with the mother a community criticism of the family. The mother immediately withdrew and became defensive, and the good rapport the home economist had so painstakingly established was nearly lost.

The Greens. The first family selected for the home economist's concentrated attention, whom we shall call the Green family, consisted of a mother, a father, and ten children. The father, who was employed on the section gang of the railroad, was considered a reliable and willing worker. However, he drank heavily on weekends and gambled. Ever since his marriage he had been sent to the county jail three or four times a year because of drunkenness and for mistreating his wife. The mother was overweight, but otherwise pretty. From the time she was six, when her mother died, she had been in one foster home after another, never being fully accepted or loved. At sixteen, she had been persuaded by her father, who did not approve of her current love affair, to marry a man much older than herself. She has never forgotten her teenage love.

The Greens had received help from the county welfare department most of their married lives, as had their parents. They lived near the railroad tracks in a dilapidated dwelling, inadequate in rooms, furnishings, and health accommodations.

In 1957, the Greens' ten children had been made wards of the court, and shortly afterward the two older boys were sent to different state institutions for the mentally retarded. The four girls still lived at home and were attending the public schools, but two of them were failing in their school work, and the other two were in special education classes. Of the remaining four children, all boys, three were attending Pine School, and the youngest, who was subject to convulsions as well as being retarded, did not attend school. All the children were attractive looking, but they were always dirty, ragged, and unkempt.

On her first visit to this home the home economist found living conditions almost unbelievably bad. Food-encrusted dishes were on the tables; food which had previously been spilled on the floor had been allowed to accumulate and spoil; broken pop bottles and beer cans were sitting about; the furniture was broken and covered with dirty quilts. Two windows were broken and, since there were no screens, the house was full of flies. Dirty clothes were scattered in confusion about the rooms, and a fetid odor permeated the house.

Without making any reference to these conditions, the home economist called on the family at least once a week as she looked for strengths to build upon and established a relationship with the mother—a process that took four visits. As Mrs. Green gradually realized that the home economist was not going to find fault with her or demand something from her, she began to show an interest in food purchasing and preparation. The home economist used this interest as a strength to build on, and with consultation from the social worker, tried to formulate simple, realistic goals that Mrs. Green could be encouraged to meet. Since Mrs. Green had exhausted her credit at the small, expensive neighborhood store where she bought her groceries, a discussion of food buying and planning was selected as a starting point. In a very short time, Mrs. Green asked that the home economist help her to plan her meals for a week and to make out a market order. The social worker and the nurse, both of whom were visiting the family, also supported Mrs. Green's efforts to plan. Now she plans by the week and purchases at the supermarket most of the time.

After some time the staff could not help but notice the improvement in the mother's housekeeping. When the home economist arrived on her unscheduled visits, dishes were usually done, the floor scrubbed, and the dirty clothes put out of sight. The interest being shown in the family by the staff and their noncritical attitude seemed to motivate the mother to greater effort.

Whenever Mrs. Green mentioned the possibility of improving some area in her home, the home economist showed an immediate interest. When the mother expressed a desire to paint and fix up the living room, she arranged for the paint to be purchased through a gift fund available to the child development clinic. Mrs. Green painted the room herself and was very proud of her accomplishment. She then saved and bought some plastic curtains for the windows and replaced the broken window panes. This show of interest and activity was a great surprise to everyone.

This family has been served by the project for two years, and the home shows definite signs of improvement. There are periods of backsliding, especially when Mr. Green is on one of his periodic drunks, but in general, the family does not go back as far as the state of apathy it was in when first visited by the project worker.

The two boys who were enrolled in Pine School are now attending public schools. While the next-to-youngest boy still needs to attend Pine School, he has learned to talk and express himself, which he could not do before. While these children are still retarded, the project staff believes that they can see some improvement and will be able to see more in the next three years.

The Marnes. The second family selected for the home economist's concentrated help—called here the Marne family—consisted of a father, a mother, and five girls. The youngest girls, twins, attended the Pine School. The older girls, [ages] eight, nine, and ten, attended the public school special education classes. This family had the kind of housing and equipment usual in lower middle-class families, but their attitudes and income defined them as of lower socioeconomic standing.

Mr. Marne, a responsible foreman in an ice cream factory, had become an orphan at an early age and had been passed from one home to another, finally ending his childhood in the city orphanage. He joined the navy as soon as he had finished the eighth grade, and had never gone back to school. Mrs. Marne also had a very deprived childhood. Her parents had a large number of children and had frequently received public assistance. They had worked their children very hard around the house and had taught them the elements of cleanliness but little else. Mrs. Marne took the same attitude toward her own children. The girls were attractive looking but often unkempt and shabbily and inappropriately dressed.

The relationship between Mr. and Mrs. Marne was stormy. Although Mr. Marne made a steady income, he would not trust Mrs. Marne with any of it.

Mrs. Marne was immediately receptive to the home economist's offer of help. There were so many things she wanted to learn that the home economist had difficulty pinning her down to one achievable goal. However, she eventually decided to learn to clean house for others, so that she might have some money of her own to spend.

Realizing that the houses in which Mrs. Marne might find work would be more elaborate than her own, the home economist took her into her own home once a week to teach her a variety of housekeeping skills. Mrs. Marne obviously wanted to learn, and she did learn rapidly although her intelligence test had produced one of the lowest scores in the project. After six weeks of this arrangement, the social worker suggested that Mrs. Marne be encouraged to seek employment as she now had the skills she had set out to learn and was in danger of developing a dependency relationship to the home economist. Though the home economist helped her find her first job, at present she has several cleaning jobs which she secured by herself and which fit her children's school hours. The reports of her work are good.

Mrs. Marne also asked for help on planning and marketing for the family's food. Breaking into tears, she told the home economist that Mr. Marne was tired of her routine fare and refused to come home for meals. The home economist responded by helping her to plan a week's menu and market order built around the kinds of food her husband liked. Learning that Mrs. Marne did not know how to use a cookbook, although she owned three, she also showed Mrs. Marne how to follow a recipe. Mr. Marne now seems to enjoy eating at home, and Mrs. Marne is continuing to try new dishes.

After two years of service, the Marne family shows great improvement.

Through contacts made in her housekeeping jobs, Mrs. Marne has become aware of how other people live. Consequently, the children are now having their hair brushed and combed and their dresses altered to fit them. Their mother has encouraged them to join the Brownie Scouts, to attend Sunday school, and to have parties. The two youngest girls have moved into a public school and seem to be doing well. In spite of her low IQ, Mrs. Marne has a tremendous drive to improve her family.

Group Meetings

Because of the obvious loneliness of the women being served in the project, the home economist decided to try to get them together in group meetings. She saw the possibilities of using the meetings not only to alleviate the mothers' loneliness but also to help them learn more about meal preparation and food planning, sewing, child care, housekeeping, and personal cleanliness. Approaching some of these subjects with groups rather than with individuals would be less likely to wound personal feelings. If the women took turns in having the group meet at their homes, enough competition might arise to serve as a motivating factor for "sprucing up" their homes. The meetings might also be used as a means of introducing the young children of these families to one another and giving them some opportunity for social interactions. The home economist hoped that each time a woman had a meeting in her home and had to cope with the various problems of entertaining, the experience would add to her ability to accept responsibility.

Because of her energetic, outgoing nature, Mrs. Marne was asked whether she would like to form a social group of the women whose children went to Pine School. When she responded enthusiastically, it was suggested that she bring the idea up at a Pine School PTA meeting. Meanwhile, the home economist also planted the idea of a social group with other mothers in the project. Thus, when Mrs. Marne made the suggestion at the PTA meeting, the mothers accepted it readily because they were familiar with it.

There was never any difficulty in selecting a meeting place, as each woman in the group seemed anxious to entertain.

At each meeting, the hostess furnished the necessary dishes; another member of the group brought refreshments, having volunteered to do so. These have ranged all the way from good and attractively decorated sandwiches to a poor pumpkin pie. Before each meeting the home economist checked early in the week to see if she could be of assistance to the hostess and to the woman bringing the refreshments, and to make sure that they had not forgotten that they were to serve. She also sent notes to all the mothers reminding them of the meeting. No one ever forgot.

These meetings were obviously very important to these mothers. Only once, at a time of extremely bad weather and a measles epidemic, was more than one mother missing. Each meeting day, the public health nurse and the home economist made the rounds in their cars, picking up children and their mothers who had no other way to get there, and taking them to the home of the party hostess. Only one woman in the group could drive a car at the beginning of the program. Since then, four women have learned to drive.

With suggestions from the public health nurse and the mothers, themselves, the home economist has planned the program for these meetings. For the first meeting she selected an activity that would be fun, without posing any threat to the mothers. She brought dried weeds to the meeting for the mothers to paint and to make into winter bouquets. At first the women were diffident about trying, but soon were painting away enthusiastically. The bouquets were in evidence in some of the homes all winter.

At the next two meetings, the mothers decorated quilts for naptime use at the Pine School. Activities at subsequent meetings have included a recipe exchange, a demonstration by a mother of how to make baking-powder biscuits, a discussion of washing techniques, a demonstration by the home economist of sewing techniques, and a discussion of how to get inexpensive ascorbic acid into diets. This last subject was chosen because nutrition surveys showed the diets of these families to be low in ascorbic acid value.

The Pine School staff had found that many of these mothers were not able to tell when a child was too ill to attend school. Therefore, one meeting was devoted to simple health instructions. The public health nurse showed the mothers how to read a thermometer, told them what a temperature meant, and gave suggestions on how to tell whether a child was too ill to attend school.

One meeting followed a showing of a child development film at the Pine School PTA meeting and was devoted to a discussion of child rearing. The women were shown government bulletins on child care for different ages and were given those in which they were interested.

In spite of these serious discussions, the meetings were essentially of a social nature. The time devoted to discussion has purposely been kept short because of the shortness of the mothers' attention spans and because the children are likely to be noisy.

A Sense of Status

Being a member of a group has given these women a sense of belonging. Probably the most important outcomes of the meetings for them have been the attainment of friendships and the development of a sense of status within themselves. As they have gained in stature in their own eyes, they have tended to become more adequate. The competition that is usually found among the members of any group has begun to appear. The women have tried to dress as well as their friends, have the house as nice as their friends' houses, and be as clean as their friends.

One of the most unreceptive women in the project has learned through the group meetings to accept the services that the project staff has to offer. She has attended each of the meetings, accepted medical assistance, and asked for help in learning how to sew. Both she and her husband have begun to attend the Pine School PTA meetings and have made friends there. She has exchanged babysitting services with other women in the group. This woman and her husband had once had their ten oldest children removed from their home by court order for being incompetent parents.

Another woman, who used to be described as slovenly, now takes great pride in her appearance as well as in the appearance of her children and her home. She and her family have moved from a dilapidated shack in town to a larger, more adequate house in the county, which she has fixed up with donated curtains and a few purchases. Her husband has been able to work out the rent by helping the farmer who owns the house. The family keeps the home neat and tidy, despite the fact that the mother must carry water for some distance.

A closely knit group can be a powerful force in an individual's life. Such a group might be difficult to organize without a nucleus to start with such as the Pine School PTA. To the home economist it seemed important that the idea of the group organization should develop through one of the mothers, and that transportation to the meetings should be provided, since they were afraid of a new experience. Other ways might be tried and found to work equally well. . . .[2]

Effectiveness of Group Approach

Unfortunately, change has not been measured, and there is no data which can be used to demonstrate the effectiveness of this group approach in helping multiproblem families. There have been changes, however, which at least give some clues to how this approach might be studied more scientifically. To describe these changes, it is necessary to first describe some of the common characteristics of these women as they appeared early in the project. These might be categorized as: 1) poor concept of self, 2) lack of skills, 3) loneliness, 4) lack of concern for others, and 5) a desire to improve.

The first characteristic, poor concept of self, was demonstrated early in the project by their consistently poor grooming and inappropriate selection of clothing. Three of the women had many open, self-inflicted sores on their arms and legs. Although several women talked about wanting to lose weight, none of them took meaningful action. Lack of confidence made it difficult, if not impossible, for them to shop in department stores. Perhaps the best illustration of this lack of confidence was an observation made at the first meeting. They were to paint weeds for winter bouquets, but none of the women could proceed without asking: "Is this the way you want me to do it?" "Does this color go all right with this one?" "Will this look okay in my living room?" Their lack of self-confidence was closely related to the second characteristic, their lack of skills.

Many of them came from broken homes, foster homes, or institutional backgrounds. They did not know how to welcome guests to their homes nor even how to respond to common courtesies. For example, in leaving one home, the staff members thanked the hostess for the nice time and, in each instance, she replied: "Yes." Only a few of the women knew how to do simple mending or had the equipment in their homes to do it. Housekeeping skills were often negligible, and one woman needed help in using the recipe books she had. Washing clothes was made more difficult because they tended to wash and rinse too many clothes in too little water, or because of insufficient hot water and equipment.

As mentioned earlier, the women were essentially lonely. Few of the families attended church or sent their children to Sunday School. They did not attend PTA meetings or other community functions, nor did they do much visiting, other than with relatives. They were suspicious and fearful of professional workers in the community.

The fourth characteristic, lack of concern for others, was demonstrated in many ways. Most of the families depended on used clothing from welfare and church groups. They tended to hoard these clothes in large boxes whether or not they fit any member of the family. When clothing was brought to a meeting, they tended to grab as much as they could—without considering the needs of others. It was rare, at first, to hear one woman offer to help another, and this was even more obvious when it involved transportation to the meetings. Although staff members furnished transportation early in the project, a few of the women did drive. They never thought to offer a ride to a neighbor, but would do so if asked by a staff member.

The fifth common characteristic, wanting to improve, can best be illustrated by describing some of the observed changes.

Observed Changes

There has been a marked improvement in grooming in most of the women, evidencing more pride in their appearance, even though several women are without teeth or dentures, or have badly decayed teeth which detract from their appearance. There is talk at the meetings of hair styling and of giving each other home permanents. Two of the women lost from 20 to 30 pounds of weight in one year, and others have cut down on waist, bust, and hip measurements, even though actual weight loss has been minimal. One of these women remarked, "I feel better, now that I'm losing weight. I know I'm not pretty, but I *feel* prettier, and that's what counts." The other woman commented that her husband has begun to "notice me again since I lost weight." A specific example of an increase in self-confidence was first noticed about two years after the weed-painting incident. The women were painting the cups from egg cartons to make Christmas decorations. No one in the group asked how the staff wanted it done, or which colors to use. Instead, they were holding things up to admire them, and got praise for what they had accomplished.

Knowledge and skill have also increased demonstrably. Some of the women learned to do some sewing early in the project, and others have expressed a need for similar classes. They use a wider variety of foods and have a good working knowledge of normal nutrition. Their attention span has increased considerably, and they are becoming more adept at discussion. Early attempts to discuss less tangible subjects such as discipline were unsuccessful, but now most of the women freely express their feelings, beliefs, and questions about child-rearing practices. However, they still want concrete facts or suggestions, rather than principles.

With more self-confidence, knowledge, and skills, several things have happened which have alleviated some of the loneliness and demonstrated an increasing concern for others. Almost all of the women now bring the used clothing which they cannot use. Some women now look out for the needs of others as they sort clothing, and they have even found ways of controlling one member who continues to grab more than her share. There is planning within the group for transportation to meetings and there are times when the staff do not have to provide transportation for any of them.

Several people have brought guests to the meetings, and, within the group, there is a great deal more socializing between meetings. Four years after the group began, they asked if they could "do something for the poor people at the county home." They made all arrangements with the personnel at the home, furnished the cookies, helped with the hostessing and, apparently, gained a great deal of satisfaction from this venture. This past year, there has been more evidence of reaching out to become a part of the community. Several women have expressed an interest in attending—and possibly joining—the local association for retarded children. Two women are helping to form a new women's group in a low-income housing area on the edge of the city. With major changes imminent in the Pine School Project, the women are giving thought as to how they can continue their group when they no longer have the nucleus of Pine School. Very few of the women can express, directly, what it has meant to them to be a part of the project or even the mother's group. The intangible gains must be inferred from changes in behavior and from their concern that their friends have similar opportunities.[4]

. . . .

The changes in the women themselves are reflected to some degree in their families. Certainly, physical care has improved; the women make a greater effort to take part in activities with their children, and there have been some changes in child management. They have made definite efforts to help the girls participate in 4-H activities and, more recently, to encourage the boys to join Scout troops formed for them. The preschool children who accompany their mothers to the meetings enjoy the socialization and appear far happier than the shy, frightened, clinging children who accompanied their mothers to earlier meetings.

The 4-H activities formed an important area of environmental manipulation involving the preadolescent and the adolescent girls of the project families. Sociograms done on most of the girls found them to be either rejected by or isolated from their classmates; hence, they were excluded from peer-group activities. The group began meeting as a girls' club, and a year or so later, reorganized as the Pine Pals 4-H Club.

This year, the girls range in age from eleven to fifteen years. Two are in special education classes, six are in regular classrooms but a year behind for their ages, and one is a "B" student in her appropriate grade. Only a few of the girls wear clothes that really fit, and these are not always appropriate. Mary, at twelve, continues to wear a frilly white organdy dress to meetings, and Sally seldom wears anything under her dress but panties—even in midwinter. They are noisy, enthusiastic, eager, hungry for new experiences, and full of ideas about places to go and things to see. In 4-H projects, they need considerably more help than the usual club member, and most of this help must come from the leaders. There have been some changes in this group, too. When we first started, it was rare for a meeting to go by without at least one member confiding that "the kids in my school don't like me very well" or "she played with me one time but she never would again." We no longer hear this very often, and the girls seem much happier than they once did. There have been some tangible changes, too. Previously, when it was necessary for them to be well dressed and groomed, we sent out a checklist several days in advance to let them know what was expected. This year, without a checklist, they came to the Better Grooming Contest clean and neat, and the two club winners compared favorably with their counterparts in the County Contest. This grooming is still seen as important only for special occasions, however, and not for day-to-day activities.

Incidentally, there is a great deal of competition between the Chit-Chat Club members and their daughters in the Pine Pals. If the girls go on a field trip, the mothers want a similar one of their own. When the 4-H had a potluck supper at the leader's home, the mothers requested a potluck supper in the same home![2]

. . . .

The most obvious and quantifiable of the data are the I.Q. scores obtained on the Binet scale. It should not be presumed, however, that these scores are deemed the only valid index of the success of the program or, for that matter, that they are the most important index. It is assumed that the children selected for Pine School have not had many of those experiences that seem necessary for the development of the abilities, attitudes, and interests that are prerequisites of academic success. It is further assumed that the Binet scores reflect, to some degree at least, the presence of such abilities, attitudes, and interests, and consequently the success the program had in altering the unfavorable course of development of the children.

The last statistical analysis of the I.Q. scores was completed in August, 1961. Data from twenty-seven children, who had been enrolled for at least one year, were used. (Data from four children were not included because they had withdrawn from the project, and twelve children were not admitted early enough to be included.) The mean gain shown by these twenty-seven children during the first year was 15.8 points. However, in view of the fact that we selected our group on the basis of low test scores, and the reliability of the measure is less than perfect, we might expect the scores, on subsequent testing, to be somewhat higher due solely to errors of measurement and the regression phenomenon. This effect accounts for only 1.5 points, and leaves a net gain of 14.3 points, which is significant at greater than the .01 level.

Eighteen of the twenty-seven were in Pine School for two full years, and the mean gain shown by these eighteen in the two-year period was 17.4 points. When regressed, this results in a net gain of 15.9 points, which is significant at greater than the .01 level.

The gain shown by these children from the end of the first year to the end of the second was 4.2, which, when regressed, results in a net gain of 3.5. This gain is not significant. Thus, most of the gain shown by the students who were in

Pine School for at least two years took place during the first year.

The correlation between the I.Q. on entry and the I.Q. one year later was only .197. The correlation between the I.Q. on entry and the I.Q. two years later was even lower, being only .179. However, the correlation between the I.Q. at the end of the first year and at the end of the second year was .792.

The total group of twenty-seven was then divided into two sub-groups: those eleven children who were older than five on entry, and those sixteen who were younger than five on entry. The regressed mean I.Q. on entry for the older group was 74.62. The mean I.Q. after one year was 83.36. The mean gain of 8.74 for the older group was significant at the .02 level. The regressed mean I.Q. on entry for the younger group was 77.26, and the mean I.Q. after one year was 95.27. The mean gain of 18.11 for the younger group was significant at the .01 level. The difference in gain between the older and younger groups was not significant.

The eighteen who were in the school at least two years were similarly divided into older and younger groups, with seven older than five and eleven younger than five on entry. The gains for the older group were not significant, being 5.03 I.Q. points the first year, —.29 the second, and 4.74 for the two-year period. The younger group, on the other hand, showed a mean gain of 15.90 I.Q. points the first year, which is significant at the .02 level; a gain of 7.05 the second year, significant at the .05 level; and a total mean gain for the two-year period of 22.95 I.Q. points, which is significant at the .01 level. The difference in gain between the older and younger groups in the first two years was significant at the .05 level.

We have been pleased with the success of the children who have attended regular schools. There is some tendency for the children to be more isolated as they grow older, because of inadequate clothing, lack of cleanliness, and so on. If this alienation can be kept to a minimum, the possibilities for continued success seem encouraging. The opportunity for the parents to see alternative techniques of child management in the school and at group meetings, to note the children's constructive use of appropriate toys, to clarify their feelings, and secure information has modified their attitudes and approaches to children in a gratifying manner. Some are better able to give their children the needed support when they leave the Pine School environment. We have no way of determining which is more important, the increased adequacy of the parents or the specific opportunities for successful learning in the school; nor are we particularly concerned. We suspect that the educational approach and the social work techniques are mutually supportive, essential, and productive. Certainly, our results would justify a critical evaluation of our traditional approach to mentally retarded children from deprived families. . . .[1]

There are unanswered questions concerning methodology and staffing patterns. More information is needed about the responses of lower-class families to techniques that we know are useful with middle-class families. I don't have the answers to these or similar questions, but I do believe that there are some implications here for nursing. Although there aren't many "ready-made" groups such as the Chit-Chat Club available to public health nurses, it might be feasible for the nurse to arrange informal meetings with a group of women in a neighborhood. As they talk and drink coffee, the nurse can learn a great deal about their values, concerns, and strengths; gradually adapt her teaching to their special needs; and select meaningful ways of motivating them toward more positive health. She can make visits to the families by appointment, thus giving them a chance to be seen at their best.

But nurses working in hospitals, clinics, schools, and doctors' offices see such families too, and need to look closely at their own attitudes toward this group of people who apparently produce more than their share of the mentally retarded. To help us to gauge the level of understanding of practicing nurses in this area, let me describe the differences we see in the senior students enrolled in the public health nursing courses. The latter bring to public health an intellectual acceptance of people whose living standards and values are different from their own. In our particular setting, they have worked in the hospital with many patients from the low socioeconomic strata and are confident that they will be able to "accept" families in their home environments. Most of the students, however, come back from their first visit to poor homes feeling extremely shocked. They are appalled at the way the families live, and they are even more concerned by their own negative, judgmental reactions to them. They do not see "how anyone could possibly live that way," nor do they see any hope for change. As the students read more about cultural differences, discuss their reactions with their instructors, and make more visits, another change takes place. They begin to recognize the many forces that influence the families and respect them for doing as well as they do under the circumstances. As they begin to use the families' strengths, changes toward more positive health do occur, and the earlier hopelessness fades or disappears. A few of the students move on to examine more critically society's role in producing such conditions and what they, as members of society, can do to prevent or alleviate similar situations.

Nurses can, then, manipulate the environment to alter the effects of socioeconomic deprivation, a frequently occurring one of which is mental retardation. To do so requires more respect for the individual, increased understanding and knowledge of individual and social class differences, plus some imagination and the willingness to look for new approaches to old problems.[3]

□ □ □

COMMUNITY ORGANIZATION IN CULTURALLY DEPRIVED AREAS

Eleanor Fackler

(Mental Retardation, 1966)

Professional personnel engaged in diagnosis and treatment of mentally retarded children are often confronted by the absence of community facilities to which they can refer these children or their parents. In addition, many underprivileged families living in low-cost public housing projects do not have access to existing play groups or private nursery schools in nearby communities. Without leadership, the inarticulate parents rarely form action groups and avoid neighborhood contacts, feeling very alone with their problem.

To discover the "hidden" resources in such a culturally deprived community, an experiment was conducted by the Child Development Clinic of Children's Memorial Hospital, Chicago, Illinois. The public health nurse's role in the clinic was extended beyond individual home visits to community planning aimed at arousing citizen interest in mentally retarded children. Since special programs are needed in these communities to create opportunities for retarded children to develop social and educational skills, a plan of action was outlined.

The first step was to seek out and develop lay leadership. Parents of retarded children who accompanied their children to a weekly, pre-school playgroup in the Child Development Clinic responded eagerly to the organization of a parent discussion group. An informal atmosphere was provided for the free expression of attitudes about their retarded child and his siblings. Generally, the first topics brought up were discipline and behavior.

In succeeding meetings, as parents became more comfortable, they discussed the meaning of mental retardation and began to ask how to care for their retarded child. Frequently, they reiterated their frustration over the lack of recreational and educational facilities in their communities. Most of these parents were unwilling to place their retarded children in state institutions. They expressed a desire to form a community-sponsored, community-centered program for the pre-school-age retarded children in their own neighborhoods. As a result, local social agencies were consulted in selecting a geographic location, containing sufficient numbers of retarded children and lacking in resources.

The second step was to explore the community. In determining how to select a residential community to begin an organization, the four principles noted by Ross (1955) were:

1. discontent with existing local facilities, expressed by a sufficient number of the residents of the area;
2. specific problems which could provide short-term, tangible goals;
3. concern about the problem from the professional as well as lay members of the community;
4. existing institutions in the area whose resources might be tapped.

Since members of the group of concern were residents of the lower socioeconomic areas, the geographic location finally selected was a public housing project, approximately one-half mile square, housing 17,000 persons. The residents lived in fifteen- to twenty-story concrete structures or several blocks of old brick row-houses. The project was an "island" among blocks of warehouses, deteriorated frame homes, taverns, small retail stores and store-front churches. It was in sharp contrast to the high-rise, luxury apartment-hotels to the east which characterize the "Gold Coast" of Chicago.

Within walking distance of the project were seven grade schools, two high schools, and six churches. The City Board of Health provided a prenatal and infant welfare station and a mental health clinic. The local community center offered day care programs and recreational activities for normal children of all ages. The Boy's Club and Y.M.C.A. had similar programs.

Among the residents were forty retarded children who had been registered in the Child Development Clinic. Significantly, only *one* community center in the area included a play-program for six retarded children, ages four to seven. Most of the residents were welfare recipients or living on marginal incomes and only a few had a high school education. Many children were products of broken homes.

The third step in program planning was to decide on a method for developing a community organization to serve the needs of these retarded children. The local health, welfare, educational, and religious centers were contacted to determine their interest in mental retardation. They were enthusiastic but evidenced some uncertainty about the kind of programs which could be offered. The "inner process" method for community development was decided upon as holding forth the greatest promise for success. This process, as described by Ross (1955), includes stimulating local initiative and leadership, keeping in mind the long-range goal of developing an awareness among community members of social responsibility and cohesive interprose in a particular problem. Katz (1961) indicates parents have become organized, in many instances, to alert a community to a specific problem and attempt to fill the gaps in community services. In contrast, parents of the forty mentally retarded children in this project had sought services but were working individually to meet their own needs.

The fourth step was to begin involving the community agencies. With suggestions and leadership from the Community and Tenant-Relations Aide of the Public Housing Authority—usually social workers or community organizers—an *ad hoc* steering committee was appointed. Representatives were invited from the local community center, the mental health clinic, the district office of the public assistance department, and a local public school, plus a juvenile officer and a parent of a retarded child.

The purpose of the first meeting was defined:

1. to explore resources in the immediate community for retarded children;
2. to consider the possibility of a community-centered parent group as a cooperative project;
3. to contact other persons active in mental retardation activities for the long-range planning.

After some discussion, it became evident that 300 children were registered at the local classes for the educable mentally handicapped. Information was not available for numbers on the waiting list for trainable mentally handicapped classrooms. It was also discovered that the three parent-sponsored, private schools did not have bus transportation in that area. In addition, many of the children were in need of diagnostic services. Some children were reported to be "hidden away" in their homes with no social contacts outside the family.

Parents of children in the special classes seldom attended P.T.A. meetings and had virtually no contact with other parents of retarded children. The juvenile officer on the steering committee felt that many of his teen-age delinquents were retarded children. Board members of the Community Center indicated an interest in mental retardation but wondered if sufficient children could be brought into a program. It was finally agreed that a parents' group should be organized which would have professional guidance and leadership, perhaps later providing its own leadership.

In the fifth step, parents of the forty known retarded children were invited to form a discussion group and meet at the local community center. Seven parents responded to the letters. The first meeting was planned for early afternoon to accommodate the mothers' schedules, particularly since some homes were without fathers. Name tags and refreshments were used to facilitate cross communication and an atmosphere of informality.

The meeting was opened with an outline of the steps leading up to dates and possible goals for future meetings. The parents focused initially on the practical problems in caring for their child, such as the danger of turning gas jets on the stove, falling out of windows, slipping away from home (particularly in high-rise apartments), or falling on the concrete playground. They were also interested in special toys or equipment.

Enthusiasm ran high as they planned to meet weekly and share problems with one another and eventually stimulate other parents to join. They hoped, later, to sponsor a mass meeting to attract other community persons and attempt to involve fathers by nightly meetings.

On the premise that groups develop self-confidence when they originate and work out their own plans, this parent group was encouraged to elect temporary officers, plan the next agenda and rotate the responsibility for refreshments and announcements. The public health nurse was invited to remain with the group as a catalyst and consultant.

Meetings continued during the summer and fall while the mailing list grew from seven to forty parents. Since the problem of baby-sitting was a stumbling block to attendance, a volunteer was recruited from the Children's Memorial Hospital Volunteer Department to take the responsibility of entertaining the children while the mothers met. Coincidentally, this volunteer happened to be a student-teacher who was soon able to develop a play-group. The children matched buttons, practiced telling time, finger-painted and listened to nursery rhymes. Gradually, equipment was donated to the play-group by the Women's Board of the hospital and other parents.

This play experience was the first

group activity for most of the children and, in most instances, was the first separation of mother and child. With this successful venture, parents and volunteers determined to seek nursery space in the community for an ongoing program. The accent of activity began to focus on the pre-school play-group and less on the parents' discussion group.

During the interim, the *"ad hoc"* steering committee reported back to the Inter-agency Council, which was composed of administrative representatives of all the health, education and social agencies in the community. At these monthly meetings, the Council members expressed approval of the parents' activities and offered support. One of the clergymen offered the use of a church schoolroom for the play sessions and parents' meetings.

As children, ages four to eight, were encouraged to join the play-group, their parents were invited to become part of the discussions and meet for educational movies or home-training demonstrations.

A statistical sampling of twenty-five children in the community with both mental retardation and physical defects was taken by the parents to determine the variety of community facilities needed. The results of these interviews were included in a proposal to the Joint Youth Development Project (which was a Federal-State enterprise aimed at rejuvenating a specific community to prevent juvenile delinquency). Needs of all age groups of retarded persons were outlined using the idea of a multidisciplinary team in habilitation centers. The suggested programs included language therapy, homemaking classes, cultural development, muscle and sensory training, vocational guidance, and group therapy for both children and adults. The data obtained in the study has continued to be used for program planning at both the official and voluntary levels.

When the parent group became more sophisticated, they invited speakers on subjects such as: psychological tests, speech training, Down's Syndrome, PKU, and financial assistance programs and insurance. A committee was appointed to visit local welfare agencies, schools, churches, and politicians to stimulate the development of new programs which would serve the retarded members of the community. Trips were taken to state schools and sheltered workshops. Picnics, trips to the zoo and to the circus were organized for the children.

Throughout the year, the public health nurse moved in or out of the groups as an active or a passive participant. Parents were assisted in planning topics for discussion, obtaining speakers, or serving as a liaison to the community. Practical hints were presented for utilizing educational toys, form boards, color charts, and self-help clothing as the needs indicated. In many instances, the public health nurse functioned as parliamentarian, assisting these people in their first attempts to take minutes or conduct a meeting. In order to begin at the point where the parents were in their social sophistication, it was necessary to be content with a lack of precise results. The atmosphere of freedom to express deep feelings and to channel energy kept the group from becoming disjointed and discouraged. A guiding principle throughout was to focus on the current concerns of the group.

At the end of the second year, the steering committee met again to evaluate what had been started or accomplished. The list was impressive.

1. The State Association for Retarded Children loaned a student trainee in social work from the University of Chicago who could take over the local parent group and form an affiliated unit of the Association. This was conceived as part of the experience in community organization curriculum.

2. The Inter-City Volunteer Program (part of the anti-poverty movement)

loaned volunteers for Saturday mornings to develop a program for motor training and cultural enrichment.

3. The local park district provided staff for a pioneer project in crafts and sports, simple plays and music for the children over ten years of age.

4. The Public School District added some classes for the educable mentally handicapped and the trainable mentally handicapped, as officials became more aware of gaps in service.

5. Several local churches offered religious education to all age groups of retarded children.

6. Information concerning the field of mental retardation was included as a regular part of the agenda of the Neighborhood Interagency Council.

When the community became more involved, the public health nurse was able to diminish her contacts but continued to attend the monthly Council meetings and offered consultant services as requested.

Summary

This experiment was conducted to demonstrate whether a low socio-economic community could be stimulated to develop individual leadership and community resources to serve mentally retarded children and their parents. By extending the role of the public health nurse, a program of action was planned in five steps. Lay leadership was developed, the community was explored and, utilizing the "Inner Process" method, local leadership was committed. Resources were explored in the community, and parent energies were united towards solutions of long-range goals. Inadequate services and facilities were outlined in an effort to "prick the conscience" of the community representatives at local Council meetings.

Ordinarily culturally-deprived families find it difficult to move outside their day-to-day problems to become mobilized into community action groups. By focusing on concrete needs and keeping the plight of the retarded children before the community, parents were given the support they required. When the total community became involved, indigenous leadership carried the responsibility for further organization. One of the long-range goals had been accomplished when mental retardation was seen as a *community* problem.

References

Adult Education Association, *Taking Action in the Community*, Chicago, 1955.

Goller, G., *When Parents Get Together*, Child Study Association of America, New York, 1955.

Katz, A., *Parents of the Handicapped*, Springfield Ill.: Charles Thomas, 1961.

Ross, M. F., *Community Organization*. New York: Harper and Bros., 1955.

□ □ □

SECTION B

The Family With a Mildly Retarded Child

In the previous section, a type of family was discussed which has come to be described in professional parlance as the limited family. Most retarded children probably emanate from limited families, and most of these children are mildly retarded. However, the limitations of such families were seen as frequently more challenging to management than the limitations of the child. In this section, we will deal with family management where mild retardation of the child is the primary focus, irrespective of family limitations.

Dalton and Epstein describe a course of counseling for which highly-motivated parents of mildly retarded children had volunteered in order to have their child admitted to a pre-school nursery program. While such parents constitute a very selected group, observations about their dynamics may have relevance to management of other parents of the mildly retarded. These authors make the point that different problems are posed according to the age at which a child is recognized as being retarded. Severely retarded children are usually suspected at or near birth of being damaged. Mildly retarded children, on the other hand, may not be suspected until evidence accumulates over the years that the child is "slow." In addition, mildly retarded children often lack obvious physical stigmata; and etiology and diagnosis are usually more ambiguous. Under these conditions, it is easier for parents to attempt denial or hope for a change. According to Dalton and Epstein, parents' belated realization of the retardation leads to depression which acts as a double edge because the child is "old enough and smart enough" to recognize that his parents are disappointed in him. The child, according to these authors, might then interpret the exhibited parental emotional reaction as his fault.

Heilman reports experiences with a special problem group about which hardly anything has been written—parents of the mildly retarded child with a physical handicap. As the author points out, there are good reasons why the dynamics of such parents are likely to be especially complex. This article has not only much teaching value, but is also of historical significance. Heilman was among the few who recognized as early as 1950 that providing help for the parent was one of the best ways to help the child.

from COUNSELING PARENTS OF MILDLY RETARDED CHILDREN

Juanita Dalton
Helene Epstein
(Social Casework, 1963)

. . . .

The experiences reported in this paper were gathered primarily in providing casework services to parents whose children attended the experimental preschool for educable retarded children conducted by the Mental Development Center of Western Reserve University.

. . . .

The center preschool is designed for educable retarded children whose chronological ages are five to seven and whose I.Q.'s on Form L–M of the Stanford-Binet Intelligence Scale are between 55 and 80. Classes, with an enrollment of twelve children, are conducted five mornings a week during the regular school year by two teachers. Children attend for one year at least, the majority for two. They then enroll in public schools, entering "slow learners'" classes when possible. Referrals are from the Center population or from the school that excluded the child from kindergarten because of "mental immaturity." A requirement for the child's admission to the preschool is that the parents participate actively in counseling; the mothers are interviewed once a week, the fathers once a month. For the convenience of both the parents and the caseworker, interviews are held during school hours. The caseworker also observes the children and works closely with the teachers.

Fees are scaled to the family's ability to pay, and all socioeconomic groups are represented in the enrollment. The preschool families, however, are not a representative sample. They are a self-selected group of highly motivated parents; witness their seeking special help and arranging daily transportation for their children. Their keen awareness that their children are different, furthermore, might have been less apparent in less adequate families. Awareness is a mixed blessing, producing in some families an unnatural parent-child relationship and stimulating in others a search for special help and education.

Pediatricians and psychologists on the staff of the center participate as needed in the preschool program. The caseworker serves as a liaison between the teaching and clinical staff and the parents. She interprets the need for a special examination and helps the parents to prepare the child for it. In addition, she tries to link the child's school behavior with events at home and to relay the teacher's observations to the parents. Cases are regularly scheduled for presentation at seminars conducted by a child psychiatrist from the School of Medicine of Western Reserve University. . . .

From the fact that previous articles on parents' reactions to retardation often deal with the *birth* of the child—a time when only severe retardation is recognizable—it may be deduced that they are concerned primarily, though not always explicitly, with the reaction to a totally dependent or a trainable child. Solnit and Stark give a particularly convincing explanation of the mother's mourning process when she realizes she has given birth to a defective child. . . .

Understanding the special problems of the parent of an "educable" retarded child begins with recognizing the difficulties inherent in identifying him as retarded. Usually his physical growth and development are within normal limits during his first two years. He usually lacks obvious physical stigmata, and the cause of the retardation is ambiguous—if, indeed, there is any organic cause to be suspected. All this supports the wishful thinking of the parents. Typically, delay in speech is the first sign of retardation for this group. Parents or professional workers are not greatly concerned about it until the age of three or so. Even then, they seek an explanation for the speech delay itself instead of questioning the child's intelligence. It is difficult for parents to recognize the speech delay as only one aspect of retarded development; they see it as the cause of the child's other problems, such as his relationship with peers and siblings.

The word *slow,* which carries the idea of a temporary condition, is commonly used to differentiate these children from the trainable retarded. Even when the parents have not been given this specific interpretation by a professional person, they find it easy to believe that in time their child will "catch up" to his contemporaries. They protect themselves against what they see and know by adjusting the level of their demands to the child's level of ability, and they rationalize his slowness on the basis that "all children are different." When the child whose speech has been delayed starts to talk, the parents and the pediatrician alike breathe a sigh of relief. The first crisis seems to be over. With changes and obvious progress of this kind, the parents' hopes are raised, only to be dashed again when the child is slow in taking the next developmental step.

The general retardation underlying the speech delay may be hard to recognize because of the variability in the child's performance. Parents accurately report behavior that demonstrates that "the child is thinking": he has a remarkable memory and can recall some past event as well as or better than his parents, or he is extremely clever in "getting what he wants." They raise doubts about his apparent stupidity by questioning his motivation: does he ignore what is said to him because he cannot comply or because he does not want to?

In the minds of parents (and some professional persons), the diagnosis is either black or white, total amentia or normality. Evidence that the child remembers, imitates, wants his own way, is lazy or stubborn at times and affectionate at others, favors an assumption of normality. They are tempted to explain away his slowness in learning new activities or grasping new concepts on the basis of lack of interest. Despite the ambiguities and uncertainties inherent in understanding the educable retarded child in his early years, most parents realize when it is time for him to enter school that he is behind his age mates in readiness for it. The prospect of kindergarten highlights the retardation. This juncture represents a second crisis as the parents come to grips with the fact that their child will be conspicuous at school and will require some kind of special attention and consideration. They can no longer hide the truth. Unlike the first crisis of delayed speech, this one does not go away.

It is at this point, or shortly before the child should be entering school, that parents seek help at the center. Once the parent and child begin participating in the total preschool program, the caseworker must deal with either a reactivation of the hope that the original diagnosis was incorrect or a continuing denial of the retardation, and often with the parents' hostility against the professional who first made the diagnosis. In either case, she continues to interpret a diagnosis that was made recently or a year or two earlier. Seldom does a parent enter the program emotionally accepting of the child's retardation. As the caseworker observes the child interacting with his parent in the school, she becomes acutely aware of the importance of the child's special characteristics and their effect upon the parent. Her understanding of the nature of the parent-child relationship increases. Knowledge of this interaction is essential for understanding the parents' need to defend themselves against both acceptance of the retardation and the subsequent depression.

Characteristics of the Educable Retarded Child in the Early Years

The prime attribute of the retarded child is, of course, his slow learning. He does not simply need more time, more exposures, more repetitions; his learning depends upon the *nature* of the task—if it is concrete and specific he can learn much faster than if it is somewhat abstract. He can more easily follow a demonstration than an explanation. His learning requires not only repetition but also concretization and simplification.

The retarded child's difficulty with verbalization is closely related to the abstract nature of language. Even after he can speak, he does not use language to communicate his feelings or experiences or to acquire new knowledge by asking questions, like the nonretarded child. Instead, he talks about his immediate external environment and he answers only direct questions. Here the parents' attitude is inconsistent with their readiness to assert his normality, for they easily assume "he wouldn't understand anyhow" and neglect to prepare him for coming events. Their vague, false answers increase the communication deficit. The mother of a six-and-a-half-year-old boy with a mental age of four and a half, who repeatedly asked during the summer vacation when school would reopen, always answered "next Tuesday" because she was so sure he could not understand the meaning of weeks and months. Her evaluation may have been correct, but her false and casual answer taught him nothing. Trying to explain, with the help of a calendar especially marked for him, would have been preferable.

The retarded child is soon discouraged from asking questions by becoming sensitized to the idea of "not knowing"; he is afraid to admit his ignorance because it upsets his parents or makes people laugh at him. A retarded child who is being tested rarely says "I don't know" or asks the examiner for the answer. He is much more likely to confabulate an answer. The gifted child, in contrast, is quick to confess his ignorance and demand an answer from the examiner.

Ever anxious to reassure themselves that he is "normal," the child's parents repeatedly ask him such questions as "What color is that truck?" or "How many blocks are there?" They then wait nervously for him to prove his intelligence by supplying the right answer. This pattern of constantly being asked to satisfy his parents rather than himself easily leads to withholding and stubbornness in the child. . . .

The Double Edge of Depression

With the parent's belated realization of the permanent handicap of retardation comes the full force of depression. The narcissistic blow is the same as with the severely retarded child: no parent likes to know that either he himself or his child as a projection of himself has a ceiling on his intellectual potential, even if it is comparatively high. Additionally, since mild retardation becomes apparent at a later age, the mother can find many reasons for castigating herself: neglecting the child in infancy, failing to teach him what he should know, failing to provide playmates, waiting too long to get help, and so on. The disappointment is thus mixed with guilt—slightly different in form from that felt by parents of more severely retarded children, but the same in impact. Typically, the latter parents are unsympathetic with this grief. They point out: "Your child will go to school. He will learn to read and write. He looks all right. He can take care of his body needs. What have you to grieve about?" But in our society, worry about the vocational future of youngsters who cannot finish high school is realistic.

For the parents of a mildly retarded child, there is a double edge to their depression. They are sad, disappointed, angry, not only for themselves, but also in empathy with the child. They imagine his future bewilderment and disappointment at school, at work, and at home. They anticipate his questions about why he is different and their helplessness in answering him satisfactorily. They feel they have been the agents of his future frustrations. Understandably, they are anxious to spare him awareness, but the educable child is likely to sense that he is different at about the same time that his parents first begin to question his mental capacity. Because the diagnosis comes later in childhood, the child is old enough and smart enough to see his parents' disappointment. He knows he is doing something wrong but cannot be sure what it is. When his mother cries because he cannot count straight or manage to button his coat, the child thinks the tears are his fault. His stupidity puts him in danger of losing her love in much the same way that bad or disobedient behavior does. . . .

An example of the parents' fear of the future is shown in their response to the child's normal wish to play "daddy" or "mommy." Ordinarily, when a child shows some resentment of his lowly childhood status and expresses a desire to be grown up like his parents, his mother comforts and encourages him by explaining, "Someday you will be daddy, you will have a car and drive to work, and you will have your own wife and your own children"—that is, she tries to assuage his jealousy by telling him that some day his turn will come. But when the child is mildly retarded the mother temporizes and says, "You will be a big man *like* daddy." Probably more important than the words is the look of embarrassment and discomfort that comes over her face when she holds out a picture of the future that is as vague to her as it is to the child.

For the sake of the retarded child and his siblings, the caseworker cannot afford to let the mourning go on any longer than necessary. The child's future makes it important to free the parents from the debilitating effects of the depression. At this point the essential goal is to restore an effective parent-child relationship.

The Twin Dangers of Immobilization

As the parents come to understand the permanent nature of the child's intellectual handicap, and as they are relieved of their feelings of guilt for causing the handicap, the caseworker must be alert to the danger of immobilization, an abdication of their parental role. In part this is a sign of their depression, but it is also an expression of their misconceptions about mental retardation. The mother has no idea of the part she can play in the child's development or the influence she can wield. She may feel superfluous or inadequate in rearing a "different" child. One father described his helplessness by saying that it seemed as if his son was "boxed in," so that he felt there was no use in trying to understand his feelings or behavior. Another father defiantly told the caseworker, "If I believed Jimmy was not going to be all right, if I thought he was really retarded, I wouldn't keep bringing him all the way to this school and I wouldn't keep coming to see you." His denial helped him maintain his feeling of usefulness; otherwise, there was no point to anything.

One result of the parents' immobilization may be genuine neglect of the child: nothing matters, there is no sense in safeguarding him, he might be better off dead. The mother of seven-year-old James expressed great surprise when she was questioned about letting him play for hours without knowing his whereabouts. "He often tells us he has already had lunch when he comes in. When we ask him where, he can't remember. Once the police found him a mile away and brought him home. Anything could have happened to him." Obviously, a neglected child is not likely to thrive either physically or psychologically.

Instead of neglect, immobilization may take the opposite form—overprotection, which is less dangerous physically but also has adverse effects on mental development. Both reactions stem from feelings of estrangement, bewilderment, and helplessness. As one would expect, the first attempts at the preschool to encourage independent behavior in a child who has been infantilized by an overprotective mother are met with resistance, anger, and negativism. During snack time on his first day at the preschool, a child with an I.Q. of 64, whose mother was still feeding him, took one look at the juice pitcher and, after knocking it and the cups to the floor, climbed onto the table. For the mother, enmeshed in her feelings of ambivalence, the handling of such aggressive behavior is more difficult than succumbing to the child's infantile demands.

As the parents' depression lifts, they are flooded with questions and decisions about the child's future. Many times the decisions are made unconsciously. Frequently cleanliness, attractive appearance, good manners, and compliant behavior are emphasized—evidence of a need to help the child compensate for his lack of intelligence. It is as if these socially acceptable traits obscured or at least made up for the retardation.

Part of this need to compensate is

again the need to deny. Often the parents' concept of a retarded person is based on the memory of a sloppy, incoherent, slobbering boy or a dirty old man, a person to be feared and avoided. If the child is neat and well-behaved, therefore, he cannot be considered truly retarded. But whether the attempt is to deny or to hide the retardation, parents' undue stress on this aspect further inhibits and restrains the child's learning and thus retards his development even more. His energies are directed toward either fulfilling their needs or opposing their efforts to force compliance. They can perhaps be helped to realize that the retarded child need not be forever apologetic. He should be taught to take pride in his appearance, to be considerate of others, and to follow instructions just like any other child, normal or retarded.

Summary

The experience of parents of educable children differs from that of parents of severely retarded children. The chief differences are in the time at which the retardation is recognized, the child's characteristics, the expectations about his future, and the objectives of the parents.

The basic treatment with most families is ego-supportive. Parents of severely retarded children appear to need the most intensive help at the time of the initial diagnostic evaluation, with gradual interpretation and referral to appropriate training resources. The parents of educable retarded children also need time to work through their denial of the retardation and the subsequent depression. They often become immobilized and need support and help in recognizing the potential, and the feelings, of the child. It is essential for the child's sake that the parents not perpetuate their mourning and that they restore an effective parent-child relationship as soon as possible. The caseworker must help them realize that the child can be a useful and contented member of society, and that their contribution to his attaining good mental health can be great. The caseworker must help them develop realistic goals, both short-range and long-range. The worker evolves such goals from a knowledge of child development in general and of the characteristics of retarded children, an appreciation of the child's individuality and the parent-child relationship, and a technical knowledge of the educational and vocational possibilities for the mentally handicapped child and adult.

□ □ □

from PARENTAL ADJUSTMENT TO THE DULL HANDICAPPED CHILD

Ann Elizabeth Heilman

(American Journal of Mental Deficiency, 1950)

The handicapped child's attitudes regarding himself and his handicap are in major part determined by parental reactions toward the child and his disability. Anyone who has worked with handicapped children and their parents is well aware of this fact. Whether the handicap is a mental or a physical one, the way in which the parents respond to it and to the child is a major factor in deciding the child's own self-attitude.

When the handicap is a double one, as when the child is both physically handicapped and mentally retarded, the difficulty of the parental adjustment is often much increased. While it is true that some parents seem to experience no greater difficulty in making an adjustment to the mentally-retarded, physically-handicapped child than they might have known in adjusting to having a child with a single handicap, many of them achieve this result by denying one handicap or the other and by focusing all of their attention on the disability which they have least difficulty in accepting. Their actual adjustment is to but one phase of the problem. For many parents, having a child who is dually handicapped does not simply double the problems of adjustment but makes them much more complex and difficult of solution.

A consequence of the greater difficulty which parents have in adjusting to a child who is both handicapped and dull is the greater hazard the child experiences in growing toward fulfillment of his own maximum potentialities. The harder the adjustment problem is for his parents, the less chance the child has of developing a desire to participate in life, of achieving realistic goals, outgoing social attitudes, self-sufficiency commensurate with his abilities, and those other qualities which make for happiness, maturity, and successful social living.

Although this inter-relationship between child behavior and parental adjustment is today commonly recognized by those whose professions bring them in contact with the handicapped child, it is doubtful whether the position of the parent is generally adequately understood. Those of us who necessarily center most of our attention upon the child, his needs, and progress, usually find it far easier to diagnose his emotional problems as being the result of infantilization, oversolicitude, rejection, or other parental sins of omission or commission, than we do to realize the catastrophic nature of the problems which beset his parents. Often our insights into the origins of the child's behavior merge unobtrusively into open or implied criticism of his parents. We fail to allow for the fact that these same parents are two individuals no more adequate, mature, or better prepared to meet the trauma of having a handicapped child than is the average member of the population. From a psychological standpoint, the parent is frequently as much a casualty as is the child. . . .

While the parents of any handicapped child must be expected normally to experience some disappointment and discouragement in relation to the child's handicap, the parents of the dull-handicapped may theoretically be expected to have an especially difficult time in handling these feelings. Compensation is hard to achieve when the child is neither physically nor intellectually normal. The parent whose polio-crippled child is making adequate scholastic progress and, within the limits of his physical abilities, is preparing for independence, has a large area in which he can enjoy and be proud of his child. The parent whose child, though dull, is strong, physically active, capable of caring for himself, and of entering acceptably into the life of the community, can find his child a source of many satisfactions if he permits himself to enjoy him as he is and not to demand of him a level of achievement which the child cannot attain. But the parent whose child is both physically inferior and intellectually below normal has no ready area of compensation. He may love his son greatly and be gratified by every sign of progress and development the boy shows; but, unless his whole adjustment to the child is an unrealistic one, he must frequently be unhappy and disappointed in him. It is not unusual for such a parent, usually the father, to make the statement that in some ways it would be better if the child were feebleminded. One father said, "If he were a vegetable, like some children, we wouldn't feel so badly about him; there wouldn't be this concern about his happiness and future; we could rest easy about him. There might even be a future for us."

Many of these parents give expression to feelings of great frustration and futility. The burden in time and money which care for the physically-handicapped frequently imposes often seems heavier as the child grows older and his mental limitations become increasingly evident. In spite of himself, the parent may find himself wondering, "What is the use? Is it worth it?" Often he is horrified at his own reaction, and tries to hide it. Such parents are often much relieved when they can ventilate their feelings. Frequently, the mother and father are unable to discuss these feelings with one another.

It is evident from an examination of the realities of the parents' situation that the pressures upon them are great. One might say that they have a right to be disturbed. The evidences which one sees of anxiety and guilt, of emotional lability and ambivalence, may be expressions of neurotic adjustment, but are not necessarily the indications of a neurosis. The professional consultant can often be of assistance simply by allowing parents to discuss their problems with him and to discharge some of their emotional tension; by showing a desire to see things from the parents' viewpoint; by indicating his readiness to be of help, within his power. In short, that person whom the parents consult, whether he be physician, psychologist, social worker, therapist, or educator, can frequently help the morale of the parent by being ready to play a supportive role toward him, if only for the duration of a single interview. This he should undertake, if not for the sake of the parent, then for that of the child, whose behavior is eventually influenced by parental maladjustments.

How does observed parental behavior relate to observed child behavior? Let us examine briefly three especially clear cases which were seen in clinical practice. No attempt has been made to explore deep-seated attitudes or unconscious motivations. The cases are purposely described in operational terms only.

Case No. 1

David M. is a four-year-old boy with a mild right spastic hemiplegia, who uses his right hand clumsily, but prefers it to the left. David walks and runs, although his balance is poor and he occasionally falls. Speech is intelligible but infantile, and at time difficult to understand. The report of the speech examination reveals that the speech mechanisms are uninvolved, and that, from a physiological standpoint, normal speech can be expected. . . .

Because of David's interest in the test materials it was possible to complete the examination with Form M of the Revised Stanford-Binet Scale. At C.A. 4–2 he earned an M.A. of 3–2, and an I.Q. of 76. The range was compact and showed no unusual patterning. It was the examiner's impression that, under more favorable conditions, David might be able to score at the lower end of the dull normal range.

Mrs. M., an attractive, well dressed woman of thirty-two, began the preliminary interview by saying that she did not know why a psychological examination had been recommended for David; neither she nor her husband had ever thought that David was of less than average intelligence or presented an problems except in the areas of speech and locomotion. They felt that if speech therapy could be begun and physical therapy be given to help David improve his balance, he would be ready at six to start first grade in the regular public school classes. Their chief concern was to start speech therapy as soon as possible. In the course of securing material for the Vineland Social Maturity Scale, Mrs. M. revealed that David, who is an only child, does not play well with other children "because they are impatient with him." He is a feeding problem, and she spends a great deal of time in trying to get him to eat. Her husband feels it would be better to let David alone; and recently David's doctor has given the same advice. But she doesn't feel right about it and hasn't been able to stop her urging. During the psychological examination, which she asked to watch in order to interpret any obscure speech, Mrs. M. interrupted frequently to urge David to complete a response or to improve one. She would not permit David to reject any items. An explanation by the psychologist that it is quite usual for children at about this age to refuse to respond to items which they can normally perform adequately was apparently not sufficiently reassuring. Throughout the examination Mrs. M. continued to insist and to prod.

Case No. 2

George J., at four years, eleven months, is a moderately severe athetoid quadriplegia without hearing loss. His gait is very unsteady, but he is able to walk unsupported. It was possible for the psychologist to interpret George's speech when she knew what response to expect; but free verbalization was unintelligible. During the examination, George often resorted to gestures to convey meaning. It was characteristic of him when presented with a new task to glance at his mother and to wait for her encouragement before attempting it. When the mother protested against leaving him with the examiner when the testing was about to begin, saying that he would be frightened without her, George promptly went to her and buried his head in her lap. George showed little spontaneous interest in the test materials but attempted to follow directions without protest or enthusiasm. On Form L of the Binet, George's successes ranged from an assumed basal at the eighteen month level to one success at IV-6. He earned a mental age of 3–1 at chronological age 4–11, and an I.Q. of 63. Some verbal items had to be omitted, while some others, which were attempted, were unintelligible. It is therefore safe to assume that this I.Q. may, to some extent, underrate George's ability. However, since several Binet and Merrill-Palmer motor items were failed at the three year level on the basis of comprehension rather than of motor skill, this probably does not represent a serious underrating. A qualitative study of successes at the upper test levels suggests that George is a child whose ability would place him in the low borderline range, at or below I.Q. 75.

Mrs. J. is an attractive widow of forty. George is her only child. She reports that she spends most of her time with him and has few outside contacts. Her chief concern is for some plan of treatment which will help him physically, some "miracle" that will make him like other children. Her eyes brim with tears; it is difficult for her to talk. In describing George's daily behavior, she says that she realizes that she has done much for George that he is capable of doing for himself. This is easier for her and less frustrating than watching George try over and over again before succeeding in accomplishing the activity himself. She has not permitted him to crawl up the stairs to the second floor, a recent accomplishment of which he is very proud, for she is afraid he will injure himself. She has spanked him for this. During the examination, Mrs. J. kept encouraging George to "show the lady" whenever he did not quickly attempt to give a verbal response to a question. (George is good at gesture language. Once he had used it, it was usually impossible to get him to try to repeat his communication in speech.) Mrs. J. stated, in response to a question as to whether George had been receiving physical therapy, that she was going to take that up herself, as she knew he would not respond well to a stranger.

Case No. 3

Tommy L., at nine, is a fragile looking little boy who has considerable involvement of the trunk and lower extremities as the result of polio at age two. During the course of the psychological examination he asked for assistance and praise but showed little insight into the quality of his performance. He gave up easily on items which were difficult for him, saying that he was tired and couldn't do that; sometimes he interrupted the test at a critical point to ask questions about some irrelevant matter. When an item seemed easy to him, Tommy often said that it was silly, that anyone would know that; however, he sometimes missed these items. The results of the examination showed that, at chronological age 9–3, Tommy earned a mental age of 7–3, and an I.Q. of 78 on Form L of the Revised Stanford-Binet Scale.

At the end of the examination, Tommy displayed his scrapbook, which contained a collection of newspaper photographs and clippings about himself. He explained that his mother helped him write letters to some of the newspaper people whenever he needed some new toys, a wheelchair, or anything. Then usually they came and took his picture, and it was in the paper. His favorite showed him sitting on the lap of a department store Santa. Tommy said, "People feel sorry for you when you're crippled like me. They give you stuff. . . . Do you think I'll have to go to school again and read about Dick and Jane? They're dumb! . . . Have you got any gum? Spearmint?"

Mrs. L. is a woman of about forty-five, separated from her second husband. Tommy is the only child still at home. In his presence she talked about how the school bus driver was responsible for Tommy's catching a bad cold, because he let him ride home from school without making him button his sweater. She described her own ill health. She talked of the interest which all the people she works for take in Tommy, of the gifts they give to both of them, and of the medical advice they offer. She read a letter she had received from a stranger who had read of Tommy's case, in which he offered to cure him by "radio waves." Mrs. L. describes Tommy as a bright, patient boy. The teachers in the orthopedic class have made him work too hard.

Observed parental behavior seems to bear a close relationship to observed child behavior. Although the majority of the cases seen in clinical practice are not so clearly drawn as the ones reported, there is usually an observable similarity between the kinds of behavior which the parent exhibits and the ways in which the child behaves.

In planning services for handicapped children, perhaps more emphasis should be placed on expanding therapeutic services to parents, as being one of the best ways of assisting the child to achieve the optimum emotional and social adjustment.

□ □ □

SECTION C

The Family With a Mongoloid Child

Most clinical syndromes associated with mental retardation are rare and show considerable variability of manifestation. Mongolism (Down's Syndrome) appears to be one of the more homogeneously-manifested syndromes, and in urban areas there are usually a sizable number of parents of mongoloid children who have similar management needs. For this reason, parents of mongoloid children are sometimes managed and counseled in groups, not only for the sake of expediency, but also because such parents have more to share with each other than parents of children who, though perhaps equally retarded, do not fall into the same grouping.

In constituting a homogeneous group, it is important to adapt management techniques and content to the special conditions on which the grouping is based. For instance, if parents of mongoloid children are grouped together, the management approach should be concerned with problems characteristically associated with that condition and with such parents. To the degree that only problems experienced by parents of generally retarded children are covered, the grouping may have been based on an appropriate criterion. In the following selection by Kopek, at least a significant portion of the group effort was devoted to problems highly relevant to group selection criteria.

from A GROUP EXPERIENCE WITH PARENTS OF MONGOLOID CHILDREN

Pauline E. Kopek

(In *The Report of Educational Program for Nurses in Region III of The Children's Bureau on Mental Retardation,* May, 1964)

. . . .

I would like to share with you an experience we had in group work in our clinic. This is not group work in the therapeutic sense as in psychiatric treatment, though there were therapeutic effects.

Shortly after the clinic opened in April of 1958, it was apparent to us that there were a number of parents of young mongoloid children who needed more understanding of what a diagnosis of mongolism meant to their child and what it would mean to them in rearing their child. It was believed that much could be gained by forming a discussion group consisting of parents who had a mutual problem—that of a mongoloid child. This would afford these parents an opportunity to share experiences, to assist them in resolving any adverse feelings they may have, and in general, to gain a better understanding of their children.

The parents of five mongoloid children were contacted and told of our plan. Each was interested in participating in this activity. The initial meeting was a get-acquainted session, with our pediatrician as group leader. The parents ranged in age from twenty-one to forty-three. The children ranged in age from sixteen months to three-and-a-half years. For some parents, this was their first and only child; for one it was their eighth. The social-economic level was that of the middle class. From this initial meeting, the group proceeded on an informal type structure and met once a month at the clinic. These were evening meetings with both parents in attendance. Arrangements were made for a clinic team member to attend each meeting. Though often more than one member attended, I had the pleasure of attending most of the meetings, which covered a period of approximately two years.

During this time, the parents took over the meeting arrangements. By this I mean that at the end of each session, plans were made for one set of parents to take over arrangements for refreshments at the next meeting, another to take over planning of the program, and so forth.

The role of the clinic team member was to assist the parents in obtaining speakers on subjects that they had expressed interest in and offering suggestions on other topics that might be of value to them. In addition, where indicated, leading questions were presented to stimulate discussion.

Many of the sessions were held by just having the parents themselves discuss the problems that they had encountered and their experiences with their children. Other programs included a speech therapist, a psychologist, a psychiatrist, a special education teacher, an insurance man, a broker, and a representative of a local bank regarding trust funds.

One particular meeting appeared to have had special meaning for these parents. Guest speakers on this occasion were two sets of parents, each of whom had a teen-age mongoloid child. The guest parents explained their experiences in regard to teaching their children self-help skills; discipline problems that had been conquered; adverse attitudes of relatives, friends, and neighbors that they had overcome; and, in general, presented a picture of the life of a mongoloid child up to approximately eighteen years of age. From this, the parents in the group gained a knowledge of some of the hurdles they must pass over and some of the joys and pleasures they would receive from their children.

The group was maintained as an open-end group, that is, as we became acquainted with parents of newborn mongoloids, or even those of older children who moved into the area, they were referred to the group. The greatest number in attendance at any one point was thirty people—or fifteen sets of parents. The core group, the original five, stayed throughout the entire period.

At a time when the group felt that they had achieved the maximum that they could from this group, the parents decided that they would like to meet with ministers, obstetricians, and pediatricians and have an open discussion of their thoughts on how parents could be helped by these professional people.

. . . .

The one thing that impressed us greatly was that these parents were literally starving for information. . . .

□ □ □

SECTION D

The Family With a Phenylketonuric Child

Phenylketonuria is another example of a condition which creates a high commonality of problems for a family. Untreated children tend to be severely handicapped, while treated children apparently benefit greatly from a special diet. The diet, however, is difficult to maintain and creates many management problems. Other specific problems are the pungently unpleasant and penetrating odor of such children, and the known hereditary nature of the condition.

Phenylketonuria is so rare that few managers have had an opportunity to gain enough experience to write about the special family management problems. It is therefore remarkable that Schild was able to structure a group counseling program for parents of phenylketonuric children. Even in a major metropolitan area (Los Angeles), the number of eligible parents proved to be small. However, these parents' need for special help was so high that some were motivated enough to drive 200–400 miles to attend the meetings.

from PARENTS OF CHILDREN WITH PHENYLKETONURIA *Sylvia Schild*
(*Children*, 1964)

. . . .

Prior to the comparatively recent development of the low phenylalanine diet, most known phenylketonuric patients were severely retarded inmates of institutions. With the availability of treatment, new interest has been focused on ways of identifying new patients as early as possible with a view toward prevention of brain damage through the initiation of early treatment.

The Child Development Clinic at Children's Hospital of Los Angeles was established in 1959 as a clinic for the diagnosis and treatment of mentally retarded children. Over the years its PKU caseload has steadily increased. The clinic staff early noted that the parents of children with PKU reacted to the diagnosis and treatment with overwhelming anxieties, revealing their sense of isolation with the problem. Several parents expressed a desire to meet another parent of a phenylketonuric child and to see another child with the disease.

The staff was also impressed with the parents' difficulties in trying to maintain adequate dietary control and in dealing with their child's behavior. Therefore, the staff considered the question of whether a discussion group for parents might not bring the parents emotional support by providing them with an opportunity to see that their problems were not unique and with further interpretation regarding the disease. It was presumed that in a group of persons with problems similar to their own some parents might feel less threatened in raising underlying questions than in individual clinic interviews.

After discussing these possibilities, the clinic director and the two social workers serving the galactosemia (also an inborn error of metabolism) and phenylketonuria caseloads initiated a six-session series of meetings at the hospital for the parents in each of these caseloads. Other staff members agreed to contribute their services as needed. Because of the shortage of staff time and the long distance families had to travel to get to the clinic, the meetings were scheduled only once a month. They were, however, held in the evening to encourage the participation of both parents. Refreshments were provided to make for a friendly, informal atmosphere.

Invitations were extended to the eighteen families who had phenylketonuric children under care at the time. Since eight of the families had more than one child with the disease, the actual number of children under treatment was twenty-five. In three of the families, a sibling of the patient had been institutionalized. Three families had two phenylketonuric children at home; in one family, all three children had PKU. All but two of the patients were age six or under, 65 per cent being under three.

Parents from all but two of these eighteen families came to the meeting at some time. Five families were represented only once or twice, and two of them only by the mother. One family, living nearly 400 miles away, attended two meetings. Three of the participating families lived about 200 miles from the hospital. Only one family lived within ten miles of the hospital.

As new PKU patients were identified and came under care, the meetings were opened to their parents. To date, a total of twenty-one families have participated in group sessions for parents of phenylketonuric children. The average meeting attendance has been sixteen. All but two of the mothers in the group were still of child-bearing age; five became pregnant during the program's first year. The other members suffered with each mother through her pregnancy and eagerly awaited the verdict as to the presence or absence of PKU in the newborn.

Participation

Despite ethnic, religious, and educational differences, the members of the group quickly became acquainted with one another. They learned about the composition of each other's families, and showed interest in each other's activities and the progress of each other's children. Their common experience with PKU created a strong bond.

While the families were generally represented by both parents, the mothers were by far the more active participants; the fathers tended to talk less, though they obviously listened with interest. Typically, a father's passivity in the group seemed to parallel his child-rearing role in the family—leaving the care and discipline of the children largely to the mother. The three fathers who participated more actively than their wives seemed to be the least stable persons in the group. Two who were especially vocal were not the natural fathers of their phenylketonuric child but did not inform the group of this.

The other aggressively participating father was an extremely immature man who continually strove to demonstrate his masculinity by his boasts of how he dominated his wife and children. His wife, although a woman of borderline intelligence, was doing an admirable task in rearing her five children despite her husband's frequent unemployment, debts, and general irresponsibility. This family had some status needs met in the group through their child, who, in addition to having PKU, had another rare metabolic disorder and was the object of much interest in the hospital. Somewhat in awe of this, the group sympathized about the double problem and gave the family much support in spite of the father's antagonistic personality. Gradually, as the father saw he was accepted by the group in spite of differences of opinion, he became quieter and his wife became more vocal.

One older couple faced circumstances markedly different from those faced by the other group members in that they had two severely retarded children with PKU who were still living at home at ages ten and fourteen. The other members turned to this couple for a kind of parental support and seemed rather confused when this was not forthcoming. They wanted leadership from the husband and at one point suggested that he be their chairman. This seemed to stem not only from deference to his age, but also from a feeling that he had lived with the problem long enough to have some wisdom to offer. He rejected the chairmanship on the grounds that he and his wife really did not belong to the group—since their children were so different, they felt the group could not help them with their problems.

This couple did not return after the first few meetings. However, when they were present, the wife was extremely active, repeatedly asking questions which revealed both the severity of her children's retardation and her ambivalent feelings about them. She listened closely to other members who had placed a phenylketonuric child out of the home, and who while they spoke of their suffering during the separation process also demonstrated that sometimes institutionalization can be an acceptable solution. The older couple has since filed for institutional care. While certainly many factors have contributed to this decision, the group experience undoubtedly opened a way for these parents to examine their ambivalent feelings and to loosen the rigid defenses they had developed.

Content of the Meetings

About three-fourths of the sessions consisted of informal lectures by clinic staff members or invited speakers, followed by informal group discussions. Characteristically, in these highly animated discussions there was an observable shift from the subject at hand (genetic, medical, nutritional, and other aspects of PKU) to daily problems related to child behavior and discipline, particularly in relation to diet maintenance. In one-fourth of the meetings, the social worker led informal discussions in which parents could bring up subjects for the group to consider.

At first the meetings were not very productive; the parents were new to one another and uneasy, obviously disinclined to reveal any deep feeling or examine their own role in relation to the problem. Their first remarks were usually repetitions of questions they had already asked repeatedly in the clinic: When can we take Johnny off the diet? Why are tests for the level of phenylalanine needed so often? What are the chances of having another child with PKU.

The social worker and the public health nurse, who observed many of the sessions, were somewhat surprised at the repetition of these familiar questions, which had been given considerable attention in the individual clinic interviews. The repetitions may partly be explained by the fact that the social worker was new to the group. However, they may also have reflected the parents' insecurity over examining their feelings about being parents of phenylketonuric children.

In later discussions, the parents touched on some deeper fears: of producing children who might continue to add to the perpetuation of a defective gene; of becoming impatient with the constant self-discipline required to consistently maintain the rigid diet; and of being inadequate to the ongoing task and unable to cope with the children as they grew older. Gradually toward the end of the year they exposed the pain of their growing awareness that in most instances the child's condition had been diagnosed too late to have prevented some brain damage from occurring. This awareness came as they loosened their hold on the dietary problem as an expression of their anxieties and after sufficient time had elapsed for them to recognize that in spite of their frequent clinic visits and efforts to enforce the diet and in spite of some evident improvement, their children still showed signs of retardation. The parents also discussed their mounting troubles with diet control and discipline as the child grew older and smarter. As the child learned to get around by himself, he was apt to sneak foods and otherwise test the limits of the parents' disciplinary methods.

In the security of the group, the parents moved to some open expression of resentment about the clinic experiences, resentment they could not express as easily in individual conferences. When asked whether being in the group helped them in ways that attending the clinic did not, some of them feelingly replied that:

1. Clinic people were too busy and could not be bothered by all their questions (this despite one-and-one-half-hour clinic appointments, in addition to individual casework interviews and other consultations).
2. In the clinic the attention was all focused on the child; the parents felt wrapped up in anxieties about how well they had managed the diet, how successful the child would perform in the psychological testing, and how low the child's phenylalanine level would be, and therefore tended to overlook or forget their own questions. The group experience offered an opportunity to concentrate on themselves.

The parents then moved to a consideration of a more formal organization. They had been impressed by the Rochester League for PKU, a group of parents who had organized to lobby for national implementation of Guthrie blood testing of all newborn babies to detect phenylketonuria. Part of this move toward more structure was probably a defense against exploring deeper feelings within the group, particularly after the display of hostility about the clinic on which the parents leaned so heavily for help. Also, most of them had by this time established a meaningful relationship in the casework situation. Other factors, such as improvement in the child, had reduced their personal anxieties and family tensions to a point where many felt they could cope with their problems more independently.

However, the movement toward more structure did not get off the ground, largely because no strong leadership emerged. No officers were ever elected. Dependence on the social worker seemed to increase. The social worker tried to interest the parents in groups of parents of retarded children in their own localities, particularly as they began to accept the fact that their children would remain retarded in some degree. This might have accounted for some falling off of attendance in the last two meetings. However, many of the parents expressed a strong desire to continue the group, although not as a formal organization.

The Group Experience

The first series of meetings for parents of phenylketonuric children took place from January through June in 1961. A similar group of parents of children with galactosemia disbanded following its fifth meeting. Experience with the latter group revealed that the members were not as anxiety-ridden as the parents of the phenylketonuric children. Several factors probably accounted for this. The galactosemic diet is much less restrictive than the low phenylalanine diet used in the treatment of PKU. Also, most of the parents of children with galactosemia had lost an infant through death due to the disease and were thus highly motivated to keep their other galactosemic children on the diet. Moreover, almost immediately after treatment is initiated for galactosemia, a dramatic improvement is evident, so that parents quickly see the effects of the diet.

In contrast, the parents in the PKU group continued to exhibit a high level of anxiety, both in overt form and in symptoms of underlying tensions. They protested strongly against the planned termination of the group after six months. The social worker agreed to continuance, but suggested the need to explore further the kind of group they wished it to be. Then the members on their own planned a park picnic for July to "tide them over" until resumption of meetings in September. Only five families attended the picnic, but they apparently enjoyed it.

Because of work pressures, the social worker could not hold the planned September meeting, and as each week passed she received more and more requests for the meetings' resumption. Realizing she delayed partly to reinforce her own resistance to continue leading the group because of her ambivalent feelings about its goals and benefits, she made a tentative reassessment of the group's experience. Her first conclusion was that the emotional support of other parents seemed to be *more* rewarding than had even been anticipated. This could be attributed to several factors:

1. A nucleus of parents who met regularly had developed. These parents seemed to be having more difficulties which they were unable to manage by themselves than were those who attended sporadically or not at all.
2. This nucleus consisted primarily of parents whose children had just been diagnosed and put on diet therapy.
3. Some of the mothers in this nucleus were pregnant. They were reassured by contact with families who had already taken the risk or were now risking having another child with PKU.
4. Just prior to the initiation of the group, the PKU caseload had been shifted to a new social worker. The parents were still feeling uncertainty about the transfer. The group meetings with the social worker helped some parents to a quicker rapport in the individual casework relationship. On the other hand, some parents initially used the less personalized group contact to maintain distance from the social worker. Much more testing of the social worker occurred in the earlier sessions than might have occurred had the group been initiated after the transfer of caseworkers had been fully effected.

Secondly, the social worker noted that the educational content of the meetings had made some facts about PKU clearer to the parents. As a result, they had to shift some of their attitudes, but had not as yet found opportunity to solidify their newer understanding. For example, the early meetings revealed that the parents largely viewed their children as "sick," partly in order to avoid recognizing the presence or danger of mental impairment, and partly as a result of the clinical description of phenylketonuria as a disease with a specific treatment. The explanation of the disease as a metabolic dysfunction had led them to liken their child to a diabetic child rather than to a retarded child. Not regarding their children as retarded, they were not seeking contact with associations of parents of retarded children.

Increased Understanding

By the end of the first six meetings, the parents were beginning to see that their children were physically well as long as their metabolism was stabilized by good dietary management. They were also beginning to recognize that all aspects of the child's behavior, growth, and development could not be attributed to the fact that he had phenylketonuria, and to distinguish those aspects which were normal patterns of maturation from those which might be accounted for by the disease.

At the same time, the social worker was learning why some of the parents were having difficulty managing their children's diet and why some of the patients were continuing to have high levels of phenylalanine in the blood. For instance, one parent, desiring to let the group know just how bright and clever her five-year-old son was, revealed breaks in dietary control as she reported how the child awoke long before his parents and got his own breakfast. Two other parents expressed concern about their little girl's refusal to chew foods, although she chewed candy well; and group members responded by telling of their methods of handling similar feeding problems, thus enabling the troubled parents to see that the child's manipulative behavior was unrelated to PKU and helping them to examine their own interactions with the child which contributed to the feeding problem.

Meetings were resumed in October, 1962, and held regularly through April, 1963, with some dwindling of attendance in March and April. In July, the parents who had attended this entire series met together to discuss the experience and the possibility of continuing it. Saying that they had benefited greatly from the group's support, they asked specifically for further group meetings focused on the general areas of parent-child relationships, with occasional special speakers to keep them up to date on PKU. Their point of view coincided with the social worker's opinion that continuing enlightenment about aspects of normal growth and development and sound child-rearing practices improves parental methods and eases some of the difficulties inherent in coping with the stringent diet regimen.

There was again a picnic during the summer, this time with seven families attending. The meetings were resumed in October, 1963, and are being continued as a reinforcement to the clinic's counseling and treatment services.

What the Staff Learned

The outstanding feature revealed by this experience was the parents' woeful inadequacy in the area of child-rearing practices. Confusion, uncertainty, and inconsistency governed the parental management of all the children in these families. Their homes were generally child centered with the parents more often than not manipulated by the children. Consequently, when faced with the difficult task of putting a restrictive dietary regimen into effect, the parents had to take on a new role orientation and become stricter, more consistent disciplinarians.

Inner conflicts may be precipitated in some parents by this necessity to perform in a new and different way. Unresolved conflicts of their own parent-child relationships may be reactivated. Alongside this new stress is the feeling of guilt inherent in the genetic aspect of the problem, which tends to reinforce defense mechanisms of overprotection and denial. Depriving the child of desired foods adds further to the guilt feelings and heightens the difficulties in maintaining firm limits on the child's behavior and diet.

The group experience provided the parents with emotional support by helping them to see that their problems were not unique and by giving them a chance to examine their own as well as their child's needs. It also increased the clinic staff's understanding of how to work with parents of PKU patients, understanding which also has implications for work with parents of children with other types of disabilities.

Physicians and other professional workers have long been advising parents of mentally handicapped children to "treat him like your normal child," without regard to the parents' "normal" methods of child care. While mention is often made of the child's need for firmer discipline, attention is rarely given to the problem this imposes on the parents. The parents of children with PKU appear to represent a cross-section of the families in American culture today, with the child-rearing practices of our current culture. Hence, counseling at time of diagnosis needs to be concerned with bringing about an awareness that treatment and rehabilitation of the child will frequently conflict with methods of child management with which parents feel comfortable.

Normal problems of child growth at various ages and levels of personality development are easily distorted in the parents' eyes by the fact that the child has a special problem such as phenylketonuria. Therefore, guidance and information in relation to children's normal developmental needs as well as to the disease or defect should be provided by all the professional practitioners of the various disciplines involved in the care of the child.

Parents tend to focus on the diet as a means of defending themselves from exploring deeper concerns. Members of the clinic staff unwittingly often strengthened this pattern out of their own anxiety and sense of responsibility for having the child under good dietary control. The group experience helped the staff recognize that more attention should be given to the parents' basic anxieties. Exclusive emphasis on the diet often makes the task of keeping the child on it appear overcomplicated to the parents and misleads them into believing that all the dietary breaks are their fault and are causing great damage to their child. They need to be reassured that some situations are not in their control, and that their humanness is respected. Advice to the parents should be geared toward helping them to understand better their child's normal and special needs and ways of adapting their own parenting behavior to meet these needs. Our experience has indicated that there is more instability in dietary control in families in which the parents are unable to cope adequately with child-rearing problems.

Thus, while established primarily for supportive and educational purposes, the parent group has also provided therapeutic benefits to the parents of children with PKU, for the knowledge gained about them has helped the clinic staff offer services more constructively.

□ □ □

SECTION E

The Siblings of the Retarded

Management of the parents of the retarded has lagged so far behind in quantity and quality that special consideration of the retardate's siblings may appear to be premature. Yet we know that a retarded child can profoundly affect the life of a sibling, and that a sibling, in turn, can influence the attitudes and decisions of his parents and the behavior of the retardate. Thus we are once more confronted with the old truism that by influencing one family member we influence the whole family.

We have already encountered some programs involving sibling management, such as the activity groups described by Triplett as part of the Pine School Project. The first selection here by Begab gives us a perspective on the problem. He suggests the inclusion of siblings in the management process, with an emphasis on family, rather than only parent, counseling. According to Begab, inclusion of the sibling can result in additional benefits for the retarded child, the parents, and the sibling himself, i.e., the family as a total unit.

Schreiber and Feeley describe a group counseling program for adolescent siblings of the retarded. O'Neill relates experiences with individual counseling of siblings. This report may be of considerable utility to case managers as it is very informative regarding the dy-

namics of siblings of the retarded. In both articles, success is reported by guiding these children with a combination of individual and group methods.

In the final article, Adams presents significant insight into the problems and needs of siblings of the retarded. She sharpens the topic greatly by differentiating normal siblings into four age groups (preschool, early school, mid-school, and adolescent), showing how particular types of stress are characteristic for each. For the normal preschool sibling she emphasizes the possible disturbance of the parent-child relationship if the retarded child obtains or requires more than ordinary care; the child of early school age is described as facing rather difficult times when an already stressful entry into the larger social world is complicated by the presence of a retarded sibling; the mid-school period is seen as one of conflict and role distortion for the normal child, which could become more severe because of the retarded sibling; and during adolescence, a particularly troubled age in our society, the normal sibling may develop fears about his own capacity for normality. In discussing management, Adams emphasizes that the problems of siblings can generally be handled as realistic reactions to "a particularly difficult and unusual situation," rather than as symptomatic of deep-seated pathology.

from CASEWORK FOR THE MENTALLY RETARDED— CASEWORK WITH PARENTS

Michael J. Begab

(The Mentally Retarded Child: A Guide to Services of Social Agencies, 1963)

. . . .

Parents are usually the major focus of treatment, and the goal of this treatment is to enable them to use their personal resources more adequately to cope with the problem. But other family may also need t direct clients in the casework This applies primarily to older normal children, but may also include other significant relatives, especially if they are members of the parents' household. The relationships of each member of the family to each other and to the retarded child are nearly always influenced in some meaningful way by the latter's presence.

Disturbances in the siblings of retarded children generally coincide with disturbances in their parents. Ordinarily, changes in parental attitudes will relieve conflicts in these children, but there are some disturbances stemming from sources outside the home which the parents cannot handle. The normal siblings of a retarded child cannot always escape the unkind words or unwanted pity of peers or adults. Nor can they easily disregard a sense of disappointment when friends boast of the achievements of brothers and sisters, or their feeling of embarrassment at large and important family affairs.

To combat these forces, the older siblings should be recognized as an essential element in family adjustment and should be included in the study, interpretation, and treatment phases of the casework process, as appropriate. Ofttimes, parents cannot bring themselves to share the painful knowledge of their child's deficiency with their other children, and later interpretation can be made by the worker on an individual basis or to the family as a unit. The method of choice will depend on the personalities of the people involved and the age of the normal sibling. But the latter approach—family counseling—has the real advantage of facilitating communication between the parents and their normal children and allowing each, in the presence of the others, to raise questions of interest and concern. (This relatively new technique has not yet been applied on any scale to families with retarded children, but may have real value in implementing "family-centered" treatment.) The early involvement of siblings can do more than promote their understanding and acceptance. It can help define their relationship to the retarded child and instill in them the conviction that they are important contributors to his welfare and to the well being of the family. The parents may be helped too, in the knowledge that their burden is shared and in the strength derived from family unity and free communication among its members.

This approach may prevent emotional disturbances in some siblings, but it does not preclude the need for constant reassessment of family dynamics and the worker's alertness to symptoms of conflict and anxiety in the normal child. Where such symptoms are persistent and severe, work through the parents or with the family as a unit may not suffice. The sibling as a primary client for casework or other professional services would then need to be considered. . . .

□ □ □

SIBLINGS OF THE RETARDED:

I. A GUIDED GROUP EXPERIENCE

Meyer Schreiber, Mary Feeley

(Children, 1965)

In the course of providing group work services to retarded children during the past decade, the staff of the Association for the Help of Retarded Children in New York became impressed by the frequent references made by parents to problems these children created for their normal adolescent brothers and sisters, and vice versa. Parents expressed concern, for example, over the normal child's feelings of being overburdened by the care of the retarded sibling, of his overt expressions of hostility and resentment toward the retarded sibling, of responsibility for the retardation, of obligation to make up to the parents for what the mentally retarded brother or sister could not give them, and of guilt for being the normal child.

At the same time, the staff became impressed by the large number of normal adolescents who were taking their retarded brothers or sisters to social group meetings and to special events, and by other indications these young people gave of being able to cope with the fact of their sibling's retardation. Many of them obviously had been able to work out their feelings about their retarded brothers or sisters with no major intrapsychic, interpersonal, or intrafamilial strains, by developing healthy defenses and using compensatory mechanisms.

Thus with evidence both of need and strength in the normal adolescent siblings of retarded children, the staff began considering what the agency could do to include such young people in its total efforts to strengthen family life in the families of retarded children.

Consequently, with agreement from the appropriate lay committee, composed in part of parents of the retarded and the agency's board of directors, the decision was made to establish a demonstration program of guided group discussion for selected normal adolescents, through which they could examine, clarify, and understand more clearly a dynamic aspect of their life situation—their role as siblings of a retarded child. The experience in such a group, it was anticipated, would help these young people to become more effective and assured in their intrafamily relationships and responsibilities, and so would enrich the total family life.

More specifically, the aims of the demonstration were delineated as:

1. To assist the individual and the group to identify the nature of their reactions to having a mentally retarded brother or sister—stress, strain, mixtures of affection and antagonism—and the effects of these reactions upon their relationships with their parents, brothers and sisters, peers, and their entire life

situation.

2. To help the individual and the group examine and clarify strategies for understanding and dealing with their siblings, their parents and peers, and the problems of daily living related to their status as the brother or sister of a retarded child—strategies which would be helpful not only to them but also to others in similar circumstances.

3. To throw light upon the extent to which the concern and reactions of such adolescents represent strength as well as intrapsychic, interpersonal, and intrafamilial strains, and to determine whether their defenses are similar to or different from those of adolescents with no retarded siblings.

Since expressions of interest in the program came from all parts of the city, it was decided to conduct the group sessions at the association's office, which was centrally located. To qualify for admission to the group, an adolescent had to be between thirteen and seventeen years of age, and be willing to participate in the group sessions every two weeks to discuss his problems and feelings in relation to his retarded brother or sister and his life situation.

Twenty-eight adolescents met these criteria. Obstacles to attendance, such as the day, time, and travel involved, reduced the number selected to participate to ten. Twenty other young people were interviewed by staff members and helped to see why they could not be included in the group. These included several who were "pushed" by domineering parents to apply because "this is good for you," others whose parents expected the group to provide a therapeutic experience, and a few whose needs were basically social. For many of these young people, the group experience might have been too anxiety-provoking or otherwise inappropriate. Unfortunately, shortage of staff members prevented followup of those who seemed in need of individual counseling.

The ten young people who formed the group included five boys and five girls, mostly from lower middle-class backgrounds. The age spread was from fourteen through seventeen, with the boys generally one to two years younger than the girls. Six of the participants were in junior high school and four in high school. Judging from their own comments about school, seven could be considered above average in academic ability and three as average students; and seven were involved in extracurricular activities at school. All participants indicated a real desire to participate in this new experience.

All the retarded siblings of these young people were living at home. Some were mildly, some moderately, and some severely retarded. Half were younger and half older than the normal brother or sister.

The Group Process

The group, which its members called the Brother-Sister Group, met every two weeks from October, 1962 through May, 1963 under the leadership of a professional group worker. The first session was devoted to a consideration of the voluntary nature of the group and what the group hoped to accomplish. The adolescents agreed on their own accord to come regularly, and to share their problems and experiences in order to help not only each other but also other teenagers in similar circumstances.

At the end of each session the group agreed upon the focus of the next. In the beginning, the group worker took an active role in suggesting possible subjects for discussion, such as "How do you tell your friends about your retarded brother or sister?" However, as the members became better acquainted and more comfortable with each other and the worker, they began to bring up spontaneously the concerns they wanted to talk about. These included such questions as: "Does the fact that our family has a retarded member lessen our chances of marriage?" "How can we deal with the feelings we get when our friends show us pictures of their brothers and sisters and brag about their accomplishments?"

The participants offered little resistance to telling the group about their experiences with their brothers and sisters, families, and friends.

The worker helped the group look at different aspects of the material under discussion, adding information as needed, or raising questions and suggesting alternative courses of individual and group action. The worker also dealt with problems of individual needs and intragroup relationships. At the same time, she helped the group hold to its aims and special function. She filled a variety of "roles"—confidant, leader, counselor, resource person, agency representative, and even parent—as the situation demanded and the group progressed.

By the fifth session a cohesive group had emerged, held together by a common bond and meaningful relationships between the members and between members and group worker. From that point on, the group was largely self-directed, taking major responsibility for the content of the meetings and for individual participation. The group worker became largely a resource person, who provided clarification of points, support for individual participants, and information to indicate alternative courses of action.

Each session lasted an hour and a half, and included a period of light refreshments provided by the agency. At the end of each, the worker summarized the progress made, emphasizing the positive, the constructive, and the realistic aspects. She encouraged the members to share their findings with parents, other normal siblings in the family, and friends; and to feed back significant reactions from them to the group. Such reporting back was frequent.

The group usually stuck with an issue until it reached a termination point. Completion of a subject of discussion sometimes took as many as three sessions. The group worker's attitude of constant acceptance provided a safe climate for the expression of concern and the ventilation of feelings, whether these were of hostility, hate, or love. The participants also found support and recognition of the right to be different from their peers. They learned a method of analyzing life situations which was not only appropriate to the current scene but which could be used in dealing with future problems as well. Attendance at sessions over the eight-month period averaged 92 per cent.

Concerns and Feelings

What were some of the common problems which emerged? The following list was prepared by members and group worker together. The illustrative material comes from the group records.

1. How do you tell your friends about your retarded brother or sister, especially friends of the opposite sex?

> At this point, Bonnie turned to Susan and said, "Should I ask the question?" Both girls giggled, and Susan encouraged Bonnie to ask it. The question was: "How do you tell a boy that you have a retarded sister?"
>
> Mark responded immediately by telling about his experience in telling a girl about his sister. The girls listened attentively, but then Susan said, "It's different telling someone that you really care about."
>
> Susan is "going steady" and she hopes Stanley will never find out about her retarded sister, Gail. Could she tell why? She feels ashamed and embarrassed.
>
> Kenneth said he knows how Susan feels, but he has been trying to help himself by asking whether he would be ashamed if his sister had no arm or no leg. He said knowing about this should have no effect on a person who had nothing to do with it, and if the boy really cares about you, this won't change him.
>
> Kenneth told us that a few weeks ago a girl asked about his sister and he did not tell the exact truth. He felt ashamed about the way he acted and made up his mind to tell the truth the next time he saw this girl, but he just couldn't get himself to do it. He knows that it was wrong but he couldn't help himself.

2. How do you deal with your parents, who have not discussed the problems of mental retardation in the family and their implications for you?

3. How do you deal with friends and people in school when you are hurt by their talk of the retarded as nutty and crazy?

4. Are these meetings really helpful or are we betraying our families' confidences?

5. Are our parents' expectations, concerning our role and their role in continued care of our brothers and sisters, real and fair to all involved?

6. What should be our responsibility toward our retarded brother or sister in the event of our parents' deaths?

> Even before the meeting began the teenagers were discussing among themselves the requests made by their parents for the care of the retarded sibling if anything ever happened to the parents. Regina and Diane have promised never to send their retarded siblings to an institution. Bonnie promised to visit her sister Barbara regularly in the institution. She would definitely not care for her if her mother were unable to do so. The other girls laughed at this and told Bonnie that she was "just talking" again, and that she would be the first one to object to having her sister placed in an institution.

7. What are we to do when our parents do not really feel affection for our retarded brother or sister?

8. How can we deal with our feelings when our friends show off their brothers' and sisters' pictures and talk about their accomplishments? Bonnie broke in here and said:

> "It is hard when you hear the other girls boasting how smart their sisters are, and the things they do, and you can't say anything about your sister. In fact, very often I do not admit that I have a sister at all. Some of the girls in school think I am an only child and others want to know if I have a brother or sister since I never talk about mine. . . ."

9. Does retardation in our family lessen our chances of marriage, and is it hereditary?

10. How can our parents help us with our problems?

11. What can you do together with your retarded brother or sister in the home or in the community?

12. How does a teenager really accept a problem that he will face the rest of his life?

13. How can a teenager plan for his adult life?

14. What are our hopes for the future?

> At this point Kenneth asked why Susan had such feelings about her sister. He thinks that they should all be very happy that they are living now when so much is being done for retarded children. Years ago people would hide retarded children, and nothing was done for them.
>
> Bonnie said that was easy to say but the fact remained that the situation was hard to face. She says that she has heard all these things before. You are supposed to feel good because the President of the United States, who is very smart, has a retarded sister.

Other feelings expressed by participants in the group were: a feeling of not being loved as much as the retarded child; jealousy, resentment, and hostility toward the retarded child; denial of the severity of the retarded child's condition; and guilt about having negative feelings toward the retarded child. Such feelings, however, were not characteristic of the group, and their intensity in the individuals who held them was often repressed. The worker recognized their significance but did not delve deeper or bring them into focus before the group in view of the anxiety that would be evoked. Rather, she held to the group's educational focus, leaving the resolution of deep and involved feelings as the function of individual therapy.

As part of the group's activity, the worker suggested, after about eighteen sessions, that the participants might want to consider ways and means of helping other young people who had a retarded brother or sister. This resulted in a group project, the writing of a pamphlet directed to other teenagers.

Some Observations

Over the eight-month period, the experience with these young people led members of the agency staff to make a number of observations. We present them as hypotheses which need further testing with a larger number of retardates' siblings—young adults as well as adolescents:

About the Normal Adolescent

1. It was not the degree or kind of retardation in his sibling which seemed to affect the adolescent's life or happiness as much as the way he felt about himself and his retarded brother or sister, and the way in which he learned to live with the fact of having a retarded sibling.
2. What the normal adolescents really needed and wanted was accurate, up-to-date information, in language and concepts which they understood, about mental retardation and what they could do to help their families and their retarded siblings. They wanted to know how to manage *now* and what they could look forward to.
3. The young peoples' attitudes were not consistent at all times.
4. Almost every adolescent in the group brought up the question: *"Why* did it have to happen in my family, to us, to me?"

> He said the question of "Why did this have to happen to me?" comes to him often. I told him this was a natural question, but said I wondered what it meant in the way of his making friends, or in school. . . . He said that it hadn't meant much up to this point but wondered what would happen when he has to tell a girl about his sister. I pondered that question too. (Kenneth is unable to use the word "retarded.") He said he would just say his sister was different.
>
> Kenneth mused that everyone has something in their family. One of his friends doesn't have a father—parents are divorced. He can see this as a real problem. I asked him if this friend might also ask himself, "Why did this have to happen to me?" and he admitted that this might be so.

5. The sessions helped the teenagers see some of the strengths, as well as limitations, in their brother's or sister's functioning, and in the family.
6. The importance of good communication and feeling between parents and adolescent depended on the existence of the kind of relationship which encouraged the adolescent to go to his parents whenever he felt the need.
7. The teenagers seemed to be helped by the very fact of knowing that the agency was interested in them as well as in their parents and their retarded siblings.
8. The group worker to be helpful had to look at life as far as possible through the adolescents' eyes, show her care and respect for them, and treat them with dignity and understanding. She had to be careful not to generalize and assume that the problems and feelings of all the siblings of retarded children are the same.
9. The group worker found it important not to underestimate the strength of adolescents or to expect too little of them. It was clear that the young people wanted their parents to involve them in planning for the total family.

About the Group and the Group Worker

1. The experience was appropriate for the adolescents in the group. They were able to express spontaneous feelings, to invest themselves in the experience, and to extract positive help and strength from their contacts with others who are in similar circumstances. For other adolescents, such an experience may be anxiety-provoking to the point that the youngster is not able to handle his feelings appropriately. In some instances, such as when family relationships and parental roles were discussed, an adolescent's group experience carried a potential threat to his parents.
2. The meetings had meaning for the group not only in giving the young peo-

ple help during a period of hardship, but also in helping them to maintain and build healthy family relationships.

3. The support of others—their peers and the worker—was helpful to these young people.

4. The size of the group was important. Ten members seemed about right for providing good opportunities for exchanging experiences and sharing the worker with each other.

5. Timing the meetings in relation to the many pressures on teenagers—school work, social life, family obligations, and work—was important.

Conclusions

Thus we concluded that this short-term group experience was useful to the teenagers involved. The spread of time helped the young people, at an age when it is difficult to put feelings into words, to open up problems, to delve into certain aspects of relationships, to pull together and integrate what had been accomplished, and to begin to think more realistically about the future.

The sessions did not always contribute to modification or change of basic attitudes, but they enabled the participants to know that others knew and experienced similar problems and that it was all right to feel the way they did. Although their problems and feelings could not always be resolved since some were "bottled up" inside, for the most part these adolescents gradually became able to express their feelings more fully as meetings progressed and to become more realistic in their appraisal of them. This seemed to result in their being better prepared to see the next steps necessary in their planning. As time went on, they seemed to be able to look at the broader implications of mental retardation not only for themselves but for others who also had retarded brothers and sisters.

Many parents of retarded children are panicked into the belief that their retarded child will adversely affect his normal brothers and sisters. However, in some families where the parents have dealt with the situation constructively, such young people have developed greater maturity, tolerance, patience, and responsibility than is common among children of their age. Our experience suggests that the young person with positive family relationships is often capable of enduring the emotional hurt and anxiety of having a retarded sibling without severe disruption of his family and social life. He needs reassurance and support, but more often his primary requirements are educational. The more clearly normal siblings of the mentally retarded can see the realities of their particular situation, the better position they are in to cope with them. This is the point of a group experience. As the young people wrote in their pamphlet:

> ". . . We helped each other. We learned how to 'talk' about retardation and felt free to discuss our problems. We helped each other to be better prepared for any unexpected behavior of our brothers and sisters. We knew that we were not alone."

□ □ □

SIBLINGS OF THE RETARDED: II. INDIVIDUAL COUNSELING

Jane O'Neill

(Children, 1965)

When a social worker is involved with the family of a mentally retarded child, he needs to maintain a continuing awareness of each of the other children in the home not only in order to learn more about intrafamily relations and their effects on the handicapped child and his parents, but also for the sake of these children themselves. If the normal children in the family have problems deriving from the presence of the handicapped child, the strain on the entire family may be aggravated.

Sometimes the social worker derives adequate knowledge about the other children in the family from the parents alone. However, the worker may enlarge his understanding of the family and perhaps modify his approach if he comes to know these children personally. This usually contributes to a greater sense of warmth and security all around, although some parents may feel threatened by the agency's contacts with other members of the family, a possibility which has to be considered in the plan for service.

Getting to know the handicapped child's siblings may be achieved by plan or by incidental meeting. At the Evaluation and Counseling Program for Retarded Children in New Haven, we have found that the informality of our office often encourages parents to bring in the entire family when they come for an appointment. In fact, if parents come from a distance they sometimes turn the trip into a family excursion, climaxed by a treat, and we encourage this. Many of these families have experienced rejection and misunderstanding in the past. We try to make them feel accepted and at ease so that we can be of help to them in facing their problems. It might seem that the presence of several children for an hour or two in our small quarters could be disruptive. It sometimes is, but we find that we gain from each of these experiences both insight into specific family relationships and knowledge about the reactions of normal children to having a retarded brother or sister.

Out of such experiences grew our realization of the special problems faced by these normal children and of the help the agency could offer them. This, of course, varies with each child.

All that one nine-year-old boy needed to dispel his fears was to visit the office, see what went on in every corner of it, and meet the staff. He knew that his brother, a hyperactive child who was frequently in trouble, was undergoing evaluation, and he had reacted to this with symptoms of anxiety. At school he had been unable to concentrate. Assurances from his parents that nothing bad would happen to his brother had not helped him; but as soon as he entered the agency office on a visit with his parents his strained expression eased. Later, his mother reported that although he seemed less anxious after the visit, he was further relieved when the evaluation was entirely completed. He continues to be a very quiet boy who seems prone to worry, but, according to information from the school, he is participating normally in the classroom.

Telling the Other Children

The question of whether older children should be included in family-staff conferences regarding a handicapped child is one which the parents must decide. The social worker can, however, help them make their decision. Various degrees of protective and dependent feelings, and sometimes sound understanding of what each child needs and can take, will enter into the parents' decision. What the conference is to be about will also enter in. If, for instance, this is to be the first interpretation of the diagnostic findings on the handicapped child, the parents may very well feel that they should come by themselves.

This leaves still to be handled the problem of interpreting the diagnosis to the other children. Usually parents will expect to do this themselves. In most instances, by the time they have come to the agency they have already established their own pattern for meeting children's questions, spoken or unspoken, about the defect, slow development, or strange behavior of a brother or a sister. They are most likely to continue to follow the same pattern to a large extent, although they may modify it in the course of their experience with the agency.

Even so, the parents may seek continuing or intermittent help with intrafamily relations. Such help may be given to them directly or in some other way. There are times, for example, when the parents will seek the worker's help in talking with an older child about a situation which has become very complex, which they feel they have been unable to interpret adequately or satisfactorily, or which has especially upset the child. Sometimes the child himself will signal his needs and a friendly conversation in the agency's playroom will lead into something more purposeful.

One eight-year-old girl, frankly acknowledged by her mother as "my right arm," was unable to remain away on any occasion when the parents brought her atypical younger sister to the office during an extended period of evaluation. She would at first express regret about missing play with her friends, but would then admit that she had insisted on coming because otherwise she would have felt anxious. She said she always liked to know what was going on. She did not, however, show interest in observing any of the evaluation procedures.

This child had a need to talk, and she showed that she thoroughly enjoyed and felt important in her role as second mother to the retarded child. She said she wished her mother would have another baby. Then she said that she enjoyed those aspects of her sister's condition which made her continue to be a kind of baby. She told of extremely conflicting feelings. On the one hand, the thing she wanted most of all was for her sister to "get better." On the other hand, she wondered what it would be like not to have a baby in the house after being used to one for so long. She said she thought about this problem every once in a while.

The child's parents had tried to explain to her that her sister was not going to get better suddenly or dramatically. In talking with her, the social worker reinforced what the parents had said. Unfortunately, there was much about her sister's condition that was diagnostically baffling. The parents had been reacting to conflicting professional opinion and had not been able to keep their rising and falling hopes from the older child.

In the course of time, this little girl has seemed gradually to accept the fact that great change in her sister's condition is neither to be hoped for nor feared. She spends less time at home now. Her mother feels less guilty and depends upon other sources for help.

Anne's Case

In other instances, we have felt it necessary to offer more formal and prolonged casework service to a sister or brother of a patient. There was, for example, Anne.

Anne was twelve years old when her parents asked for evaluation of her five-year-old brother Freddy, a severely retarded, spastic child who was hyperactive and extremely difficult to control. To an increasing extent the life of all members of the family was being geared to Freddy's needs.

Freddy had been on the waiting list for admission to one of the State training schools for about four years. However, the parents were not sure that this was what they really wanted. They had sought an evaluation of Freddy by the agency to help them make a decision and be prepared if the opportunity for admission occurred.

The worker's first impression was that this was a very close family. All members, including Freddy, had a generally pleasing appearance. The mother looked careworn, but was very bright and controlled. The father, a clerical worker, was affable and mild in manner. He was extraordinarily patient with Freddy. Anne was pretty, serious, and even sombre. Later it was discovered that she was capable of great animation. Her eight-year-old brother George had a ready smile.

Anne seemed to feel a great deal of responsibility for Freddy. The mother said that when Freddy wanted to be comforted he would go to Anne; when he wanted to play, he went to George.

The parents were direct in their discussion of Freddy, but they tended to deny their own deep feelings about him. While they accepted the offer of continuing service from the public health nursing consultant, they made only limited use of the agency's help. By the time of the staff-interpretation conference, they had about settled on residential care as the ultimate plan for the child.

In spite of their independence in planning for Freddy, these parents admitted a sense of inadequacy in regard to Anne. They said they knew that she was deeply concerned about the home situation, but that she would not talk to them about this. They eagerly accepted the offer of an opportunity for Anne to talk alone with the worker, and Anne also responded positively.

The social worker had four interviews with Anne. The girl used them primarily to ventilate her feelings. These related to her sense of being repressed at home, to her relations with each of her parents, to George and Freddy, and to friends at school.

> Anne announced from the start that she had accepted the fact that the plan for Freddy was to go to training school. She seemed to look forward to it as possibly providing some relief and relaxation of the tension at home. Her understanding was that they would be able to bring Freddy home for visits frequently.
>
> Anne expressed a sense of rivalry with her mother. She was convinced that she understood Freddy and that when her mother was not there to interfere she managed him well. She felt that he could be taught to do more for himself but that her mother lacked the patience for this. For instance, Freddy had not learned to wash his hands because if he dropped the soap he would have a tantrum and refuse to try again. Anne thought that he could be helped to learn by repetition, and she told of an instance in which he had, but this kind of procedure was very frustrating to her mother.
>
> Anne said she thought that one possible advantage of the training school would be that Freddy would be taught how to develop his potential. She used part of one interview to ask about learning processes, and told of how she was able to apply some principles of child development she had learned in school. When asked if she thought her mother might be interested in knowing about these principles, Anne seemed to shrink. She said her mother would not converse with her on that level; that her mother regarded her as only another child.
>
> Anne felt that she was different from her mother, stronger in that she did not talk about her troubles—"I'm more like Daddy." At the same time, she recognized that things were hardest of all for her mother because she was in the house all the time. She was pleased when her mother joined a sewing club.
>
> Anne said she knew she was considered to be a serious person, but that this was only at home—"Outside I'm like everyone else." She expressed ambivalence about George and commented that he had a good understanding of Freddy, "more than I did at his age," and that "this probably will mature him mentally." She was frankly envious of George's ability to enjoy his own life to the fullest and of his imperviousness to scoldings.
>
> George and Freddy would fight, and this distressed Anne. Their behavior interfered with her homework and for a while she was getting up at five o'clock every morning to study French.
>
> Anne found real satisfaction in her relations with Freddy and in his response to her. She delighted in talking about him, and about what he liked to play. She liked to provide him with new experiences. One spring day she let him splash in the mud and she thought this did something for him. Her mother, who has very high standards of neatness, was upset.
>
> Although she could see weaknesses in her parents and felt that in many ways she could do better, Anne was not entirely uncomfortable in her role in the family and in the protective structure which her parents had placed about all their lives. Although many of her observations and reflections showed capacity for independent thought, many of her concepts and values, even expressions, reflected those of her parents.

An acute problem for Anne related to community attitudes toward Freddy. She found it hard to tell people about him and was especially afraid of telling her schoolmates. About two years previously, the family had moved to a suburb from the city. She found herself a newcomer in a school in which most of the children were from families of higher economic status than her own and, she thought, more secure socially than hers.

There was one girl whom she admired very much. Once when retardation was mentioned in school this girl said, "But those children look awful." Nevertheless, Anne wanted to be liked by her. She held back from social opportunities out of shyness but accepted an invitation to the girl's home. She realized then that she was well accepted but she continued to fear that this would change if the family problem became known.

Anne thought that she would never have the courage to tell her schoolmates about her brother's condition herself, and that she would be considered deceitful if they learned about it in another way. She and the worker discussed this problem at great length, but Anne could not work out any entirely satisfactory plan for handling it. She was pretty sure that not many people in the community knew about Freddy, although a few of her new friends had seen him when they stopped at the home one evening to pick her up for a party. When the worker asked what their reaction to Freddy seemed to be, she said all they seemed to have seen was a cute little boy. He had looked appealing at the moment. He had just had his bath and was ready for bed. She was sure they had not noticed anything. The girl about whom she was so concerned had not been in the group.

Anne's closest friend was a girl from her old neighborhood. She knew all about Freddy and about Anne's problems concerning him. Fortunately, Anne had been able to continue in a close relationship with this trusted friend.

When the worker asked Anne if she had ever had any experience of her own which would be useful to her in understanding the reactions of others to Freddy, Anne recalled that many years ago, before Freddy was born, a child visited the family who did not talk. She had not been aware then that there was anything else wrong but now she knows he must have been retarded. She and George played with him, and she remembers now that his parents seemed very pleased. The worker asked how she thinks of this person now. She closed her eyes and then said, "Someone nice." She said she was afraid, however, that some people are prejudiced against a retarded person before they even meet him.

At her third interview, Anne reported that her father had an opportunity for a job transfer which would have some advantage for him. It would mean moving out of the state. Her mother was not in favor of it, on the grounds that the family might suffer a financial loss in giving up the present home and acquiring a new one elsewhere, and also that the family needed to make sure of Freddy's continuing eligibility for admission to the training school for retarded children.

Anne said, however, she thought the real reason her mother was against the transfer was that she did not want to move away from friends and familiar surroundings. Anne did not know what her father really wanted to do, but she felt that he must want a change because for eighteen years he had been working in close association with a person whom he "couldn't stand." This would be his last chance to change because he had declined a previous offer. Anne said she was feeling more and more puzzled at her father's way of giving in to everyone. She told about how he spent every Sunday driving two sets of relatives between their homes and her family's.

Anne was not quite certain what she preferred herself but she leaned toward the move. The problem of informing new friends about Freddy would come up again but perhaps she could make a different kind of start. She pointed out that although she knew about the question of the move and some of the circumstances related to it, she did not know just where her parents were in their thinking since they did not include her in making a decision of this kind.

At the next interview a few weeks later, Anne said that she did not know what the final decision about her father's job was or if it had yet been made, but she knew one thing was certain: whatever the family did and whatever happened in their house in regard to almost any thing would be what her mother wanted. She seemed a little relieved by her own ability to recognize that this was a fact of her existence.

> Anne seemed less concerned about the home situation now and more about school. She groaned when she said that she sometimes felt that she would never get into college. The end of the school year was approaching, however, and she was looking forward very eagerly to a three-day trip to Washington with a group to which she belonged.
>
> At the end of this interview, Anne was not sure whether she needed to come to the agency again, so it was decided that the interviews would be terminated until she felt she wanted to resume them.

We have had no further direct communication with Anne. Her father was waiting as she left the office. In passing conversation, he revealed that the plan for job change had been definitely rejected. A few months after this, Freddy was admitted to the training school. The mother reported that they had to act on short notice and that perhaps this was good. She said she thought her husband was feeling the separation hardest of all. As for Anne, her mother said she seemed happier, "a changed girl."

Counseling service for the father was offered at this point but declined. The mother explained that she and her husband understood and valued the agency's interest but that they always felt that they should handle problems themselves as much as possible. She sent a message to the worker with the assurance, "We're doing all right."

The Meaning

Perhaps the agency might have given more help to this family, especially toward precipitating better communication among the members. The help which was provided, however, was in an area concerning which the parents recognized a need. It harmonized with the family's basic goals, although the parents' immediate goals were not identical.

For the girl, the agency's service provided an urgently needed outlet. In helping her, it released some of the tensions in the entire family. It also helped to increase the agency's own understanding of some of the problems faced in the homes of retarded children, the strengths which may be found in them, and the importance of giving them support.

□ □ □

SIBLINGS OF THE RETARDED: THEIR PROBLEMS AND TREATMENT

Margaret E. Adams

(Child Welfare, 1967)

That mental retardation is essentially a social problem we all know. No aspect of this complex and many-faceted condition is without far-reaching and serious social ramifications, whether they are related to the long-term implications of certain clinical conditions of identifiable genetic origin, to the manifestations of sub-average intelligence in maladaptive behavior, or the problems of adjustment to, or acceptance within, society that are imposed on the retarded individual and on those people in his environment charged with his care. In America and in other industrialized western countries, the unit of society that bears the initial brunt of the social stress stemming from mental retardation is the nuclear family—the parents and offspring—and within this vulnerable primary constellation it is inevitable that some of the difficulties and hardships associated with the presence of a retarded child in the family impinge also on the normal children, creating adjustment problems for them in turn. Farber and others have written about the displacement of sibling roles in families with a chronically handicapped offspring,[1] and most professionals know firsthand of the practical restrictions that a retarded child places on the normal life patterns of his family as well as the psychological repercussions that this tragic occurrence sets off.

This paper will describe some of the problems of siblings that have been reported by parents or observed by staff members in a special clinic in the course of treatment for the handicapped child.

This presentation will not deal with siblings who demonstrate inherent pathology of their own, of either a behavioral or an intellectual nature. Rather it will be concerned with children whose overall functioning appears to be within the normal range as determined by developmental level, adjustment at home and in school, and so forth, except for some specific areas or symptoms of stress that can be identified primarily with the circumstance of having a retarded brother or sister. In some families the stresses evoked by the advent of a retarded child may be so severe that the normal members do develop a seriously pathological reaction, but in these situations there is usually a predisposing factor that militates against the family's capacity to absorb the trauma and precipitates the acute response.

My concern is not with the obviously pathological children, but with those whose problems, whatever their guise, can be seen as a *normal* response to a highly stressful situation, and merit professional help to prevent their becoming worse. As can be envisaged, the stresses encountered among such a diverse clinic population (which includes children with all degrees of defect) vary a good deal according to the number and age of normal children in the family, and according to the age of the retarded child and his degree of defect. Only the more obvious and frequently recurring ones can be touched on. By and large, these are occasioned by the more severe types of retardation, which are both more socially conspicuous and more disruptive of normal life. In most of the cases from which my observations are drawn, the child was at best moderately retarded.

There are several reasons for clinical concern with the adjustment problems of the normal children. *First,* there is the factor of prevention. Because of its adverse social consequences, mental retardation has to be viewed as a "total family handicap," and clinical treatment must therefore be geared toward protecting the healthy members from its potentially harmful effects, as well as dealing with the primary manifestation in the disabled child. A family with such a burden is *ipso facto* a social and psychological risk, and if the pressures of caring for the handicapped child overwhelm the normal needs of the other children, there is a real danger that their vital developmental years will become blighted by emotional neglect, distorted family relationships and roles, and curtailed opportunity for social contact. As a result they may grow up as warped in their capacity for self-fulfillment as, in another way and for another reason, the retarded child is. The prevention of this secondary contamination is an important therapeutic goal.

Second, the development of healthy children and the satisfactions of normal child rearing are valuable in neutralizing the feelings of disappointment that parents experience through having a retarded offspring, and these satisfactions provide them with a more balanced perspective about their situation. Because of the health and well-being that normal children symbolize, they can contribute significantly to the overall psychological viability of the family group and can help to create the emotionally stable environment that a retarded child needs for optimal development. If there are maladjustments in the normal children, this healthy source of renewal is blocked, the family resources are diminished even further, and the task of successfully rearing the retarded child becomes much harder.

Third, the normal siblings can do a great deal to help the social and emotional development of the retarded child if they have a realistic and positive attitude toward his handicap. Their proximity in age, the natural empathy that exists between children, their opportunity to stimulate interest by sharing play, and the importance of their role as the link between the retarded child and other children in the wider social community, all invest the normal siblings with an unusually high therapeutic potential if it can be tapped constructively. The trainable mongoloid child of five who has been accepted by her eight-year-old sister's friends and encouraged to join in those of their games that are within her competence is likely to develop a higher level of social skill that will be an enormous asset when she gets into school, and in subsequent life situations.

Finally, there is evidence that having a retarded sibling is an experience that normal children can assimilate without too much stress, although they do encounter difficulties that need special understanding. Studies carried out in St. Louis in 1960[2] and in Los Angeles in 1962,[3] which explored the adjustment of preadolescent and teenage children to the retarded child in their families, showed a fairly high degree of constructive acceptance. More recently, reports on group and individual counseling with adolescents on this problem confirm these earlier findings that this age group, at least, can be quite articulate about its difficulties and that its members, given support, can mobilize themselves to handle the difficulty constructively.[4]

This combination of high vulnerability and a good potential for adjustment makes the normal sibling group a very appropriate target for professional concern.

The problems of siblings are potentially so manifold and diverse that it has been difficult to decide from which of the many possible standpoints to approach them. By and large, however, they can be roughly separated into those that are common to most children in most family settings throughout the total childhood period, and those of a more specific nature, which impinge crucially at different phases of the developmental continuum of the normal child. This paper will deal mainly with the latter category, but two major areas of common difficulty also need to be mentioned briefly. These are the pervasive sorrow and anxiety that most parents experience on behalf of their handicapped child, and role distortion within the family. The former stress, which has been described with such clarity by Olshansky,[5] is a constant background feature in the environment of the normal siblings, and the latter is a dynamic occurrence that affects every family, whatever its age and sex structure, and affects it at all stages. This problem impinges with greater significance on certain phases, however, and also creates particular stress for the normal siblings who are younger than the retarded child. From an early age these younger siblings have to accustom themselves to the incongruity of a physically larger child who is able to achieve less than they, and for whom parental demands for conforming behavior are less exacting. Unless the confusion of this anomalous situation is appreciated and deliberately counteracted, there is a risk that the normal children may identify with the handicapped child in the early stages of their development and pattern their behavior on his. If the older defective child receives an inordinate amount of attention, the incentive to adopt him as a model is unduly high and increases this risk. Role distortion also affects children in the mid-school-age group, as will be discussed later.

The separate stages that have been delineated as areas of specific stress for normal children are:

The preschool period—up to age five,

The early school period—between ages five and approximately eight,

The mid-school period—between ages eight and twelve,

The adolescent period—between ages twelve and eighteen.

I will briefly indicate what are the most characteristic and predominant difficulties of each phase, and then go on to discuss steps that professionals can take to mitigate their harmful effects.

Preschool Period

In the preschool period, disturbance of the parent-child relationship and resultant mishandling are the major hazards that the normal young child faces if there is a retarded child in the family who needs more than usual care. Because of the pressures on them to meet these exigencies, parents may unintentionally neglect the normal child, meeting only his minimal needs and not providing him with the affection and stimulation that he also requires. The normal child may react to this treatment by reducing demands on the parents who, in turn, may accept this helpful behavior with relief, failing to understand the psychological dangers in too much cooperative inhibition. Alternatively, the normal child may protest with negativism, which creates further stress and reinforces the parents' sense of being overwhelmed by too many problems so that they perceive the child's behavior as a deliberate aggravation rather than a normal reaction for his age and situation.

This type of family maladjustment is illustrated by a young couple with a girl of three and a severely retarded older child of four and one-half who, because of gross neurological impairment, absorbed a great deal of the parents' time and emotional energies.

> When the normal child came to the clinic's attention she was regressively soiling, hostile toward the retarded brother, and negativistic to her parents, but extremely anxious if separated from them. In discussing whether she was ready for nursery school—where the parents were desperately seeking to enroll her—both parents expressed great resentment that she was demonstrating these regressive patterns of behavior. The father, particularly, complained about her anger when he paid attention to the older child before her when he came home at night. He explained that since she could run to him and the crippled child could not, he owed it to the latter to put him first.

This is a rather extreme illustration in that the parents had many additional problems besides the retarded child, but it is illustrative of the type of situation that can easily arise and which needs prompt professional attention.

The Early School Period

The early school period may in some ways present the most difficult adjustment problems which, because of their subtle and complex character, are not always recognized. At this juncture the normal five-year-old is faced with the usual hazards of school adjustment and separation from home, and is therefore somewhat unsure of himself. His own entry into the larger social world beyond the family and his extending contact with new people and situations combine to make him suddenly aware of the social implications of retardation, which were not obvious when it was contained within the four walls of his home. Many parents report that an older child starting school will ask about future arrangements for the retarded child, which seems to suggest that for the first time the child is seeing the discrepancies that will occur when the handicapped sibling is exposed to new social demands and systems. With this enlightenment comes the dilemma of how to explain the sibling's deviance to peer groups and the teacher, and anxiety about how they will react to this unusual feature in his background.

At this stage of transition between babyhood and childhood, intrapsychic forces still exert a strong influence, and the visible presence of a clearly disabled child in the family may adversely affect the normal child's self-image, making him wonder about the origin of the damage, why he has escaped, whether he will remain immune, and why this phenomenon has not occurred in other families. At a deeper psychological level there is the possibility of guilt feelings at being whole, and anxiety that destructive sibling rivalry fantasies may have caused the condition.

Such fears of damage and violence

were verbalized by the five-year-old brother of a very retarded three-year-old boy who attended a weekly play session at the Clinic.

> The normal child was exhibiting considerable separation anxiety when his mother came for counseling. This anxiety was also expressed in his fear of going to school. To avert constant interruptions he was allowed to join the counseling session. During the second interview he spontaneously volunteered the information that he had difficulty in going to sleep and suffered from bad dreams, emphasizing one in which he could not talk. Since lack of speech was felt by the parents to be the fundamental cause of the retarded child's severe malfunctioning, it seemed clear that the older boy was very preoccupied with this defect in his sibling.
>
> The following week he described a frightening dream in which he was in a room with a lot of big children, and then went on to elaborate various fantasies of violence and to describe the revenge he was contemplating on his father for his alleged harsh punitive treatment (a description not confirmed in reality).

The juxtaposition of this material, produced spontaneously with no cues except for a sympathetic interest in his difficulties, raises speculation as to whether he might not be viewing his brother's disability as a feared paternal punishment for Oedipal rivalry. This ventilation of fears appeared to reduce his anxiety, and for the next seven sessions he stayed in the waiting room, joining the social worker and his mother for the final fifteen minutes of her sessions when his affairs and his relationship with his brother were discussed. When the brother was brought to the mother by the special teacher, the normal child participated in the joint conference on the retarded child's progress and the treatment aims in day-to-day living.

Mid-School Period

During the mid-school period the type of social problems that start with entry into school are exacerbated because of the normal child's increasing involvement in a wider range of social activities and relationships outside of the family that have to be reconciled with the unusual features of home life with a retarded child. This is a phase when role distortions and practical issues deriving from them impinge heavily on the normal children, threatening the proper development of their own personal interests and activities. The most obvious problem—and one that recurs often—is how much the normal child is expected to share in the responsibility for the retarded child, either by directly supervising him in place of the parents or through being under pressure to include him in his own pursuits.

By the very nature of his handicap the retarded child is some hindrance to the normal children, interfering with personal possessions, interrupting their homework, and trying to copy their activities. His presence creates a situation that has to be explained to friends visiting the home, and if he is allowed to obtrude too much into peer group activities, children outside the home may stop visiting, and the normal child's social life may be curtailed in a vital area. The phenomenon described by Farber as "arrest in family cycle" probably affects children in this age group most, in that their roles constantly shift as their skills develop and they outstrip the retarded child in achievement.[6] Further, this instability of roles within the family is experienced at the crucial stage of their own social development when experimentation with new roles outside of the home normally occurs.

At this period also, the problem of parental pressure to achieve well in school starts to predominate, leading to several unsatisfactory reactions in the normal child. He may, for example, become preoccupied with academic success to the exclusion of other equally important activities, or he may fail to work up to his potential because of feeling unequal to meeting these excessive demands. The implication that the normal child has to compensate for the intellectual failure of the handicapped child, which is drawn by many children from their parents' preoccupation with their progress, can also create doubts as to whether he or she is loved for himself or for being the achiever in the family. There may also be conflicts over the success role, with guilt feelings about being the well-endowed, healthy child, and with consequent reluctance to demonstrate this superiority.

A ten-year-old boy with a severely retarded sister, whose low functioning was a great disappointment to the parents, went through a stage of being very hostile to his parents, accused them of caring only for her, and one day expressed the vehement wish that he were average or dull. His comment might be taken to imply that he felt his unusually high intelligence to be the opposite end of the intellectual seesaw on which he and his sister were placed, with the obligation to strike a compensatory balance.

Adolescent Period

Four studies have already been cited on the problems of adolescents and their retarded siblings, and since I do not have much to add to these observations, this section will be brief. It may, however, be pertinent to touch on the special problems of teenage siblings that relate to the medical aspects of retardation. Even where there is no known hereditary factor causing the retardation, the fact that an imperfect child has been born to his or her parents inevitably casts some doubts on the teenager's own capacity for healthy parenthood. When there is a known genetic factor present, such as Trisomy 21 or phenylketonuria, the situation is more fraught with anxiety. Because popular scientific information is so easily available now, most teenagers are quite sophisticated about the various causes of retardation (without always understanding how they apply specifically to their own family), so it is very important, in order to prevent misconceptions, that they receive accurate knowledge from an informed source about the retarded child and the implications of his condition for their own future as potential parents. The often-voiced complaint that a retarded child at home makes it hard for teenagers when they are dating would be much reduced if the teenagers had a factual explanation to give to their peers that would dispel the aura of stigmatized mystery that still surrounds retardation when the facts about it are not known.

Treatment of Problems

I have already indicated that the problems that the normal siblings experience should not be viewed as pathology so much as an unsuccessful attempt on the part of the family to meet the strains of a particularly difficult and unusual situation. Treatment, therefore, is less concerned with the symptomatic aspects than with trying to increase the total family's adjustive capacity to this long-term, all-pervasive problem. This has to be approached along two lines—first, through a direct confrontation with parents to help them gain some insight into their normal children's predicament; second, by involving the normal children in the clinical program as a part of the overall therapeutic plan.

It may seem rather superfluous to place such emphasis on the need for mobilizing the parents' active concern, but in my experience of counseling families I have been struck by the stereotyped and ambiguous ideas that many parents have concerning the relationship between the retarded and normal children in the family. These parents tend to veer from the uncritically favorable dictum that the retarded child is loved by everyone to the opposite idea that his presence is harmful to the other children and constitutes a social injustice for them. Such oversimplifications suggest that parents do need help in confronting the realities of this situation, clarifying more precisely their ideas and feelings, and recognizing the much more dynamic character of intra-family relationships that surround a handicapped member.

The significance of these relationships can be introduced in the course of taking the initial social history, when the orthodox factual questions about siblings (age, ordinal position, level of development) may be extended to explore also the parents' feelings and attitudes about their circumstances. This tactic not only indicates the family-focused approach the clinic adopts toward the problem of retardation, but also gives implicit recognition to difficulties that parents may not have raised spontaneously for fear of their being insignificant or irrelevant. A further inquiry into how they themselves handle the problem can open up possibilities for subsequent counseling on this subject.

Parents are inclined to underestimate the normal sibling's capacity for assimilating both the emotional and intellectual aspects of retardation, and it is therefore very important for them to be helped to realize that clear, objective, factual information about the retarded child's diagnosis and treatment is the best protection that most children can have against their own anxieties and also against the curiosity of their contemporaries. A good many parents are inhibited from explaining the complexities of retardation by their feelings of being improperly informed themselves, but most of them respond with interest when they are offered guidance on this. The doctor who presents the final diagnostic findings can be very helpful if he bears in mind the parents' need to relay the information to the siblings subsequently and discusses how this can be done in a way appropriate to the children's levels of understanding. Explanations that can be put in terms of obvious functional deficiencies rather than the abstract and highly stigmatized term of retardation are likely to be more acceptable.

Depending on circumstances, clinic involvement may be quite informal or deliberately structured, but its overall purpose should be to offer the normal children a milieu that provides an accepting attitude toward the idiosyncracies of the retarded child, and a positive interest in his condition. How a clinic can provide this atmosphere of uncritical acceptance is well described in a report from New Haven.[7] I would add that the clinic also provides a social frame of reference in which the normal children can see the retarded child. If the latter is severely handicapped, the normal children perceive him as someone who is receiving medical treatment to make him less sick; if his handicap is only moderate, he is seen as coming to the clinic to be taught basic social skills to prepare him for later life. This therapeutic orientation lessens the sense of social isolation and bewildered defeat that can surround a retarded child.

One mother described her normal ten-year-old son's face as lighting up when she told him of the progress the younger, autistic, retarded child was making in the weekly play therapy sessions with the special teacher. It is very beneficial if a sibling can be included at least once in the actual therapy and allowed to participate in a helping capacity, since this gives him a more positive outlook on the retarded child's handicap and takes away some of the aura of mystery with which deviant behavior tends to be vested. Two eight-year-old girls, whom their mothers described as being very upset about their younger brothers' slow development, expressed a desire to visit the clinic to see what took place there and showed enthusiastic interest when the special teacher took them to the playroom, demonstrated materials, and interpreted the treatment aims to them.

For more articulate children, a special opportunity to meet with staff members to ask questions and express their own ideas about the retarded child can be helpful. Most children over ten are probably, at heart, very interested in the reasons for their siblings' being different, and where feasible it is probably a good strategy to schedule routinely one appointment for the normal children to talk with the doctor on the clinical aspects. The very intelligent ten-year-old boy mentioned earlier was extremely distressed to learn via a casual telephone conversation that his retarded sister was also brain-damaged. This further upsetting revelation could have been spared if he had been given a simple explanation of the organic basis of retardation by the clinic doctor. His need to understand her condition more scientifically had been demonstrated earlier when he took a book on animal-learning psychology from the library and insisted on reading excerpts aloud to his mother.

Whether children should be given individual appointments or included in the total family conference depends on a variety of factors, but since retardation can never be a private affair, I am in favor of the normal siblings joining in family conferences from time to time when the topic is within their emotional and intellectual grasp. (I would not, for example, advocate preadolescent children being present when the genetic aspects of phenylketonuria or Tay-Sachs disease are under discussion.) In certain situations the older child may benefit from the chance of ventilating to a neutral outsider ideas that may be of doubtful acceptance at home. But interviews should always be geared to a specific problem and emphasized as part of the total therapeutic approach, otherwise the normal child may feel he is being seen because he also is a problem.

An example of this sort of individualized help[8] can be found in the case of an eleven-year-old girl who was becoming withdrawn and depressed and was deteriorating in her school work because of her mother's decision to request placement for the hyperactive four-year-old, brain-injured brother.

> The sister felt that it was treating him like an animal to send him away and that it was a final act of rejection. Her mother was receiving counseling about placement, so with her concurrence an appointment was offered to the sister to discuss what placement would actually mean. In this interview she talked about her conflicts concerning the retarded child and revealed her more general fears about her very precarious home situation. (The family was supported by welfare, there was no father, and her mother had a chronic respiratory condition.) Through help at this crucial juncture she became less critical of her mother's decision, in which she was now actively involved as a responsible family member, and the two of them were able to discuss interim plans for the retarded child between themselves and with other relatives in a more constructive way.

An effective approach with older siblings is to let them attend a parents' group from time to time to exchange views with the adults. This practice started impromptu when mothers attending a weekly group to discuss problems of the retarded in the home made an occasional request for their older normal children to come to the room instead of staying in the waiting room; it was subsequently incorporated as a routine tactic into the group program, with a special effort made during the school holidays to have several children attend simultaneously. Their contributions were extremely enlightening; one hypersensitive, very bright, thirteen-year-old Negro boy discussed the need for more information on the retarded to reduce prejudice, and a remarkedly poised and cheerful twelve-year-old provided some insightful and realistic revelations on the interaction between the seven-year-old retarded boy and his five older brothers (such as when he said he thought the older ones had a right to get mad [at] the younger child if he deliberately provoked them, otherwise he would never learn to get along with people). He also made some interesting suggestions on how the whole family could try to break through his retarded sibling's obsessive eating habits, which were also regarded as a major social handicap.

This type of informal discussion

within a mixed age group serves as a model for cooperative interaction at home and provides a forum where the different, and sometimes conflicting, opinions of both generations can be exchanged with mutual advantage. In one instance it was used very constructively to resolve a conflict on management between a middle-aged mother and her eighteen-year-old daughter.

> The daughter was taking classes in child psychology and felt that the mongoloid girl of seven would develop better if she were handled more permissively. The eighteen-year-old sister was invited to come to the group her mother was attending to talk over these opposing ideas and to express her viewpoint. She was helped to understand that retarded children (because of their limited intelligence) need both a very structured and consistent pattern of discipline. This gesture of inviting her to share her ideas with grownups highlighted her role as a would-be helpful older sister, while giving her the support of informed guidance on how to fulfill this wish most effectively.

This last example provides a note of optimism on which I should like to end, since it also echoes the belief that I hope has colored the whole presentation—namely, that while the advent of a retarded child is a tragic and stressful experience, the majority of families have enough resources to meet its problems if they are given help. The function of social workers and all the professions related to this field is to ensure that this help is forthcoming, so that the positive resources of strength and good will are maintained and the family can absorb the individual pathology of the child into its own corporate health.

Footnotes

1. Farber, Bernard, and Ryckman, David B., "Effects of Severely Mentally Retarded Children on Family Relationships," *Mental Retardation Abstracts,* 1965, II: 1-17. Shere, M. O., "Sociometric Factors in Families of the Twin with Cerebral Palsy," *Exceptional Children,* 1955, XXII: 197-199.
2. Caldwell, Bettye, and Guze, Samuel E., "A Study of Adjustment of Parents and Siblings of Institutionalized and Non-Institutionalized Retarded Children," *American Journal of Mental Deficiency,* 1960, LXIV: 849-861.
3. Gralicker, Betty, Fishler, Karol, and Koch, Richard, "Teenager Reaction to a Mentally Retarded Sibling," *American Journal of Mental Deficiency,* 1962, LXVI: 838-843.
4. Schreiber, Meyer, and Feeley, Mary, "Siblings of the Retarded: Part I—A Guided Group Experience," *Children,* XII (1965), 221-225. O'Neill, Jane, "Siblings of the Retarded: Part II—Individual Counseling," *Children,* XII (1965), 226-229.
5. Olshansky, Simon, "Chronic Sorrow: A Response to Having a Mentally Defective Child," *Social Casework,* 1962, XLIII: 190 ff.
6. Farber and Ryckman, *op. cit.*
7. O'Neill, Jane, *op. cit.*
8. The author is grateful to Miss Olive Jacob, formerly of the Department of Pediatrics, Division of Psychiatry, Jewish Hospital of Brooklyn, for this and other case material quoted describing the reaction of an adolescent girl in a parents' group.

□ □ □

Part IX The Parent and the Institution

The question of residential placement is likely to occur to most parents of lower functioning retardates. Historically, the institution has been the major service resource for such families, and it is only now beginning to be supplemented to a significant degree by other management alternatives. That the institution serves a function for many families with a retarded member is fairly evident by the growing number of such facilities in the country, and by the fact that waiting lists rarely seem to shorten. Still, estimates of the number of retarded in this country tend to agree that at the very most 4 per cent are presently in institutions. Thus, management programs for families in which there is a retarded member must, realistically, be designed in terms of the other 96+ per cent. However, in each case of an institutionalized individual, a decision had to be made to request entrance. And, in the vast majority of cases, the decision-making process had probably been a very demanding and emotionally difficult one.

Completion of institutionalization by no means marks the end of the management needs of the family. Management now requires a new emphasis, one which recognizes the discontinuities implied by institutional placement. In a society which places great value on children as a means of family actualization, and which emphasizes cohesiveness and togetherness in family interaction, the removal of one member must be seen as a highly significant event for all members. Sociologists point to the function of the family as a socializing agent of society, and they have written about the major influence of family patterns on the socialization process. Institutionalization means that the child will be socialized somewhere else, that the child will no longer be a sociological member of the family. It means that the family has decided that it will surrender the socializing role to another agent. This entire process stands in sharp contrast to the American value system. It is no wonder that such family decision-making problems are highly emotionally charged. Management must rally to a complex challenge. In this section, we attempt to examine family management procedures during the placement decision-making, during the placement process, and after the institutionalization has taken place.

SECTION A

The Placement Decision and Its Alternatives

To this day, residential placement usually, but quite unnecessarily, constitutes a radical discontinuity in the lives of a child and his family. Until this discontinuity has been bridged by our service patterns, and maybe beyond, managers must be deeply concerned about the nature of the placement decision. This concern must be expressed toward both the child and other members of the family. Let us contemplate, for a moment, how radical an alternative institutional placement currently is. Institutionalization means that a member of the family social system, a member around whom emotional problems have centered, is removed, usually to spend the rest of his days in an entirely different social system. Only rarely do families deliberately make decisions that have equally system-affecting implications.

There are a host of cliches which have been developed to rationalize institutional placement: 1) It will be better for him; 2) They can take care of him better than we can; 3) They have doctors there who know how to handle his problems; 4) It's not like losing a child, it's just putting him into expert hands; 5) We can visit him anytime we want to; 6) It will be better for our other children; 7) We'll all be better off; 8) Now his sister will be able to have dates; 9) Now our family can become normal again; 10) We'll still be able to have him as part of the family on weekends and during vacation periods, and so on. Even with these emotionally satisfying rationalizations, some of which may be quite realistic, the decision to institutionalize still carries with it overtones of parental failure and guilt, and under the conditions of a radical discontinuity, the decision to institutionalize is bound to be filled with strong emotional problems on the part of those who remain in the family and community social system. It is quite possible that during the decision-making discussions, and after the institutionalization has taken place, many families may actually need more guidance than when the child was first identified as being mentally retarded.

Beddie and Osmond remind the manager that parental decisions which are in conflict with prevailing cultural values and mores are likely to prove unsatisfactory, perhaps disastrous. Even if parents decide to pursue a socially censured alternative, the manager is most unwise in urging it upon them. Their discussion centers around a case in which a child, identified as mongoloid at birth, is to be institutionalized without the mother ever seeing her baby because of the strong advice of the obstetrician and pediatrician. The authors suggest that our society has not developed adequate roles and rituals for a mother giving birth to a child who does not socially exist. For this reason and others, they take a strong position against institutionalization at birth.

The second selection has been widely quoted in the literature. In it, Jolly disputes a number of the reasons widely cited in favor of early placement of retarded children. He demonstrates that the tendency for professionals in the past to recommend early placement was often not only inappropriate, but also meaningless because of the lack of residential facilities. Similar considerations are presented in the article by Slobody and Scanlan, who also discuss the deleterious effects of depriving a child of maternal contact upon institutionalization. In the selection following, Grant decries the phenomenon of "instant institutionalization" as ". . . a palpable disgrace to the medical profession, a disservice to parents, and often a burden upon the taxpayer."

To argue against premature placement is one thing, but to provide parents with alternative services is another. Giannini and Goodman describe a project conducted at the Flower-Fifth Avenue Hospital in New York where the aim was to prevent unnecessary institutionalization of mongoloid infants. The main alternatives offered were individual casework, group counseling, and medical care. One might argue that in many cases more direct services aimed at the alleviation of caretaking problems would have been desirable, but this would apply only in part to the families served. Most were of high socioeconomic status, and early placement was not primarily sought because of excessive child-rearing demands, but because of family value conflicts. If the parents found it impossible to consider alternatives to placement, the personnel of the Flower-Fifth project attempted to give support, and to help in implementing the decision constructively.

Begab describes a program which was institution-based, but which also attempted to forestall placements which might not have been necessary. The pre-commitment phase, and the dynamics of parents in this phase, are explored. Begab feels that a carefully structured pre-commitment program can contribute importantly to the retarded child and to other members of the family.

from MOTHERS, MONGOLS, AND MORES

Alastair Beddie
Humphry Osmond

(The Canadian Medical Association Journal, 1955)

. . . .

There can be few doctors who have not seen the heart-breaking sight of a middle-aged mother accompanied by a doll-like mongoloid child. Many doctors advocate separation of the mother from the child as a means of reducing family stress. However, very few doctors think about the consequences of carrying out this separation, but passively accept the view of a small minority of their colleagues that separation is a good thing.

Take Rosebud for instance, who is in a corner of the baby ward. No one knows her real name. In accordance with the newest ideas, as soon as the observant obstetrician noticed that she was mongoloid, he had her separated from her mother, who then left hospital without seeing her baby, and Rosebud, so named by the nurses, remains behind. She is not dead, so her mother cannot mourn her loss as would be both becoming and healthy, yet is she properly alive? Unchristened, unrecognized by her parents, she remains in a corner of the baby ward waiting for a place in the mental deficiency hospital. Why?

How Was This Decision Made?

Apparently the obstetrician who delivered Rosebud decided that it would be better for her mother not to see her until he had been advised by a pediatrician. The pediatrician agreed that Rosebud was a mongoloid and recommended that she should go to an institution. Her mother was told gently that she could not see her child, and only kind and overworked nurses handled her from time to time.

The Spartans exposed unwanted children on hillsides; other peoples have dealt with their excess population by killing infants and old people. With a deeper wisdom than we seem to possess, they took care that there should be some means of supporting those who were forced to make such tragic decisions. If a mother, especially a newly delivered mother, must be deprived of her child for her own good or for the good of society, then society must provide some recognized way of doing this; a way that is sufficiently robust to sustain the mother in her grief and guilt, and also to sustain the nurses and doctors in the uneasiness they must feel at doing such a thing.

Why Was This Done?

Two men, one of whom specialized in delivering babies and the other in looking after children, have made a clinical judgment which has somehow effected a social, ethical, and moral revolution. They have done it with the best intention but no thought at all of the consequences for the mother, the baby, or society. They have decided that although normal infants must be cherished and nurtured by their mothers, this infant is expendable in the interests of its mother. But what about Rosebud's mother, that shadowy lady who has disappeared from the hospital without a glance at her daughter? What has happened to her? What have her advisers done to her?

Rosebud's Mother

To begin with, she went into hospital happily pregnant. To prepare herself for her baby she had undergone all the ceremonies and rituals which our society prescribes. Duly anesthetised in the manner which we order, she has had her baby; but there is no baby. True, many mothers bear dead babies and get over it, but Rosebud is not dead. If she were dead there would be condolences, flowers, the priest or parson, the neighbors' sympathy—"poor little thing, perhaps she's better dead."

Death in the just-born must be faced as it must in the adult or the aged. That men have striven with death through the centuries is evident in art, literature, and architecture. We have learned how to control our fear of the dead by closing our ranks as members of the living. Although each death reminds us always that we cannot escape, yet at the same time we rejoice that this time we have escaped.

We do this by mourning. In all cultures the form of mourning is prescribed. As the writer of Ecclesiastes said:

> To every thing there is a season and a time to every purpose under heaven.
> A time to be born, and a time to die,
> A time to weep, and a time to laugh,
> A time to mourn, and a time to dance.

Lindemann has demonstrated that if mourning is not carried out at its proper time, then it must be done at some other time. His findings suggest that many puzzling depressions are "delayed mourning." "Grief work" must, he says, accompany any loss, and if not at the time, then later. In our case, the mother has in a very real sense lost her child. Let us consider the consequences of her loss.

Rosebud is lost, but she is not dead. Her mother's womb is empty, but there have been no funeral rites. Perhaps the kindly doctor said, "It is as if she'd been born dead." Rosebud is alive, however, and the question must inevitably arise, "Why won't they let me see her?" To the mother it must mean that she has given birth to something so monstrous that it were better never to see it. In fact Rosebud is no uglier than many babies which gave their mothers great joy and pleasure. Rosebud's mother knows how queer some quite normal babies look, and so she is bound to imagine something much more dreadful than a mongol child. There have always been things that must never be seen, for instance the head of Medusa, the gorgon at the horror of whose visage men were frozen to stone.

Recently a mongoloid child who had never been seen by its parents was admitted to a mental deficiency hospital. Against their pediatrician's advice and with great trepidation, they finally visited the baby. They were delighted to find that the monster they had feared was a little baby much like other little babies and with many endearing ways. When he died, a few months later, they said, "We would never have forgiven ourselves if we hadn't come to see him." They took the dead child home and buried and mourned him. All was completed in decency and decorum. A child had been born, acknowledged, named, lived a little, and died.

Failure to perform those rites of passage which we call mourning is psychologically damaging. Rosebud's mother is doubly deprived, for she has been bereft of her newborn child and has been denied the opportunity of mourning its loss. This, Lindemann observed, is a dangerous situation psychologically. Grief that cannot be openly expressed and accepted may find other expression in unaccountable depression or in psychosomatic illnesses. One might predict that among mothers who are encouraged to deny and abandon their children in this way, there would be an enhanced likelihood of subsequent psychiatric illness. One of us has seen a grave depression develop in a girl following therapeutic abortion, and this began at the time when the aborted child was due to be born. It seems to us imprudent to deprive the mother of both her child and her right to mourn its loss; to put her in a position where it is not proper for her to discuss and adjust to the loss she has undoubtedly sustained. . . .

Human societies have developed approved ways of meeting the various predicaments which constitute life. These are mores (or customs) and laws. Nothing from birth to death is unaffected by these mores. A mother who has an idiot child has to meet this misfortune in the setting of our culture and must therefore, unless she is to alienate herself from our mores, respond to this misfortune in the way which our culture demands. To remarry too soon after being widowed causes raising of the eyebrows; to abandon an infant invokes the law. Cultures which do allow the denial of full social membership to certain newborn infants have various rituals and ceremonies for supporting those who must endure the unpleasant situation, and for expressing social approval of their act.

It is doubtful whether mothers should ever be allowed to abandon their babies at birth. If after due consultation with those whose province is mental health and illness (as well as those who specialize in infant care), this is thought to be essential, then some way must be devised to ensure that the mother is not deprived of both her child and of what is her inalienable right—her grief. If a harsh government should decree that no mother of a mongolian idiot should ever see or tend her child, its decree could be met, resisted, or evaded, but it is much harder to deal with the kindly doctor with his "all is for the best" attitude.

In the present state of our knowledge, there seems no reason why mongoloids should come to a special psychiatric hospital until they are of school age, unless some unusual need arises. When the time comes, the family doctor, the pediatrician, and the psychiatrist in charge of the hospital for defectives must decide how best to present this unhappy event to the family, but it will at least be impossible to evade it. It does not seem to be a doctor's place to encourage his patient, on whatever pretext, to flout the mores of his society; that is, to make ethical decisions for him.

If he believes it is desirable, he may in his role as a *citizen*—not as a doctor—attempt to alter these mores. If he is prudent he will try to determine the unintended and unexpected consequences of such changes before advocating them; and to do this he must have recourse to the social scientists for help.

. . . .

□ □ □

from WHEN SHOULD THE SERIOUSLY RETARDED INFANT BE INSTITUTIONALIZED?

Donald H. Jolly

(*American Journal of Mental Deficiency,* 1953)

Earlier institutionalization of the severely retarded child has been the trend for the past fifteen years. . . .

We believe that there are three major inter-related factors which have combined to produce this trend as follows: *first,* increased emphasis on developmental diagnosis has provided earlier recognition of retardation so that the problem of institutionalization has now to be faced earlier; *second,* increasingly strong advice from consultants for immediate institutionalization has produced strong community pressures from parents who wish to follow the course their physicians recommend; and *third,* these community pressures have led to some increase in the special facilities needed for the care of infants within our institutions. The second factor is certainly the most powerful one; and like most social effects lags a considerable time behind the causative pressure.

It has been economically impossible to provide additional crib facilities at the rate demanded. Consequently long waiting lists have been built up in most institutions which accept infants. Immediate re-evaluation is needed for this increasing trend among obstetricians and pediatricians to recommend institutionalization of an infant as soon as serious mental defect is confirmed. In types such as mongolism, where the defect can be recognized at birth, this policy reaches its extreme situation; and the physician may recommend that the child be transferred directly from the newborn nursery to some institution designed for the care of mentally retarded babies.

While this course may be the simplest one for the physician, it is seldom the best solution for the parents and other members of the family. The widespread recommendation of early institutionalization which is said "to prevent the family from becoming too attached to the child" shows total lack of understanding of the emotional conflicts confronting the parents of the defective child. In most cases, a healthy solution of these parental problems is more important in the total situation than any effects a choice between early or later admission may have on the child himself.

Many well-meaning advisors will tell the parents of a mongoloid child: "It will be better if you never take the child home. You may become attached to it." In most cases the mother is already attached to the child. Her attachment has literally and figuratively grown during pregnancy and through the mechanism of identification of the unborn child with a previous offspring or with the child of some friend. It is better to recommend that the mother take the child home for some time so that she may gradually become detached from the child. This time will allow her to see for herself that her child is exceptional, and she will come to realize that the child needs the special facilities of an institution. Very early separation may leave strong doubts in the parent's mind as to the validity of the diagnosis. Early admission or commitment may be interpreted by the parents as rejection and may add to their anxiety by emphasizing their already strong guilt feelings. When first discussing institutionalization, it is common to hear a parent use the phrase "put him away." As long as this negative interpretation exists, institutionalization of the child is a dangerous step to take. One of our cases will illustrate this point.

M . . . is the second child of healthy, intelligent middle-income parents who wanted to have a large family. Her older sister was born six and one-half years before, and there followed a period of relative sterility during which the mother had three miscarriages. After an uneventful pregnancy Mary was born during a normal delivery and had a birth weight of eight and one-half pounds. There were no neonatal difficulties.

Mongolism was recognized at birth and confirmed by two pediatricians during the first week of life. These consultants and the obstetrician who delivered the child all agreed that early or immediate institutionalization was the proper course and recommended this to the parents. They further advised that the mother not be allowed to see the child any more. This was agreed to by the father; and he was able to arrange institutionalization directly from the maternity service of the hospital where the baby was born.

During the first few months of the child's stay she had no visitors; but her father telephoned on two occasions to inquire about her health. His strained emotions could be noted over the telephone; and he said that his wife was in "bad shape," "broken up over the whole thing."

When the child was eight months old, she developed pneumonia, was placed on the danger list; and the father was notified. Since he had been told at the time of her birth that life expectancy was short, he thought that the child would die. He therefore decided to permit the mother to see the child.

The mother arrived at the hospital the following morning to visit her child whom she had never seen. She had no true idea of what mongolism really was. She had no idea of what to expect in this child she had borne. In her own mind she had built up several fantasies based on hearsay and fragmentary reading about mongolism. She surely expected some sort of monster to be presented to her, as her child. Overnight, the child had made a remarkable response to massive doses of antibiotics and was full of life. When the child was brought to her, the mother said, "Why, she's not so bad." At that point, the mother broke down, and enjoyed a much needed cry. A great load was lifted, and from that time on, the mother visited regularly. After the birth of M . . . the relationship between the parents had deteriorated; and they had decided to have no more children. This situation improved.

The child has thrived and has become a lovable, somewhat overweight mongoloid child. The mother, who visits her regularly, has become pregnant, and a few months ago gave birth to a normal baby.

No one can say what would have happened if the child had been taken home; but from our very first interview the mother has shown a degree of insight and intelligence which would have allowed her to adjust very well to the child in her home. We believe that this couple could have been spared many months of anxiety and guilt if the case had been handled differently; and if the time of institutionalization had been chosen in a less arbitrary fashion.

Furthermore, to recommend institutionalization of an infant may be impractical, especially in areas where there are no public-supported facilities for infants. Most physicians realize the futility and harm in recommending a complete rest in Florida, free from care and responsibilities, to a working-man with a large family to support, who consults the physician because of symptoms of peptic ulcer. But many good pediatricians recommend a course equally impossible to the parents of a severely retarded child when they advise immediate institutionalization as the only solution of the parents' problems. Even in those states where commitment of babies is possible, the number of cribs available is far short of the demand. Attempts by parents to carry out the recommended early institutionalization meet with frustration, or put an unbearable financial drain on the family if care is secured in a private institution.

One of the arguments offered in favor of removal of the child from the home at the earliest possible time is to avoid any ill effects his presence may have on older siblings. We must consider on the other hand in this situation that it may require a large portion of the family income to support a retarded child in a private institution. As a result the siblings are deprived of many advantages. Very often the effect of these deprivations will be much more serious than the presence of their mongoloid infant sibling. Either the frustration of failing to carry out recommended early admission or the financial insecurity which comes from private institutionalization at high cost, will have the effect of delaying the solution of the parent's emotional problems.

To about the age of three, the physical care of most retarded children is no greater than that of a normal child of the same age. It is usually better to have the parents work out their emotional conflicts gradually, while caring for the child at home, during the first years of life. Under the guidance of a physician who will take time to explain the possible causes of the defect, give an honest prognosis, and emphasize the positive features of institutional life, the parents will come to accept their misfortune and to see the logic of separation. The request for institutionalization will then come from the parents themselves and will have complete acceptance.

Since it is sometimes impossible for him to give the amount of time required to secure this emotional adjustment on the part of the parents, the busy physician may have to call on ancillary staff such as social workers, visiting health nurses, and clergymen to carry part of the load. The situation can be explained to these aides by the physician so that when they regularly visit the family they will point out the eventual need for institutionalization. They should emphasize the positive features such as the security in a situation where he will be free from the frustration of competition that he cannot meet; and the voluntary nature of commitment, which still applies to the admission of young children in most states. The parents will see the need for the . . . special class training which so far is available in very few communities outside of institutions. They will be comforted with the thought of continuing care in the event of their death. Gradually the parents will realize that life in an institution is the proper positive action in planning for the future of their exceptional child rather than an act of "putting him away."

While this transition is taking place we must be alert to recognize the proper time for placement and prevent the child from being kept at home so long that he comes to dominate the family. This serious situation is one that cannot be solved by sudden separation. . . .

There is a *best* time in every case at which the separation can be brought about with the least emotional damage to both the family and the retarded child. It is the duty of the physician, with whatever aid he can secure in the community, to keep the need for eventual institutionalization active in the thinking of the parents and to recognize the optimum time for separation when that time presents itself.

We believe that this optimum time is seldom, if ever, in early infancy.

□ □ □

from CONSEQUENCES OF EARLY INSTITUTIONALIZATION IN MENTAL RETARDATION

Lawrence Slobody, John B. Scanlan

(*American Journal of Mental Deficiency*, 1959)

To a great extent, our society's ways of viewing and dealing with the problem of mental retardation parallel its approach to mental illness. At first, both the retardate and the psychotic were regarded as potentially dangerous and even sub-human, to be quietly and quickly put out of sight behind the walls of secluded institutions. More recently, as our concepts of the nature and prognosis of these conditions have changed, we have begun to doubt that traditional methods of handling are in the best interest of society, of the family, and of the patient.

The recent trend in psychiatry toward the treatment of the emotionally ill person in his own community, and even in the general hospital, has its counterpart in the field of retardation where clinical and educational facilities for the management and treatment of the retarded within the community are increasing more rapidly than institutional facilities.

Institutionalization of the retarded has a significant impact, not only on the patient and his family, but on the community as well. The community feels it largely in financial terms, the individual and the family mainly in emotional ways. But none of these effects should be overlooked in considering the advisability of institutionalization generally or in the specific case. The physician who may be called upon or may feel called upon to give advice regarding the placement of a mentally retarded child is dealing with a matter which requires considerably more than a correct medical diagnosis and a plan of treatment.

In conducting a large clinic for the evaluation and management of retarded children, we have been impressed with the frequency with which the recommendation to institutionalize the very young retarded child is made summarily and without proper regard for the consequences.

There are, of course, a small percentage of severely retarded children, (e.g. hydrocephalics) who, because they are twenty-four hour nursing problems, cannot reasonably be maintained at home. We are principally concerned here, not with that small group, but with the much larger group of retardates whose condition is discovered early, who could be maintained at home, but who are institutionalized, sometimes on the basis of erroneous assumptions, and often with such rather disastrous results as will be described below.

Almost any family confronted by the problem of mental retardation will, because of their emotional distress and their lack of knowledge, turn for comfort and counsel to the physician. Many times they will be ready to accept what he may present as a quick and permanent solution to their problem—immediate institutional placement for the child. The need for placement in such cases may arise very largely from the subjective reactions of the advisor rather than from the objective demands of the situation. It is often true that placement is advised as a method of expediency without proper regard for what it can mean in the future to the child, to the family, and to the family's relationship with the physician.

Hasty placement of the very young retardate is particularly likely to occur with those children who bear physical stigmata. The mongoloid child is usually diagnosed early because of his conspicuous features and may be institutionalized early for the same reason. The fact that he might be more manageable or even ultimately might function on a higher level of intelligence than a retardate who looks "normal" is often not taken into consideration. The conspicuousness of the condition, the presumed damaging effects of this retardate on the family, and the abhorrence for deformity or disability which seems particularly strong in our culture are factors likely to lead to the family's being pushed toward early institutional placement.

But what are the possible consequences of early and hasty placement? First we shall consider how it may affect the family.

In a good many cases the alleged urgency of placing the child leads a family to commit itself to the expense of private institutional care which they ultimately cannot bear. They are then faced with the problem of taking the child back into the home. Frequently enough, the emotional adjustment to this is complicated by the parents having to reveal the truth to relatives and friends, who have been led to believe the child is dead, or do not even know of its existence. Other frequent problems are the guilt feelings of the family. On one hand they may feel guilty of abandoning the child if they place it before they have proved to themselves that they are unable to care for it; on the other hand they may feel guilt about opposing the professional advice to place the child.

It is a fallacy that the retarded child who is out of sight is out of the mind of the parent. The mother of a mongoloid child institutionalized soon after birth will continue to wonder about him and his development, and as Farrell[1] points out, may react with tremendous guilt when she sees that he is "not the horrible monster she had been led to expect, but a lovable child ready to return parental affection."

If placement has taken place purely on the authority of the physician or other professional advisor and not as a result of thorough discussions which have helped the parents to make their own decision and resolve their own guilts and anxieties, we may expect future repercussions within the family.

What of the consequences for the child of early placement? In recent years there has been a growing recognition of the crucial importance of "mothering" in the early life of the child. Bowlby,[2] in his important monograph for the World Health Organization, says that "direct studies make it plain that when deprived of maternal care the child's development is almost always retarded—physically, intellectually, and socially." Furthermore, it seems to be true that if maternal deprivation occurs early enough and is prolonged enough, the retardation in development and the emotional damage to the child may become irreversible.

The mentally retarded child is certainly no less in need of mothering than the child with a normal intellectual potential. If he is to realize *his* potential he must receive the same kinds and amounts of emotional supplies as the average child. The best of the institutions for the retarded are those that are most like home. Even these best are far from being adequate substitutes for home for the young child. Multiple parent substitutes, no matter how interested and kindly, can never fill the child's need for a single, consistent, and clearly known mother-figure. The development of thinking, of controlled behavior, and of the capacity to relate emotionally to others all depend very greatly on a close, satisfying relationship with an ever-present mother during the earliest years of life. One who has seen children in the more deprived institutional settings huddled together rocking themselves for hours on end will have had an impressive illustration of the possible consequences of maternal deprivation.

It would be unrealistic not to admit that a good many retardates will require institutionalization at some time in their lives. This is sometimes used as an argument for early placement, the theory being that the eventual separation from home will be a heartbreaking experience for all involved. The fact seems to be that the retardate who has had the emotional advantages of a good family life makes a sounder adjustment to living with others within the institution.

Summary

It seems to us evident that early placement of the retarded child in an institution, although it often may seem the expedient method of dealing with the problem, can and far too often does have unforeseen and disastrous consequences for the child and the family. Its further possible consequences, in terms of the relationship between the family and the physician who advises it, are obvious.

Deciding whether a child should be placed or should remain at home is only a small part of a complex problem. Counseling the parents means not only giving accurate information and advice on management, but helping them work through their shock, their unreasonable guilts and anxieties, and all of the emotional consequences of their having a retarded child. It does not mean fostering one's own opinion or one's own emotional reaction to a problem. It is clear that too often early placement results from just such an unsound method of advising by physician or other advisor.

It should be observed that the working through of parental emotional reactions may require months or years of professional assistance and frequently requires the skills of the social worker or the psychiatrist.

Our experiences bear out the validity of the recommendations made by the Expert Committee on the Mentally Subnormal Child of the World Health Organization,[3] that a) home care of the retarded is to be advised unless serious problems will arise as a result of it; b) even severely handicapped children can be cared for at home by parents of reasonable mental health and competence with the help of available community facilities; c) the best institution is no substitute for the parent-child relationship; and d) that early placement often intensifies parental guilt feelings and their sense of having rejected the child. . . .

FOOTNOTES

1. Farrell, M., "The Adverse Effects of Early Institutionalization of Mentally Subnormal Children," *American Journal of Diseases of Children*, Vol. 91, March, 1956.
2. Bowlby, J., "Maternal Care and Mental Health," *World Health Organization Monograph Series*, 1951.
3. Expert Committee on the Mentally Subnormal Child of the World Health Organization, "The Mentally Subnormal Child," *World Health Organization Technical Report*, Series #75, April, 1954.

□ □ □

from OUT OF THE SHADOWS

Donald K. Grant

(*American Journal of Diseases of Children*, 1965)

. . . .

One privilege of writing an editorial is to give free rein to pet hobbyhorses. Thus, one may castigate accepted practices. In this era of "instant" this and that, there is the phenomenon of "Instant Institutionalization (I.I.)." This occurs when the doctor, having diagnosed severe retardation, incontinently advises incarceration. The practice reaches its apogee in the mongoloid child diagnosed at birth. I.I. is a palpable disgrace to the medical profession, a disservice to parents, and often, a burden upon the taxpayer. Furthermore, to a physician intimately involved in the management of retarded children and their families, it is a familiar, frustrating experience to find that, whereas he spends many hours helping parents care for a handicapped child at home, he has but to visit an institution to find infants arbitrarily admitted. The parents, as often as not, have been given little chance to assist in a most vital decision. . . . One might illustrate a remarkable contrast of attitudes by comparing the arrangement through which regular employment is found for mongoloid adults (e.g., assembling television sets) with the advice given to the father of a newborn mongoloid infant (e.g. "Don't let your wife see 'it'; institutionalize 'it' immediately; tell her 'it' died"). . . .

□ □ □

from COUNSELING FAMILIES DURING THE CRISIS REACTION TO MONGOLISM

Margaret J. Giannini

Lawrence Goodman

(*American Journal of Mental Deficiency*, 1963)

Under the auspices of the New York

State Department of Mental Hygiene, the Clinic for Retarded Children at Flower-Fifth Avenue Hospital undertook in March, 1961, a two- to three-year Demonstration Treatment project evaluating the effect of comprehensive services to families who apply for state institutionalization of infant mongoloids. At this time we are presenting a description of the project, the rationale for undertaking it, and our initial clinical observations. We wish to emphasize that this is a preliminary report with tentative impressions that are subject to later statistical validation.

The policy of accepting children under five in New York State institutions, primarily Willowbrook State School, began in 1946. Within a brief period, however, the number of requested admissions to the nursery wards has necessitated the establishment of a waiting list of many months. About two-thirds of the families involved (averaging about 300 at any given time), are New York City residents. . . .

The total population of the institutions for the retarded of New York State is ten per cent mongoloid, yet they represent a disproportionate twenty-five per cent of all under-five admissions, and a majority of the youngest. A similar distribution is reported by Kramer (1959) in California. We know, pediatrically, that the mongoloid child's needs in infancy do not differ greatly from those of normal infants. He generally does not require elaborate physical care—but he does desperately need the same atmosphere of love and security possible only through maternal closeness. The mother, too, must experience an irreplaceable loss when deprived of the opportunity to nurture her child. These factors, which are so obvious to us who practice in the field of mental retardation, obviously become closed out and distorted in the context of medical misinformation (sometimes deliberate); preoccupation with social stigma; and the premature forcing of a vital decision in an atmosphere of catastrophe; complicated by the already heightened emotionality of the birth experience. We recognize that there are certainly situations of social and psychological impairment where immediate institutionalization is vital—and that the community has the responsibility to provide such care. Yet we can state categorically that most mongoloid infants should be cared for at home—in the interest of both the child and the family—and that many such children have in the past been inappropriately placed.

In recognition of the deficiencies in meeting this many-faceted, serious social problem, our demonstration project was established with the following goals:

1. to evaluate the impact on families of the birth of a mongoloid child and the effect of introducing intensive services at the point of crisis;

2. to determine whether these services influence the flow of these mongoloid infants from the waiting list to the institution.

3. Are there implications for future admission policies?

In setting up procedures for referral of cases to us, it was agreed that all families of infant mongoloids would be handled by the supervising social worker of the State Department of Mental Hygiene application unit, so that there would be uniformity in handling the question of referral. The New York City office processes cases from the five boroughs and surrounding counties. The services of the clinic were to be suggested to all families except those who lived at too great a distance from the clinic, or, who, in the judgment of the supervisor, were so brittle that any discussion of the possibility of further exploration would be psychologically detrimental. The decision to use the clinic was to be on an entirely voluntary basis—and it was clearly pointed out that it would in no way affect the child's place on the waiting list.

Initially we decided to offer service to families already on the waiting list, recognizing that many uncontrollable variables were present which would limit statistical inferences that could be made. We anticipated that psychological defenses of this group would already be rigidly drawn and self-protectingly defended against therapeutic intervention. The previous experience of the Department of Mental Hygiene showed that unless the child had died, when an opening became available it was almost invariably accepted.

Of this waiting list group forty per cent of the children were at home—sixty per cent in private temporary placement, usually at great financial sacrifice. In nearly every such case the child had been placed at birth. It should be pointed out that applications are accepted when the child is under a year old in particularly emergent situations only. Usually parents of infants under a year are placed on a "deferred" list and must reapply later. They are then added to the waiting list. It was decided early in the project that the initial application was the point when families most needed help and that referral should be made of these "deferred" families. Previous experience also had shown that only rarely did these families not reapply and that very few sought specialized interim help. The proportion of youngsters in private placement was about the same as the waiting list groups.

The present paper deals with the first 100 families referred to the clinic. More than half were on the waiting list when the project began. These families were, on the whole, less accessible to help than those later families with whom the clinic was discussed at the point of application. Forty-five of these 100 children were fully evaluated, including several youngsters who were removed from private institutions for the workup. In thirty-three cases only the parents of children in private placement were seen, with a number of them continuing to use casework services. Twenty-two families, mainly from the original waiting list group, did not respond or consistently failed to keep appointments.

The first appointments were with the social worker who was to maintain continuing contact with the family. Often several appointments were necessary before the family was able to restructure its thinking sufficiently to permit an evaluation of the child. For some the concept that this supposedly hopeless, grotesque child warranted the attention of a group of specialists carried with it the threat that their rigidified thinking about the child might be open to question and reactivate the desperate uncertainty that they had originally experienced. This was sufficient to keep a number of families from going beyond the first contact. Others were so openly protective of their defenses that they kept a single appointment in order "to help research" but had no intention of continuing beyond the first session.

For those families able to use help, comprehensive services included pediatric examination and follow-up medical care, psychiatric evaluation and consultation, psychological testing through the adaptation of infant scales which would have some prognostic validity for the age group studied, and on-going casework services. Our casework goals were viewed as follows:

1. To share with parents our understanding of what they can expect from their child if he is placed immediately or at a later age in terms of his potential intellectual functioning, physical condition, available services, special problems that may arise, and individual family considerations. We are thus giving them the opportunity to decide on placement in terms of a realistic appraisal of the total situation and to deal with it on a reality basis.

2. To provide counseling to help families understand the conflict and ambivalence that is almost always present—overtly or covertly—regardless of the final decision.

3. Where a family does not appear to have the strength to consider alternatives—or where placement is clearly indicated for a variety of reasons—to support them and to help them face and plan for separation as constructively as possible, with a minimum of guilt.

At this time let us examine the composition of the families. One highly significant observation is that the socio-economic-educational level was considerably higher than the community as a whole (which also was true of the families we did not see). Ethnically, too, there were differences, with very few Negro and Puerto Rican families. Family integration and cohesiveness were generally high; practically all families were intact.

These observations are in sharp contrast to the findings of Saenger (1960). Parents of institutionalized children were found to be socioeconomically and ethnically representative of the general population and with a high incidence of family deterioration, broken homes, and parental inadequacy. The families of infant mongoloids planning to institutionalize are obviously of different composition and must, therefore, be seeking placement for different reasons. They are not unable or incapable of caring for their children at home—but yet they are blocked from doing so [by] inner pressures and external influences.

It is unlikely that middle-class families produce more mongoloid babies—what appears then to be happening? All families react to a retarded child in terms of their own life experiences and the values and attitudes of their own immediate environment. The mongoloid child, the most stigmatized of the retarded, physically and socially, represents an assault [on] middle-class strivings and aspirations and culturally determined goals. He is seen as a serious impediment to social mobility. The child is retarded for all the world to see—the family cannot find solace in euphemisms like brain damage or post-encephalitis—and as a result the family's self concept becomes seriously threatened. At the same time this is antithetical to the family's sense of justice and responsibility, which adds to the dilemma. Families with less status concern seem to be far less traumatized.

Another noteworthy factor is that these middle-class families are the ones who use private general practitioners, pediatricians, and obstetricians who are identified with the family and its values. The physician may feel a sense of having failed the family with whom he has a relationship—and his own emotions and feelings come into play—seemingly to a greater extent than with lower class families. His recommendations may be influenced unconsciously by his discomfort with the situation and his strong desire to "save" the family. At this time of strain the physician can be viewed as an omnipotent figure, and the family feels compelled to follow his recommendation—which is usually an unqualified dictum for institutionalization.

There are, of course, examples of thoughtful and informed handling. On the whole, however, most physicians know little about mongolism; do not see the guilt, denial, and struggle present even in parents who appear to have completely rejected the child; and are not aware of community resources.

Previous papers dealing with the handling of mongolism by physicians (Schipper, 1959; Koch, 1959; Farrell, 1956) contain numerous dramatic illustrations of uninformed handling. Unfortunately there appears to be no observable change in attitude. Families from our regular clinic population, who have never considered placement, report parallel experiences. Some parents are still being told that their healthy child probably will die before he is two years old, that he will never be capable of any self-care skills; that there are no educational facilities for him; that the institution will be able to teach the child while they cannot; that it is harmful to keep him at home, etc. We shall give only two brief examples:

> 1. Mr. and Mrs. A. were told that the child should be placed immediately —that for their own sake they should tell everyone that the child had died. At a time when their judgment was seriously impaired, they followed his recommendations. They have continued to visit the child regularly. He is an alert, high functioning, appealing child whom they feel they have abandoned. They cannot find the strength to take him home and face their family and their own children, and are experiencing intense guilt.
>
> 2. Mr. and Mrs. B. live in a semi-rural area. They were told that if they took their child home, he would have a devastating affect on their two adolescent children. He presents no management problems, but the cost of his private care has exhausted the money saved for the college education of their other children, in their misguided effort to save them from "the horror" of this infant who is so like every other young child.

It would be possible to go [to] great length with similar incidents to illustrate what parents can be subjected to, that can only confuse further and add to an already overwhelming problem.

Our treatment of parents has utilized accepted, conventional casework methodolgy, with therapists who have acquired the necessary body of knowledge of mental retardation content and have worked through their own feelings and prejudices around institutional placement.

Social Work Methods being used are:

1. individual counseling—both intensive and supportive;
2. group counseling for fathers and mothers (jointly);
3. counseling at home.

Individual counseling has varied from weekly interviews with both parents to occasional "as needed" contacts. Some families were able to make optimal use of a limited number of sessions—while our more disturbed families required intensive treatment, with less observable gain. Three mothers showed such pathological involvement that we tried to work with them toward accepting psychiatric therapy. None of them, however, were accepting of referral. In all cases, we attempted to include the father —and in nearly every situation he participated in treatment. The extent of the father's involvement from the very first contact has a number of implications that will be developed in later reports. It should also be mentioned that in order to accommodate fathers, evening and Saturday sessions were held.

Our counseling groups have included both parents—with six couples participating. For those families who are ready to involve themselves sufficiently in the group process, there have proved to be a number of advantages in group treatment. One obvious antidote to feelings of social isolation and uniqueness is to meet with other essentially adequate, intelligent, likeable individuals who are reacting to the same trauma and struggling, each in his own way, with a similar crisis. That the group was meeting a deeply felt need is evidenced by the almost perfect attendance record in spite of the considerable distance that most families had to travel.

We have structured the groups purposely so that there will be some balance between families who already are moving toward a decision to keep their child at home, and those who will go ahead with placement. This introduces dynamic conflict which the leader uses to point out that there is no single solution—that each family must decide in terms of its own reality. Yet in spite of the impartiality of the leader in relationship to each individual family, the collective inclination seems inevitably to move toward a decision for home care. In the one completed group, three of the couples previously had indicated that they were considering withdrawing their application, and eventually did so. We think it will be of interest to discuss the three other families briefly.

> Mr. and Mrs. T. are an attractive, young, status concerned, Negro couple

who in their individual contacts with us had presented a "united front." They felt deeply for their only child, but they could not face the social consequences of keeping him with them. He was at home, but largely under the care of his maternal grandmother. Mrs. T. had gone back to work, consciously recognizing that she had done so mainly to avoid her child and the guilt he aroused in her whenever she looked at him. Through their interaction in the group it became apparent that behind the surface agreement there was much conflict over placement between Mr. and Mrs. T. which threatened to permanently disturb their marriage. Mr. T. had been bitterly opposed to institutionalization, but felt that he had to go along with his wife's unalterable decision. He began to seriously question her values–she felt he was insensitive to her feelings. Through their identification with other members of the group and expanded frame of reference in which to evaluate their thinking–as well as the active support of the leader and other group members–each was helped to better understand and accept the other's point of view. They came to the joint decision that they would place their child temporarily–see what it would be like without him–and then consider taking him home. The youngster was placed in Willowbrook while the group was meeting, but Mr. and Mrs. T. continued until the sessions were completed. Shortly afterwards their child died of pneumonia–and they were able to discuss their feelings about it with their individual worker. It is quite possible that if this family had not been in treatment, the death of the child would have destroyed the marriage.

Mr. and Mrs. P. were extremely defensive about their decision to place their child who already was receiving temporary private care. At one point Mrs. P. projected her guilt and self anger onto the group by confronting those parents who were keeping their children at home with a callous vision of what the child would be like when he was past the "cute" age. In a later meeting when she understood her feelings, she was deeply apologetic to the group. They, in turn, could empathize with Mrs. P.'s conflict and could support her decision to place–and, in a sense, give their approval for what was right for Mr. and Mrs. P.

Mr. T. is a college professor–an overly intellectual, unemotional, somewhat pontifical man who dominates his wife. There seemed to be no question about their decision to place Donald, who had been in a private institution since birth. He was coming to the group purely to give the other parents the benefit of his superior thinking. In the fourth or fifth session, however, Mrs. T. emerged from her passivity and, incorporating strength from the group, was able to say for the first time that she wanted her child and could never forgive her husband unless he recognized her need. While the group was still meeting, Donald was accepted into Willowbrook. Two weeks later the T.'s announced proudly that they were taking him home. After the meeting ended, the families in the group were invited to the T.'s home for a reception for Donald.

Recognizing the special values of the group method, in the coming year we plan to place greater emphasis on the group program. We also plan to expand our home counseling facilities. This experimental part of the treatment program, which has provided service to seven families who were unable or too immobilized to come to the clinic regularly, has had rich therapeutic overtones and obviously has had special meaning to the families involved.

Where families have shifted from their plan to institutionalize—some eagerly and with tremendous relief; some anxiously, hesitantly—they have sought reassurance from us that our help would remain available to them. In undertaking a demonstration treatment project it is not sufficient to accept responsibility for care for the duration of the project only. The families involved become a part of the clinic's population, and future help with planning must be made available to them.

Of the families we have worked with, twenty-four have indicated that they are no longer planning to place their child. In most instances they realize that this decision is subject to later reevaluation as they live further with the problem and test out their own reactions. In some cases the decision is neurotically based and these families will need a great deal of continuing help. In most situations, however, the decision appears to us to be sound and in the interest of the mental health of the child and the family. If help had not been provided at this time, it is likely that nearly all of these youngsters would have prematurely been institutionalized, obviously against the innate wishes of the parents. They could not have been influenced to keep their children—even if that had been our intention—unless there already was dissatisfaction with what they were doing. It could only have erupted into further doubt and guilt if the child had been placed without opportunity for parents to face and work out their conflict. . . .

References

Bowlby, J., *Maternal care and mental health.* Monograph, World Health Organization, Geneva, 1951.

Centerwall, S. A., and Centerwall, W. R., "A study of children with mongolism reared in the home compared to those reared away from the home," *Pediatrics,* 1960, 25: 678-685.

Farrell, M., "Adverse effects of early institutionalization," *American Journal Diseases of Children,* 1956, 91: 278-281.

Koch, R., et al, "Attitude studies of parents with mentally retarded children," *Pediatrics,* 1959, 23: 582-584.

Kramer, M., "Measurement of the flow of the mentally retarded into institutions," *American Journal of Mental Deficiency,* 1959, 64: 278-290.

Pense, A. et al, "A cohort study of institutionalized young mentally retarded children," *American Journal of Mental Deficiency,* 1961, 66: 18-22.

Saenger, G., *"Factors influencing the institutionalization of mentally retarded individuals in New York City,"* Monograph Interdepartmental Health and Resources Board, Albany, 1960.

Schipper, M., "The child with mongolism in the home," *Pediatrics,* 1959, 24: 132-144.

Slobody, L., & Scanlan, J., "Consequences of early institutionalization," *American Journal of Mental Deficiency,* 1959, 63: 971-974.

Spitz, R. A., "Hospitalism," in *The psychoanalytic study of the child,* edited by O. Fenichel, New York University Press, 1945, 1: 53-74.

□ □ □

from PRECOMMITMENT SERVICES IN A TRAINING SCHOOL FOR MENTAL DEFECTIVES

Michael J. Begab

(American Journal of Mental Deficiency, 1955)

. . . .

It is unfortunate but true that few persons, professional or not, who urge commitment are familiar with the personality or behavior characteristics of retarded children. Equally important, they have little knowledge of the institutional program and facilities nor the legal and social significance of incompetency. Advice from such uninformed sources can be very detrimental to patient and parent alike. Parents often find it very difficult to accept the reality of their child's deficiency. They are overwhelmed by feelings of frustration, guilt, and anxiety. They are ego threatened by their real or imagined loss of social status. They have intense feelings of inadequacy regarding their child or future children. When absorbed with these emotions and conflicts, parents cannot be expected to plan objectively for their children. They tend to fall in line too readily with the "surgical concept" of treatment—that if you remove the cause, you solve the problem. This rather physical approach negates the importance of emotional factors and as a result many parents agree to the commitment of their children without the benefit of adequate preparation.

The case of Mrs. B., which has many parallels in our records, illustrates the need for better planning prior to commitment:

> Mrs. B. had two daughters ages four and two respectively, at the time her third child, Carol–a mongolian type defective–was born. Both parents–mature, understanding and intelligent people–were understandably shocked and grief stricken over their child's condition. They had no knowledge of mongolism but were informed by their doctor of the infant's expected limitations, the negative effect on the other children, and other problems of care in the home. Because of the fear [that] they would become emotionally attached to Carol, the B.'s were advised to seek immediate commitment.
>
> This procedure was initiated at once, but due to the overcrowded conditions at Southern Wisconsin Colony, admission was delayed for five months. During this time, Carol was cared for in the home. A routine home study by

> our Social Service Department following admission soon revealed that Mrs. B. had never fully accepted Carol's need for institutionalization. She observed that the child had been less difficult to care for than her other children and had been fully accepted by her siblings. She and her husband both regretted their hastiness in seeking court action so soon after birth.
>
> Mrs. B. had a good intellectual awareness of Carol's expected retardation and recognized the problems that would arise when she became old enough to play with other neighborhood children, etc. She realized, too, that eventually some plan for institutional care might be required. . . .

In the above case, as in numerous others of its kind, the patient was granted a temporary discharge and returned to the home—but not until considerable cost to the court, institution, and taxpayers of the state had been incurred. Further and perhaps more important, both of the parents had been put through an unnecessary traumatic experience, occasioned by the court proceeding and separation from their child.

The large number of custodial-type patients, who leave the institution after a very brief period, reflect the inadequate preparation of parents for commitment. It is not sufficient that the child be a fit subject for commitment; before institutional placement can succeed, there must be emotional acceptance as well as intellectual recognition of the problem by the parents. Often such acceptance comes only through the reality of experience—when the behavior of the child in the community, the physical and emotional strain on the parents, or some other form of crisis to patient or family does not permit continuation in the home.

We are too often prone to view the retarded child as an entity separate from his family and to view the total situation by our own judgmental standards. We must recognize that many parents have a strong sense of loyalty, devotion, and responsibility to their children, and depriving them of the right to fulfill their parental drives could have an extremely negative effect on their mental health.

Another great problem affecting our institutional program results from inadequate diagnostic evaluation prior to commitment. This occurs primarily in persons of borderline intelligence with various types of personality disorder. State sponsored colonies for the mentally deficient must accept all persons duly committed to their care and do not have the selective privilege enjoyed by private institutions. As a result, our institutions tend to become a "catch all" for every kind of disturbed personality who shows some degree of mental retardation.

There is a high incidence of psychosis, character disorders and sociopathic personality types in our defective population. In some of the cases, the emotional components rather than mental limitations *per se,* are the primary cause of the maladjustive behavior. Patients of this type are frequently a threat to the safety of other patients and represent a severe disruptive influence to the training program. They consume a disproportionate amount of attention and care from the professional and nonprofessional staff and to this extent adversely affect the care and treatment of the entire population. Even a good precommitment diagnosis could not always determine the facility most appropriate to the care of a patient who is severely disturbed as well as mentally deficient. However, it is sometimes apparent that a patient is dangerous to himself or others or for other reasons requires a maximum security facility. The failure to screen these cases before commitment is uneconomical and detrimental to the entire program.

Purpose of Precommitment Services

The purpose of casework services, [and] psychological and psychiatric examination, prior to commitment is to eliminate or reduce as far as possible some of the many problems previously mentioned.

Parents, in general, have a difficult

time recognizing and accepting mental deficiency in their child. Their intellectual judgment is distorted and warped by feelings of grief, inferiority, frustration, or resentment. They require help in working through some of their conflicts and in accepting the reality limitations of their child. This is a prerequisite to constructive planning for the immediate and long range future.

The caseworker, who is familiar with mental retardation, can by virtue of his knowledge and experience help the parents to a more objective understanding of the total family situation. As in most casework, understanding and emotional acceptance of a problem is often the forerunner of constructive action. Knowledge of the child's physical and emotional needs and the capacity of the family, institution, or other resource to fulfill these needs offers the basis for a sound decision. In some instances, the problem is not one of accepting a condition but of determining the nature of the condition. The case of Joan H. is one in point:

> Mrs. H. visited the Southern Colony to discuss the commitment of her sixteen-year-old daughter, Joan. The interview revealed that [the] patient's difficulties in school followed the onset of scarlet fever at the age of eleven. She completed eight grades though her academic ability at this level seemed questionable. Factors precipitating the mother's petition for commitment were the girl's increasing maladjustment socially, scholastically, and in her relationships with the family. Exploration of the family relationships brought out the girl's jealousy and abuse of her siblings, severe temper tantrums, and widely fluctuating mood swings. She had also been seen by a psychiatrist who reported increasingly depressive reactions and possible suicide as well as mental retardation.
>
> Because of the personality features indicated, the worker felt that this facility might not be the most appropriate for this girl's care and that further investigation was needed. He accordingly referred the girl for a complete diagnostic evaluation, secured reports from the psychiatrist who had examined her earlier, and submitted all the information to the court for their consideration and decision. To date, this girl has not been committed though more than six months have elapsed.

In this case the single precommitment interview served a variety of purposes. It helped the mother obtain adequate diagnosis of her daughter's condition, enabled the institution to properly interpret its program in light of the girl's particular needs, and contributed to a better working relationship with the courts. Although it is too early to determine what other useful purposes were achieved by the contact in this particular case, other gains may be anticipated. Should this precommitment service, as it has in other instances, result in a foster home placement or other institution more suited to the girl's care, it will have eliminated an unnecessary expense to the parents, county or state. Further, it will have avoided a possible transfer at a later date and the impact of changing environments on the mental health of the patient and relatives.

In addition to the objectives mentioned above, precommitment services also help to acquaint county agencies with the institutional program and counteract to a degree the overcrowded conditions at institutions such as ours.

Planning to Meet the Need

The organization of a precommitment program depends upon the division of responsibility between county and state agencies and the community resources available for diagnostic evaluation. Another important consideration, of course, is the limitation of staff personnel. The following outline is not presented as an ideal program, but rather one that could be introduced without resort[ing] to extensive changes in organization. Its chief attribute lies in its utilization of existing community resources and the obvious economies resulting therefrom.

The effectiveness of any precommitment program depends in the first instance, of course, on satisfactory channels of referral. Unless parents, courts, social agencies, physicians, etc., seek the help of the training school in planning for their child, our objectives cannot be fulfilled. This is a matter of public education and can gradually be accomplished by contact with parents' groups and other community agencies.

Requests for an interview are generally referred to the social service department, and arrangements are made for a home visit or office interview. In either event the parents are always encouraged to visit the institution for a tour of the wards and other departments.

The interview itself is directed toward a mutual understanding by the parents and worker of the child's physical and mental condition, the nature of the problem, and reasons for considering institutionalization. In this discussion the parents' emotional readiness for commitment may also be determined. Where the information obtained is vague or ambiguous, referrals are made to guidance clinics, hospitals, etc., within the community. Not infrequently, particularly in outlying, sparsely populated areas, such resources are unavailable. In these cases the institution may utilize its own personnel and facilities to aid in diagnosis. We also secure information from other sources in order to evaluate the patient's social and moral behavior.

In general, however, the major problem is not diagnostic in nature, but rather whether the child requires institutionalization and, if so, to which facility. Evaluation of the family situation and the patient's needs may disclose that the child can be better cared for in the home or community.

It is our philosophy that every child, defective or not, is entitled to the advantages of a home life, provided of course that his interests and that of the family and society are best served in this manner. Obviously many children by virtue of severe physical and mental retardation, extreme anti-social behavior, or poor family environment require the protection of an institution. In general, however, institutions should be looked upon as a terminal rather than initial facility for meeting the needs of the mentally defective child.

Results of the Program

As a part of the Division of Mental Hygiene, one of our major concerns is the mental health of our patients. Their happiness in turn is largely dependent upon the emotional security and well-being of their parents.

We have found in our precommitment contacts that in helping parents to recognize and accept their problems —whether they decide to commit or not—we have through assurance, support, and mere ventilation of anxiety, enabled them to achieve peace of mind. By encouraging the parents to participate in planning for their children, we are also able to promote better working relationships with them. We have learned that parents seen in a precommitment contact are invariably grateful for the opportunity to discuss their problems and cooperate more fully with our policies than those not seen in this capacity.

As suggested earlier, only a small minority of the mentally retarded population requires institutionalization. Unnecessary commitment creates a financial burden on the state and usurps the rights of the individual. The following summaries indicate the advantages derived from precommitment services in two cases:

> Elmer L. is a sixteen-year-old boy, youngest of five children, whose family resides in one of the larger urban areas in southern Wisconsin. He attended special classes in a public school for retarded children for approximately eight years and had reached the maximum level of his achievement. His adjustment in the school, home, and community had been satisfactory.
>
> Mr. L., the father, was an automobile mechanic by trade, but currently employed as a factory worker. He appeared to be of average intelligence, mature and devoted to his wife and

children. Although the mother and several of the children were of limited mental endowment, the family presented no community problem in either the financial, social or moral spheres.

The patient had been referred for possible commitment to Southern Wisconsin Colony by a civic-minded citizen in the belief that he would receive vocational training in preparation for employment in private industry. There was also the fear the boy might become a sex problem, although he was quite passive in nature and had not exhibited more than a normal interest in the opposite sex.

A visit to the institution and a tour of our facilities soon made it apparent to the father that our program could not fulfill his son's vocational needs. In actuality, the boy's limited mentality (IQ 50) made it unlikely that he could profit from specific training, and this was interpreted to the father with various suggestions regarding the type of employment within the boy's capacities.

In this case it was felt that the home was fairly adequate and had more to offer the patient in terms of continued development and emotional security than did the institution. Mr. L. made plans for his son to help him with simple auto repairs and to secure work in neighborhood garages doing car washing, etc. The interview with the family took place more than a year ago and to date Elmer's presence in the home and community has not created any problems.

Mr. and Mrs. A., age twenty-seven and twenty-six respectively, were referred by the county welfare department for commitment to Southern Wisconsin Colony, primarily for the purpose of sterilization. Both were of borderline intelligence and experienced some difficulty in properly caring for their three children, two of whom seemed to be within the dull normal or average range of intelligence. The children had been placed in foster homes and the welfare department was concerned lest more children be born of this union creating a further burden on the community.

Mr. A. had been employed for several years as a factory worker but due to the marginal level of his performance and increasing unemployment in the labor market, had become a public charge. He had never been in conflict with the law and the social and moral behavior of his wife and him was above criticism.

Following our contact with the county judge and welfare agency, it was agreed that the A.'s were not fit subjects for commitment, even though limited in mental endowment. Direct interview with Mrs. A. revealed some insight regarding the inadvisabilty of future pregnancies and a willingness to follow the court's recommendations.

Shortly after this contact, Mr. A. secured work as a farm laborer and is no longer receiving financial aid. To our knowledge their continuation as a family unit has not raised any further objections to date.

The results obtained in these two cases reflect a few of the many advantages to be derived from a precommitment service. There is little doubt that all three of these persons would have been duly committed to the Colony in the absence of our social service contact. The cost of their care, possible sterilization, return to the community, and follow-up supervision would represent an estimated expense of well over $5,000 for a single year. Assuming they remain in the community and live out their average life expectancy, the projected savings to the state for these three people alone, represents the staggering total of $650,000.

Of course, financial considerations are not our only concern. In these two cases, the latter particularly, we protected the rights of the individual and contributed to the emotional welfare of parents and relatives who were strongly opposed to commitment. We helped the parents to find other resources and plan constructively for the patient's future welfare. It also served to promote a closer working relationship with courts and agencies and to interpret our philosophy to them.

It seems strange that the ideas incorporated in pre-sentence investigations for adult and juvenile offenders have found such limited application in the field of mental deficiency. Perhaps the difficulty lies in recruiting professional personnel in sufficient quantity to administer such a program—or it may be due to an unawareness of the value of these services.

Our experience at Southern Wisconsin Colony, during the year we have served parents, courts and agencies in this capacity, has proved beyond all doubt the advantages of this program. With the limitation of our present social service staff to four psychiatric social workers, we have been unable to foster expansion of precommitment services as desired, without the curtailment of ongoing programs. Despite this fact, however, the results thus far obtained have been most gratifying. The number of cases served have not been numerous enough to warrant a statistical evaluation, but in this instance the qualitative analysis presented in this paper, and the advantages denoted far outweigh any statistical considerations. Of the cases interviewed, nearly half did not require immediate institutionalization, and other plans were effected for them. It is quite significant that even though our function was limited to an advisory and consultation service, none of the patients who could be cared for at home or elsewhere were processed for commitment. In those instances where the best interests of the patient and family required institutionalization, we were able to facilitate the proceedings by helping the parents recognize and accept the problem.

In summary, the formal precommitment program now in effect at this institution offers the following contributions:

1. Promotes the mental health of the parents by helping them to recognize and accept their child's condition and participate in planning for their care.
2. Gives concrete service in obtaining adequate diagnoses or referral to community resources better qualified to meet the patient's needs.
3. Protects mental health of [the] patient by directing him to [the] facility most suited to his care.
4. Eliminates unnecessary expense to family, courts, counties and state.
5. Facilitates interpretation of institutional goals, objectives and facilities, thus contributing to community planning.
6. Develops better working relationships with parents, courts and local agencies.
7. Effects economies through delay of commitment and avoidance of unnecessary temporary discharges (resulting when parents commit though emotionally unready for this step).
8. Improves institutional program by eliminating patients with psychiatric disorders whose needs are better fulfilled elsewhere.

Whether the above advantages can best be realized by a traveling clinic team approach, the social service department of the institution, or some other arrangement depends on the organization of the welfare agencies within the state and the availability of diagnostic resources and qualified social workers. The manner in which precommitment services are prescribed is of secondary importance; the combination of adequate diagnostic techniques for the patient and casework services to parents and agencies can fulfill a vital need in more successful planning for the mentally defective population in this country.

□ □ □

SECTION B

Management During the Placement Process

Once the decision to institutionalize has been made, a new phase of the management process has been reached. Now the decision must be implemented in a way which is most constructive for both the family and the retardate. As mentioned previously, the transfer of custodianship or even guardianship appears to be unnecessarily abrupt, but since this abruptness is likely to remain a reality for some time, the manager must make the best of it. On this level, we must recognize that placement may not only constitute a discontinuity in the parental role, but also in the management relationship. Usually, family management passes from community agencies to the institution, as the selections in the next section illustrate.

The first selection, by Walker, discusses problems associated with the placement process and parental dynamics likely to be encountered at this time. The second and third items, by Probstein and Kusuda and by Standifer, describe unusual techniques which not only proved expedient but also appeared to add to the quality of management as well. Probstein and Kusuda discuss a program of group orientation of parents to the institution. Such a program not only serves to acquaint parents with their new role and the role of the institution, but it also constitutes one last chance to reverse the decision should a parent conclude that the institution is not the kind of place he thought it was. Standifer describes a program in which a state institution calls upon parents of residents to serve as guides to other parents in the admission phase. These "pilot parents" also act as public relations agents for the institution. This management alternative appears to be particularly useful where an institution has such a large catchment area that many parents live too far away to be easily counseled by institution personnel. In addition, in some situations a mature, well-adjusted parent could be more effective in the counseling role than the institutional staff involved in the management process.

from SOME CONSIDERATIONS OF PARENTAL REACTIONS TO INSTITUTIONALIZATION OF DEFECTIVE CHILDREN

Gale H. Walker

(*American Journal of Mental Deficiency,* 1949)

The parent facing institutionalization of a child for reason of mental defect is facing some of the most critical problems and decisions of his life. . . .

The problem resolves itself into four equally great problems for the parent, which are as follows: 1) the recognition of the child's defect; 2) the recognition that institutionalization is necessary; 3) the recognition that institutionalization be consummated at some definite given date; 4) the recognition that once consummated, emotion should not undo the action. . . .

Pride often forces the parent to consider the private school first, even though the family financial picture is such as to preclude such institutionalization. Frequently when first approaching a public or state facility the parents will openly state rather apologetically their acceptance of the tax supported institution.

Having accepted the defect the parent is often seized with a desire to consummate the process with a minimum of delay. If the institution is faced with a waiting list, as so commonly occurs, the parent may begin a blind assault upon the institution, sparing no avenue for pressure. If successful in gaining speedy admission, this type of parent often is so poorly conditioned that he immediately begins another campaign for the removal of the patient or develops critical fault-finding of the care given.

Sometimes social agencies err in overselling the parent on the benefits of institutionalization, picturing a cure, learning to read and write, or the learning of a trade when the child has shown no such promise. Such overselling resolves none of the parent's emotional problem and merely postpones the necessary adjustments.

One type of parental reaction towards institutionalization of their child might be termed a catastrophic reaction. Ignoring the reality of the situation facing them, they postpone any definitive action until the problem becomes acute either within the family group or until community or other pressure occurs. Often really remarkable sacrifices have been made to adjust to the defective without apparent complaint or discomfort. Suddenly, however, the situation seems, with little additional pressure, to be totally unbearable. The parent then can stand no more, loses hope, and resorts to all the avenues of pressure that may give the slightest hope of relief from the situation.

Once the parent has accepted the fact that institutionalization is desirable, there is a second adjustment to be made when a set time for admission is arranged. The emotional conflict reopens, and sometimes the defenses against recognition of the defect are reestablished to a sufficient degree to allow the parent to renounce the admission date. Only rarely is the parental adjustment sufficient to cause him to attempt conditioning of the defective child to the separation from the family that must follow admission. Time seems a cardinal factor in assisting the parent in adapting to this and the preceding phase of parental adjustment.

Frequently parents are thrown into a degree of conflict between their recognition of the defective needs and a sense of filial devotion if one or more of the grandparents rejects institutionalization. Grandparental rejection can easily occur if they are domineering or have been tyrannically strict as parents, and if circumstances have been such that the grandparents have never been responsible for caring totally for the defective for any length of time. The emotional stress that would have otherwise existed is usually intensified and may be sufficient to entice the parents to defer admission or other action.

The date of admission is a very eventful day for the parent as well as for the child. Again a catastrophic reaction may be exhibited by the parent. Often the parent is anxious to be done with the deed and leave the institution. Parents who have shown no great degree of emotion openly in previous contact may be visibly affected. Apparently admission to an institution is considered in a light very similar to death. Parental adjustment is aided if the parent can be induced to remain away from the institution for a month to six weeks following admission. Even despite such suggestion, the emotional reaction may be so severe that the parent may return in a day or two or even several weeks and press for the removal of the child.

The parent usually approaches the institution with considerable fear and often with some hostility. The fear of the institution is for the most part the fear of the unknown. As this may be dispelled by good institutional procedure, the question of what may occur on the other side of the door through which the patient goes becomes less and less disturbing. Hostility to an institution is often to some degree justifiable, inasmuch as institutional routine sometimes becomes impersonal ritual outliving usefulness. Parental hostility exhibited is a projection of the parent's hostility to the idea of defect in his child, the injury to the parent's self pride; and the natural critical attitude of one who must passively permit another to assume his prerogative of care [for] his own.

Parents sometimes retain, over long periods of time, a hostile alertness for slights in care to the child. A visitation may be followed by an emotionally bitter letter left at the institution or arriving within a day or two. These letters may express great concern over care given. The parent may not, however, retain the feeling and if invited in the reply to personal discussion on their next visit may not avail themselves of the invitation.

Parental emotional responses do not remain static, but remain in a state of constant flux and subject to quick reversal under the action of additional stresses such as illness of the child, domestic trouble, financial reverses, and the like, even though the defective be institutionalized for months. . . .

Identification of the parent with the defective is often encountered among the less intelligent parents, especially after periods of institutional care, particularly if court instigated. Sometimes this is made obvious by statements such as "there are lots of people walking the streets that are worse than him," or statements like, "he wasn't any different than the rest of the children." Racial feelings are sometimes injected into the parent's reactions in the more unstable parents of minority racial groups, and the parent may reject the diagnosis of the child's defect or suggestions of institutionalization as evidence of discrimination. When racial feelings are present, other defense mechanisms are usually prominently displayed. In my experience racial feelings are not evident in the more intelligent minority group members.

Parental denial of the defect as a protective mechanism seems precariously established, for short periods of parole of the defective will quickly shatter the denial and bring about a more acceptable return of objective evaluation. Nevertheless the denial can on occasion create almost a halo effect of idealization which may reach practically a degree of deification in the event the defective dies while young.

Very often one or both parents may effect some degree of transference towards one or more of the staff of an institution. When this occurs the adjustment of the parent towards institutionalization is usually facilitated.

While time has not permitted the inclusion of illustrative histories or full expansion of the mechanisms involved, it would seem that certain practical conclusions might be drawn from the considerations given. One may conclude that parents of defective children approach consideration of institutionalization in the light of their own emotional background, reacting within the range of their conditioned ability, reflecting their emotional weaknesses or strengths, and evoking a range of mechanisms of defense. Since parental adjustment is as much a humane necessity as adjustment of the patient, it is logical that time and effort be expended to promote this end. Indeed, bread cast upon the water in this pursuit comes back twofold with better understanding of the parent with whom we deal as well as the patient we serve.

□ □ □

from USE OF GROUP TECHNIQUES IN THE PRE-ADMISSION PROCESS

Irwin Probstein, Paul Kusuda

(*American Journal of Mental Deficiency,* 1962)

The advantages of providing Preadmission Services to parents with a retarded child, include promoting the mental health of the family and preventing precipitous decisions by parents who are not emotionally prepared for separating from their child. In addition such services can act as a catalyst in stimulating agencies in the community to develop interest in and to provide services for the mentally retarded through exploration of alternate planning hitherto unknown or underdeveloped. . . .

Whether the child remains with his family usually depends upon two factors: 1) the quality of pre-admission services, and; 2) the manner in which the medical diagnosis is presented to the parents. Begab (1956) has commented on the latter, stating that the doctor has a surgical concept of treatment "based on the belief that removal of the defect cures the patient. Similarly removal of the child from the home is expected to solve the parent's problems."

The confidence placed by parents in their physician's ability to give sound advice in the medical area tends to create a halo effect, which in turn interferes with their abilities to consider alternate plans with the social worker. In this latter respect the social worker often meets with great resistance in attempting to help parents consider more fully the meaning of their decision. Frequently this parental resistance is the reaction to the guilt provoked by the decision to separate from a child, the hostility toward the world for being made a victim of such a catastrophic event, as well as the accompanying grief at being forced to give up long awaited plans for the child which will never reach fruition....

Central Wisconsin Colony is Wisconsin's newest facility for the mentally retarded. New units are still under construction. Patients for this institution first arrived in June, 1959. Fourteen months later a nursery building was activated for children from infancy to seven years of age. Admission to this 450 bed unit is from the other two state facilities for the retarded as well as from the community. It was at this point that parents began to be seen at Central Wisconsin Colony regarding their decision to place or not to place their child and a pre-admission service was established.

Initially, Pre-Admission Social Services consisted of an interview with the parents in the home or at the institution and a short tour of the ward areas. The diagnoses of the children ran the gamut from mongolism to various complex forms of organic brain damage. Families were seen from all parts of the state and from all socioeconomic levels. The most outstanding fact observed was the inadequacy of the pre-admission service to meet the emotional problems of the parents.

The challenge to the Social Service Department was to understand the sociocultural as well as the psychiatric impact of this problem upon parents with a retarded child, then devise a means of creating a new therapeutic strategy which would allow the aroused defenses of these parents to become sufficiently relaxed so that they would at least be able to perceive the value of alternate planning. The device decided upon was a variation of a structured group session. First attempts were made in mid-1961. Parents who had previously been seen in pre-admission interviews were invited back for a day-long session with the staff. A simple format involving informal group discussion and individual interviews with the parents was employed.

The response of parents to this new program indicated a high level of interest. However, few parents attended the programs, and because of the lack of attendance these initial efforts were felt to be in need of further modification. It is believed that the trauma of the first visit to the institution expends what ego strength parents have. Their decision is fraught with guilt-provoking conflict and in some instances dormant unresolved problems can be exacerbated.

In light of these clinical implications the Social Service Department retooled the pre-admission program to start group sessions at the point of earliest or "first" contact between the parents and the institution rather than to wait, as had been the practice, until initial interviews were completed. It was decided that four to six couples would constitute a group and arrangements with parents to attend were handled accordingly.

A copy of the program is shown

below.

9:00-9:30 A.M.
Registration and reception in the Nursery Building Lobby.
The morning session will be held in Classroom 2 in the Nursery Building.

9:45-10:00 A.M.
Welcome by the Superintendent.

10:00 A.M.
Introduction of parent group by Social Service.

10:00-11:15 A.M.
Parents will meet with a Physician, Psychologist, Social Worker, and Nurse for presentation and discussion of their child's particular problems.

11:15-12:00 Noon
Feeding—Visitor's Lounge

12:00-1:00 P.M.
Luncheon

1:10-2:15 P.M.
Individual interviews by staff with individual couples in offices of Nursery Building.

2:15-2:30 P.M.
Coffee

2:30-3:00 P.M.
Recreation Demonstration

3:00-4:00 P.M.
General Closing Session
Parents and Staff

As can be seen by simple inspection of the program, information is presented lecture-style to assist in the reduction of feelings of anxiety, strangeness, hostility, etc., by addressing the group rather than any one person or couple.

Each presentation by medicine, psychology, nursing, and social work runs between fifteen and twenty minutes. At the conclusion, parents are free to ask questions of the staff thereby using the strength of the group to raise questions they might not be able to raise if they were seen alone. At the end of the presentations, parents were quite able to ask questions and make comments. Because most of the parents seen have very young infants, they are taken to observe feeding on the infants' ward. It was found that this also enhanced socialization between parents, and parents and staff.

This particular demonstration consistently has brought enthusiastic response from parents. They are always most interested in seeing children presenting feeding problems very much like those they have at home. In addition, they also see that the institution has no "magical" powers or "magical" solutions, which in turn facilitates a more realistic evaluation of the pro's and con's of institutional placement.

After observing feeding, the parents and the staff have lunch together. By now it is usual to find conversation flowing fairly well. Parents are observed sharing information, experiences, and comments with one another and with staff members. The staff has been able to join with the parents in discussing the experiences of the day, what their reactions were, and so forth. All this time the staff has an excellent opportunity to assess strengths and weaknesses of the parents, which has been found to be most helpful in the interviews which follow.

The purpose of the individual interviews is to examine with the parents their specific situation, to determine if theirs is an emergent condition in the home, and generally to evaluate the mental health of the family in psychosocial terms. The interviews are conducted by the staff members participating in the program.

After the interviews the parents are then seen as a group for a final session with the staff. The purpose of this final meeting is to discover the effect of the program on the parents, to evaluate what value they received, what additional questions they have, comments, etc.

Since this all-day program was begun over a year ago, certain changes have occurred. For example, it has moved to a "first contact" basis from the previous approach, which was inviting couples to return. Greater individualization has been achieved by splitting the groups by diagnosis. For example, the parents of mongoloid children are seen apart from those parents whose child carries a diagnosis of cerebral palsy or other brain damage. Thus two groups are seen in the morning session now, whereas before the parents in each class were seen as one group. The feeding has been more specialized in that the ward staff brings a selective and representative group of patients in their cribs out to the parents in the waiting room. Thus parents have the opportunity to observe even more closely the feeding of children very much like their own. A short play demonstration has been added after the parent interviews and before the final session. The purpose is to show parents through a one-way vision mirror that the recreation needs of the children are no different than with any other children. The emphasis throughout is to reenforce the parent's feelings of adequacy regardless of the eventual decision; be it to place or not to place their child, and to provide them with as sound a basis as possible upon which to make their decision. . . .

□ □ □

PILOT PARENT PROGRAM: PARENTS HELPING PARENTS

Francis R. Standifer

(Mental Retardation, 1964)

Many residential facilities for the mentally retarded, as they face the dilemma of increasing demands for services without concomitant increases of staff, are beginning to look toward the community for supplementary services (Hartford, 1960). For the past two years the Abilene (Texas) State School has successfully used parents of children in the institution as adjuncts of the Social Service Department.

Families considering institutionalizing their children have many and conflicting feelings (Thurston, 1960). In some cases they feel they must make the decision alone; in other cases, as they seek assistance, they are advised by both lay and professional people who, by and large, have only limited knowledge of mental retardation and of institutional programs and procedures (Murray, 1959). Ideally, the unresolved doubts confronting parents are handled through pre-admission interviews at the institution (Dittmann, 1962). However, at the Abilene State School, which has an admission area of 128,353 square miles in western Texas and one social worker for each 600 students, parents are encouraged to come to the school and discuss their problems with the staff, but pre-admission conferences are not a prerequisite for admission.

In an effort to assist parents who are unable to visit the school prior to the admission of their child and who have need of a more detailed and personal orientation than can be provided through informational brochures, the Pilot Parent Program was initiated in June, 1961.

Developing the Program

In setting up the program, the staff operated on the premise that counseling by parents who have undergone a similar experience is "meaningful, productive, and markedly successful," (Weingold, 1963), and on other reports in the literature that parents gain understanding from each other (Goodman, 1961; Thurston, 1960). In the initial phase, social workers listed as possible Pilot Parents those parents in their caseloads who had worked through the major problems surrounding placement, were able to accept their children's retardation in a mature manner, and were able to identify with the staff.

An effort was made to secure Pilot Parents in areas of highest potential student density, with no family farther than an hour's drive away. The primary concern, however, was with the anticipated effectiveness of the Pilot Parent rather than the effort to cover the admission area. In communities having an active Council for Retarded Children, the chairmen of committees on residential facilities were recruited if they had children at the school.

During the past two years, twenty-nine sets of parents have been contacted either by personal interview or by a letter suggesting that they can render a service by assisting other persons in their section of the state through answering questions regarding the school —its staff, program, procedures and, particularly, the pre-admission process. Permission is asked to give their names to other parents as they request application forms. It is further explained that in order to maintain confidentiality, names of parents requesting application forms will not be given to the Pilot Parents.

As soon as their acceptance is received, Pilot Parents are mailed a kit containing parent and personnel brochures, sample chapel and recreation bulletins, volunteer newsletters, the institution's monthly newsletter, application and commitment forms, visitor's permits, furlough and discharge papers, each with an attached explanatory statement. They are assured that members of the professional staff are always available as resource persons, and conferences are usually on the agenda as Pilot Parents visit the school.

Of the twenty-nine sets of parents who have been asked to serve as Pilot Parents, only one couple has refused, and, after almost two years, only two couples have not continued in the program. In the two latter cases, marital difficulties culminated in break-ups of the marriages.

On the positive side, it soon became apparent to the Social Service Department staff that they were being confronted with fewer distraught families on admission day and thus were able to establish a more effective relationship quickly. Within a matter of weeks, Pilot Parents were not only assisting in filling out application forms but were setting up diagnostic evaluation appointments, arranging transportation, contacting county officials, and forming car pools for school visits. In addition, they were becoming public relations people as they interpreted the school to their friends and neighbors and to civic and church groups, particularly to their Councils for Retarded Children, legislators, county officials and educators. Prior to the school's Open House last October, they secured excellent newspaper, radio and television coverage; and seventeen Pilot Parent couples attended the event, some of them driving more than 400 miles.

Parents' Evaluation

At the end of the first year, an effort was made to evaluate the program. Questionnaires were sent to twenty-seven families who had been referred to Pilot Parents and to eighteen Pilot Parent couples. Members of the first group were asked, "Was it helpful to talk to the parents of a child already at the school?" and "How was it helpful?" The latter group was asked, "Do you feel the Pilot Parents program is helpful to other parents?" and, if so, how had they been of assistance? Seventeen parents (father and mother or the responsible relative) and twelve Pilot Parents returned the questionnaires.

Of the seventeen sets of parents, three had not contacted the Pilot Parents. All of the remaining fourteen stated that talking to the Pilot Parents had been helpful. In several instances, parents who had not returned the questionnaire expressed verbally their appreciation of the program as they visited at the school.

Typical comments by the parents were: "It was helpful to find that other children became happy and adjusted to the school because we could expect our child to do as the others did." She explained that her child was happy at the school and that he showed great improvement. "We saw how happy they were with the care their child was receiving at the school."

One could imagine how doubts had dissolved as parents reported, "It was helpful to know what to expect during the adjustment period." "She assured me that all the children were treated the same." "She told me how efficiently the school was run, how each student was made to feel an individual." Another parent ruefully stated, "It would have been more helpful if I could have talked to the Pilot Parent sooner. I am so grateful for her call."

Pilot Párents also found the experience rewarding. One said, "All I can say is, if I can give some parent hope by what I have learned, which is that the school is the greatest blessing I have ever known, it is good for each of us." Others expressed the same thought differently: "We feel this is a good and necessary program and from our personal experience, we feel that we would have appreciated very much the help of Pilot Parents." "Pilot Parents would have been worth so much to us if we could have talked to anyone with experience about the school."

Other Pilot Parents stated more specifically how they helped: "We have answered all sorts of questions, have loaned our brochure, and have listened for hours to parents talking about their troubles. It is a general understanding that parents feel for each other." "We have helped people still trying to make up their minds that this is a step [institutionalization] in the right way." "We are able to answer questions about things we have already experienced. They know what to expect after we have told them about our child."

However, as they were confronted with a variety of questions about a program they had previously evaluated only from the viewpoint of their own child's needs, Pilot Parents began to experience some of the doubts with which the staff had struggled in planning the program. About half of them requested additional information and materials. To partially meet this need, a series of color slides and a script explaining the admission procedure were provided which have been used with groups throughout the area during the past six months. Presently some consideration is being given to the mailing of a monthly newsletter and to the possibility of having periodic one-day institutes at the school for this group of parents who are so effectively supplementing and enhancing the efforts of the paid staff.

Summary

In conclusion it can be stated, after having had the assistance of Pilot Parents for almost two years, that parents have proved to be even more helpful in supplementing the services provided by the Social Service Department than the staff had anticipated, perhaps because the program was initiated with some hesitancy. Since there was little precedent to follow, Pilot Parents were selected with caution; only those persons about whom the staff was in complete agreement were chosen. However, as the Pilot Parents have identified themselves with the school, its program and problems, they have come to be an integral part of the institutional family and the school's most ardent ambassadors to the community.

References

Dittmann, L. L., "The Family of a Child in an Institution," *American Journal of Mental Deficiency,* 1962, 66: 759-765.

Goodman, L. and Rothman, R., "The Development of a Group Counseling Program in a Clinic for Retarded Children," *American Journal of Mental Deficiency,* 1961, 65: 789-795.

Hartford, R. J., "A Volunteer Program in a State School for the Mentally Retarded: An Administrative Viewpoint," *American Journal of Mental Deficiency,* 1960, 65: 318-321.

Murray, Mrs. M. A., "Needs of Parents of Mentally Retarded Children," *American Journal of Mental Deficiency,* 1959, 63: 1078-1088.

Thurston, J. R., "Attitudes and Emotional Reaction of Parents of Institutionalized Cerebral Palsied Patients," *American Journal of Mental Deficiency,* 1960, 65: 227-235.

Weingold, J. T., "Parents Counseling Other Parents," *Children Limited,* 1963, 12: 2.

□ □ □

SECTION C

The Management of the Institutionalized Child's Family

Once placement has been effected, families tend to settle into one of several patterns. For instance, one kind of family completely cuts itself off from the retardate; another lives in constant ambivalence, and often becomes a dreaded problem to the institution staff; a third provides continued support and unequivocal affectional ties, and so forth. It is evident that the family's behavior can have a profound effect upon the retardate's adjustment in the institution. Severe breakdown in functioning after a parental visit, or even after a letter from home, is not an uncommon experience. Constructive management of parents once placement has been effected can thus be beneficial to the parents themselves, to the resident, and to the institution as a whole.

Problems and dynamics of parents and siblings of institutionalized children are exceptionally well discussed in an article by Dittmann. She meaningfully describes the type of reactive emotional adjustments that remaining members of the family might make. Furthermore, Dittmann recounts the possible nature of the adjustment of the child once in the institution, and staff reactions to certain patterns. With much insight, she also points out: "Absurdly little thought has been given to the importance of preparing a child for his new residence." We understand that this article has been reprinted and widely circulated and we concur with the implied judgment of its excellence.

In the next article Farrell, a superintendent of an institution, discusses the obligations parents have to their child and the institution, and how the institution expects them to work for the resident's welfare. Another superintendent, Barber, describes a range of techniques of maintaining effective communication between parents and institutions. Communication is oriented to parent education, goodwill, and public relations, all leading to promotion of what Barber refers to as "happier teamwork" with the parents.

from THE FAMILY OF THE CHILD IN AN INSTITUTION

Laura L. Dittmann

(*American Journal of Mental Deficiency,* 1962)

. . . .

Parents usually make the decision to place a child in a residential institution with mixed feelings. Reluctance is present, that is, if it is a decision at all, rather than compliance with advice given by a physician or someone else. Placement may be undertaken shortly after the birth of a child when the parents are in a state of numbness and ignorance about the true nature of the child's condition. If the baby is placed at that time, most parents have to arrive at the decision independently at a later time. Many do feel they would have acted differently had they been helped to consider all the factors. Those who are never able to review their actions, after hastily placing a child in the first days or weeks of his life, probably are never able to develop true parental feelings about that child at all.

Before a conclusion is reached, even *post hoc,* the parents argue it pro and con, individually and together. Frequently the question is explored at length with a physician, pastor, or social worker. Generally, relatives become involved in the discussion. Grandparents who have a "hands off" attitude about the other children, or other matters pertaining to the family, almost always become actively involved. The extended family—kin on both sides—recognize placement as such a fundamental decision [that] they feel entitled to put in their "two cents" worth. Usually, they regard their contribution as worth a lot more.

Finally, somehow, the decision is made. The course is set, application papers are filled out. Then the waiting period begins. During this interval, the question may remain unresolved in the minds of the parents. One day the child seems more manageable and the parents wonder if they should withdraw the application. Possibly, the child reflects the let-up of pressures and expectations as the family realizes that the trouble can end. Everyone relaxes a little with the prospect of relief, however distant.

As time goes by, however, and the wait for a court hearing or an empty bed is extended, all interest becomes focused on *when,* no longer *if*. And, when the day for admission finally arrives, all energies become caught up in the physical details of arranging for the move.

In the weeks following the departure of the child, there comes a letdown, a period of release and relief alternated with nagging doubts about the necessity of placing the child after all. "We could have managed somehow. I must have been exaggerating the problem." Round and round, back and forth. When this ambivalence exists and persists, it is difficult for the parent to behave consistently and spontaneously toward others, toward the child, toward his brothers and sisters still at home, and toward the staff of the training school.

This basic story is affirmed by most parents who have placed a child. Almost without exception, there is a note of apology to their voices when they reveal that their son or daughter is away at a school or home. There is a hesitancy lest they be judged, and found wanting in faith or patience.

One would expect that parents who have placed a child would be able to get support for their decision from other parents of retarded children. Yet within local organized groups of parents this ambivalence can be observed. Most of the meetings are concerned with interpreting the needs of retarded children to the public and to the development of community programs for the retarded. Of course, parent groups are dedicated to improving care for the retarded wherever they are, but this refinement may be lost, at times anyhow, as the members see and work with parents who have kept their child at home. The parent whose child is away must realize that the day school, camps, and workshops which the organization is working toward won't profit his child at all.

Even if things go well in the absence of the child, an illogical, but nonetheless real, doubt may be felt which might be something like "We shouldn't have it so good. We don't deserve this relief." Before the placement, the tune went "We don't deserve to have him at home, he might spoil chances for the other children." A double-bind of this type, when either course selected brings misgivings, is not an enviable position to be in.

Things may not go well at home, however. Other problems, submerged by the demands which the presence of the retarded child placed on the emotional reserves of the members of the family, are revealed glaringly when the shield is removed. Once hidden or shadowed, these problems may be disclosed with clarity. The other children may still quarrel; the older daughter, whose lack of popularity was blamed on the retarded child, may still be unpopular and need sympathetic help in learning how to get along with others. The relationship between the parents, tried by the retarded child, still isn't good, and recriminations and resentments continue. New questions confront everyone.

The brothers and sisters of the child who is placed may have doubts. If young, they may secretly wonder if they, too, will be sent away from home if they misbehave. They may wonder if they contributed to the decision by complaining about their retarded sibling, by flareups of hate, by not helping enough. Students of child development recognize that children frequently feel to blame when events around them go wrong, and reproach themselves silently, although the casual adult observer may feel them to be blissfully carefree.

When these ambivalences, misconceptions, and conflicts are present, they are bound to influence behavior.

Such feelings may make it hard for the parents and children to visit the training school. A parent might make promises, which he would be unable to keep or would forget to keep. He might make promises which he knows he couldn't keep, and blame the rules of the institution, the staff, the physician, or social worker for his own failure to follow through.

It might happen that no one would remember the child's bad points—how destructive he was, how hard to feed, how difficult the sleepless nights. The family may idealize him. No one would dare to speak of his shortcomings. The tendency to eulogize the absent one is not confined to retarded children, of course. The absent parent, when there is divorce, may become the ideal, loving, Santa Claus type of parent in the mind of the child. The tyrannical, irascible, selfish old lady, once she dies, may in the minds of her relieved children, be transformed into a loving, dear little grandmother.

It might work in another way. The parents would not dare to speak up about the defects and inadequacies of the institution, let alone critically examine the place, lest in some way the child's situation there be affected adversely or the staff would retaliate or neglect the child. Parents might not dare to become thoroughly acquainted with the institution, lest they find it so clearly undesirable that they would have to face the fact that placement there was unsuitable. Parents could not admit its weaknesses to themselves. . . .

Parents and institution staff profess that they want a closer relationship. Parents, daring now for the first time to assume that they have rights and duties, and that their children have rights, want to know the truth about the institution—its problems, its strong points, its "skeletons," its triumphs. The parents want to know the reasons behind its policies and procedures. Some are traditions, hoary with age. These need review in the light of modern practices and philosophy. Some are for the convenience of staff, not necessarily for the good of child or parent. Some suit one kind of child and not another.

The policy regulating visiting may be one area where tradition has interfered with, not cemented, closer relationships. It may be appropriate to compare institution practices with those of hospitals which plan for young patients with acute or chronic illness.

Formerly hospitals found visits upsetting to their routines, and pointed out that they upset the child as well. So visiting hours were infrequent, and brief. Now hospital staffs no longer regard parents as a necessary evil, but recognize that the presence of the mother and father may determine to a large degree the value of the treatment being administered. A child's sense of continued closeness to his family is regarded as good medicine.

A good deal of thoughtful attention has been given to the meaning of hospitalization to a young child. Robertson (1959) took movies of a two-year-old in the hospital, which show the process by which a child, initially resistant and negative, refusing the attention of nurses and staff, finally, "settles in" and becomes docile and manageable. The child stops crying and accepts the attentions of the staff. Everyone felt this to be a desirable state of affairs. In fact, hospital staffs pointed out that when the child's parents came to visit, the patient might pull away or withdraw from them, or act as if they weren't there. This behavior had successfully fooled everybody, and was used by the staff for their own convenience to keep parents out from underfoot. Nurses observed that when the parents left, the child was upset all over again, and at first glance it seemed to everybody, parents as well, that it might have been better if they hadn't come.

A closer look revealed that the child's docile and withdrawn behavior wasn't a good sign at all. If it continued for any length of time, without the frequent and regular appearance of the parents, the child could be seriously damaged by the deprivation. This could result in profound personality change, which would mean that the child would make but superficial contacts with others, not daring to invest himself closely in another, that is, to love. His good behavior in the absence of his parents might be partly to prove that he is good enough to go home, and partly to hide from himself how desperate he feels. He would protect himself from further painful departures by appearing not to care. Frequent, regular visits not only assure him that he still has a mother and a father, but help him release his anxious feelings which otherwise can remain frozen within him too long, causing real disturbance.

Continued reassurance from his parents gives the child a knowledge of who he is, the will to grow and live.

In the light of such studies, institutions might well review their visiting policies. Most restrict visiting hours stringently. Many forbid visits at all for the first six weeks or more, until the child "settles in" and becomes, in some instances, potentially unreachable.

Absurdly little thought has been given to the importance of preparing a child for his new residence. For a long time, we have been convinced that children profit from an explanation of what is going to happen to them. Even if they are too immature to understand the real meaning of what they are told, any effort to prepare a child for a major change pays off, whether it be the coming of a new baby, the need for him to have his tonsils out, the departure of mother to go to work, or any other forthcoming crisis.

Preparation of a retarded child would rarely be accomplished by talking about the school. Doubtless institution staffs and parents would come up with simple and creative suggestions—more often than not, of things they wish they had done. One easily accomplished step could be that of asking the child's assistance in packing a suitcase, with pointed omissions of possessions, too. In this way the child might know that some of his belongings were being kept at home for his return.

It would seem that if parents were able to attempt any kind of advance preparation for their child, or through counseling were helped to find words and ways to use, they would be in a better position to help other children in the family understand what was involved also.

The behavior of children who leave the institution to come home for a visit is frequently puzzling to parents. Again, a parallel might be found in the behavior of children who return home from a long hospital stay. When the sick child is dismissed and returns home, everyone expects a brief letdown. Fond parents are indulgent for a few hours or a day, but then they expect things to right themselves rather quickly. Interviews reveal that events seldom warrant this expectation, however. The child often lets down completely, after his bravery through the separation, and may become extremely difficult to handle. He may wish to be fed, start to wet himself again, be wildly upset when his mother leaves the room, or appear to be angry at his parents for what has happened to him (what they've done to him). He may throw temper tantrums or become destructive. It requires extreme patience to deal with a child who shows these effects of a hospital stay, and it is very important to see him through this trying period by giving him what he shows he needs—loving reassurance.

It is often not easy for parents to see that loving reassurance is not the same as licensed indulgence. They frequently need understanding help to see that when they stop teasing or naughty behavior, they assure him in a concrete way that he is important to them. They demonstrate that they care enough to stop him and expect him to assume responsibility for his behavior in keeping with his abilities and age.

Frequently a retarded child, home for a visit, tests out his parents with behavior which is demanding and requires the greatest ingenuity to handle. It is difficult to keep the retarded child in line, and at the same time give him reassurance that he belongs and is valued for himself alone, especially when the visit is apt to be a short one. Their uncertainty about what is reasonable to expect is compounded by the fact that parents frequently have a poor day-to-day notion of the capabilities of a child who has been separated from them for a considerable length of time. It would be easy, after a few disheartening experiences, to decide it wasn't worth it to bring the child home at all, yet such a decision would add to the child's deprivation in a real way. The institution could assist parents by devoting time to preparing and interpreting to them the behavior they might be likely to experience.

The mother of a retarded adolescent mongoloid boy described graphically her growth in ability to handle both her boy, and her own feelings, on visits home. At first, she felt she must assure him of her love by permitting him to raid the icebox at all times. As a result, the effort to help him lose weight at the institution was sabotaged. Even more troubling to her was her son's refusal to return to the training school. When she began to limit him to three meals a day, plus occasional special treats as they traveled about the city, she found the boy less reluctant to return to school when his holiday ended. She was proud of herself, too, as she was able to see how her wish to indulge the boy had been more a reflection of her own needs than his.

Visits are but one way of keeping in close touch. Most institutions have a desperate shortage of help, and can use volunteers, either parents or other friends, in creative and stimulating ways. This requires that a parent be willing to give of him or herself to other children, and represents a stage of maturity which many parents can be helped to reach if they have been made to feel, all along, adequate—not inadequate—[for] the job of parenthood.

If contact is to be on a close basis, a lot of things must be faced honestly. It's relatively easy to put something away and hide all the unresolved doubts and feelings along with the hidden package. If you are going to get the package out frequently—figuratively speaking, ambivalences, rivalries, and doubts must be faced.

The condition of the child must be talked over honestly and continuously, with the other children in the family who will know of visits, and may be included themselves from time to time. As the placement is faced, and brought to the surface again and again by close contact with the child in his new home, chances are the parents can grow in their assurance that the decision was a correct one. As a result, they can become more positive in their discussions with their other children and associates.

With close contact, parents themselves can undertake the role of public relations and interpretation to the community. As they identify themselves with the institution, they will become informed members of the larger family, the institutional family. And as such, they can be the most effective people to interpret the institution to their friends and neighbors, to the legislators and committeemen. Through an active, informed parent who considers his own child still a part of his immediate family, institutional doors can be thrown wide open with tremendous improvement for his and all other children.

□ □ □

WHAT THE INSTITUTION EXPECTS OF PARENTS *Malcolm J. Farrell*

(American Journal of Mental Deficiency, 1957)

I consider your invitation to talk with you for a short while this morning on the subject of what the institution expects from parents a signal honor and a great opportunity. After all, you as parents and we in the institution are interested in the same goal, namely, the development of the child entrusted to our care until he achieves the maximum of his abilities. We in the institution fully realize that we cannot be successful without the cooperation and help of the parents.

A very important responsibility of parents is the preparation of a child for admission to an institution. A child who knows not only that the school has the backing of his parents, but that his admission to it is at their request, has already taken the preliminary step toward a satisfactory adjustment when that time arrives, and the task of the institution is made that much easier.

Certainly all discussion of this important decision must be completely honest. The child should be informed that his parents recognize and accept his particular educational problems and that his new school has been chosen by them not only because it will meet his educational needs but will provide an opportunity for association with other children whose interests are like his own. Also, he will have the opportunity for making new friends and playmates who will not reject him as those in the community may have done. The child who has been told bluntly that the doctors at the School want him to go there, implying that his parents do not, or the child who has been told that he is going for an automobile ride or going to visit a relative, only to find that he is being placed in an institution, will have his confidence in his parents shaken to its roots. It is obvious that such a child will have a severe problem in adjustment for, from his point of view, his parents and other persons in the community have proven untrustworthy and the unfamiliar persons in his new environment are an unknown quantity, and will present new threats to him.

We who are entrusted with the care of your children, can profit from your candor. If your child has temper tantrums or shows other patterns of behavior which have caused great difficulty at home, never be afraid to tell us for we are very familiar with such problems and are equipped to deal with them. The more complete information we have concerning the type of situation which these children find intolerable and the methods they habitually use for dealing with this frustration, the more effectively can we modify the defensive aspects of such behavior and help the children evolve more satisfactory methods for dealing with their conflicts. "Protest behavior" reflects no discredit on either the child or his parents, and a frank discussion of it at the time of admission is of enormous help to the doctor in indicating the areas in which special guidance may be needed.

You, as parents, need to realize that once a child is admitted to an institution, your relationship to that child has not changed. You are still the parent and the child is not a "state ward." Only recently I had a discussion with a father who, in revising his will, was planning to make no mention of a child who had been admitted to our institution, feeling that he was now a state ward, and therefore, could not be included among the beneficiaries. A short discussion convinced him that his relationship as father to that child had not changed, nor had his responsibilities changed, except to the extent that he now was a member of a cooperating team who shared his interest in planning for his child.

This matter of true cooperation between the school and the parents is of paramount importance in implementing an adequate program for any child entrusted to our care. As a member of a family, he has certain obligations as well as rights in his relationship with parents and siblings. This same balance between duty and privilege must be maintained in his relationships within his own community—the School. The rules and regulations of the institution, like those of all good residential schools, are designed to provide experience in this matter of "civic rights," so to speak. The parent who interprets them as restrictions and asks that they be waived in the case of his own child is doing more than merely asking a special concession; he is creating difficulties for the conscientious parents who accept regulations as part of the total learning situation. He is complicating the relationship between the Staff and all the children in the group and, particularly, is denying his own child the opportunity for learning respect for regulations and the law as a social force. I wish to point out, however, that we do not want our institution to become "hide bound" with regard to regulations. We are prepared to change with the times, and your suggestions could be most helpful. Your concern in this matter should extend to our boys and girls who have no parents. The absence of family ties is, in itself, a terrific handicap in the task of successful maturing. Such children are already denied the motivations and satisfactions connected with parental affection, and no thoughtful person would add to the psychological burdens these children bear. In their immature attempts to make experience meaningful, they reach the pathetic conclusion that since they have no family, life holds nothing worthwhile for them and that they are worthless individuals, if not actual outcasts. Their feelings of insecurity and of isolation are intensified when they observe others, who have the security of families, receiving special privileges which are denied to them.

Earlier I asked that parents be honest with the institution and honest with their children at the time of admission. The obligation for honesty does not end at that point. For the child away at school, any word from home has a tremendous psychological value. This means that great care must be taken in your letters or your conversation never to make a promise which cannot be fulfilled, never to take the easy way out of the difficult situation of denying a request by saying "I will if the doctor will let me" when the truth is, "it cannot be done." Children like to think of their parents as willing and able to comply with their every wish, and it is a role parents enjoy; but when the wish is impossible to fulfill, the parent must assume the task of telling the child, tempting though it may be to shift the onus to the impersonal "school." If parents yield to this temptation, the child's attitude toward school authority will be resentful and hostile, an attitude which makes it impossible for him to profit from the opportunities the school can offer. If plans must be changed, the parents themselves should notify the child as soon as possible and give him a truthful explanation suited, of course, to his level of comprehension. In commenting on this matter of honesty, it might be well to add a word of caution. Every happening which involves his family is of keen interest to any child and at times these events may be unhappy affairs. To report such things to a child, away from home, requires both tact and discretion. As a general thing, one does not think of letter writing in terms of an exercise in semantics, but the feeling aroused by the statement "your father is out of work again and I don't know how we'll pay the grocer," is quite different from the one induced by "Daddy isn't working at the same job now, and until he finds a new one we are all trying very hard not to buy things we don't really need." Even more delicate to handle is the problem of disharmony between parents. I have in mind a boy who was kept in a state of emotional turmoil for over a year because an indiscreet mother in her letters and during her visits gave him a "blow-by-blow" description of the troubles which she was having with her husband, until finally a divorce was obtained. It is not necessary to keep your child in ignorance. During your visits and in your letter tell him the happy things about home.

Great difficulty is created by parents who are either unable or unwilling to understand the nature and purpose of the institution. So often, we have long discussions with parents who describe the institution as a "jail." Most frequently the child of such parents has been in difficulty in the community, often as the tool of other children. The misdemeanor may have been followed by admission of the whole group to an industrial school. When it was found that this particular child would be better cared for in a school for the mentally retarded, a transfer was arranged. One would think that this was a most appropriate solution and that the parents would be gratified that their child's needs had been recognized. However, too often, as soon as the companion of normal intelligence is released from the industrial school, the parents of the retarded child appear to demand his immediate discharge since, in their words, "he has served his time."

Then, too, there is the parent who cannot accept the fact that his child is retarded, although he realizes that he is unable to cope with the situation at home. Such a parent naturally experiences a great deal of guilt and frustration in sending his child to an institution. Subconsciously the parent has a need to demonstrate to himself and to others that he is not neglecting the child. As a result, he finds fault with everything about the institution; he criticizes the equipment, the program and the professional staff; he blames attendants for not taking proper care of the child, even of neglecting him; and in general, makes the situation very uncomfortable not only for himself and the entire personnel, but for the child as well. Lengthy interviews with the physicians many times relieve this situation, but a valuable aid in this respect is the joining of a parents' organization, which will be discussed later. The parents themselves must remain open minded and accept the present condition and potentialities of their child. It is certainly natural to hope against hope that some miracle will happen and that the child will become normal, but sooner or later the parent must be helped to realize that such dreams lead only to repeated disappointment and that sincere acceptance of the situation makes it possible for them to experience real satisfaction in observing the progress of their child, even though it may be slow. The personnel, particularly the professional personnel at the institution, certainly will do everything possible to achieve a happy adjustment for parent and child.

Professional personnel in an institution realize that it is a most serious matter for a parent to have a retarded child, and are well aware of the emotional complications attendant on it. We would be most happy if you, as parents, would discuss your problems with us. Don't discuss them with the child. Our Social Service Department stands ready to offer a great deal of help. They know of many community resources which can help in solving problems. Since a social worker is present every Visiting Sunday, parents may consult with him to attempt to arrive at a satisfactory solution.

I believe it is a duty and an opportunity for parents to join the Parents'

Organization connected with the School. The Fernald League, for example, has been a source of much happiness for many of our parents. Through membership in it, they have met other parents who have similar problems, thus realizing that they are not alone. The programs offered by the Fernald League describe in detail what the institution is attempting to do for the patients; and they provide an opportunity for the parents to make a unique contribution through informed constructive activities to benefit the child, themselves, and the institution.

In my opinion, parents also have responsibilities as far as public relations are concerned. When they are well acquainted with the institution, they can do a real service in interpreting the policies and needs of the school to the public, who are taxpayers, to legislators, and to other parents. These public relations responsibilities are most important. The institution will be just as good as you as parents and taxpayers make it by your interest, support, and suggestions. Please make your suggestions to a person in authority, so that we will not receive a garbled version, second or third hand.

Cooperation between parents and institutional personnel, particularly in the light of the above considerations, will achieve our common goal of providing maximum help for your children and through them, for yourselves as well.

□ □ □

BETTER PARENT EDUCATION MEANS MORE EFFECTIVE PUBLIC RELATIONS

T. M. Barber

(American Journal of Mental Deficiency, 1956)

The material presented in this paper is drawn largely from methods used at Rainier State School in the State of Washington. A variety of techniques have been valuable in dealing with families of our children and are helpful in understanding the needs of these children.

The first technique employed was a Liaison Committee with personnel of state and local chapters of the Washington Association for Retarded Children in this area and, through these individuals, periodic round-table conferences were planned. Persons selected either as officials or elected representatives of this organization visited with the Superintendent and around the institution for discussion of problems of mutual consideration. In addition, personal contacts and visits with other groups of members of this organization were frequently held. Also, at time of regular visits for meeting with their children, occasion was afforded to keep posted on current topics with many of these individuals. In addition to these occasional contacts, the superintendent and other staff members frequently attend chapter and special meetings of the parent organization. Besides these contacts, with one chapter (the Tacoma-Pierce County group), we have now had a pilot project on "Parent Education" in operation since July 1954. This has been conducted monthly; it has been apart from regular chapter meetings and it has involved from forty to sixty parents and friends from this area. Primarily, this project was begun as a clinic to assist the parents of children on our waiting list, and for whom certain delays in admission made desirable the instruction and re-assurance this clinic could provide. It is probable other chapters may care to utilize such a plan later, especially in some of the more populous counties.

A second method of frequent use is that of participation and cooperation with parent group activities. In this matter members of our staff, as well as groups of students and friends, have met gatherings of the parent groups. On occasion, in a chapter meeting, some special presentation such as Senior Girls' Chorus may be scheduled. Our tumbling team has frequently been presented; likewise, Scout activities, Camp Fire projects, and other demonstrations have been carried out as part of this exchange of program with parent groups. At some of our more recent chapter meetings, various staff members including doctors, teachers, supervisors, and others have presented talks or round-table discussions on matters of current interest. An example worthy of special attention at this time is a recent service of physical therapy which is a type of auxiliary care being implemented in our new Cerebral Palsy Center. This plan and incidental facts pertaining thereto have been discussed carefully with the interested parents. Another manner of relating our efforts to the parent groups has been the bazaars which are an annual affair and which are usually participated in by hundreds of interested friends in the several communities where they are held. These usually take place in the fall, and proceeds derived are for special Christmas gifts and other benefits to the state schools.

The third method of counseling and education for parents, as well as for other groups of individuals interested in Rainier State School, is that of our educational activities. In this category a variety of techniques have been employed successfully including the movie, "Children Limited," which was produced at Rainier State School in 1951 and has been shown in numerous places over the globe. Locally, this film is frequently used for P.T.A. or community club programs and has received a wide approval, especially since November, 1954, at the time of the drive for the National Association on Mental Retardation. It has received increasing demands; it has been shown in Canada and abroad, and this spring a copy of the film was loaned for extensive use in Israel. It is hoped that a sequence may soon be made to bring the program up-to-date.

Another vehicle of communication is that of radio and television; these have been used and, no doubt, will be further employed. Both television and radio stations locally have cooperated for presentation of appropriate messages—especially timely in May during National Mental Health Week. On one occasion there was participation with a local station on the program "Breakfast with McMurtrie" and more recently a radio recording on the school program as a part of a series sponsored by the local Mental Health Association. Another means of communication, of course, is newspaper and press. Regular items are submitted through local papers for special events; a monthly bulletin "The News Letter" is a local publication showing school activities and items of personal interest for the whole parent group. Still another channel is the pamphlet "HOPE for Retarded Children" which is the state bulletin published regularly by the Washington Association for Retarded Children. Indeed, there are regional and national bulletins of similar nature now performing this function for the parent group over the country. The name of the publication for the national organization is also called Children Limited.

Some items of more recent publication in various types of journals and press have contributed to broader understanding for both parents and the general public. Nearly every month we provide paragraphs of interest for the local chapter news letters as well as for our own publication. We usually have items in the Washington State Association bulletin mentioned above. In addition, we have completed a series of bi-weekly articles in our local newspapers on various phases of school operation. . . .

Still another means of education and helpfulness to the parents is the speakers' bureau. Various staff members, especially supervisory personnel, frequently have opportunities for presentation of talks about the school program to such groups as PTA, Rotary, Kiwanis, and other organizations. Special papers, articles or findings of research, likewise, are occasionally available for professional and lay personnel. One such paper recently presented by the Superintendent for the medical profession was that on the mongoloid child; other items are in progress. Our speakers' bureau in recent months has taken the Superintendent and others to a wide variety of groups and places about the state; in January, a lively discussion and presentation of the film "Children Limited" at Pierce County Medical Society in Tacoma; in February, a presentation before a regional meeting of ICEC [now called CEC] in Ellensburg; also, that month a meeting in Everett before the legislative group of the local Altrusa Club; in March, a fine meeting of PTA at Shelton with about 200 persons present including a nucleus group for a new parent chapter; in April, active participation in a regional meeting of AAMD held at Rainier State School and, in May, addresses before Rotary and Active Clubs in Port Angeles. These are regular activities and several of the staff participate faithfully.

Still another channel of education and help to parents has been that of presenting displays of articles made by special departments of the school and presented at the bazaars, as well as at regional and local fairs, such as Western Washington Fair which, in our area, corresponds to many large state fairs. This has been a continuing project for many years.

An important channel of education has been that of direct orientation and instruction of groups and individuals, parents concerned, professionals, and others who have come to the school regularly for such opportunities. Preadmission contacts are encouraged because of the waiting list situation and necessary delays in admission. At such times, the visits to the school and inspection of various services, particularly those that might be available to their children, have been valuable contacts. We also have frequent visits of professional groups and various disciplines including medical, nursing, social, psychological, educational, and others. These, in turn, have been means of communicating more help to the parents through their special contacts. Just a few of the professional and semi-professional groups that have visited Rainier State School in recent months for orientation, clinic, tour and so forth include the following: in the field of special education extension class groups have come from Ellensburg and from the University of Washington; as just mentioned also the annual regional meeting of the American Association on Mental Deficiency, April 22nd and 23rd, afforded a fine opportunity for many professional as well as lay participants. The nursing profession, registered and practical, pediatrics, public health, orthopedic provide frequent groups for instruction. The medical profession has provided large and smaller groups including an annual visit of the whole medical junior class of the University of Washington and also including smaller groups of pediatricians and others from Madigan General Hospital and other nearby facilities. Social service and psychology groups have been oriented from high school through college and graduate levels. All of the above special groups certainly have been of further assistance through their own community and personal contacts with family groups in their own area.

Still another means of helpfulness and education is that of direct counseling with the parents of school staff members on occasion of extra-curricular visits or other activities. These include such events as already mentioned: PTA group meetings, addresses to luncheon clubs such as Rotary, Kiwanis, Lions, Active and so forth, and personal contacts with various members of these groups with the staff. More recently, for about ten months of the past year, the "Parents' Clinic" which has been operating in conjunction with the Tacoma Pierce County Chapter of the Washington Association for Retarded Children, has been a very valuable group relation. Another is organized participation in the activities of the parent groups; this is enjoyed by a number of staff members who may be either active or associate members of the various groups. Staff members have participated actively in state, local and regional meetings of the organization. In recent years they have participated actively in annual meetings in Spokane, Bellingham and for this year will share in the Aberdeen meeting. Through the larger organization of the American Association on Mental Deficiency members of the staff participate both as active members and as officers. As mentioned above in the recent regional meeting at this school, a large number of staff participated actively and others were invited to share in the deliberations.

Counseling both intra and extra murally, likewise, is conducted through various departments of the school. The key areas are social service, administrative and psychological offices. Members of these departments are constantly in demand for individual or group counseling with parents. The pre-admission counseling, as mentioned earlier, with the first visit of the parents, usually before the child's active admission but while on the waiting list, is conducted by the social service department. Members of this staff, or the Superintendent, or others concerned are able to instruct and to answer many questions presented by the anxious parents. A tour and orientation of individual parents or groups of parents at Rainier State School is frequently arranged by appointment and valuable to all concerned. The parents themselves, even before admission of the children, are likewise frequently members of parent organization groups and this is valuable to them as a type of group-therapy. It is a means of education as to the extent of the problem of mental retardation and, I am sure, it is very helpful to the individuals who are actively participating. In this regard, parents of children newly committed and not admitted are routinely approached as to interest before their names are submitted to parent organizations. If approval of the project is obtained, then names are submitted and arrangements made for earlier participation in the local parent groups. (New Chapters or units are being added right along.)

Another way in which parents may participate with the general educational program is by consultation and by education from specialists and lecturers available in this area. Some such opportunities have been presented by Dr. Edgar Doll, psychologist of national repute and now located at Bellingham, and Mr. Ernest Roselle, administrator in one of the newer and finer schools for mentally retarded in Connecticut, whose latest visit here was in August, 1954. Individual conferences with parents are arranged at various times for counseling with staff members, as requested. Group contacts are made through various channels such as communications through newspapers and telephone in case of significant events or activities and through bulletins available at key places within the administrative offices or at information desks at time of visits and announcements available for meetings of the local chapters pertaining to subjects of general interest such as "institutional quarantine" or special activities.

Parents participate in these [events] and by their sharing obtain reassurance as well as information concerning the activities of the school. Such events are the Easter, Christmas and other holiday assemblies. Parents frequently participate in these in a very real way—open-house or special entertainments are frequently afforded, for example, at Fourth of July, Labor Day and Christmas entertainments, special ceremonies, dedication of new projects or buildings. Reception of new equipment, such as a new school bus, a miniature train or a new swimming pool, also affords opportunity for group contacts and parent reassurance. Parents are frequently consulted and advised concerning gifts or projects of this nature, and appropriate publicity is made available concerning them. One large project of parent participation has been the equipping of all halls at Rainier State School with television sets as they become needed. There are presently more than a score of fine units so installed. These have been provided both for this school and for Lakeland Village as well as for our Yakima Branch, all sponsored through state organization of the Washington Association for Retarded Children. Parents share the pleasures and the contacts of school assemblies and our Sunday chapel, or special activities and other events on occasion. They are kept advised of activities also that our children participate in such as baseball, knot-hole, gang, the Scout and Shrine Circuses, the Fair participation and special treats, such as attendance at Standard Hour broadcasts. Parents, likewise, participate directly and indirectly in regular birthday parties and in special planning for such events as July Fourth and Christmas, for the additional pleasures of our large number of children on these occasions.

The above classified lists of events and techniques are many of the types used at Rainier State School. These are, definitely, means of parent education. They also are means of understanding goodwill and public relations. They have been the means of promoting happier team-work with the parents and, I am satisfied, have brought many dividends and pleasant experiences to the school. As a result, there is no question but that [as] we invest more and more energy and effort in this direction, [a] greater degree of satisfaction is evident both for the children who are our immediate care and the parents and families who are certainly also interested.

□ □ □

Part X Parents Helping Parents

Ultimately, it is almost impossible to help parents unless they want to be helped. Therefore, those who are committed to helping parents must, realistically, be sensitive to the pleas and judgments of the potential and actual recipients of their services in order to structure these services so as to be maximally effective. If programs are developed in an opinion vacuum, they can be worse than useless—they can actually interfere with client adjustment and future service development.

This book has been dedicated to the parent. The parental voice was strongly represented in the introduction to the book, and occasionally in other sections. To conclude the readings with statements by parents thus appears equally appropriate and logical. It is particularly fitting that our last two authors have both been presidents of the National Association for Retarded Children. Elizabeth Boggs, a parent and an outstanding leader in the field, lays down certain guidelines for parents to follow if they have, or suspect having, a handicapped child. In the concluding section, Alton Lund, who was instrumental in the formation of the NARC, delineates the role of the parent movement within the larger context of social action. He personally asked parents how they could be mutually helpful, and found that every respondent stated ". . . almost without hesitation, that he or she had been helped most by finding out that they were not alone."

POINTERS FOR PARENTS

Elizabeth M. Boggs

(Adapted in 1968 from the chapter "Guide for Parents," in *The Child with a Handicap,* 1959)

The conviction is firmly embedded in American culture that children grow up more effectively if the ultimate responsibility for their welfare remains with their parents. The kind of education, the character of their religious instruction, the type of medical care and attention children receive are characteristic of the broad range of decisions which are left almost entirely to the discretion of parents.

The parental right to make decisions concerning their children is well established in law. Although our culture supports the propriety of social and judicial concern for the welfare of each individual child, the right of others, even of official agencies to interfere with parental choice is carefully hedged with safeguards protecting the right of decision by the parents. Only neglect, the failure to make or to implement decisions, or provable cruelty is allowed to justify the abridgment of parental jurisdiction.

Underlying these recognized rights is the basic responsibility of all parents to nurture their young in a manner that fosters their optimum growth in all dimensions. Some parents have more aptitude for this role than others, but all should have access to the supporting services offered by society through its public and private social institutions—the schools, the churches, the health services, and recreational programs, to name but a few.

Parents of atypical children are drawn, by the hand of chance, from the same ranks as those of "normal" children. They have the same kinds of strengths and weaknesses, and above all, the same diversity. They may be stable or unstable, conscientious or shiftless, intelligent or dull, economically comfortable or marginal, aggressive or meek, determined or aimless, happily or unhappily married, mature or immature, articulate or inarticulate, ambitious or placid. They exhibit these characteristics in all the myriad combinations and shadings which characterize other parents. Like these other parents they are entitled to the presumption that they can be entrusted with making decisions concerning the welfare of their own children. Like these other parents, they are also entitled to enlist for their children, both handicapped and normal, the benefits of social systems and institutions which can complement and enhance the natural parental role.

Parents of the handicapped sometimes have to fight for the right to act like parents, for so frequently they are told that they are not objective about their handicapped children. And why should they be? No one expects parents of "normal" children to be entirely objective about *their* children. Parents should not only be partial to, but also should be partisans for their children. The right of the child to this special championship is no less real because he is handicapped.

Because society has not always been truly conscientious in providing services adapted to the needs of handicapped children, nor really concerned about the rights and responsibilities of their parents, the parents have often labored under dual stress—the stress of extra effort in practical matters coupled with "chronic sorrow" for their child, and the stress of society's neglect and oftimes its opprobrium. In the last two decades, however, significant progress has been made in extending health, education, welfare, employment, and other societal services to the mentally retarded and physically handicapped. There has also developed an increasing respect for their parents and the unique contribution parents should be allowed to make in the lives of their handicapped children.

Notwithstanding these encouraging trends, parents of handicapped children—particularly those whose handicap carries with it a significant lifetime disability—are still faced with many special problems. Some of these are inevitable, but all can be alleviated by parental skill in using the resources available and by parental initiative in creating new resources.

It is toward enhancement of these skills and initiatives in the well motivated parent that the following pointers for parents have been developed.

The Pointers

1. *Have a careful diagnostic study made as soon as you think "something is wrong."* Try to develop a reliable prognosis, that is, a prediction as to the nature and degree of handicap which your child will have later in life. Such a prediction will be subject to revision as time goes on. Get its outlines early so that both you and your child will not waste time, effort, and hope preparing for the impossible.

2. *Don't be ashamed to lose your cool—temporarily.* If the news is bad, you'll be facing a family crisis and it's *natural* to react with mixed emotions—anxiety for the future, doubt of your own ability to cope, indignation that this should happen to your child, concern about what your in-laws or the neighbors will say, uncertainty as to whether the diagnosis is really right, self-questioning as to the cause, determination to fight for your child's rights to the best treatment and training available. Accepting a serious handicap, such as mental retardation or blindness in your own child is like facing death, only harder in some respects, because you go on loving him and grieving for *his* loss at the same time. You will grieve for your own loss, too. Grief is a normal and appropriate human emotion whose suppression is unhealthy. Parents of a handicapped child have to live with their continuing form of grief and must be free to express it.

Human beings also need the opportunity to explore fully the factors that cause them concern. Although it might be more comfortable for those around you if you immediately accepted all the implications with stoic calm, studies have shown that in the long run the parents who in time of crisis express their concerns, badger their physicians and pastors for answers, and allow themselves to realize that their lives will never be the same again—these parents will eventually emerge stronger and better able to reconstruct their own lives and those of all their children. So take time for tears, but don't let the crisis stretch out till it forms an excuse for self pity and inaction. Your child needs you to take the *next* steps soon.

3. *If you are not convinced of the accuracy of the first diagnosis, seek an additional expert opinion, preferably from a center offering specialized services in the area of handicap which is suspected in your child's case.* No matter what the "presenting problem," the staff of such a center will want to make a complete physical, mental, and emotional evaluation of your child. After such an evaluation has been obtained, a member of the staff will be prepared to discuss your child's case with you in some detail. About some types of handicap, doctors are able to be quite definite both in diagnosis and prognosis. About other types, considerable research is still necessary. Try to get the whole picture and to understand the suggestions for action. Medical and surgical treatments may well be the least important. Some of the suggestions, you can put into effect at home, some will depend on what is provided for handicapped children in your community.

4. *Have confidence in your own abilities as parents.* You are the key to the situation. As parents newly facing the fact of a handicapping condition, you should take courage from the many positive experiences of other parents, and [from] the normal young people who look back upon their association

with a mentally or physically handicapped brother or sister as an experience which added depth to their perception of life.

As parents of a handicapped child you will need specialized help as well as courage to play a difficult and essential role—one which no one else can play. But with the help of those in supporting roles you can see it through.

5. *If your child's handicap is a long-term one with implications for his adult life, establish contact with the most suitable agency in your home community which can offer you continuing practical counseling in planning for your child and in taking advantage of the resources of your locality and state.* The chances are better than four out of five that you live in a county served by a local member unit of the National Association for Retarded Children (420 Lexington Ave., New York, N.Y. 10017). This organization, which was brought into being in 1950 by parents like yourselves, concerns itself with the full range of mental retardation, regardless of cause, degree of handicap, age or complications. Similarly the National Society for Crippled Children and Adults (2023 West Ogden Ave., Chicago, Illinois 60612) promotes services for those with sensory disorders and neurological impairments as well as orthopedic problems, while the National Association for Mental Health (10 Columbus Circle, New York, N.Y. 10019) places special emphasis on autistic and other seriously mentally ill children, as well as those with milder emotional disturbances. There are numerous other more specialized groups.

All local or state affiliates of these organizations will help put you in touch with the direct service agencies which you seem to need. Some of them actually sponsor such services. In other cases they will help you find the right state agency for the blind, or local cerebral palsy treatment center, or public health nursing service, or clinic for the retarded, or public school special education program.

If there appears to be no local organization competent to advise on the overall management of the type of handicap your child has, they may well find it helpful to approach your local family service agency.

Of course, your pediatrician or family doctor (or the diagnostic center, if it is near enough) should continue to care for your child's medical needs and to advise you on related matters. However, a staff member of a specialized agency trained in counseling the retarded or other handicapped and their families will usually have more time to spend with you than a busy physician can give. And it is the counselor's business to know the educational, social, rehabilitation, and recreational resources, as well as the health services of the community.

6. *Inform yourself about the general class of handicapping conditions of which your child's case is a particular example.* Nowadays there are many avenues through which the intelligent parent can learn more about the condition, treatment, and potentials for the future of a handicapped child. The organizations just mentioned have prepared pamphlets and reading lists. Their local groups hold meetings and discussion groups especially for parents and invite your active membership. There are good movies. Through a local agency counselor one can usually arrange to visit a school or camp or treatment center or residential facility to see programs and similar children in action. It is well to remember, when visiting for the first time, that you have probably become accustomed to your own child's differences, but that you will be unprepared for some of the *other* peculiarities of other children who are in many respects comparable to your own.

In the absence of local resources, write for reading material to the appropriate national organization or the U.S. Children's Bureau, Dept. of Health,

Education and Welfare, Washington, D.C. 20402.

7. *Get all the expert advice you need, but make your own decisions.* You will have to live with them. Take time to think things through at each stage, but don't let things drift indefinitely. It will take time to separate fact from opinion, and to minimize anxieties caused by popular misinformation and prejudice and by conflicting professional advice. Worrying is part of deciding and deciding is part of being a parent. Indeed, what normal child grows to maturity without some anguish on his parents' part?

8. *Give thought to modifications of the physical environment.* Anyone can remove the scatter rugs that slip under the crutch, although houses differ enormously in the ease with which a crippled person can move in and out. Not so obvious is the importance of layout in the control and supervision of an active mentally retarded youngster whose physical ability to get about exceeds his good judgment. Can he play safely where you can see him while doing housework? Are storage areas exposed? More than the contents of the medicine cabinet must be kept from his grasp. Will the decor favor the child with poor vision? Can the child who must be less active still be a participant, indoors and out, rather than left in seclusion to speculate on tantalizing noises? Will it be easy to transfer the child from house to car in any weather?

As children grow older specific problems change. Parents can help themselves as well as their children by trying to anticipate the new needs when buying and furnishing a house and by developing new arrangements from time to time.

And don't forget that when *your* time and energy are saved you have more to give your children.

9. *Get help in working out a program of home training in self care, safety, and activity for your child.* Most physically and mentally handicapped children need to follow a pattern of their own, specific each to himself as well as to his handicap. Parents must find out what is important, when to try to teach it, and how. Weaning, chewing, toilet training, walking are all special hurdles, with a revised schedule for the handicapped [child].

A child who is physically crippled, mentally retarded, or impaired in vision or hearing may require rather specific training in personal self care, locomotion in home and community, and communication, in various combinations. "What to do" is obviously specific to the handicap and "when to do it" depends on the developmental stage of the child. Ideally the parent should have the continuing guidance of the staff of a local center where the child has been studied and continues to be observed from time to time, or of a visiting nurse, teacher, or a family counselor.

Most national organizations distribute articles or pamphlets with home training suggestions specific to the handicap. These suggestions can be adapted by parents who have some insight into where their child stands developmentally.

Whenever a child is attending a school, nursery, or treatment program make every effort to develop consistent and complementary patterns of instruction between school and home. A handicapped child has to work so much harder for everything he learns that it seems scarcely necessary to teach him two different approaches to tying his shoes just because mother and teacher didn't get together.

10. *Begin early to accustom your child to the company of people outside the family circle and to being cared for occasionally by outsiders.* Even the physically or mentally dependent person cannot be forever emotionally dependent on the same two or three people. The handicapped, as well as the normal child, must learn to establish new relationships. Your child will need these new relationships when you are

gone. Encourage their development while you are living. As a beginning find out whether yours is one of the communities which have groups of young people who have prepared themselves especially for the more difficult task of "sitting" with a handicapped child. This can make possible some very much needed "ordinary" social life for you too.

11. *Start working up an educational plan early, several years before your child will be ready for formal schooling, if possible.* If you live in one of the larger cities, the chances are that a "director of special education" will be glad to explain to you just what your city offers in the way of special instruction. Generally speaking, "special educators" prefer to keep your child with his agemates in a regular class, *if* your child can take advantage of most of the activities and can receive any needed special help on an individual supplementary basis. Speech problems are generally handled in this way. In some states and school districts, blind as well as partially seeing children attend regular classes and receive special instruction in braille from an itinerant teacher or in a special classroom. Children who use hearing aids may not be segregated although supplemental instruction in lip reading may be arranged on an individual basis.

A special class or special school is more likely to benefit the totally deaf child, especially in his preschool and early elementary years. Such a class is recommended also for the mentally retarded, whether "educable" or "trainable," since the pace and content of all areas of learning have to be substantially modified. The cerebral palsied child also may be benefited by special class placement, especially since he may have specific handicaps in concept formation, speaking, reading, and writing, as well as in ambulation. Parents can help by recognizing the advantages of these special facilities and by cooperating with the school when special placement is recommended, even though special placement may be inconvenient for the parent or seem unduly to separate the child from his neighborhood companions.

Where it is impossible to get the child to a school or where there are not enough handicapped children to form a special teaching unit, home or hospital instruction should be considered. A two-way communication system between home and school may be arranged through the board of education and the telephone company. Although such arrangements do not give the child the full advantages of social interplay found in the classroom, they do represent a very real contribution to the life of the homebound child.

With the increasing parental interest and with the passage of supportive or mandatory legislation in many states, educational opportunities for the handicapped of school age are multiplying rapidly. However, special education opportunities are not by any means available today in every community for every type of child who may need help. Since several years are required to get a new program underway, parents who arrive on the school's doorstep with a seven-year-old, without having lifted a finger in anticipation, may find the school unready.

In some sparsely populated areas, special local facilities may not be practical for a small but heterogeneous group of atypical children. A realistic appraisal of the situation may lead parents to consider relocating or looking into the merits of residential schools.

Many states maintain such schools for the deaf and blind, a few for the cerebral palsied; all have public residential facilities for the mentally retarded of school age and beyond. Directories of private residential schools for the handicapped, including residential treatment centers for the emotionally disturbed, may be found in your local library.

12. *Do not let your child lean on his*

handicap. Expect and insist on performance up to his ability not only in the area of handicap but in others as well. Do not lead him to think that he will be able to get by in life on pity. Be sure he has his family as well as his personal duties. Children of different ages in the family understand concessions or differentiations based on age. They will understand those based on special disabilities, too.

13. *Don't overlook the importance of fun and change.* All therapy and no play make Jack pretty solemn. Basic routines of living are fine for insuring that the essentials are included, but even the most severely handicapped child needs the stimulus of variety and choice. The importance of provoking or motivating spontaneous play and exploration in the very young handicapped child is being increasingly recognized.

Opportunities for group participation and adventure through organized recreation activities for older children are opening up for the handicapped. Today, for example, some suitable camping experience, either in a regular or specialized program, is available to nearly every type of handicapped child. Seek out these resources for your child. But don't forget to include him in family fun too.

14. *Help your child to understand his handicap.* The handicap is neither to be ignored nor to be exaggerated. Unless the child is very severely mentally retarded, he cannot escape discovering that he is different. He should find it out so early in his life that he does not remember *not* knowing it. He needs to know, in a matter of fact way commensurate with his understanding and with increasing detail as he grows older, the nature of the defect and the reasons behind the various kinds of special therapy or training. Help him to meet friendly curiosity as an expression of interest in him and as a desire to understand how he feels. When he is small, you can explain things for him to his friends. Gradually he may be able to do it for himself in a way that will make him feel more comfortable.

Steering the right course in this respect requires particular care when the child is mentally retarded; for you will have to make some special rules for him, especially as he grows older, which, by the very nature of his handicap, he may not entirely understand. Generally speaking it is a good idea to try out the hypothesis that he does understand or can understand more than he appears to.

15. *Keep step with each other in your learning and planning for your child and yourselves.* The discovery of a handicapped child in a family often accentuates already existing patterns. Family dissentions may become more pronounced in the face of a new distress. Equally significant, a basically stable family may go on to new strength and new unity in the face of a new challenge. The important thing is to keep communication open, and for each parent to try to put himself or herself in the other's place. Father has to imagine what is it like for mother to handle a hyperactive, oversized youngster in the supermarket, or not to be able to leave a child unsupervised long enough to go to the bathroom. Mother has to realize that home problems added to job problems at 6 P. M. may be one bale of hay too many. And there are more subtle pressures. You won't be the first father who has turned down a tempting job offer because the new community didn't have what your youngster needed.

Some sacrifices will have to be made, personal, social, or financial; but there are ways to cut down on the heroics. Find out about homemaker services, or the possibilities for "short stay" care for your child away from home, to enable you to have some sort of vacation or respite together, for example.

16. *Start coming to grips with some of the big problems while you still have time to think.* A special vacation can offer an opportunity to think out and

talk over such knotty problems as religion, heredity, and sex and marriage for the handicapped. The question of religion concerns *you* primarily and if it *does* concern you, it's a good idea to start thinking it through during that precious and probably all too short period when your youngster still sleeps ten hours a night.

Most theological systems recognize pain and suffering and interpret its meaning for men. Many persons, however, not fully understanding the tenets of their own faith in relation to anguish of this kind, are ill prepared. For many the place of "natural law" has never been clarified. Confusion between scientific and theological explanation leads you to ask, "Why did it happen to me?" when you mean "Why did this happen?"

Parents who are deeply religious must bring their experience into harmony with their beliefs before their energies can be fully liberated for constructive action. The advice of professional people—physicians, social workers, psychologists—does not always recognize the real problems with which the parents may be grappling. To those persons for whom no sparrow falls but by God's design, so significant an event must somehow be placed in its religious context. Those individuals belonging to sects which stress retribution and the belief that the sins of the fathers are visited on the children may regard their own suffering as expiation. Those men or women for whom each adversity is part of "God's plan" may see its meaning as bringing to themselves a profounder understanding of spiritual values, as revealing to them their mission in life, or as a mystery to be accepted as an act of yielding to a higher will. Other persons may see their present suffering as preparation for a world to come. They may believe that God has singled them out for the special privilege of ministering to a special child or that the child himself has a mission, as in the Biblical story of the man born blind of whom Jesus answered, "Neither hath this man sinned, nor his parents: but that the works of God should be made manifest in him."

Whatever may be the teachings of your own faith, if it has importance in your life, your own peace of mind and that of your other children, as well as the way your handicapped child feels about you, will depend on an understanding and acceptance of its tenets as they relate not only to your own suffering but to the meaning of his handicap to the child himself.

Heredity is another knotty subject that may come up when one asks the question *Why?* The majority of handicapping conditions in children are not presently thought to have a genetic origin, and if this is so in your case, the sooner it is confirmed and your worry on that score eliminated, the better.

But if you are spared this concern, express your gratitude by doing your bit to lighten the stigma that still so often unjustly adds to the burdens of those parents who must learn that something went wrong with their genes or chromosomes.

If your child's disorder is of genetic origin, you will be confronted with two problems—one primarily emotional and one intertwining emotional and practical concerns. It is not comfortable to find that in addition to your child's apparent handicap, you also have a biological deficiency, albeit hidden. The practical side, of course, arises out of the risks that may be run by yourselves (if you plan to have more children), by your normal children in their turn, and even possibly the handicapped one too. Not all genetic mechanisms work the same way, and most parents will want to learn all they can from a qualified genetic counselor. Whether to have more children, consider the family complete as is, or complete it by adoption is a personal decision when all the facts—as far as science has discerned them—are in.

17. *Be frank with your other chil-*

dren: Answer their questions truthfully and arm them with the fullest information appropriate to their understanding. This frankness is just as important when the handicapped child has been placed outside the home as when he is in it. Young children develop fears about the mysterious absence of another child. Older children are sensitive to overtones of reticence. Let brothers and sisters be partners in the family's planning, but do not ask them to assume responsibilities which are properly yours, particularly in relation to commitments for an unforeseeable future.

Open up the opportunities for them to join in some of the youth groups which are developing exciting volunteer activities with and for the mentally retarded. A career of work with the handicapped often gives the normal sibling a sense of special value.

Youngsters should also be armed with knowledge affecting their own hopes of parenthood. Many have been plagued unnecessarily with unjustified and long unexpressed fears which could well have been dispelled in children. On the other hand a sensitive preadolescent whose chances of having healthy children are indeed impaired should know where he stands.

18. *Look your handicapped child's future squarely in the face and help him to do so.* If the child can become economically and socially independent, guide him in directions where he can succeed because of his capabilities. If the child is mentally handicapped but potentially able to maintain himself, start early to build respect for the kinds of employment which will be open to him. Don't urge a particular educational course just to "prove" something. A handicapped person, who makes a fine academic record for himself in a profession which for reasons of impaired mobility or communication he cannot freely practice, has not been helped. The physically handicapped can and do pursue a variety of different careers with distinction according to their intellectual gifts and bents.

If your school system has not established a close working relationship with your state vocational rehabilitation agency, find out for yourself what this state agency may have to offer. Most such agencies offer vocational evaluation and counseling but do not actually operate training and rehabilitation services. They can, however, subsidize such services in various ways. Parents may need to be forehanded in anticipating the needs of the community by promoting the establishment of a rehabilitation center or sheltered workshop in their locality.

On the question of marriage for the handicapped person, you may want professional advice. Parents are often too fearful. Some of the happiest marriages in the country involve one or even two very handicapped people. There are people who as children were excluded from school because of the severity of their mental retardation who have nevertheless grown up, married, and raised children of normal intelligence. Obviously there are many individual factors to consider—too many to make a general discussion here very meaningful. But one thing is clear, if marriage may one day be thinkable, it is the handicapped person's personality which will make the difference, and this you can do something about, beginning in his earliest years.

Wherever communication is possible with the child and he is able to comprehend what it may mean to go away to live, whether for a longer or shorter period, ample time should be given by parents to preparing him for this eventuality, should it be planned. If possible the child should be allowed to participate in the advance visit of inspection and to share in the final decision. An understanding should be arrived at ahead of time about visiting and vacations. Being sent [away] from home should never be used as a threat.

The moment a handicapped child or adult leaves the family to take up residence elsewhere, in a boarding school or on a longer term basis, is likely to be a traumatic one for the parents, no matter what the age of the child. On the other hand, if it is the right time, with the right preparation, it may well be for the child a stage in growing up, despite some temporary homesickness.

If your child will be partially or wholly dependent, economically, socially or physically, your planning will have to be of a special kind. You need to be concerned not only with your own ability or inability to establish financial security, but also with the continuity of enlightened concern in the state in which you or he resides, with the character of the state's program for long term care, with your status under social security, and upon other factors which will require individual analysis in each case.

The whole question of the care and support of the dependent adult is in a state of flux at present. Joint study and action by organizations and agencies, public and private, interested in the handicapped are especially needed.

19. *Take part in community action.* No man is an island, least of all the parent of a handicapped child. The role of the individual parent in relation to his individual child is pivotal, but the family needs resources. Since ours is a highly organized society, the handicapped will not be part of it or enjoy its benefits unless he is planned for cooperatively. Cooperative effort has been the great strength of organizations such as the National Association for Retarded Children. There is a continuing urgent need for parents to exercise their citizenship roles and to demonstrate leadership in community planning.

Remember that the opportunities afforded the handicapped child for education, for special training and rehabilitation, for recreation, for ultimate employment, and for participation in community life have increased dramatically during the past twenty years largely because so many parents, first alerted to the lacks and gaps in services for handicapped children by their own needs, have gone well beyond the bounds of cooperative effort directed at their own child's problem. They have derived great satisfaction from what has become an altruistic community service in the interests of all such children. In this larger work, as in that with their individual children, they are often guided by a saying so apt and so often quoted, "God grant me courage to accept what I cannot change, strength to change what I can, and wisdom to know the difference."

□ □ □

from THE ROLE OF PARENTS IN HELPING EACH OTHER

Alton F. Lund

(Counseling Parents of Children with Mental Handicaps, The Woods Schools, 1958)

. . . .

I, as a parent and a layman, would like to discuss the role of the parent in the past, his present-day role, and perhaps a few ideas for the future.

Not long ago I had two experiences which brought home to me the irony surrounding the relationship of the retarded child and his parents. My daughter, who is wonderfully normal in all respects, was taken ill. Suddenly we found ourselves face to face with a serious illness—a ruptured appendix. But everyone was wonderful—the doctors took over with all of their tremendous skill, the neighbors were most helpful and proffered every aid. Afterwards, when everything turned out for the best, my wife and I had a warm feeling indeed for these neighbors and friends.

The second experience involved our other child—our retarded boy. That we were not prepared for the devastating realization that our child was retarded, goes without saying. Seventeen years ago no one, with some rare exceptions, was prepared for such a happening and the parents found themselves alone. That was our experience, and while I will not attempt to recite the emotional upset, the shock and bewilderment, I do want to point out the ironic contrasts in the two situations.

In the one, people, armed with knowledge and understanding, stepped in and were able to give efficient and skilled help. Tragedy was averted and the best elements of society came out. In the other—bogged down by ignorance, misunderstanding and fear, we all groped for help.

I do not resent this difference because the years have taught me that we were all in the same boat and my family, my neighbors, and my associates simply did not have the answers, or the knowledge, to cope with the situation.

In my position I talk with literally hundreds of parents in all areas of the United States. I would like nothing better than to report to you that all of the past records of ignorance, cruelty, and superstition have passed—and that we no longer face these situations. When I see progress being made my hopes rise. Then, just as I am in a complacent mood, things happen which bring me down to earth.

Not more than a month ago, I was at home on a Saturday afternoon when the phone rang. It was a woman begging for help. It seems that her sister-in-law was retarded and had been in an institution. She had been released because she was an excellent worker and could easily find employment. However, she was the victim of one designing person after another until her life had become nothing but a morass of immorality, crime, and debauchery. This woman asked me what help was available. But when I undertook to get some of the facts, she became very evasive. It finally came out that she was appealing for help over the strong objections of her entire family. The mother of the girl flatly refused to permit the matter to be discussed by the family. The girl's conduct did not seem to bother the family nearly as much as the terrible danger that people might discover she was retarded. That disgrace they could not face! Since she would not identify herself so that I could make an appointment with people who could help, I did get her to promise she would take the matter up with proper authorities. She also promised to come to some of the meetings of our unit in Salt Lake City. When such a case comes to my attention I wonder just how far we have come in ferreting out the cases in the back rooms, basements, and the like.

While I am sure that we have made tremendous progress, there is still a vital role for the parent to play in helping fellow parents with this problem. I would like to discuss some phases of this role with the hope that the position of the parent may be made a little clearer.

Recently I had the pleasure of sharing a television program with the noted American actor, Mr. Walter Abel. In his opening remarks Mr. Abel stated, "It is our duty as parents to see to it that no couple should be unprepared for the birth of a retarded child." I believe this very clearly expresses that desire to help other parents which is so basic to the entire parent movement today.

Since accepting this invitation to speak to you today, I have conducted an experiment, asking several parents what other parents can do to help them and how they had been helped by other parents. You will be interested to know that every single parent stated, almost without hesitation, that he or she had been helped most *by finding out that they were not alone*.

I recall vividly the letter, written by a parent and published in the newspapers, in which she stated that she was the parent of a retarded child and would like to meet with others with the idea of finding out what could be done. What an indictment that she had to resort to the public press to even find other parents! This took courage on her part and it well illustrates the type of parent who is responsible for the parent movement today.

In any consideration of this subject, we must first answer the question as to why there is such a need for one parent to help another. Social problems are rarely solved by individual action but rather by concerted action on the part of all society to rid our civilization of a blight or problem. Of course, individuals through discoveries in medicine, social science, and the like sometimes make possible some solutions, but society itself must act if the solution is to be widespread and effective. In most fields we are very advanced in this type of social action. Why then in the field of mental retardation are we some fifty to seventy-five years behind?

The reasons for this social phenomenon would warrant a vast study in itself. I believe there is no single cause but a multiplicity of them. Such factors as the change in our economic set-up with the advent of the machine age with its premium on skilled labor; false theories of heredity; universal public education; medical advances which have greatly prolonged life among all members of our society; developments in the fields of psychology; and many other factors have had a great deal to do with the whole problem of the mentally retarded child and his inability to adjust satisfactorily to modern day social patterns. Such changes have brought the entire problem to the forefront. While consideration of all of these factors would be most enlightening, it is to the question of the attitude of the parent that I would like to address myself. In that attitude lies the key to help. It is only in understanding that attitude that one parent will be able really to help another.

I return, then, to the comment made above that parents were helped by finding that they were not alone. They were not glad that others were in the same predicament, but rather that this was not something that had befallen them particularly. In other words, there were many parents involved. This discovery is most important psychologically. It is the key which opens the door to cooperation and action.

What has resulted? As victims of a stigma placed upon them and their children by society with false theories of heredity and old wives' tales, they found that they and their retarded children were without programs or help. So they began to look around and make inquiry. This led to organization—and the parent movement of the twentieth century was born!

This all seems so simple and basic that it is indeed puzzling that the movement was so slow in starting. But it is a fact that the parent movement, as we know it today, is less than twenty-five years old.

It is interesting to note that this discovery of not being alone, with its therapeutic value to the parent, does not result at first in a program for the child. The parent is still in the stage of thinking about himself. Further development in his attitude is essential. He must come to see that his child needs help not only from him but from others as well. He then begins to make comparisons. He compares his child with others. He sees that they are not all alike but are as different and varied as all children. He begins to see the many problems which face retarded children. But at this stage, he is very much wound up in the problems of his own child.

Unfortunately I must admit there are many parents who never get beyond the "my child" stage. Too often parents are interested only if their own child is involved. Sometimes these very parents are most active if the activity revolves around a facility or program which encompasses their child. But they are indifferent if their particular child is not involved.

There is one very important step in the development of a wholesome attitude—and that is the acceptance of the child as he actually is. By this, I do not mean that the parent must give up all hope and quit, but he must realize that his child has limitations and needs help;

that even with help he may be far from a normal child. I have heard it said many times in our association work that nothing really happens until the parent does accept this fact and gives up false notions and wishful thinking. He is then ready to help other parents and other children.

The ideal lesson for the parent to learn is: he helps his own child most by working for all children. This does not lessen interest in his own child, but his perspective changes. He sees that a truly worthwhile program, which will build a community in which his child may function to the best advantage, can only be accomplished when that program encompasses all children. Although his child may not be particularly benefited by a particular program, other children will benefit and thereby build up a program in which his child can eventually participate. He must sometimes wait his turn.

For example, most school districts are now beginning to accept educable children readily and form classes for them. Would a parent of a trainable child be justified in ignoring a program for educable children because his child could not participate in the classes? I think not. Such a parent must come to realize that with such a program he is just that much closer to a broader program which will eventually help his child. I know this is sometimes difficult, but parents must work to help others understand that a program for all children should be their goal and not a narrow specific one which includes only a few children.

In my own community the parents who worked so hard for the establishment of school classes are now realizing that they should have taken a much greater interest in workshops and other similar programs to help their children after they leave school. We who have learned such lessons can help by passing along this type of information.

Now here is a word of caution. The fact that we have been through the mill does not qualify us as amateur psychiatrists and sage counselors, especially where new parents are concerned. The many emotional involvements in this problem should make all of us wary, and the old statement that fools rush in where angels fear to tread is very pertinent. But through our organizations and units we should stand ready to offer the helping hand and make it possible for new parents to take part in a program for their children. There is great consolation in being actively engaged in such efforts.

Another word of caution—psychological development takes time, and we cannot rush it. An unwise or foolish remark can often shut the door on the very thing we are trying to accomplish. It may take months and years to see these wholesome attitudes develop, but they are worth waiting and working for.

No discussion of parental attitudes and the role of parents in helping each other would be complete without some discussion concerning attitudes toward public institutions for the retarded. Because of public apathy, a number of unfortunate incidents, and downright public neglect, there are some disheartening situations existing with reference to public institutions for the retarded. Long waiting lists, overcrowded conditions, economy drives and so on—have resulted in all institutions of this nature, both good and bad, being looked upon as a last resort. I have actually heard parents say, and this is very recently, that they would rather die than place their child in an institution. In this way, we have actually "created" a stigma on children in state institutions.

We sometimes forget that these are the same children as those within the community. Their problems do not differ. They have the same limitations, they have the same feelings—the same desires to be loved and wanted. Fortunately things in the past few years have taken an about-face. In most areas, with the development of community programs, there has come an overall change for the better. We, as parents, are becoming better acquainted with our public institutions and their problems.

The stigma I mentioned can be removed. We, as parents, must continue to stress that a public institution is a *public responsibility*. It cannot and must not be shirked. The public institution must not be considered a "last resort" but rather a definite part and facet of a larger problem. While the private school and residential home can care for some of our children, it is clear that we must also have our public institutions.

Therefore, I say to parents who are critical of state institutions and to parents who place their children there, please shift from the negative to the positive side. If your institution warrants criticism and needs help to bring it up to standard, you should do all you can to see that this information is brought to the attention of the proper officials, legislators, and to the public generally. Urge upon them the necessity for action to correct the situations.

I am not urging placement of children in institutions. That is a question which must be the decision of each parent, consistent with the needs of each child. My appeal to you is to consider the public institution in its rightful place—a needed place for some children and also a place which we can take pride in because we have done our duty as citizens in making it so.

So far we have concerned ourselves with a discussion of parental attitudes toward this problem and our relationships with other parents. But there are additional ways in which we can help. We can urge all new parents to affiliate with parent units and show them that there is much satisfaction in working in these units and in an organized program.

In our local units, our state units, and our national organization there is a progressive program at all three levels. It would take more than my allotted time to give you even a brief description of the vast program which is now being carried on by parents all over this nation. We have more than 550 separate units in our National Association for Retarded Children, all dedicated to helping retarded children. And this has happened in less than eight years.

To the parent who is worried about what may become of his child when he is no longer here, we say: "Get in touch with the Guardianship Advisory Committee of the national and of your state organization. We have far-reaching plans for making provisions by way of wills, insurance, trusts and other arrangements. We are constantly studying this very question and are actively investigating many phases of it. We may not have all the answers but we can certainly help you."

To the parent who does not know where to go or what to do for help: "Contact the Parent Guidance Committee of the national association. This committee will not only help you but will put you in touch with people in your local area. Contact these people on your local level. They are parents with the same problems and they will help in many ways."

To the parent who is concerned about legislation—both federal and state: "Your national association maintains an active legislative committee which is in constant contact with the Washington situation and furnishes materials and information to Congressmen and other governmental departments. The present interest and large appropriations of the present day were spearheaded by your national association in cooperation with state and local associations. Perhaps we are not entirely responsible for this change but it is interesting to note that it has all come about since our organization and activity. On the state level we are setting up a new committee to coordinate state commissions and legislative activity, and to exchange information. This interest in national and state legislation affects every citizen and any parent concerned with this problem should interest himself and become active in this area."

To the parent who is concerned with research (and what parent is not?): "Your national association has established the Grover F. Powers Chair of Research at Johns Hopkins University under Dr. Robert Cooke, and we are in the process of setting up others. These research projects will concern themselves with basic research into causes, prevention, and the other phases of mental retardation. We are establishing a research fund to finance this work and in this we must have help. Every parent and interested person is vitally concerned here."

To the parent who is concerned with his child who is in an institution: "Our Public Institutions Committee, with state correspondents in most of the states, is constantly working on problems concerning institutions. We have completed a fee study to bring public attention to this whole question and to show the inequities and differences which exist. Programs concerning the operation of state institutions, such as education and recreation, are being studied by this committee. Such parents should get in touch with this committee, for certainly a program to help their children is underway."

To parents concerned with income tax questions and social security provisions: "Your Legal Advisory Committee has succeeded in having many of these regulations clarified and has sent the information to all units. These provisions now offer great help to parents and guardians, who should keep in touch with their national, state and local associations concerning such regulations."

Similarly we have programs in the fields of recreation, education, vocational rehabilitation, and in publications. All are coordinated by a professional staff in our national office in New York City, and no request is ever ignored.

These matters are constantly discussed and reported in our national newspaper, "Children Limited," which goes to all members of the national association. No parent should be without this paper. It is the concrete and dramatic story of a dynamic program now going on in behalf of retarded children—and it stems from this desire of one parent to help another and his child. These are methods by which one parent has helped another and they illustrate better than words of mine what can and must be done.

It is the parent who has filled the role of the catalyst in this vast social structure of ours in bringing about this change. He has, by his pilot projects, proved his point that the retarded child can and should be helped—and in his various activities, he has succeeded in bringing about what amounts to a social revolution in the public's treatment of one of its great problems. And this is not a parent's problem alone, for the cost to the public is staggering, and the public must be made to see that it has a basic responsibility here.

We have come a long way, but we have truly only scratched the surface. If I had to name one element essential to our success, it would be *enlightened public opinion*. When the American people understand the needs of these children and the scope of this problem, I have absolute faith that they will act not only to help the children living today, but will establish a research program which will insure that tomorrow's children will be born, live, and grow beyond the limits of this shadow.

As we ring down the curtain on a past era of ignorance, prejudice and misunderstanding, we raise it immediately on a new era dedicated to hope, understanding, and realistic evaluation—to the end that our children may attain their rightful heritage. We must bestow upon our mentally retarded children that respect, that human dignity, that real importance which is their birthright.

□ □ □

Epilogue

In the decision-making sessions which led to the selection of items to be included in this collection of readings, we concentrated on publications which we felt reflected the current status of the field. In writing the introductions to the specific sections, we tried to capture the essential features of each author's contributions, with some attempt at providing a synthesis of conclusions, suggestions, and ideas. As we discussed and revised our editorializing, certain crucial and recurrent themes began to emerge. Two of these themes, highly interrelated, are extremely significant to an understanding of the past development of the field and as portenders of the future.

The clearest theme of this nature is a disturbing lack of empirical underpinnings for past and present practices in the management of the family of the retarded. This lack, which has had far-reaching consequences for the entire management area, seems to be the end result of a number of factors. One is the newness of the field: there was little family management in mental retardation prior to the mid 1940's. However, newness alone is not an adequate explanation, for there are other young fields that are much more empirically oriented. Another consideration that may account for the lack of empirical underpinnings is the fact that in mental retardation the practitioner preceded the empiricist. Even evidence-oriented practitioners do not always have the necessary skill to conduct research themselves. As noted in the earlier-mentioned companion review to this book,[1] the preponderance of empirical studies in the field, though relevant, did not yield meaningful results. Poor quantification, lack of controls, and other design inadequacies were the rule rather than the exception. The second important theme which emerged in the discussion of articles selected for inclusion is an outgrowth of an historical accident: management of the retarded and their families had been based on models taken from medicine and its subspecialties, such as psychiatry. These models had been strongly established and almost universally accepted as valid. Lately, however, questions have been raised about whether these original models were appropriate; and if so, whether they were adequately founded in empiricism themselves, or whether they, too, were based largely on clinical lore, dogma, or ideology. By adopting these medical models, the field of retardation may not only have embraced an inefficient strategy; it may also have embraced an obstacle to empirical research by erroneously assuming either relevance or empirical foundations that did not exist. Obviously, if one believes that clear-cut answers to certain questions are already available, one will not be inclined to conduct research, or see the necessity for conducting it.

In the past, not only family management, but also management of the retarded generally has been based on the disease model. Surprisingly, this disease model was not only adopted by medical practitioners, but also by social, behavioral, and even educational personnel. Mental retardation was defined as a "disease"; retardates (and even their parents) were widely referred to as "patients"; management, even if purely social or educational in nature, was interpreted as "treatment" or "therapy"; residential facilities, even if lacking a single full-time physician, were called "hospitals"; and living units of such facilities were labeled "wards." The lower-class, mildly retarded were said to "suffer from" cultural deprivation, as if from a disease. Since mental retardation was conceptualized as a disease, its treatment was seen to be analogous to treatment in medicine, and the concept of "cure" was widely utilized. Many workers in the field even defined mental retardation as being "incurable." Those who believed that treatments for mental retardation might be discovered looked forward to treatments that would be analogous to medical treatments. Thus, many held the hope that an operation would be developed or a pill would be discovered that would "heal" the "patient."

Revascularization operations and the glutamic acid studies are typical examples, and even the 1963 President's Panel Report spoke in terms of "intellectual vitamins" when referring to early environmental stimulation.

The developmental nature of mental retardation was so poorly understood on the theoretical level, as many workers claim that if to be effective, it was rejected or ignored because it did not fit the preconceived models of what treatment in mental retardation should be like. The management now widely believed to prevent, reverse, or reduce mental retardation in many children is educational-developmental in nature, and it requires long-range, day-to-day stimulation. Change comes slowly and over the years, not quickly and spectacularly as in many medical treatments. Such management is so different from the more glamorous cure-by-medication-or-surgery model that it took many years to receive some acceptance in practice. Even today, and even when implemented, it is still not always understood on the theoretical level, as many workers claim that if developmental retardation in a child can be reversed, the child could not have been retarded in the first place, but only "deprived," "disadvantaged," "undermotivated," etc.

Gradually, increasing numbers of workers in the field are both unconsciously and consciously rejecting and/or redefining the medical disease model in retardation. The condition giving rise to intellectual impairment may, in some cases, be recognized as constituting a disease or pathological process. However, the contributions of the social sciences have opened our eyes to the fact that whether behavior is adequate or inadequate is largely determined by prevailing cultural demands and expectations. In less demanding environments or cultures, only a small proportion of individuals will be judged to be inadequate. In a complex, technologically and achievement-oriented society, a large proportion of members may fail to meet even routine demands. This implies that within a society committed to such a way of life, increasing proportions of members will be judged to be retarded over time.

By definition, about 17 per cent of the population falls below the average range of psychometric (measured) intelligence. Perhaps an equal proportion is identified as requiring a significantly above-average amount of societal services in the form of assistance, guidance, supervision, or control. Such societal services may take the form of special or remedial education, rehabilitation, financial assistance ("welfare"), guidance and counseling, institutionalization, policing or correction. At present, perhaps 10 per cent of the population appears to be subaverage in both measured intelligence and adaptive adequacy. In the sense of the 1959 definition by the American Association on Mental Deficiency, most of these people are mentally retarded. They are not only retarded in a technical, arbitrarily-defined way; they are also retarded in a socially meaningful sense.

Our society is growing increasingly technologically complex and intellectually demanding. The amount of schooling that is considered average has steadily increased and is projected to continue to increase indefinitely. In all probability, a higher percentage of United States residents inadequately fulfill the social demands of today than during earlier periods of history. Projecting this line of reasoning, it is quite likely that in decades to come, the proportion of persons who are retarded in the eyes of society will increase further. Eventually, 15 per cent, 20 per cent, 25 per cent, and perhaps even more of the population may come to be defined as retarded—and, again, meaningfully so.

Such a social definition of mental retardation leads to far-reaching corollaries, only some of which can be considered here. For example, a major increase in the number of retarded persons may necessitate radical revision of target goals in service development. There is also a possibility that management ideologies may undergo changes, no matter what the proportion of retarded individuals is. In our society, foods and goods are produced with increasing efficiency, and there is a massive manpower shift from the middle to the higher range of the skill, education, and training continuum. Both the demand and the supply of human services are increasing. Human management is a service; thus our ideals pertaining to the needs of the retarded and their families may outpace even a greatly increased supply of such services. Both trends may combine so that the perceived service gap may widen rather than diminish, despite considerable increases in the absolute quantity of service provisions.

Considering the low state of current knowledge and the prospects for the future, we would like to propose that the time has arrived for programmatic high-quality research on family management and related topics. Needed first are criterion measures of variables that are of significance in management. Among such measures might be scales to assess information and misconceptions about mental retardation, attitudes toward mental retardation, parental perception of the retarded child, parental realism about the child's current abilities, parental expectations regarding the child's future attainments, family adequacy, impact of a deviant child upon the family structure and function, and parental child-rearing practices.

While some scales of this nature have already been developed, they tend to suffer from many shortcomings. To justify the expense of large-scale research, these measures should be highly quantified, should be objectified to reduce observer or rater error, and should possess high and proven reliability and validity. Facing up to the reality of the absolute shortage of research manpower, and the relative shortage of service personnel, these instruments should be structured so as to require as little human intervention as possible during their administration, scoring, and interpretation. We now have the means to accomplish these goals through the use of automated and computerized processes and equipment. These means will not only increase the efficiency of data and family management, but will also reduce human error and result in greater objectification. Once such criterion measures are available, more definitive answers can be sought to many presently unanswered questions: What is the relationship of such variables as parental agreement, age, and socioeconomic status to optimal case evaluation; to type of evaluation feedback, to amount, extent, duration, spacing and type of counseling; and to use of resources? When is individual and when is group management preferable? What type of group management (e.g. fact oriented, child-development oriented, or therapeutically oriented) is most effective with different types of parents? What are optimal management structures and techniques for various types of groups? Is diagnostic feedback most effective in a single concentrated session, or should it be spaced-out over time? If the latter, what is the optimal spacing for most or for certain types of parents? Such a listing of unanswered but significant questions could be continued at some length.

The apparent hopelessness of closing the service gap calls not only for experimentation with automated data collection and case evaluation, but also for new management approaches which utilize the new resources our age has provided. Instead of verbal face-to-face counseling—essentially a stone-age technique—use of "canned" and automated management needs to be explored. Films and video tapes can be used to inform, educate, and counsel parents. For instance, such media could be used to present general facts about retardation and child management to parents. In addition, a vast and varied amount of high quality video material of a more specific nature could be stored to be selectively retrieved for presentation by pushing buttons which enter relevant information such as: child's age; child's sex; child's developmental pattern and level as ascertained by psychological evaluation; child's etiological diagnosis; parental education and income, age, and urban-rural residence; and others. Aside from more traditional film-like presentations of information, information can also be programmed for operant teaching, and the pace of presentation can be individualized for each parent by analyzing his responses and by branching the teaching process. While it would require a tremendous amount of material to "stock" the system, one basic system could be reproduced at a fraction of the original cost and could be utilized at numerous locations throughout the country.

An objection that may be voiced is that automated management is utopian. This may be. However, entire automated learning environments for children have already been constructed and have been found to be highly effective. Before long, an entire generation will have grown up with automation in school, home, play, and work. To them, automated management will appear commonplace. We certainly possess the technical knowledge for developing such management; all we need now is a willingness to identify the cost-efficiency ratios of various management alternatives, along with a commitment to the development costs.

A second objection might be that automated management will not work because of its impersonal nature in a problem area that calls for personal encounters. There are several answers to this objection. First, we really do not have the evidence as to what elements of the management process need to be personalized, or for that matter, whether some elements can actually be handled better impersonally than personally. Furthermore, it is conceivable that cultural changes will also change the patterns of needs for personalized management so that it may become feasible in areas where it may be unfeasible now. Finally, by automating certain aspects of case evaluation and management, it may be possible to liberate manpower from some tasks so as to reinvest it with greater effect in those areas where personalization may actually have been demonstrated to do the most good. This last point is especially important since automated processes, though perhaps the method of choice for some types of management, may never be able to replace other types of management, or the need for such other types.

In the long run, management of the family of the retarded should, and undoubtedly will, become more continuous with education for parenthood in general. The rearing of children is one of the most significant and demanding tasks most of us confront in our lifetime. Yet, paradoxically, this is a task for which the average citizen has received little or no formal preparation. Even when the child has an unimpaired growth potential, and even where parents are highly intelligent, well-educated, and possessed of abundant material resources, child rearing is typically fraught with error, and frequently marked by failure. How much more problematic the situation then becomes when the child is handicapped!

There is now reason to believe that by necessity, man will institute new patterns of child rearing. Indeed, we may live to see the first major change of what have been essentially prehistoric habits handed to us from the darkness of our past. For the first time, parents may be systematically and universally taught what we hope to be optimal skills of parenthood. As some of the more primitive and irrational aspects of parenthood diminish, and as knowledge replaces myth, parents—by becoming better parents in general—will become better parents of handicapped children as well. The process and risks of reproduction and development may come to be better understood, and future generations may be spared many conflicts we see in our generation of parents—conflicts engendered by ignorance or one's perception of the attitudes of others. Perhaps in the future there will be diminishing need to help parents with their feelings about a child's impairment, so that the management task can be focused on the more technical problems of child development.

FOOTNOTE

1. Wolfensberger, W., "Counseling the parents of the retarded," in A. Baumeister (Ed.), *Mental Retardation: Appraisal, Education, and Rehabilitation.* Chicago: Aldine, 1967.

ACKNOWLEDGMENTS

Acknowledgment is gratefully made to the following journals, authors, and publishers who have granted permission to reprint entire articles or excerpts from copyrighted publications. When excerpts comprise only a part of an article, complete page references for the article are given in brackets.

AMERICAN JOURNAL OF MENTAL DEFICIENCY:

C. Anderson Aldrich. *Preventive Medicine and Mongolism,* 1947, *52,* 127-129;

T. M. Barber. *Better Parent Education Means More Effective Public Relations,* 1956, *60,* 627-632;

Michael J. Begab. *Precommitment Services in a Training School for Mental Defectives,* 1955, *59,* excerpts from pp. 691-697 [690-697];

Norma L. Bostock. *How Can Parents and Professionals Coordinate for the Betterment of all Retarded Children?*, 1956, *60,* excerpts from pp. 428-432;

Dan Boyd. *The Three Stages in the Growth of a Parent of a Mentally Retarded Child,* 1951, *55,* 608-611;

Vincentz Cianci. *Home Training,* 1956, *60,* 622-626;

Laura L. Dittmann. *The Family of the Child in an Institution,* 1962, *66,* excerpts from pp. 759-765;

Carl Drayer and Elfriede G. Schlesinger. *The Informing Interview,* 1960, *65,* excerpts from pp. 365-370 [363-370];

Malcolm J. Farrell. *What the Institution Expects of Parents,* 1957, *61,* 675-678;

Marion M. Font. *Parental Reactions to Psychologic Measurement,* 1951, *56,* 48-51;

Estate of Anne C. French (deceased), Morrison S. Levbarg, and Harold Michal-Smith. *Parent Counseling as a Means of Improving the Performance of a Mentally Retarded Boy: A Case Study Presentation,* 1953, *58,* excerpts from pp. 17-19 [13-20];

Margaret J. Giannini and Lawrence Goodman. *Counseling Families During the Crisis Reaction to Mongolism,* 1963, *67,* excerpts from pp. 740-747;

Lawrence Goodman and Ruth Rothman. *The Development of a Group Counseling Program in a Clinic for Retarded Children,* 1961, *65,* excerpts from pp. 789-795;

Edith P. Gramm. *Peter Beautiful: The Story of an Enchanted Child,* 1951, *56,* 271-274;

Evelyn Disner Hanschaka. *Reporting to Parents,* 1956, *61,* 362-367;

Donald Hastings. *Some Psychiatric Problems of Mental Deficiency,* 1948, *52,* excerpt from p. 262 [260-262];

Ann E. Heilman. *Parental Adjustment to the Dull Handicapped Child,* 1950, *54,* excerpts from pp. 556-562;

Donald H. Jolly. *When Should the Seriously Retarded Infant be Institutionalized?*, 1953, *57,* excerpts from pp. 632-636;

Leo Kanner. *Parents' Feelings About Retarded Children,* 1953, *57,* 375-383;

AMERICAN JOURNAL OF MENTAL DEFICIENCY:

Stanley C. Mahoney. *Observations Concerning Counseling with Parents of Mentally Retarded Children,* 1958, *63,* 81-86;

Dorothy Garst Murray. *Needs of Parents of Mentally Retarded Children,* 1959, *63,* excerpts from pp. 1085-1087 [1078-1088];

Cleo E. Popp, Vivien Ingram, and Paul H. Jordan. *Helping Parents Understand Their Mentally Handicapped Child,* 1954, *58,* 530-534;

Irwin Probstein and Paul Kusuda. *Use of Group Techniques in the Pre-Admission Process,* 1962, *67,* excerpts from pp. 227-230 [227-231];

W. Newland Reilly. *Let the Parent Live Again,* 1942, *46,* 409-413;

Stanton L. Sheimo. *Problems in Helping Parents of Mentally Defective and Handicapped Children,* 1951, *56,* excerpts from pp. 42-47;

Lawrence B. Slobody and John B. Scanlan. *Consequences of Early Institutionalization in Mental Retardation,* 1959, *63,* excerpts from pp. 971-974;

Elizabeth M. Smith. *Emotional Factors as Revealed in the Intake Process with Parents of Defective Children,* 1952, *56,* excerpts from pp. 809-810 [806-811];

Nellie D. Stone. *Clinical Team Treatment of a Mentally Retarded Child and His Parents: Casework with the Mother,* 1959, *63,* 707-712;

Gale H. Walker. *Some Considerations of Parental Reactions to Institutionalization of Defective Children,* 1949, *54,* excerpts from pp. 108-114;

Joseph T. Weingold. *Parents' Groups and the Problem of Mental Retardation,* 1952, *56,* excerpts from pp. 484-486, 489-492 [484-492];

Mary L. Yates and Ruth Lederer. *Small, Short-term Group Meetings With Parents of Children with Mongolism,* 1961, *65,* 467-472.

AMERICAN JOURNAL OF PSYCHIATRY:

John L. Hoffman. *Mental Retardation, Religious Values, and Psychiatric Universals,* 1965, *121,* excerpts from pp. 885-889;

Reynold A. Jensen. *The Clinical Management of the Mentally Retarded Child and the Parents,* 1950, *106,* excerpts from pp. 830-833.

AMERICAN MEDICAL ASSOCIATION:

publisher of AMERICAN JOURNAL OF DISEASES OF CHILDREN:

Keith N. Bryant and J. Cotter Hirschberg. *Helping The Parents of a Retarded Child: The Role of the Physician,* 1961, *102,* excerpts from pp. 52-66;

Donald K. Grant. *Out of the Shadows,* 1965, *110,* excerpts from page 2 [2-3].

publisher of the JOURNAL OF THE AMERICAN MEDICAL ASSOCIATION:

"Counseling Parents," Chapter 4 in *Mental Retardation: A Handbook for the Primary Physician,* 1965, *191,* excerpts from pp. 183-232.

AMERICAN NURSES' ASSOCIATION, INC.

Ruth Woodfall. "The Nurse, the Mentally Retarded Child, and his Family." In *Nursing Approaches to Denial of Illness.* New York, 1962, excerpts from pp. 6-16 [5-18].

GEORGE S. BAROFF:

"Mental Retardation: A Family Problem." In The Training School, *Conference on Psychological Problems in the Habilitation of the Mentally Retarded.* Vineland, N.J., 1962, excerpts from 85-89 [85-90].

Michael J. Begab:

"Casework for the Mentally Retarded—Casework with Parents." *The Mentally Retarded Child: A Guide to Services of Social Agencies.* Washington: U.S. Gov't. Printing Office, 1963, excerpts from pp. 58-68.

Harriet E. Blodgett:

"Helping Parents in the Community Setting." In The Woods Schools, *Counseling Parents of Children with Mental Retardation.* Langhorne, Pa., 1958, excerpts from pp. 74-84 [74-85].

British Medical Journal, by permission of the authors, editor and publisher:

C. M. Drillien and E. M. Wilkinson. *Mongolism: When Should Parents be Told?,* 1964, *2,* excerpts from pp. 1306-1307.

The Canadian Medical Association Journal:

Alastair Beddie and Humphry Osmond. *Mothers, Mongols and Mores,* 1955, *73,* excerpts from pp. 167-170.

Canada's Mental Health, bi-monthly journal of the Department of National Health and Welfare, Ottawa, Canada:

Michael J. Begab. *Counselling Parents of Retarded Children,* 1964, *12,* No. 3, excerpts from p. 4-5 [2-5];

Renée Lipsett. *A Volunteer Program: Home Care for the Retarded,* 1964, *12,* No. 3, excerpts from pp. 6-9.

Children, a publication of the U.S. Department of Health, Education, and Welfare, Social and Rehabilitation Service, Children's Bureau:

Alice V. Anderson. *Orientating Parents to a Clinic for the Retarded,* 1962, *9,* 97-101;

Irene L. Arnold and Lawrence Goodman. *Homemaker Services to Families with Young Retarded Children,* 1966, *13,* excerpts from pp. 149-152;

Helen L. Beck. *Counseling Parents of Retarded Children,* 1959, *6,* excerpts from pp. 67-72;

Laura L. Dittmann. *Home Training for Retarded Children,* 1957, *4,* excerpts from pp. 43-48;

Arthur Mandelbaum. *The Group Process in Helping Parents of Retarded Children,* 1967, *14,* excerpts from pp. 227-232;

Jane O'Neill. *Siblings of the Retarded: II. Individual Counseling.* 1965, *12,* 226-229;

Mabel H. Parsons. *A Home Economist in Service to Families with Mental Retardation,* 1960, *7,* 77-83;

Letha L. Patterson. *Some Pointers for Professionals,* 1956, *3,* excerpts from pp. 31-35;

Sylvia Schild. *Parents of Children with Phenylketonuria,* 1964, *11,* excerpts from pp. 92-96;

Meyer Schreiber and Mary Feeley. *Siblings of the Retarded: I. A Guided Group Experience,* 1965, *12,* excerpts from pp. 221-225.

Child Welfare:

Margaret E. Adams. *Siblings of the Retarded: Their Problems and Treatment,* 1967, *46,* 310-316, 334.

CLINICAL PEDIATRICS, published by J. B. Lippincott Company:
Gerald Solomons. *What Do You Tell The Parents of a Retarded Child? Some Personal Experiences and Reflections,* 1965, *4,* excerpts from pp. 227-232.

COLUMBIA UNIVERSITY PRESS:
Marlin H. Roll. "A Study of Retarded Young Children," in *National Conference on Social Welfare* from SOCIAL WORK PRACTICE, 1962, excerpts from pp. 146-157.

GUNNAR DYBWAD:
"Group Approaches in Working with Parents of the Retarded: An Overview." In *Challenges in Mental Retardation.* Columbia University Press, 1964, excerpts from pp. 41-52.

EUGENICS QUARTERLY:
Robert L. Tips, Donald L. Meyer, and Audree L. Perkins. *The Dynamics of Genetic Counseling,* 1962, *9,* excerpts from pp. 237-240.

EXCEPTIONAL CHILDREN:
James J. Gallagher. *Rejecting Parents?,* 1956, *22,* excerpts from pp. 273-6, 294;

Leonard Zudick. *A Conference Program with Parents of the Mentally Handicapped,* 1955, *21,* excerpts from pp. 260-263, 272.

GROUP FOR THE ADVANCEMENT OF PSYCHIATRY, INC.:
Mental Retardation: Family Crisis—The Therapeutic Role of the Physician. New York, 1963, Report No. 56, excerpts from pp. 136-137.

GROUP PSYCHOTHERAPY:
Arthur Blatt. *Group Therapy with Parents of Severely Retarded Children: A Preliminary Report.* J. L. Moreno, M.D., Ed., Beacon House Inc., Publisher, 1957, *X,* 133-140.

HARPER AND ROW, publishers:
Seymour B. Sarason. "The Problem of Professional Training" and "Interpretation of Mental Deficiency to Parents," from *Psychological Problems in Mental Deficiency,* 3rd edition, by Seymour B. Sarason. Copyright © 1949, 1953 by Harper and Brothers; Copyright © 1959 by Seymour B. Sarason. Reprinted by permission of Harper & Row, Publishers. Excerpts from pp. 331-346, 361-372.

MOGENS HAUGE:
"Genetic Counseling." In J. Oster (Ed.) *International Copenhagen Congress on the Scientific Study of Mental Retardation.* Copenhagen: Berlingske Bogtrykkeri, 1964, 151-155.

INTERNATIONAL CHILD WELFARE REVIEW:
R. Winterbourn. *Home Training Through Correspondence: A New Zealand Programme,* 1965, *19,* excerpts from pp. 164-166.

REYNOLD A. JENSEN:
"Counseling with Parents at Time of First Knowledge of Retardation." In The Woods Schools, *Counseling Parents of Children with Mental Handicaps.* Langhorne, Pa., 1958, excerpts from pp. 44-5, 52 [44-53].

Journal of Clinical Psychology:

Joseph T. Weingold and Rudolf P. Hormuth. *Group Guidance of Parents of Mentally Retarded Children,* 1953, *9,* 118-124.

Journal of Consulting Psychology:

Harriet L. Rheingold. *Interpreting Mental Retardation to Parents,* 1945, *9,* 142-148.

Journal of Experimental Child Psychology, published by Academic Press, Inc.:

Robert P. Hawkins, Robert F. Peterson, Edda Schweid and Sidney W. Bijou. *Behavior Therapy in the Home: Amelioration of Problem Parent-Child Relations with the Parent in a Therapeutic Role,* 1966, *4,* excerpts from pp. 99-107.

Journal of Mental Deficiency Research, St. Lawrence's Hospital, Caterham, Surrey, England:

K. S. Holt. *The Influence of a Retarded Child upon Family Limitation,* 1958, *2,* excerpts from pp. 28-36.

Journal of Mental Subnormality:

Wolf Wolfensberger. *Diagnosis Diagnosed,* 1965, *11,* excerpts from pp. 63-70 [62-70].

Journal of Pediatrics, The C. V. Mosby Company, publishers:

Charlotte H. Waskowitz. *The Parents of Retarded Children Speak for Themselves,* 1959, *54,* excerpts from pp. 319-329;

Israel Zwerling. *Initial Counseling of Parents with Mentally Retarded Children,* 1954, *44,* excerpts from pp. 469-479.

Leo Kanner:

"The Emotional Quandaries of Exceptional Children." In The Woods Schools, *Helping Parents Understand the Exceptional Child.* Langhorne, Pa., 1952, excerpts from pp. 25-27.

Pauline E. Kopek:

"A Group Experience with Parents of Mongoloid Children." In *The Report of Educational Program for Nurses in Region III of the Children's Bureau on Mental Retardation.* Winston-Salem, N.C., May 1964, excerpts from pp. 167-173.

Alton F. Lund:

"The Role of Parents in Helping Each Other." In The Woods Schools, *Counseling Parents of Children with Mental Handicaps.* Langhorne, Pa., 1958, excerpts from pp. 62-70.

McCormick Quarterly Supplement:

Hans S. Falck. *Mental Retardation: A Family Crisis—The Role and Function of the Social Worker,* 1966, *19,* Special Supplement, XIX, excerpt from p. 32 [26-39];

Paul W. Pruyser. *The Challenge of Mental Retardation for the Church,* 1966, *19,* excerpts from pp. 20-25.

Edgar E. Martmer, editor:

Elizabeth M. Boggs. "Pointers for Parents" adapted from "Guides for Parents," *The Child With a Handicap.* Springfield, Ill.: Charles C. Thomas Co., 1959, 351-366.

EDGAR E. MARTMER, editor:

Samuel M. Wishik. "The Role of the Physician," *The Child with a Handicap.* Springfield, Ill.: Charles C. Thomas Co., 1959, 3-10.

THE MENNINGER FOUNDATION:

Thaddeus P. Krush. "The Search for the Golden Key." Reprinted with permission from the *Bulletin of the Menninger Clinic,* Volume 28, pp. 77-82, Copyright © 1964 by The Menninger Foundation.

MENTAL RETARDATION, a publication of the American Association on Mental Deficiency:

Eleanor Fackler. *Community Organization in Culturally Deprived Areas,* April 1966, *4,* No. 2, 12-14;

Simon Olshansky. *Parent Responses to a Mentally Defective Child,* August 1966, *4,* No. 4, excerpts from pp. 21-23;

Harry Raech. *A Parent Discusses Initial Counseling,* April 1966, *4,* No. 2, 25-26;

Philip Roos. *Psychological Counseling with Parents of Retarded Children,* December 1963, *1,* No. 6, excerpts from pp. 345-347, 349-350 [345-350];

David B. Ryckman and Robert A. Henderson. *The Meaning of a Retarded Child for His Parents: A Focus for Counselors,* August 1965, *3,* No. 4, excerpts from pp. 4-5 [4-7];

Frances R. Standifer. *Pilot Parent Program: Parents Helping Parents,* October 1964, *2,* No. 5, 304-307;

Harold W. Stubblefield. *Religion, Parents and Mental Retardation,* August 1965, *3,* No. 4, 8-11.

NATIONAL LEAGUE FOR NURSING:

June L. Triplett. "Environmental Manipulation as an Approach to Mental Retardation." In *Nursing and Community Mental Health and Retardation Program,* (papers presented at the 1965 convention of the National League for Nursing, No. 33-1190), 1965, excerpts from pp. 21-26.

NURSING OUTLOOK, a publication of the National League For Nursing:

Harriet Logan. *My Child is Mentally Retarded,* July 1962, *10,* excerpts from pp. 445-448;

June L. Triplett. *A Women's Club for Deprived Mothers,* January 1965, *13,* No. 1, complete article from pp. 33-35.

RALPH OWNBY:

"The Interpretative Conference with Parents of A Mentally Retarded Child." In *The Report of Educational Program for Nurses in Region III of the Children's Bureau on Mental Retardation,* Winston-Salem, N.C., May, 1964, excerpts from pp. 81-93 [80-94].

OXFORD UNIVERSITY PRESS:

Jack Tizard and Jacqueline Grad. *The Mentally Handicapped and Their Families: A Social Survey*. London, 1961, excerpts from pp. 68-71, 94-102.

PRESIDENT'S PANEL ON MENTAL RETARDATION:

A Proposed Program for National Action to Combat Mental Retardation. Washington: U.S. Gov't. Printing Office, 1963, excerpts from pp. 88-89, 91-95.

PSYCHOANALYTICAL STUDY OF THE CHILD, published by International Universities Press, Inc.:

Albert J. Solnit and Mary H. Stark. *Mourning and the Birth of a Defective Child,* 1961, *16,* excerpts from pp. 523-535 [523-537].

QUARTERLY REVIEW OF PEDIATRICS:

Rudolf P. Hormuth. *Home Problems and Family Care of the Mongoloid Child,* 1953, *8,* 274-280;

Joseph T. Weingold. *Rehabilitation of the Mongoloid Child: Introductory Remarks,* 1953, *8,* excerpts from pp. 253-254.

SHELDON C. REED:

"Genetic Counseling." In The Woods Schools, *Counseling Parents of Children with Mental Handicaps.* Langhorne, Pa., 1958, excerpts from pp. 55-60 [54-61].

SLOW LEARNING CHILD, Remedial Educational Centre, University of Queensland, Brisbane, Australia:

E. R. Chamberlain. *Maximising Treatment Susceptibility During the Diagnostic Process,* 1963, *10,* excerpts from pp. 33, 35-6, 37 [32-37].

SOCIAL CASEWORK, published by The Family Service Association of America:

Margaret E. Adams. *First Aid to Parents of Retarded Children,* 1967, *48,* excerpts from pp. 148-153;

Juanita Dalton and Helene Epstein. *Counseling Parents of Mildly Retarded Children,* 1963, *44,* excerpts from pp. 523-530;

Arthur Mandelbaum and Mary Ella Wheeler. *The Meaning of a Defective Child to Parents,* 1960, *41,* excerpts from pp. 361-367 [360-367];

Robert M. Nadal. *A Counseling Program for Parents of Severely Retarded Preschool Children,* 1961, *42,* excerpts from pp. 78-83;

Simon Olshansky. *Chronic Sorrow: A Response to Having a Mentally Defective Child,* 1962, *43,* 190-193.

SOCIAL WORK, published by National Association of Social Workers:

Lawrence Goodman. *Continuing Treatment of Parents with Congenitally Defective Infants, 9,* No. 1 (January 1964), excerpts from pp. 92-97;

Alexander Hersh. *Casework with Parents of Retarded Children, 6,* No. 2 (April 1961), excerpts from pp. 61-66;

Sylvia Schild. *Counseling with Parents of Retarded Children Living at Home,* 1964, *9,* No. 1, excerpts from pp. 87-91 [86-91].

MANNY STERNLICHT AND TONI ALSTON:

Evolution in Group Work with Parents of Retarded Children and Adolescents, paper read at AAMD convention, Kansas City, 1964.

TEXAS MEDICINE:

Robert L. Tips. *Clinical Genetic Counseling,* 1965, *61,* 319-321.

WORLD HEALTH ORGANIZATION:

Excerpts from *The Mentally Subnormal Child.* Geneva, Switzerland, 1954.

CONTRIBUTORS

Adams, Margaret E., Research Associate, Child Welfare League of America, New York

Aldrich, C. Anderson, formerly Director, Rochester Child Health Project, Rochester, Minnesota (Deceased)

Alston, Toni, Chief Psychiatric Social Worker, West Bergen Mental Health Center, Ridgewood, New Jersey

Anderson, Alice V., Assistant Professor of Social Work, National Catholic School of Social Work, Catholic University of America, Washington, D. C.

Arnold, Irene L., Executive Secretary, Retarded Infants Services, Inc., New York

Barber, T. M., formerly Clinical Director of Mental Retardation, Eastern Oregon Hospital and Training Center, Pendleton, Oregon

Baroff, George S., Professor of Psychology, University of North Carolina at Chapel Hill; and Director of Psychology, Murdoch Center, Butner, North Carolina

Beck, Helen L., School Social Worker, Westport Board of Education, Westport, Connecticut

Beddie, Alastair, Superintendent, Saskatchewan Training School, Moose Jaw, Canada

Begab, Michael J., Head of Mental Retardation Research Center Program, National Institute of Child Health and Human Development, Washington, D. C.

Bijou, Sidney W., Professor of Psychology, University of Illinois, Urbana, Illinois

Blatt, Arthur, Lecturer, Hunter College, New York

Blodgett, Harriet E., Program Director, The Sheltering Arms School, A Day School and Research Program for Mentally Retarded Children, Minneapolis, Minnesota

Boggs, Elizabeth M., Past President, National Association for Retarded Children, Upper Montclair, New Jersey

Bostock, Norma L., formerly Psychotherapist, University of Chicago Counseling Center, Chicago, Illinois

Boyd, Dan, member Bergen-Passaic Unit, New Jersey Association for Retarded Children

Bryant, Keith N., Physician—Child Analyst, La Jolla, California

Chamberlain, E. R., Department of Social Studies, University of Queensland, Brisbane, Australia

Cianci, Vincentz, Supervisor of Child Study, New Jersey State Department of Education, Trenton, New Jersey

Dalton, Juanita, Social Caseworker, Mental Development Center, Western Reserve University, Cleveland, Ohio

Dittmann, Laura L., Assistant Professor of Education, Institute for Child Study, University of Maryland, College Park, Maryland

Drayer, Carl, Attending Pediatrician, Jewish Hospital and Medical Center of Brooklyn, Brooklyn, New York

Drillien, C. M., Department of Child Life and Health, University of Edinburgh, Edinburgh, Scotland

Dybwad, Gunnar, Professor of Human Development, The Florence Heller Graduate School for Advanced Studies in Social Welfare, Brandeis University, Waltham, Massachusetts

Epstein, Helen, Social Worker, Mental Development Center, Western Reserve University, Cleveland, Ohio

Fackler, Eleanor, Public Health Nurse Consultant, Children's Memorial Hospital, Chicago, Illinois

Falck, Hans S., Professor, School of Social Work, University of Maryland, Baltimore, Maryland

Farrell, Malcolm, Superintendent, Walter E. Fernald State School, Waverly, Massachusetts

Feeley, Mary F., Director, Community Education and Public Relations Services, New York City Department of Social Services

Font, Marion McKenzie, Psychologist, Ochsner Clinic, New Orleans, Louisiana

French, Anne C., formerly at Clinic for Mentally Retarded Children, Flower and Fifth Avenue Hospitals, New York (Deceased)

Gallagher, James J., Associate Commissioner, Bureau of Education for the Handicapped, United States Office of Education, Washington, D. C.

Giannini, Margaret J., Professor of Pediatrics, New York Medical College, New York

Goodman, Lawrence, Associate Professor of Pediatrics, Mental Retardation Center, New York Medical College, New York; and Director of Social Work, Flower and Fifth Avenue Hospitals, New York

Grad, Jacqueline C., formerly at University of Sheffield, Sheffield, Yorkshire, England

Gramm, Edith P., member of Letchworth Chapter, National Association for Retarded Children

Grant, Donald K., Physician, Buffalo, New York

Hanschaka, Evelyn Disner, teacher, Bloomfield, Connecticut

Hastings, Donald, Physician, University of Minnesota Medical School, Minneapolis, Minnesota

Hauge, Mogens, Physician, Copenhagen N, Denmark

Hawkins, Robert P., Director, School Adjustment Research Project, Kalamazoo Valley Intermediate School District, Kalamazoo, Michigan

Heilman, Ann E., Assistant Professor, Department of Psychology, Loyola University, Chicago, Illinois; and Consultant, State of Illinois Mental Health Center, Chicago, Illinois

Henderson, Robert A., Chairman, Department of Special Education, and Professor, Institute for Research on Exceptional Children, University of Illinois, Urbana, Illinois

Hersh, Alexander, Director of Admissions and Social Service, Elwyn Institute, Elwyn, Pennsylvania

Hirschberg, J. Cotter, Director—Training in Child Psychiatry; and Associate Director, Children's Division, The Menninger Clinic, Topeka, Kansas

Hoffman, John L., Social Research Scientist, Pineland Hospital, Pownal, Maine

Holt, K. S., Physician, Institute of Child Health, University of London, London, England

Hormuth, Rudolf P., Specialist in Services for Mentally Retarded Children, Health Services Division, Children's Bureau, United States Department of Health, Education, and Welfare, Washington, D. C.

Ingram, Vivien, Coordinator of Special Projects, Flint Public Schools, Flint, Michigan

Jensen, Reynold A., Professor, Department of Psychology and Neurology; and Director, Division of Child Psychiatry, University of Minnesota Medical School, Minneapolis, Minnesota

Jolly, Donald H., Commissioner of Mental Retardation, Department of Public Welfare, Harrisburg, Pennsylvania

Jordan, Paul H., former Director, Child Guidance, Flint Public Schools, Flint, Michigan

Kanner, Leo, Professor Emeritus and Honorary Consultant, Johns Hopkins University and Hospital, School of Medicine, Baltimore, Maryland

Kopek, Pauline E., Registered Nurse, Mentally Retarded Children's Clinic, Arlington County Health Department, Arlington, Virginia

Krush, Thaddeus P., formerly Clinical Director, Community Service Division, Nebraska Psychiatric Institute, Omaha, Nebraska (Deceased)

Kusuda, Paul H., Chief, Bureau of Research, Wisconsin Department of Health and Social Services, Madison, Wisconsin

Lederer, Ruth, formerly at Bureau of Maternal and Child Health, Government of the District of Columbia, Department of Public Health

Levbarg, Morrison S., Attending Pediatrician, Lenox Hill Hospital, New York

Lipsett, Renée, formerly Social Work Coordinator of Community Services for the Mental Assessment and Guidance Clinic, Montreal Children's Hospital; and Chairman of Home Care Service, Quebec Association For Retarded Children, Canada

Logan, Harriett, former Family Counselor for parents of preschool blind, University of Washington, Seattle, Washington

Lund, Alton F., Past President, National Association for Retarded Children; Attorney at Law, Salt Lake City, Utah

Mahoney, Stanley C., Clinical Psychology Consultant, National Institute of Mental Health, Denver, Colorado

Mandelbaum, Arthur, Chief Social Worker, The Menninger Foundation, Topeka, Kansas

Meyer, Donald L., Physician, Los Angeles, California

Michal-Smith, Harold, Professor of Pediatrics and Psychiatry, New York Medical College; and Director, Division of Psychology, Department of Pediatrics, Flower and Fifth Avenue Hospitals, New York

Murray, Dorothy Garst, Past Vice President, Southeast Region, National Association for Retarded Children; and parent, Roanoke, Virginia

Nadal, Robert N., Director of Social Service, Rochester Rehabilitation Center, Al Sigl Center, Rochester, New York

Olshansky, Simon, Executive Director, Community Workshops, Boston, Massachusetts

O'Neill, Jane, Social Work Consultant, Evaluation and Counseling Program for Developmental Problems in Early Childhood, New Haven, Connecticut

Osmond, Humphry, Physician, Bureau of Research in Neurology and Psychiatry, State of New Jersey, New Jersey Neurological and Psychiatric Institute, Princeton, New Jersey

Ownby, Jr., Ralph, Associate Professor of Pediatrics, Medical College of Virginia; Director of Consultation and Evaluation Clinic; and Medical Consultant, Mental Retardation Program, Virginia State Department of Health, Richmond, Virginia

Parsons, Mabel, Assistant Professor—Foods, Home Economics, University of Iowa, Iowa City, Iowa

Patterson, Letha L., a founder of the National Association for Retarded Children; parent and free-lance technical editor and writer, Topeka, Kansas

Perkins, Audree L., Histologist for Reproductive Physiology and Behavior, Oregon Regional Primate Research Center, Beaverton, Oregon

Peterson, Robert F., Research Assistant Professor, Psychology Department, University of Illinois, Urbana, Illinois

Popp, Cleo E., formerly Chairman of Special Projects, Flint Public Schools, Flint, Michigan

Probstein, Irwin, Day Care Consultant, Community Services Division of Mental Hygiene, Wisconsin Department of Health and Social Services, Madison, Wisconsin

Pruyser, Paul William, Director, Department of Education, The Menninger Foundation, Topeka, Kansas

Raech, Harry, San Jose, California, Trustee, Exceptional Children's Foundation, Los Angeles; and Trustee, Southwest Association For Retarded Children, Torrance, California

Reed, Sheldon C., Director, The Dight Institute for Human Genetics, University of Minnesota, Minneapolis, Minnesota

Reilly, W. Newland, former President, Spokane Unit, Children's Benevolent League of Washington, Spokane, Washington (Deceased)

Rheingold, Harriet L., Research Professor, University of North Carolina, Chapel Hill, North Carolina

Roll, Marlin H., Dover, Delaware

Roos, Philip, Associate Commissioner, State Department of Mental Hygiene, Division of Mental Retardation, Albany, New York

Rothman, Ruth, Consultant for Group Therapy, Flower and Fifth Avenue Hospitals, New York Medical College, New York

Ryckman, David B., Assistant Professor of Education, School of Education, University of Michigan, Ann Arbor, Michigan

Sarason, Seymour B., Professor of Psychology and Director of Psycho-Educational Clinic, Yale University, New Haven, Connecticut

Scanlan, John B., Chief Psychiatrist, Mental Retardation Center, New York Medical College, Flower and Fifth Avenue Hospitals, New York; and Assistant Professor of Psychiatry, New York Medical College

Schild, Sylvia, Career Teacher, University of Southern California, School of Social Work, Los Angeles, California

Schlesinger, Elfriede G., Research Associate, The Graduate School of Social Work, Rutgers, The State University, New Jersey

Schreiber, Meyer, Associate Professor, School of Social Service, Fordham University, New York

Schweid, Edna I., Child Psychiatry Clinic, Children's Orthopedic Hospital, Seattle, Washington

Sheimo, Stanton L., Physician, Western State Hospital, Fort Steilacoom, Washington; Clinical Director, Child Study and Treatment Center, Department of Institutions, State of Washington; and Clinical Associate Professor, Department of Child Psychology, University of Washington

Slobody, Lawrence B., Vice President for Hospital Affairs, New York Medical College, New York

Smith, Elizabeth M., Director of Social Service, The Sailors' Snug Harbor, Staten Island, New York

Solnit, Albert J., Physician, Yale University School of Medicine, Department of Pediatrics and Child Study, New Haven, Connecticut

Solomons, Gerald, Associate Professor of Pediatrics; and Director of Child Development Clinic, Department of Pediatrics, University Hospitals, University of Iowa, Iowa City, Iowa

Standifer, Frances R., Director, Social Services Division, Richmond School, Richmond, Texas

Stark, Mary H., Social Worker, Yale University School of Medicine, Department of Pediatrics and Child Study Center, New Haven, Connecticut

Sternlicht, Manny, Yeshiva University, New York

Stone, Nellie D., Associate Professor, Newark State College, Union, New Jersey

Stubblefield, Harold W., Chaplain, Clover Bottom Hospital and School, Donelson, Tennessee

Tips, Robert L., Director, Medical Genetics Center, Pasadena General Hospital, Pasadena, Texas

Tizard, Jack, Professor of Child Development, University of London, London, England

Triplett, June L., Registered Nurse and student in the doctoral program of Adult Education, University of Michigan, Ann Arbor, Michigan

Walker, Gale H., former Physician, former Superintendent, Polk State School, Polk, Pennsylvania (Deceased)

Waskowitz, Charlotte H., Certified Clinical Psychologist, Baltimore, Maryland

Weingold, Joseph T., Executive Director, New York State Association for Retarded Children, New York

Wheeler, Mary Ella, Psychiatric Social Worker, Children's Services, Menninger Clinic, Topeka, Kansas

Wilkinson, Elsie M., Social Worker, Department of Child Life and Health, University of Edinburgh, Edinburgh, Scotland

Winterbourn, R., Professor, Department of Education, University of Auckland, Auckland, New Zealand

Wishik, Samuel M., Director, Division for Program Development and Evaluation, College of Physicians and Surgeons of Columbia University, New York

Wolfensberger, Wolf, Mental Retardation Research Scientist, Nebraska Psychiatric Institute, Omaha, Nebraska

Woodfall, Ruth, Registered Nurse

Yates, Mary, Program Supervisor, Hospital Section, Social Work Service, Veterans Administration Hospital, Washington, D. C.

Zudick, Leonard, Principal, Mark Twain-Fisher Schools, Detroit, Michigan

Zwerling, Israel, Professor of Psychiatry, Albert Einstein College of Medicine; and Director of Bronx State Hospital, New York

NAME INDEX

SUBJECT INDEX